ILLICIT DRUGS IN CANADA

ILLICIT DRUGS IN CANADA

A Risky Business

Edited by

Judith C. Blackwell, Brock University, and
Patricia G. Erickson, Addiction Research Foundation

NELSON CANADA

© Nelson Canada.
A Division of International Thomson Limited, 1988

Published in 1988 by
Nelson Canada.
A Division of International Thomson Limited
1120 Birchmount Road
Scarborough, Ontario
M1K 5G4

Canadian Cataloguing in Publication Data

Main entry under title:

Illicit drugs in Canada
Includes bibliographical references and index.
ISBN 0-17-603410-2

1. Drug abuse – Canada. 2. Drug abuse – Canada –
Prevention. I. Blackwell, Judith C., 1944-
II. Erickson, Patricia G.

HV5840.C3157 1988   362.2'93'0971   C88-093560-X

Any views expressed in this book are those of the editors or
authors and do not necessarily represent those of the Addiction
Research Foundation or any of the other institutions with which
the authors are affiliated.

Printed and bound in Canada

1 2 3 4   88   92 91 90 89

CONTENTS

Preface and Acknowledgments   ix

SECTION 1: THE PSYCHOPHARMACOLOGY OF ILLICIT DRUGS: OF RATS AND MEN

INTRODUCTION   1

1. Making Connections: Drugs, Mind, and Body,
   Kevin O'Brien Fehr   5

2. The Dealer's Choice: An Introduction to Street Drugs,
   Kevin O'Brien Fehr   28

3. Toxicity Associated with Long-Term Intravenous
   Heroin and Cocaine Self-Administration in the Rat,
   Michael A. Bozarth and Roy A. Wise   51

4. Heroin "Overdose" Death: Contribution of
   Drug-associated Environmental Cues,
   *Shepard Siegel, Riley E. Hinson,
   Marvin D. Krank, and Jane McCully*   57

5. Rat Park Chronicle, *Bruce K. Alexander,
   Patricia Hadaway, and Robert Coambs*   63

SECTION 2: CANADA'S RESPONSE TO DRUGS: HISTORY AND LEGISLATION

INTRODUCTION   69

6. The Road to Regulation: Patent Medicines in Canada
   in Historical Perspective, *Glenn F. Murray*   72

7. The First Century: The History of Non-medical
   Opiate Use and Control Policies in Canada, 1870–1970,
   Robert R. Solomon and Melvyn Green   88

8. Canada's Federal Drug Legislation, *Robert R. Solomon*   117

SECTION 3: DRUGS, DEVIANCE, AND DEFINITIONS: THEORETICAL PERSPECTIVES

INTRODUCTION   131

9. When Experimental Psychology Is Not Empirical Enough: The Case of the "Exposure Orientation," *Bruce K. Alexander*   139

10. Sin, Sickness, or Social Problem? The Concept of Drug Dependence, *Judith Blackwell*   158

11. Drugs and Disrepute: The Thin Line, *John Hagan*   175

12. Towards Rational Drug Scheduling, *Melvyn Green*   186

SECTION 4: THE EPIDEMIOLOGY OF ILLICIT DRUGS IN CANADA: METHODS AND TRENDS

INTRODUCTION   209

13. Epidemiologic Methods and Indicators, *Irving Rootman*   213

14. An Overview of Canadian Illicit Drug Use Epidemiology, *Judith Blackwell*   230

15. The Enforcement of Narcotics Violations in a Canadian City: Heroin Users' Perspectives on the Production of Official Statistics, *Kenneth Stoddart*   244

SECTION 5: THE CRIMINAL JUSTICE SYSTEM: ARRESTS AND PROSECUTIONS

INTRODUCTION   259

16. The Noble Pursuit of Evil: Arrest, Search, and Seizure in Canadian Drug Law, *Robert R. Solomon*   263

17. Becoming a Cannabis Criminal, *Patricia G. Erickson*   291

18. Canadian Punishment of Illegal Drug Use: Theory and Practice, *Neil Boyd*   301

19. Cannabis Criminals Revisited, *Patricia G. Erickson and Glenn F. Murray*   314

SECTION 6: POLICY ANALYSIS: LESSONS FROM THE PAST AND PROPOSALS FOR CHANGE

INTRODUCTION   323

20. Canada in a Global Setting: Notes on the International Drug Market, *Judith Blackwell*   326

21. The Le Dain Commission Recommendations, *Patricia G. Erickson and Reginald Smart*   336

22. What Happened on the Way to Law Reform? *P. James Giffen and Sylvia Lambert*   345

23. Legal Considerations in Canadian Cannabis Policy, *Robert R. Solomon, Eric Single, and Patricia G. Erickson*   370

24. Heroin "Treatment" in British Columbia, 1976–1984: Thesis, Antithesis, and Synthesis? *Neil Boyd, Christopher J. Millard, and Christopher D. Webster*   392

25. A Justice-based Argument for the Uniform Regulation of Psychoactive Drugs, *Chester N. Mitchell*   407

Concluding Remarks: A Risky Business   444

Appendix A: Selected Statistics on Convictions for Illicit Drug Use in Canada, *Joan A. E. Moreau*   449

Biographical Notes   456

Index   461

PREFACE and ACKNOWLEDGMENTS

This book appears at a propitious time in the history of drug policy development in Canada. After a period of fomentation in the late 1960s and 1970s, and of relative quiescence in the 1980s, concern about illicit drug use has again taken a high profile on the public agenda. In 1987, the federal government initiated the planning of a national drug strategy. The Minister of National Health and Welfare announced that $210 million over the next five years would be allotted to the drug strategy. While continuing to emphasize enforcement and control, the Minister's statement also stressed the importance of prevention, education, and treatment. No details of any specific legal changes were provided.

The contents of the book will, we believe, provide an invaluable aid to informed public discussion on the future of Canadian drug policy. Our purpose is to provide an understanding of the current dilemma and of why some new responses are needed. The reader will receive a solid grounding in Canada's drug laws, how they came into being, the ways they are put into practice, and the impact they have on individuals and society. The volume also contains information about the extent of illicit drug use in the Canadian population, and about the nature and effects of these chemical substances on the human body. Armed with this basic knowledge, the reader will be challenged by critical analyses of existing policies and by proposed alternatives. If readers are then better equipped to enter the debate on drug policy issues, and perhaps even provoked to develop their own positions, we will have fulfilled our basic purpose.

This volume is interdisciplinary in nature. This attests to the academic reality that the authors themselves represent a variety of fields: law, sociology, psychology, criminology, pharmacology, and economics. In addition, these selections reflect an increasing recognition that a serious social problem cannot be addressed from the narrow perspective of a single discipline, but instead must be considered from diverse viewpoints. The topics of illicit drug use, and of reform in our approaches to the problem, are particularly suited to this broader perspective.

The selection of chapters was guided by certain principles. As mentioned above, one was to reflect the variety of scholarly disciplines that have taken up illicit drug use as a topic of study. Another was the quality and timeliness of work on any given topic. We included a number of papers to provide a body of factual knowledge. We chose others for their controversial aspects, which in themselves suggest areas in need of further critical thought. We avoided articles that were unduly technical or that dealt primarily with methodological issues.

We ourselves have provided an introduction to each section, and some concluding remarks. The essential value of such a collection of work, however, is that each author speaks in his or her own voice. Thus, the reader can become acquainted with the thinking of numerous scholars, each of whom has devoted part of his or her professional career to the topic of illicit drug use.

The authors are grateful to the Addiction Research Foundation for its support during the preparation of this manuscript. Compiling this book of readings was made possible by the unstinting effort of several people. First and foremost, we owe Sylvia Lambert an immense debt of gratitude for editing and overseeing all the manuscripts in their journey from other journals or original papers into this collection. The task of standardizing all the references and footnotes was a daunting one which she accomplished with great diligence. We are also indebted to Joan Moreau for her conscientious backup in proofreading and correcting chapters, and for her insistence on keeping all the files organized, as they mounted.

We are grateful to the many contributors and their publishers who not only allowed us to reprint their work, but in some cases also updated earlier articles on their own initiative. Working within narrow time constraints, other contributors produced original papers to fill the gaps we perceived in the published literature. Their efforts have added considerably to the value of this collection. Particular mention must be made of Professor Robert Solomon, the author or co-author of four chapters in the volume, who gave sound advice during the planning stages and was tireless both in revising previously written material and in preparing new selections. The work presented in these pages provides, in our view, compelling evidence that the Canadian coterie of drug researchers has indeed come of age since the Le Dain Commission.

We are most fortunate to have had the assistance of two very capable secretaries, Shirley Pierre and Lecia Hanycz, who entered the entire manuscript onto the word processor. Their good humour as the disks multiplied, and the responsibility they assumed in sharing the workload, made them a pleasure to work with.

We have enjoyed the experience of working closely with Joerg Klauck, our editor at Methuen, who has been a source of encouragement and advice since the beginning of this project. Wayne Herrington and Avivah Wargon have provided excellent editing services and support.

J.C.B.
P.G.E.

THE PSYCHOPHARMACOLOGY OF ILLICIT DRUGS: OF RATS AND MEN

INTRODUCTION

Nowadays one does not use "men" to mean "human beings," but in the present context the word is appropriate. This is because most pharmacological research subjects *have* been men, or rats. Mice and chimpanzees have had their chances to contribute, and in recent years more studies have even focused on the effects of psychoactive drugs in women.

The science of psychopharmacology is a branch of pharmacology that studies how drugs interact with behavioural and psychological activity in living organisms. Because the purpose of psychopharmacology is to explore the mystery of consciousness, in a sense it is the science of human essence. People have been taking drugs for millennia, but with little understanding of how these substances exert their therapeutic or mood-modifying effects. In recent years, however, there have been dramatic incremental increases in our understanding of the central nervous system, and much of this knowledge comes from drug research. On a subcellular level, pharmacological research is delving into the Cartesian nexus between mind and body.

Pharmacology is divided into two broad subject areas: pharmacokinetics (what the body does to a drug) and pharmacodynamics (what a drug does to the body). This division, however, can convey a misleadingly mechanistic impression of what happens when person meets drug, especially when the drug is a psychoactive one. In that relationship, drug-related factors such as the dose or the mode of administration will influence the drug reaction, but so too will factors found within the individual drug user (the set) and the total environment in which the drug is taken (the setting). The operation of these factors has been observed by drug users themselves. For example, a standard drink of alcohol when taken in a social setting tends to be stimulating, whereas the same drink taken at bedtime might be sedating. Set factors that influence drug reactions include a person's past history of drug experience, expectations of drug effect, attitudes, personality, mood, and motivations for drug use. The setting includes both the physical and social environments.

To control for set and setting factors, many psychopharmacological experiments are designed to compare responses to a drug with responses to a pharmacologically inactive substance, a placebo. Because the knowledge and expectations of the experimenter may also have an effect on the outcome, "double-blind" studies have been developed where neither experimenter nor experimental subject knows whether a drug or an inactive placebo has been administered until the experiment is over.

Psychopharmacology is a rigorous science, but there are limitations on the questions it can answer. Take, for example, the question of whether one drug is more or less harmful than another. Suppose it was discovered that marijuana smoke contained twice as much tar as an equal amount of tobacco smoke. This would not necessarily mean that marijuana smokers were twice as likely to get cancer. If most marijuana smokers were found to smoke less than one cigarette a day compared to the twenty or more of the average tobacco smoker, or if marijuana cigarettes were generally smaller in size, or usually shared with a friend, the risk for cannabis users would be reduced. Conversely, the risk would be increased if it were found that marijuana users inhaled more deeply or held the smoke in their lungs longer. Thus, answering the seemingly simple question of comparative dangerousness of drugs involves a whole series of subsidiary questions about dose, frequency of use, characteristics of users, modes of drug administration, circumstances of consumption, and so on.

Psychopharmacology cannot be expected to answer some of the big questions, but there are many specific issues that can be resolved in the laboratory or in controlled studies, particularly with regard to populations at risk. It is said that Irish midwives used to recommend tobacco smoking to pregnant women who had previously had trouble delivering large babies; on the basis of modern research, pregnant women are now advised to stay away from tobacco because mothers who smoke tend to have smaller babies. Pharmacological research demonstrating other physiological effects may suggest that individuals suffering from specific diseases or disabilities, or in certain age groups, should avoid particular drugs. Such findings may not be definitive if, for example, they come from rodent studies or experiments using very high doses, but it is wise to err on the side of caution.

Scientific investigation into the nature of drugs and their actions is an important contribution to the knowledge necessary for making informed decisions about drug use and drug policy. However, even the best pharmacological research will not tell us everything we need to know. Even when rigorous controls are maintained in the formal analysis of scientific research, the interpretation and application of the data are often subjective. Scientific findings alone cannot inform public policy and, as we will see in the following sections of this book, political, legal, philosophical, economic, and moral issues also impinge on policy decisions.

This first section introduces the reader to the various classes of drugs that appear from time to time throughout the volume and presents an overview of pharmacological principles. The material should serve as a basic reference source on the pharmacology of illicit psychoactive drugs. To illustrate one of the lines of research on which this overview is based, we have also included some important examples of Canadian rodent research.

Chapter 1, the first of two papers commissioned for this book from Kevin O'Brien Fehr, addresses the fundamental questions of pharmacology. Her title refers to "making connections," but the connections here are not those between drug user and drug dealer. Instead, they are the connections between chemicals and the central nervous system. This chapter explains how drugs alter the messages that pass from one neuron to another, and how this in turn determines behavioural and cognitive effects of drugs. In language understandable to the lay person, Dr. Fehr reveals the microcosm of the central nervous system, how it reacts to drugs, and how it produces its own drug-like substances.

These basic principles of psychopharmacology are essential to an understanding of the drugs themselves, the topic of Chapter 2. There, Dr. Fehr summarizes the most up-to-date research on mood-altering drugs, with special attention to the illegal ones that are the subject of this book. She provides information on the origins, preparations, and modes of administration of the various drug types, as well as their psychological and physiological effects.

As one pharmacological wag put it, "A drug is anything that, when injected into a rat, produces two scientific papers." Animal rights activists argue that animals should not be used at all in experiments, but mainstream contemporary ethics allow vertebrate animal experimentation under certain conditions. The animals must be carefully cared for, and not subjected to excessive pain and undue distress. If pain cannot be alleviated, experimenters are required to perform prompt euthanasia. Ethical considerations also include whether the research questions might be answered in some other way and whether the predicted value of the research findings justifies animal experimentation.

The ethical requirements of both human and animal experimentation have advanced rapidly in recent years. Most readers need no reminder of the victims of research atrocities under the Third Reich during World War II. Closer to home, in the United States, a notorious study withheld available medical treatment from hundreds of black men with syphilis; this "research" continued into the late 1960s. Here at home, in 1950s Montreal, drug experiments were conducted on psychiatric patients who, unaware that they were research subjects, believed they were receiving legitimate therapy. After this doleful history, one can only feel relief that ethical review is now routinely demanded for project proposals and that ethics committees are vigilant.

Animal studies permit experimentation that for ethical reasons would not be considered with human subjects, and the paper by Michael Bozarth and Roy Wise represents research of this nature. Here, rats were given continuous access to either heroin or cocaine by intravenous injection, their drug intake was measured, and their general health was evaluated. Within the 30-day testing period, the cocaine-using rats became unhealthy and almost all of them died. The heroin users were much less likely to die, and those who survived were still in good health.

Shepard Siegel and his colleagues used rats to explore the phenomenon of tolerance, the loss of sensitivity to drug effects described in Chapter 1. This study involved giving animals with different drug histories a high dose of heroin under different experimental conditions. Rats who received these large injections in an environment where they had previously received heroin were less likely to succumb to them, suggesting that environmental cues are associated with tolerance.

To the degree that rat experiments can be extrapolated to human beings, one could say that the Siegel experiment was studying setting variables. Bruce Alexander and his colleagues used two radically different settings in which to study rodent morphine consumption. One was a traditional laboratory setting with isolated, caged rats. The other, Rat Park, they designed to be as close to a normal environment as the experiment would permit. Rats are sociable beings, and the Park was a spacious and comfortable area where groups of rats of both sexes could work out their own social relationships. The differences in drug consumption in the two settings were remarkable. Perhaps even more provocative for the future of rodent research were the results of subsequent attempts to replicate the study. Dr. Alexander discusses the implications of this work in the 1987 Update, written especially for this book.

1

Making Connections:
Drugs, Mind, and Body

KEVIN O'BRIEN FEHR

From the beginning of recorded history, drugs have played a significant and varied role in virtually every society. They have played a crucial role in both primitive and modern medicine, in healing and for symptomatic relief. In addition, they have been, and still are being, employed as important components of rituals and ceremonies, enhancers of mood, and aids in attempts to achieve self-insight and personal growth.

What is it, then, that makes the non-medical use of behaviour-altering drugs so attractive and pervasive? The answer to this question is multifaceted. The many factors influencing potential users' drug-taking decisions include the type of drug available, its anticipated effects, its price, and the perceived medical, psychological, and social consequences of its use. The pharmacology of the drug (i.e., the interaction between the agent and its user) plays an important role in determining whether people will use a drug, and what happens to them when they do.

This chapter focuses on the interaction between drug and user. Here, the reader will find an overview of the major groups of behaviourally active drugs subject to non-medical use, as well as the factors that influence their effects, the intensity of their actions, and their ability to produce a state of drug dependence.

Chapter 2 describes the effects of the drugs themselves. First, however, it is important to understand a few fundamental principles of drugs and their actions. Therefore this chapter discusses what drugs are, how they are taken, how they get to their site of action, and how they influence body function when they arrive there. It begins with a few basic definitions.

WHAT IS A PSYCHOACTIVE DRUG?

A drug is essentially any substance (either occurring naturally or synthesized chemically) that is taken with the intention of producing a desired change in body function. However, foods consumed as part of a normal diet are generally excluded from this definition. Substances such as vitamins are difficult to categorize one way or the other.

Most drugs taken for non-medical reasons fall into a group called psychoactive substances. These agents make up a special category of drugs, comprising those substances that alter brain function in such a way that behaviour is affected. Normally, the user expects the agent to produce a desired change in mood. However, other aspects of brain function are usually affected as well. Processes such as perception, attention, arousal, concentration, learning, memory, abstract thought, and psychomotor control may be altered. In addition, these drugs may influence a great number of physiological functions mediated by the brain that are outside the realm of conscious control, including cardiovascular function, respiration, and hormonal balance.

WHERE DO PSYCHOACTIVE DRUGS ACT?

Psychoactive drugs act primarily on the central nervous system (CNS), which consists of the neurons of the brain and spinal cord. The CNS functions by perceiving stimuli, processing the information, and executing decisions based on the information received. All processes can occur on both conscious and unconscious levels, depending on the type of data and the system in the brain processing the information. Any or all systems can be affected by the administration of psychoactive drugs, although the degree of interference can vary, depending on the specificity of the substance.

Perception is the process by which various types of conscious stimuli are translated into a form that can be processed by the brain. It involves the transduction of various types of energy into the kind of electrical signals that can be understood by the neurons of the CNS. The perceived stimuli that certain psychoactive drugs are known to alter can be visual, auditory, olfactory, or gustatory, or can reflect touch, pressure, pain, or temperature. Also, physiological data such as blood pressure, body temperature, and blood carbon dioxide levels are constantly received on an unconscious level. This process too can be altered by drug use.

Information processing is an extremely complex phenomenon that is highly sensitive to the effects of most psychoactive drugs. Functions required for efficient processing include concentration, learning, memory, judgment, and abstract thought. Processing may also be influenced by emotion, level of alertness, and other factors affecting current mental status.

The execution of decisions made in the brain may be voluntary. Messages are sent from the cells of the motor cortex to the skeletal muscles necessary to complete the required actions. These may be signals to the muscles important for the articulation of speech, or to the muscles that move the various body parts. Many psychoactive drugs, especially the depressants, can interfere with the smooth co-ordination of body movement.

Unconscious decisions are co-ordinated by the autonomic nervous system, which regulates our involuntary physiological functions. Some messages travel via this system to the muscles of the cardiovascular system, the gastrointestinal tract, and the urogenital system, for example. Others go to both the endocrine and the exocrine glands to regulate the release of various secretions and hormones.

Psychoactive drugs often interfere with the function of this part of the nervous system, and, in doing so, produce a broad spectrum of side effects. For example, cocaine increases blood pressure by acting via the autonomic nervous system rather than by affecting the blood vessels directly. Likewise, heroin slows breathing by depressing the activity of the respiratory centre of the brain located in the brain stem. It does not act directly on the lungs or respiratory muscles.

HOW MIGHT PSYCHOACTIVE DRUGS AFFECT BRAIN FUNCTION?

The brain contains many kinds of cells, but only one type, the nerve cell or neuron, has the function of receiving, processing, and transmitting messages. The billions of neurons in the human brain are organized into complex networks of connecting cells which together carry out the functions described above.

Messages travel through these networks in two ways. They travel within each cell as *electrical* signals. However, since one neuron does not physically touch the next, electrical transmission between cells cannot occur. Therefore, neurons must communicate with each other by a different method: the *chemical* transmission of messages from cell to cell.

A neuron receiving a chemical signal, therefore, must first translate the information into a minute electrical impulse which it can transmit along its membrane to the body of the cell (the soma) for processing. Here, the hundreds of messages arriving simultaneously from the different receptor sites are integrated. Complicating this process, however, is the fact that there are two different types of incoming signals: stimulatory input which increases the excitability of the cell's membrane, and inhibitory input which decreases it.

If the net excitation of the membrane (stimulatory input minus inhibitory input) exceeds a certain threshold level determined by the properties of the cell membrane, a new message is generated by the cell body and is transmitted along a long projection called an axon which connects to the next cell in line. This signal is called an "action potential." However, if the net excitation after integration does not reach the threshold level, nothing happens. For this reason, the soma is said to be responding in an "all-or-none" fashion.

The soma's "decision" whether to generate an action potential can be influenced by changing the cell's stimulatory and/or inhibitory input. For example, cells that send the inhibitory messages are particularly sensitive to the depressant effects of many sedative drugs. If the soma receives fewer messages than usual from its inhibitory connections, the sum of the stimulatory signals has a better chance of exceeding the cell's threshold. The soma will respond by generating and transmitting more messages, and the connecting cells will become more excited. The reduction of inhibitory activity is called "disinhibition," and explains a paradox, the behavioural stimulation that is observed with low doses of many sedatives.

The messages generated by the soma rapidly reach a swelling on the end of the axon called an axon terminal. The axon terminal of the transmitting cell together with the immediately adjacent part of the receiving cell are called the synapse (from the Greek word for connection). However, the two neurons are not in physical contact with each other. The gap between them is called the synaptic cleft.

Situated within the axon terminal are small vesicles containing one of several different kinds of chemical messenger called neurotransmitters. There are at least two dozen kinds of neurotransmitter in various parts of the CNS. Scientists believe that each one fulfils a specific function. The most fully studied include acetylcholine, norepinephrine, dopamine, and serotonin.

The arrival of the action potential at the synaptic terminal triggers the release of neurotransmitters into the synaptic cleft. These molecules diffuse (randomly move from an area of high concentration to one of low concentration) across the synaptic cleft to the adjacent cell. Specialized areas on the surface of this cell (called receptors) detect their arrival. The transmitter, by binding to the receptor, initiates a series of changes that generates a new electrical signal on the membrane of the receiving cell.

Following the transmission of each message, the neurotransmitter molecules are removed from the cleft either by enzymatic breakdown, or by re-uptake into the axon terminal where they are recycled for later release.

Drugs can alter the chemical transmission of messages in a variety of ways. By interfering with the synthesis or release of a neurotransmitter, some drugs can decrease the number of molecules reaching the receiving cell, thereby decreasing the level of activity in that particular circuit of neurons. Certain drugs given to treat high blood pressure act by producing this effect. Other drugs decrease the level of activity by blocking the receptors on the adjacent cell, thereby preventing the neurotransmitter from acting—for example, antipsychotic agents.

Other substances can produce the opposite effect, that is, they can increase the number of messages detected by the receiving cell. Some drugs (e.g., nicotine) act directly at the receptor sites of the receiving cell by mimicking the action of the real neurotransmitter. Others act indirectly by increasing the amount of neurotransmitter in the synaptic cleft. Cocaine, for example, increases the concentration of dopamine in the synaptic cleft by inhibiting the re-uptake of this transmitter into the axon terminal of the transmitting neuron.

WHAT DETERMINES THE EFFECTS
OF A PSYCHOACTIVE DRUG?

Psychoactive drugs differ considerably in their selectivity. Some act at special target sites, whereas others act non-specifically on all neurons and produce more generalized effects. The characteristics of each kind of action are described in this section.

Examples of non-specifically acting drugs include the alcohols, inhalants, and general anesthetics. These substances are lipid-soluble (fat-soluble) agents that dissolve in the fatty double-layered cell membrane forming the outer shell of the neuron. The membrane expands, and is said to be "stabilized," since it is then much less able to transmit electrical information. Thus the neuron becomes less responsive to messages from adjacent cells, and is less able to generate and to transmit signals of its own. The potency of a non-specific drug depends on its ability to dissolve in fat (i.e., on its lipid solubility) rather than on its shape or other chemical properties.

The effects of non-specific drugs tend to be generalized (i.e., to alter many different brain systems), since the function of all neurons of the brain is affected to some extent. However, some neurons are more sensitive than others. At low drug concentrations, inhibitory pathways are the first to be suppressed, resulting in paradoxical "stimulation" as the activity of the excitatory pathways is unmasked. For this reason, users of these agents often exhibit disinhibited and boisterous behaviour, especially early in a drug-taking session.

Complex pathways requiring the involvement of many neurons are more sensitive to the effects of non-specific drugs than are simple pathways. Complex messages need to be transmitted through more cells, providing a greater opportunity for disruption. Suppression of the reticular activating system, a part of the brain that is essential for arousal, results in sedation and loss of complex co-ordination of cortical processes, which include learning, memory, abstract thought, and psychomotor control.

The effective doses of non-specific drugs are relatively high. For example, it takes 30–50 g of alcohol or more to produce an obvious state of intoxication since many molecules of the drug must be dissolved in a neuronal membrane before its function will be affected.

A specific drug interacts with a "specific receptor" located on the membrane of or inside the neuron. Drugs for which specific receptors have been identified include the opioids (for example, morphine and codeine) and the benzodiazepines (anti-anxiety agents such as diazepam). Many additional groups of drugs are thought to interact with neurons by means of specialized receptors.

Specific receptors play a role in natural internal (endogenous) processes that have evolved in the brain over millions of years, and employ a number of naturally occurring substances as chemical messengers. For example, the endorphins are a family of endogenous compounds that interact with the opioid receptor to help regulate mood and various physiological processes.

Drugs with specific receptors are usually effective at low doses (5–10 mg or less in non-tolerant individuals). Since LSD produces behavioural effects at doses as low as fifty micrograms (50 μg), this drug probably has a specific receptor.

Only cells with specific receptors for a certain drug are affected by that agent. For those drugs with receptors on only a few types of cells, drug effects tend to be selective rather than generalized. An example of a specific effect is opioid-induced blunting of the response to pain (analgesia).

A specific drug not only must be able to bind with its receptor, but also must initiate the chain reaction of cell changes that produces the desired effect. The interaction of a drug with its receptor is illustrated by Figure 1.1.

Many drug receptors consist of specialized proteins. They can be thought of as containing two essential components: (1) the binding site, and (2) the effector site.

A drug, in order to be effective, must first bind with the receptor. The term "affinity" refers to the ability of the drug and its receptor to form what is called a drug-receptor complex. These complexes are dynamic. They are constantly forming and breaking up. Therefore, the binding between drug molecules and their receptors is said to be reversible, and is indicated in Figure 1.1 by a bidirectional arrow.

The affinity of a drug for its receptor is governed by the three-dimensional shape of the drug molecule and its pattern of electrical charge. Not only must the shape of the drug molecule match that of the binding site of the receptor, but the electrical charges on each must be complementary as well.

Once binding has occurred, the drug must then interact with the effector site. The term "efficacy" refers to the ability of the drug to do this. A drug with high efficacy alters the shape or electrical charge of the effector site in a way that initiates a chain of cellular events leading to the expression of the ultimate effect.

Agonist drugs are agents that have medium to high affinity, and high efficacy. This means that they have a moderate to strong attraction to the receptor, and that they can interact with the effector site. An example of an opioid agonist is morphine. If the affinity of a drug for its receptor is low, then potency is low, even if efficacy is high. An example of such an opioid is codeine. However, such a drug can reach maximum effectiveness if the administered dose is high enough.

Antagonist drugs (for example, the opioid naloxone) have high affinity for the receptor but little or no efficacy. In other words, they bind tightly to the receptor, but do not interact with the effector site. Antagonists can be used to occupy receptors and thus reduce or block the effects of agonists

Figure 1.1

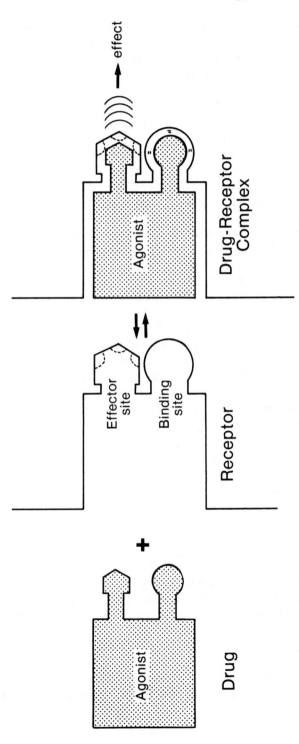

acting on the same receptor. Naloxone is used to restore breathing in cases of heroin overdose.

The processes that link the formation of the drug-receptor complex to the eventual changes in cell function are not fully understood. In some cases there may be changes in the transport of charged atoms (ions) across the neuronal membranes; in others, there may be interference with the action of endogenous neurotransmitters, or alterations in the metabolism of secondary messengers in the cell, cyclic AMP for example. All of these changes could affect the ability of the neuron to receive, process, and/or transmit information.

HOW CAN DRUG EFFECTS BE MEASURED?

Drug effects can be measured, and studied by means of graphs called dose-response curves. By plotting these graphs, researchers can gain a great deal of information about the actions of a substance in the body, and can compare the effects of many agents.

The intensity of the effect that the investigator wishes to study is plotted arithmetically on the vertical axis of the graph, while the dose is plotted as a logarithm on the horizontal axis. This means that the units of dosage increase by geometric rather than arithmetic progression (i.e., 1, 10, 100, 1000, rather than 1, 2, 3, 4).

This type of plot usually results in a sigmoid (S-shaped) curve with a central portion that is almost linear. The part of the curve that approximates a straight line can be treated as such mathematically. This simplification makes the statistical analysis of the results much easier.

An analysis of the curve can reveal a great deal of interesting information about the drug or drugs in question. Look, for example, at the dose-response curves plotted in Figure 1.2 for two mythical drugs, "Extacin" and "Uforin."

Potency

The potency of a substance is reflected by the location of the curve on the horizontal axis. For example, the curve of the more potent drug, Extacin, is to the left of that of the less potent substance, Uforin. In other words, less Extacin than Uforin is required to produce a given intensity of effect. The potency of a drug is not of great clinical importance, since the dose of a substance can always be adjusted to within the effective range.

Maximal Efficacy

This property refers to the maximum degree of effect potentially possible with a drug. Maximal efficacy is indicated by the height of the plateau on the

Figure 1.2

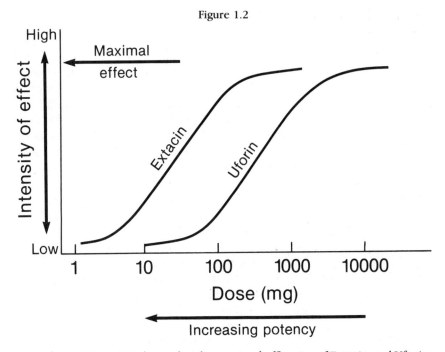

vertical axis. Figure 1.2 shows that the maximal efficacies of Extacin and Uforin are equal. The maximum effect that can actually be achieved with a drug may be less than the theoretical maximal efficacy because of restrictions imposed by the appearance of toxic side effects at higher doses.

The curves of Extacin and Uforin are parallel and demonstrate the same maximal efficacy. These similarities suggest that the two drugs belong to the same pharmacological family and act at the same receptor. Extacin appears to have a higher affinity for the receptor than Uforin.

Slope

The slope of the nearly linear portion of the curve provides information on the margin of safety of the drug. For example, if you were to plot both a dose/effect curve and a dose/toxic-effect curve for one of these drugs, the danger of toxicity would be indicated by the degree of overlap. If there is significant overlap, a dose high enough to be effective in the least sensitive members of a population will be toxic to the most sensitive members. On the other hand, if the slope of the dose-response curve is too steep, the exact dose required to produce an intermediate (submaximal) response becomes difficult to calculate, since even a slight increase in dose will produce a large increase in effect.

WHAT DETERMINES THE INTENSITY
OF A DRUG'S EFFECTS?

The intensity of a drug's effects and the duration of its action are governed by two major factors: (1) the concentration of the drug at the site where it is acting; (2) the sensitivity of the target cells to that particular substance.

The concentration of a drug at the site of action depends on a number of factors that include the dose administered and the way in which the substance is absorbed, transported, metabolized, and excreted by the body.

Usually, the dose of a drug is either known or can be estimated easily. In the case of a prescription or non-prescription medication the dose per tablet (or, if liquid, the concentration) appears on the label. A dose of alcohol can be estimated easily by multiplying the number of standard drinks consumed by the roughly 14 g contained in each drink. A "standard drink" consists of a bottle of regular beer, a glass (150 mL) of table wine, a small glass (90 mL) of fortified wine, or a shot (45 mL) of spirits.

In the case of illicit drugs, the dose is often unknown because of great variability in the potency of these preparations. When drugs are derived from natural sources, differences in strains of plants and cultivation techniques can affect the potency of the preparation. The composition of synthetic drugs varies according to the techniques selected by the chemist and the care with which he or she carries them out. In addition, illicit substances often deteriorate significantly if they are stored improperly. They are also frequently diluted ("cut") with inert compounds prior to sale.

The amount of a psychoactive drug that reaches the brain and the length of time that it stays there are determined by a number of factors that govern the movement of substances in the body. These "pharmacokinetic" factors can be divided into four major processes: absorption, distribution, metabolism, and excretion.

To a large extent a drug's movements in the body are governed by its degree of lipid solubility. The more easily a substance can dissolve in fat, the more readily it will be able to cross cell membranes. A highly lipid-soluble drug will be absorbed rapidly, and will penetrate the brain quickly.

Absorption

Most psychoactive drugs are fat-soluble enough to diffuse passively across cell membranes with relative ease. The speed with which they will enter the bloodstream and the brain, however, depends on the thickness and surface area of the particular membrane. For example, lipid-soluble substances are absorbed very quickly from the lungs since the alveolar membrane (the membrane that lines the air sacs of the lungs) is very thin, has a rich blood supply, and comprises a huge surface area for diffusion to occur. On the other hand, only the most highly fat-soluble drugs are able to penetrate intact skin which consists of several layers of almost impermeable cells.

Drugs can be given or taken in a variety of ways. The most common routes of administration are oral (by mouth), by inhalation, across mucous membranes, and parenteral (by injection).

Oral administration (swallowing a drug) is the most common and convenient method of taking a drug. Absorption of drugs occurs mainly in the small intestine. That is because the small intestine has a larger surface area and a greater blood supply than the stomach. However, the rate of absorption of substances by this route tends to be rather slow since, for the most part, they must pass from the stomach into the small intestine before they can enter the bloodstream. Therefore, it may take 30–60 minutes to feel the effects of an orally administered drug. This slowness may be a disadvantage if a rapid drug effect is desired.

The rate of absorption depends mainly on the speed of gastric emptying. Factors that delay the passage of substances from the stomach to the small intestine (for example, the presence of food in the stomach) retard absorption. Slower absorption means that a longer time is required for a user to reach peak blood level. Moreover, the eventual peak level will be lower, since some of the drug has been broken down during the period of delay.

Stomach contents that are too acidic or too alkaline may interfere with the absorption of some drugs. For example, ASA is best absorbed from an acid environment; the simultaneous administration of antacids will result in a mixture that is not acidic enough for efficient absorption. Some drugs are destroyed entirely by stomach acid or digestive enzymes, and must be given by injection if they are to be effective (e.g., insulin, some antibiotics, some hormones).

Oral administration can also be inefficient for some substances because of a phenomenon known as "first-pass metabolism." A newly absorbed drug circulates with the blood through the liver before it reaches the rest of the body. If the drug is broken down very quickly by the liver during this "first pass," it may never reach the brain in amounts sufficient to produce an effect unless the user takes a very large dose. This is one reason why cocaine and heroin users prefer other, more direct routes of administration.

Volatile substances (gases) and aerosols (suspensions of particles or liquid droplets in a gas) can be administered by means of inhalation. This route is so effective that the user may feel drug effects within 10 seconds of administration. Volatile drugs that can be taken in this manner include solvents, propellant gases, and many general anesthetics. Note that the common term "glue sniffing" actually refers to administration by inhalation. Aerosol preparations include cannabis and tobacco smoke, and some drugs given in the treatment of asthma.

The dose of an inhaled drug can be controlled by an experienced user. The absorption, and therefore the intensity of effects, can be modified if, for example, the user adjusts the depth of inhalation or the duration of breath retention. This process is called "titration." For this reason, it is difficult to quantify the amount of drug in a smoke or vapour that is actually absorbed.

Mucous membranes (the linings of the mouth, nose, eye sockets, throat, rectum, etc.) are more permeable than surface skin because they are made up of fewer layers of cells, have a higher blood supply (and, therefore, a shorter diffusion distance), and lack the protein called keratin, which renders surface skin tough and impenetrable to all but the most lipid-soluble substances.

Absorption across mucous membranes is both fast and effective for lipid-soluble drugs. Effects may be felt within a minute or two. Drugs that are "snorted" into the nose include cocaine, heroin, and nicotine in the form of snuff. Cocaine and nicotine can also be absorbed across the lining of the cheek. Some drugs (e.g., nitroglycerin) are absorbed rapidly when given sublingually (i.e., placed under the tongue). Many drugs can be absorbed rectally.

Injection by-passes normal biological barriers, drastically decreasing the diffusion distance. Consequently, the risk of infection from contaminated needles or solutions increases significantly. Drugs can be injected into many of the body's tissues or cavities.

Subcutaneous (s.c.) administration refers to injection under the skin ("skin popping"). This route is used for some therapeutic drugs and by street users who are either inexperienced with the syringe or can no longer use their badly scarred veins. Absorption tends to be slower than when the same drugs are given intravenously, but faster than when they are taken orally. Effects are usually felt in 5–10 minutes.

Intramuscular (i.m.) injection involves administration of a drug into muscle tissue. This route permits a larger volume of solution to be injected than s.c. administration does, but there is usually more pain involved. Effects are felt within 10 to 15 minutes. This method is frequently used with therapeutic drugs but is not popular with street users.

Intravenous (i.v.) injection (or "mainlining") gives drugs immediate access to the bloodstream, and hence is the most rapid route of injection. The effects of a drug given i.v. can be felt within 10 to 15 seconds. This route is used clinically when speed is essential. I.v. injection requires considerable skill, and therefore tends to be employed by more experienced illicit drug users. They favour this route since a very rapid rise in blood level is achieved if the drug is injected quickly. Blood with a high concentration (or "bolus") of drug may reach the brain within a few seconds of administration. The resulting rapid rise in brain level of the drug accounts for the "rush" or brief period of intense drug effect that the illicit user experiences. The "rush" dissipates within minutes as the drug has time to distribute more evenly throughout the body.

Intravenous injection is the most hazardous route of administration because of the increased risk of overdose. I.v. users of illicit drugs are also likely to contract infections because of impure solutions or non-sterile injection techniques. In addition, small particles or air bubbles (emboli) in the injected solution may block the passage of blood through the tiny capillaries of the lungs and other organs.

Distribution

The term "distribution" describes the movement of drugs around the body, mainly via the bloodstream. Like any substance in the blood, drugs can travel either by dissolving in water or by binding to plasma proteins. Alcohol is a substance that dissolves well enough in water to be transported in the former manner. This drug enters the brain directly by diffusing through the walls of the capillaries. Although alcohol is a water-soluble drug, it possesses enough lipid solubility to reach the neurons rapidly.

Most psychoactive drugs other than alcohol are not freely soluble in water, and therefore must be transported by means of plasma proteins. An equilibrium is established between the amount of drug bound to the protein at any one time and the amount free in solution. This means that the ratio of bound drug to free drug remains constant at all times. Since protein molecules are too large to leave the bloodstream, once a drug molecule is bound it must remain there. Only the free drug is able to diffuse into the tissues. As the free drug diffuses into the tissues or is excreted, bound drug is slowly released from the protein molecules in order to keep the ratio between the bound drug and free drug constant. Thus the proteins can act as a reservoir or storage depot for many drugs. Those that are strongly protein-bound (e.g., methadone) usually have a relatively long course of action.

Distribution of a drug to the various organs is always uneven because of variation in their blood supply. Concentrations of drug rise most quickly in those organs (such as the heart, lungs, brain, liver, and kidneys) that receive the richest blood supply, and most slowly in tissues such as fat that contain fewer blood vessels. Some drugs may be stored (sequestered) in certain tissues where they may remain bound to tissue proteins or dissolved in fat. These substances are released slowly from their depots as the plasma concentration of the drug drops. Fat storage explains why breakdown products of THC (the major psychoactive component of marijuana) may be found in the urine of a heavy cannabis user days or even weeks after he or she stops using the drug.

Excretion

Although volatile drugs (such as solvents or general anesthetics) are exhaled through the lungs, most psychoactive drugs are excreted either in the urine (via the kidneys) or in the feces (via the liver, through the bile duct and the large and small intestines).

However, it is impossible to excrete lipid-soluble drugs efficiently by either of the last two routes. These substances cross membranes so easily that they are rapidly "resorbed" into the bloodstream from the kidney tubules and/or from the small intestine before they can be excreted in the urine or in the feces respectively. Hence, the drugs would continue to recycle through the kidneys, liver, and gut for several days if the process known as metabolism did not occur (see below).

There are also several minor routes whereby small amounts of drug may be excreted. For example, high concentrations of very lipid-soluble drugs can pass into the milk of nursing mothers. Traces of drug residue may occur in other body fluids such as saliva, sweat, tears, and semen.

Metabolism

In order for lipid-soluble drugs to be excreted more easily, they must first be transformed into substances that are less fat-soluble and more water-soluble. The term "metabolism" is used to describe a series of chemical reactions occurring mainly in the liver that change these agents into water-soluble breakdown products suitable for excretion. The liver contains two major systems responsible for the metabolism of drugs. One system is responsible for the metabolism of the alcohols; the other, for most other drugs.

Beverage alcohol is an unusual drug in that it is not excreted by the normal pathways. When the drug is consumed, about 10 percent of it is exhaled or excreted unchanged in body fluids. The rest (about 90 percent) is transformed in the liver by means of the alcohol dehydrogenase system into a chemical called acetyl-CoA. This substance is then "burned" in the liver's citric acid cycle to provide energy, just as any sugar would be. The by-products, carbon dioxide and water, are eventually excreted.

Unlike the transformation of most other drugs, the rate of conversion of alcohol is constant over time, and is independent of the drug's concentration in the blood. The rate of metabolism is genetically determined, but can be stimulated to some degree by chronic alcohol consumption. Normally, the blood alcohol level drops at the rate of 10–25 milligrams per cent per hour (mg%/hr), no matter how high the initial level was. In the average person, the drop is about 15 mg%/hr. The rate can be above 30 mg%/hr in chronic alcoholics.

Other alcohols, such as methyl alcohol and isopropyl alcohol, are also metabolized by means of this enzyme system, but into highly toxic breakdown products that include formaldehyde, formic acid, and acetone.

The microsomal drug oxidizing system is responsible for the metabolism of most drugs other than the alcohols. The enzymes of this system catalyse the transformation of the parent drug into metabolites (products of metabolic change) at a rate that is dependent on the drug concentration in the liver. This means that the higher the concentration of drug, the faster the chemical reactions proceed.

Metabolic conversion consists of a series of reactions that render the parent drug progressively less lipid-soluble (i.e., more water-soluble). This has the final effect of making the drug less able to cross cell membranes. Therefore it becomes more easily excreted and less able to enter the brain. Some of the primary products, however, can be as active in the brain as the parent drug, or even more potent. These are called "active metabolites." When they are produced, the drug must undergo further transformation steps before it can be excreted.

After a drug is totally absorbed into the body, the blood levels soon start to fall. Initially, this drop is very rapid, and reflects movement of the drug from the bloodstream into the tissues. Later, however, the rate of decline slows considerably. At this point the decline is caused by the metabolism and excretion of the substances.

The rate of decline at any point depends not only on the drug itself, but also (with the exception of alcohol) on the concentration of drug in the blood at that time. In other words, the higher the drug concentration, the faster metabolism and excretion will proceed. The variability makes it difficult to compare the rate of metabolism of one drug with that of another. To get around this difficulty, pharmacologists have borrowed from the nuclear physicists a term that was originally used to describe the rate of radioactive decay. They use the expression "half-life" for the length of time required for a drug's blood concentration to fall by one-half. In the later or "terminal" stages of metabolism and excretion, the half-life of a drug is constant, no matter how high the concentration actually is. The following example illustrates this principle:

The terminal half-life of THC, the major psychoactive component of marijuana, is about 24 hours in a young regular cannabis user. When that user smokes a "joint," the THC level rises within minutes to a concentration of about one hundred nanograms per millilitre. A nanogram (ng) is a thousandth of a microgram. Within an hour, the level has dropped to about 20 ng/mL, and by 6 hours, to about 5 ng/mL. Thereafter, the level drops by half with every passing day. A scientist with a very sensitive analytical instrument will be able to detect minute levels of THC in blood for several days after the drug was taken.

As is the case with alcohol, the rate of transformation of other drugs is genetically determined. However, a drug's rate of metabolism can be increased significantly by chronic exposure to other agents that are also metabolized by the microsomal enzyme system. The barbiturates, in particular, are effective stimulators of the metabolic rate of many other drugs.

WHAT DETERMINES THE SENSITIVITY OF THE TARGET CELLS?

The second major determinant of intensity of drug effect is the sensitivity of the cells on which the agent is acting. There are many factors that seem to affect the response of target cells in the brain, but a lot of these are not well understood. Genetic factors may determine cell structure or function, which probably influences sensitivity to some agents. Target neurons may be influenced by the activity of the cells that connect with them. Important factors include mood, state of arousal, and environment. Damage to the CNS can result from traumatic injury or long-term drug use. Such injury may decrease the ability of the neurons to compensate for intoxication and may thereby increase sensitivity. Finally, sensitivity can decrease after sustained exposure to a substance because of compensatory mechanisms within the cells. This phenomenon underlies the development of functional tolerance discussed below.

HOW CAN DRUG SENSITIVITY CHANGE OVER TIME?

Tolerance is defined as the loss of sensitivity to a substance in such a way that (1) drug effects become less intense if the same dose is administered repeatedly; or (2) escalation of the dose is required to restore the initial magnitude of effect. Tolerance can be explained in terms of two major mechanisms that act alone or, more frequently, in combination.

The first mechanism is termed "dispositional tolerance." Repeated exposure to a substance often increases the rate of its elimination, usually because of an increase in the efficiency of the liver. This change both shortens the duration of action of the drug, and increases the dose required to maintain the intoxicated state at a desired level for a sustained period of time.

Loss of sensitivity to some substances can also occur within the neuron itself. When this happens, the drug effect begins to diminish even if the concentration in the brain is kept constant. This phenomenon is called "functional tolerance."

Loss of sensitivity can occur over the course of a single sustained administration. In this case it is termed "acute tolerance." For example, the effects of alcohol are felt less intensely at the end of an evening of heavy drinking than at the beginning. Scientists call this difference in sensitivity the "Melanby effect." More colloquially, it is referred to as "drinking yourself sober."

Drug sensitivity may also decrease over the course of a small number of administrations. For example, a user of LSD may exhibit almost complete tolerance to the drug after as little as three consecutive days of administration.

More commonly, the sensitivity of the neurons decreases slowly over the course of several days, weeks, or months of administration. This is the case with alcohol, barbiturates, opioids, and cannabis.

Many factors influence the rate of tolerance development. Generally the loss of drug sensitivity will be fastest if high doses are administered frequently and on a regular schedule. Tolerance to the effects of a specific drug will also develop more quickly in a user who has a previous history of heavy consumption than in a naive individual. Learning clearly makes an important contribution to this phenomenon (see Chapter 4).

Sometimes sensitivity to one drug can be altered by prior chronic administration of another substance. This cross-tolerance can occur either because the metabolism of the second drug has been stimulated by the first, or because functional changes have occurred within the brain.

WHAT HAPPENS IF MORE THAN ONE DRUG IS TAKEN AT ONCE?

The term "drug interaction" is used to describe what happens when the presence of one drug modifies the actions of a second one. For example, one drug can sometimes enhance the actions of another. In this case the effects are said to be *synergistic*. This type of interaction is illustrated by the enhancement of the effects of alcohol by the benzodiazepines. In other situations, the administration of one substance can attenuate (decrease) the effects of another. For example, the opioid antagonist naloxone can block the effects of heroin. This type of interaction is called *antagonistic*.

Drug interactions can occur when drugs share the same receptors (e.g., the opioid agonist morphine and its antagonist naloxone), or when drugs act by different mechanisms, but on a common neural pathway (e.g., the enhancement of the effects of alcohol by the benzodiazepines). They may also occur when drugs act by different neural systems (e.g., in the antagonism of some of the effects of alcohol by the amphetamines).

Illicit drug users often combine drugs, and when they do, drug interactions are inevitable. Alcohol, for example, is taken with virtually all other psychoactive drugs, and generally enhances their intoxicating effects. Other combinations reported include heroin and cocaine ("speedball"), pentazocine and tripelennamine ("Ts and blues"), pentazocine and methylphenidate ("Ts and Rs"), and phencyclidine and cannabis ("killer weed"). Users of these combinations often report a greater degree of mood enhancement than when taking any one of these drugs alone.

WHAT IS A TOXIC EFFECT?

So far, psychoactive drugs have been described as substances capable of producing desired changes in mood and behaviour. However, these agents are not entirely specific and often generate a whole spectrum of unintended effects, many of which are unpleasant, and some of which may be life-threatening.

Toxicity is the term used to describe the capacity of a drug to produce one or more effects that have been defined as adverse. Here, the term is defined broadly to include both physical and behavioural effects and their immediate social consequences.

In most cases, there is little question as to whether a drug action is undesirable. For example, virtually everyone would agree that drug-induced carcinogenesis is an adverse effect. In other situations, however, there may be some ambiguity. For example, the drowsiness produced by many of the antihistamines is considered unpleasant by allergy sufferers who are taking such a drug during working hours, but is the desired effect in those who are taking it in the form of a non-prescription sleep preparation.

The analysis of toxic effects is often complicated by the fact that both desired and adverse effects are sometimes caused by different ingredients of the same crude preparation. For example, it is the tar rather than the nicotine that accounts for most of the pulmonary toxicity associated with tobacco smoke.

If undesired reactions result from a single dose of a substance, they are termed "acute toxic effects." Often, however, days, months, or years of constant exposure are required before adverse reactions become apparent. These delayed manifestations are termed "chronic toxic effects." The problem of drug dependence can also be considered under the heading of chronic toxicity.

Acute Toxicity

Acute toxic effects can be physiological, behavioural, or both. Although the distinction between behaviour and physiology is not always clear, the two have been separated here for ease in discussion.

Adverse physiological effects are generally dose-related, and in their broadest sense include all effects unrelated to the primary reason for taking the drug. They include disruption of the functions of the autonomic nervous system, the endocrine system, the immune system, and the liver. As long as the effects are reversible and mild and occur infrequently, they are not likely to be of clinical significance.

Some effects, at sufficient intensity, are capable of causing death. For example, respiratory depression may lead to cessation of breathing; abnormal electrical activity in the brain, to seizures; hypertension, to stroke; and irregularities in heart rhythm, to cardiovascular collapse.

Drug interactions can sometimes enhance these effects in ways the user might not expect (for example, the increased respiratory depression that occurs when cocaine is combined with heroin).

A few individuals are unusually sensitive to the effects of some drugs because of pre-existing allergic tendencies, diseases, or genetic conditions. In these instances, effects are not generally dose-related. For example, epileptics are particularly sensitive to many drugs that lower the seizure threshold. In rare instances, individuals with a genetically linked sensitivity to certain general anesthetics can die from increased body temperature when exposed to them. Many similar instances of drug hypersensitivity are known to occur.

Acute behavioural effects are also generally dose-related. They are due to drug-induced disruptions of brain function that are almost always transient, and manifest themselves as emotional changes as well as impairment of perception, concentration, learning, memory, abstract thought, and psychomotor skills. All of these effects can contribute to impaired performance while driving, at school, or at work. The risk of a serious accident can increase significantly if a car, truck, or heavy machinery is involved.

Emotional changes can damage interpersonal relationships and can contribute to violent behaviour directed at oneself or others. Some individuals may be unusually sensitive to behavioural effects. For example, individuals with pre-existing but possibly unrecognized psychotic tendencies are particularly sensitive to the psychotomimetic (i.e., mimicking psychosis) effects of the hallucinogens.

Chronic Toxicity

Chronic adverse effects are those observed after several drug exposures; they can affect both physiological functions and behaviour. They are determined not only by the administered dose but also by the duration of exposure. Chronic side effects may appear only when the dose is escalated following development of tolerance to the desired effect.

Physiological effects show up as damage to a variety of organ systems, depending on the drug administered. For example, pulmonary toxicity results from the use of cannabis and tobacco; cardiovascular disease, from tobacco; gastrointestinal problems, from alcohol; and endocrine disturbances, from opioids, alcohol, and a variety of other drugs. Toxic effects can be so mild that they may only be apparent as decreased disease resistance. Affected users may exhibit increased absenteeism due to more frequent and more severe viral infections (colds, flu, etc.). Moderate effects include those that affect the user as long as the drug is still being administered, but disappear once its use is discontinued. They are often severe enough to require medical attention. Examples of moderate effects include alcohol-induced gastritis and tobacco-induced bronchitis. On the other hand, chronic toxic effects may be irreversible and potentially life-threatening. Examples of such severe conditions include carcinogenesis, cirrhosis, severe cardiovascular disease, and atrophy of the brain.

Chronic behavioural effects can also be reversible or irreversible. Reversible changes reflect a continuing drug effect (often termed the "chronic intoxication syndrome") that is seen when a drug's excretion is slow and administration is repeated frequently enough to sustain or increase brain levels. These changes can include difficulties in abstract thought and memory, anxiety, irritability, and mood depression with associated behavioural consequences (poor learning, violence, etc.). Function tends to recover slowly when drug use is discontinued.

Residual changes in brain function are at least partially reversible if no destruction of neurons is involved, or if, since dead neurons cannot be regenerated, other cells can compensate for lost function. This compensation probably explains the partial recovery of function that has been observed in brain-damaged alcoholics. The user who has suffered severe behavioural impairment accompanied by demonstrable loss of cortical cells will improve by abstaining from the drug and by taking dietary supplements, but will never recover entirely.

Chronic psychotic states have been associated with the long-term use of many drugs, especially the hallucinogens. There is much debate about whether these substances can precipitate a chronic psychosis in previously healthy individuals, since the psychiatric status of these patients before they became ill is generally unknown. Experts suspect that in most of these cases, the drug has unmasked a latent psychotic condition.

Withdrawal Reactions

Withdrawal reactions are a special type of toxic drug effect. Depending on the substance, suddenly discontinuing use after chronic exposure may produce an abstinence syndrome that can be relieved by readministration of that drug or one of a similar pharmacological class. A person experiencing such withdrawal phenomena is said to be physically dependent on the drug. These reactions appear to arise from the brain's attempt to maintain the physiological systems of the body in a steady state in the face of disruption by the drug. In other words, the brain cells adapt their functioning in such a way as to minimize the drug's effect.

When the drug is removed, these changes are unmasked. The brain is still compensating for drug effects that are no longer present. During the time that the brain requires to readjust, symptoms occur that are opposite in nature to those that the drug produced originally. For example, the withdrawal from depressant drugs such as alcohol or the sedative-hypnotics produces a picture of general hyperexcitability, characterized by tremors, anxiety, and insomnia, and in severe cases by seizures and hallucinations. Withdrawal from opioids produces restlessness, increased sensitivity to pain, and a variety of rebound autonomic symptoms such as hyperthermia (increased body temperature), increased pupil diameter, and increased gastrointestinal motility. Withdrawal from stimulants results in hypoactivity, mood depression, and ravenous hunger. The severity of a withdrawal reaction depends on the drug administered and the extent and duration of exposure. The symptoms can range from mildly annoying (as with cannabis) to life-threatening (as can occur after high doses of barbiturates).

Compulsive Drug-seeking Behaviour

Most psychoactive drugs have been used compulsively by at least a few of their consumers. Compulsive use is influenced by the properties of the drug and the behavioural characteristics of the consumer.

Psychoactive drugs provide reinforcement which increases the probability that they will be taken again in the future. The user experiences positive reinforcement when a substance produces a pleasurable mood. The relief of unpleasant states such as anxiety or depression can also act as negative reinforcement. A person who uses drugs to relieve these states is negatively reinforced. The relief of withdrawal symptoms by the readministration of a drug also functions as negative reinforcement, although this appears to be less significant in determining compulsive use than drug-induced improvements in mood.

Other factors are said to act as secondary reinforcers: for example, environment, friends, and drug paraphernalia. Secondary reinforcers do not contribute to drug effects directly, but are strongly associated with them by the user. They can contribute significantly to the dependence liability of a substance.

Drugs also act as punishers by producing adverse effects (such as nausea or hangovers) that decrease the probability of continued use. The dependence liability of a drug depends on the balance between reinforcing effects and punishing effects. A drug that induces a highly pleasant state will have a much higher dependence liability than one that produces anxiety or other unpleasant symptoms. The dependence liability may vary from person to person, since sensitivity to the various reinforcing or punishing effects seems to differ for genetic or other reasons.

Since drugs can both reinforce and punish at the same time, the user makes a cost-benefit analysis that takes into account not only the drug-related variables but also the costs and benefits associated with alternative non-drug-related behaviours. In many cases the compulsive user decides to take the drug in the face of punishing effects that appear to the non-user to be extremely severe (e.g., cocaine-induced seizures, paranoid psychosis, financial burden, or family breakdown). This behaviour emphasizes how highly reinforcing the effects of certain drugs can be.

The timing of the onset of the effect is important. An outcome is always most reinforcing when it follows quickly after the act which produces it. Likewise, the impact of a punishing outcome is diminished if there is a delay in its occurrence. Reinforcing drug effects usually occur quickly, especially if the substance is smoked or administered intravenously. On the other hand, punishing effects (e.g., lung cancer caused by tobacco) are often delayed, and therefore can be less of a deterrent to the user than one would expect from their severity.

It is interesting that first-time use of many psychoactive drugs (for example, nicotine) may be more punishing than reinforcing. This is because the user has not yet developed tolerance to some of the aversive effects such as nausea. In these cases, other factors (such as social reinforcement) may help maintain drug use until the pharmacological effects become more rewarding.

Non-drug-related Toxicity

Toxicity may be associated with the use of many psychoactive drugs, but may not be caused directly by them. Adverse outcomes of drug administration may be related to contaminants in illicit mixtures, methods of administration, or other elements of the user's lifestyle.

Contaminants of one kind or another are almost always found in illicit drug preparations. Identified contaminants with toxic potential include: liquid fertilizers, pesticides, herbicides, by-products of chemical synthesis, pathogens (disease-producing agents) such as bacteria and fungi, and bulk diluents ("cutting" agents). Intravenous drug administration results in a host of local and systemic infections due to contamination of solutions and equipment. Small particles and air bubbles in the injected solution can produce adverse effects by blocking capillaries. And there are many additional risks in belonging to a drug subculture. Interpersonal conflict and violence are common in this kind of environment and homicides occur frequently.

MAKING CONNECTIONS:
WHERE DO WE GO FROM HERE?

As the brain continues to reveal its secrets to the hordes of investigators who vigorously pursue them we are increasingly amazed at the complexity of a system that seems to function so effortlessly. Years of intensive research into the neurochemical basis of behaviour have blurred the once sharp distinctions between mind and body, and have made the task of the psychopharmacologist ever more challenging.

The discovery of a group of receptors specific to the opioids suggested the existence of an opioid-like substance occurring naturally within the brain. Why else, scientists reasoned, would so many species have evolved receptors for a drug to which they would probably never have been exposed? Shortly thereafter, a family of mood-regulating substances that interact with the receptors was identified. Release of these endorphins has subsequently explained the effectiveness of acupuncture, and has even been suspected of accounting for "jogger's high."

How many new mood-altering compounds remain to be discovered in the brain? Probably many, and the study of the interaction between psychoactive drugs and their receptors is one of the best ways to uncover them. This knowledge should, in turn, promote better understanding of the physiological basis of behaviour, and lead to more specific treatments of behavioural disorders.

Compulsive behaviour (drug-seeking or otherwise) remains a focus of particular concern. We are currently witnessing intensive study not only of the neurochemical mechanisms involved in drug dependence, but also of the connections between these physiological changes and the many environmental factors relevant to the drug user. Discoveries in this area will undoubtedly help the treatment of drug-dependent individuals.

Over the last 10–20 years there have been exciting and sometimes surprising developments in the field of psychopharmacology. In all probability, however, we have seen just the beginning of a whole new wave of discovery.

FURTHER READINGS

Benet, L. Z., and Sheiner, L. B. Pharmacokinetics: The dynamics of drug absorption, distribution, and elimination. In: Gilman, A. G., Goodman, L. S., Rall, T. W., and Murad, F. (eds.). *Goodman and Gilman's The Pharmacological Basis of Therapeutics.* 7th ed. New York: Macmillan, 1985.

Jacobs, M. R., and Fehr, K. O. *Drugs and Drug Abuse: A Reference Text.* 2d ed. Toronto: Addiction Research Foundation, 1987.

Julien, R. M. *A Primer of Drug Action.* 4th ed. San Francisco: W. H. Freeman, 1985.

Kalant, H., and Kalant, O. J. *Drugs, Society and Personal Choice.* Toronto: PaperJacks, 1971.

Levine, R. *Pharmacology: Drug Actions and Reactions.* 3d ed. Boston: Little, Brown, 1983.

McKim, W. A. *Drugs and Behavior: An Introduction to Behavioral Pharmacology.* Englewood Cliffs, N.J.: Prentice-Hall, 1986.

Ross, E. M., and Gilman, A. G. Pharmacodynamics: Mechanisms of drug action and the relationship between drug concentration and effect. In: Gilman, A. G., Goodman, L. S., Rall, T. W., and Murad, F. (eds.). *Goodman and Gilman's The Pharmacological Basis of Therapeutics.* 7th ed. New York: Macmillan, 1985.

2

The Dealer's Choice:
An Introduction to Street Drugs

Kevin O'Brien Fehr

Mood-altering drugs, as mentioned in Chapter 1, come in many varieties. The number of available substances continues to increase, as both pharmaceutical companies and underground chemists seek to extend their markets. However, this intensive activity would soon cease, were it not for the extensive demand by members of our society for agents that relax, relieve pain and psychic distress, energize, enhance self-esteem, alter consciousness, or simply elicit a "high."

This chapter explores the drugs available to the non-medical user that fill these apparent needs. The psychoactive agents discussed include illicit substances such as cannabis and the other hallucinogens, and the prescription drugs that are subject to non-medical use (for example, the opioid analgesics, anti-anxiety agents, sleeping pills, and stimulants). Legal drugs such as alcohol, tobacco, and caffeine are mentioned in their appropriate categories, but are not discussed since they fall outside the scope of this volume.

There is no ideal way to classify mood-altering agents. Since these substances have very complex chemical properties and effects, they tend not to fall neatly into a few categories. However, this difficulty has not prevented pharmacologists from trying to classify them. Some of the criteria used over the years include the source of a drug, its therapeutic applications, its chemical structure, or its mechanism of action. However, no one system has proved to be ideal and each has limitations. Therefore, a compromise has been developed that allows some flexibility in deciding where a given substance best belongs. Some drugs still remain difficult to classify since they have properties that place them in more than one category.

The psychoactive drugs discussed in this chapter have been arbitrarily divided into four categories: depressants, opioid analgesics, stimulants, and hallucinogens. Some of these categories have subgroups that are defined as each one is discussed in more detail.

CENTRAL NERVOUS SYSTEM (CNS) DEPRESSANTS

Depressants are a group of drugs that produce a reduction in arousal of the cerebral cortex, primarily by suppressing the electrical activity in the reticular

Table 2.1
CNS Depressants

Alcohol (beverage or ethyl)	beer, wine, spirits
Alcohols (other)	methanol, isopropanol
Barbiturates	secobarbital (Seconal®) amobarbital (Amytal®) thiopental (Pentothal®) phenobarbital (Luminal®)
Non-barbiturate sedative-hypnotics	methaqualone glutethimide (Doriden®)
Benzodiazepine anti-anxiety agents and hypnotics	diazepam (e.g., Valium®) chlordiazepoxide (e.g., Librium®) oxazepam (Serax®) flurazepam (e.g., Dalmane®) triazolam (Halcion®)

Antihistamines	chlorpheniramine (e.g., Chlor-Tripolon®)
	diphenhydramine (e.g., Benadryl® and in
	    cough syrups and non-prescription sleep
	    preparations)
	dimenhydrinate (e.g., Gravol®)

Solvents and aerosols	acetone, toluene, gasoline, fluorocarbon propellants, etc.
General anesthetics	ether chloroform nitrous oxide halothane (e.g., Fluothane®)

activating system, a network of cells located in the brain stem. The term "depression" is used here to denote a slowing of CNS function. It does not imply mood depression. These drugs are used therapeutically as anesthetics, sedatives, anti-anxiety agents, and sleeping pills. For the most part, people make non-medical use of these agents because they produce disinhibition and relieve anxiety. Table 2.1 lists commonly used groups of drugs belonging to this category; they are described briefly in the following section.

Beverage Alcohol

Ethyl (or beverage) alcohol is the most commonly used depressant drug, and generally the first that young users have occasion to try. This drug causes more health and social problems in Canada than all the illicit drugs together. However, the legal status of alcohol places it outside the scope of this book. For more information, consult Jacobs and Fehr (see Further Readings).

Anti-Anxiety Agents

Historically, sedative-hypnotics have been divided into two major categories: hypnotics (sleeping pills) and anti-anxiety or "anxiolytic" agents (tranquillizers). Pharmacologically, the distinction between the two is not always clear, although there are some differences in selectivity of action. The benzodiazepines are more able to relieve anxiety without producing excessive sedation than earlier drugs. For this reason, they have become the drugs of choice for the treatment of daytime anxiety. Although not originally marketed as sleeping pills, the benzodiazepines have largely replaced the older hypnotics in the treatment of insomnia as well, since they are as effective and safer. Currently, however, doctors are showing increasing reluctance to prescribe benzodiazepines, especially for long unsupervised periods, because of the recently recognized risk of dependence.

The first benzodiazepine, chlordiazepoxide, was introduced as Librium® in 1960. Diazepam (marketed under the trade name Valium®) followed three years later. Since the early 1960s, literally thousands of chemically related compounds have been synthesized and screened for potential as anti-anxiety agents. At present, 13 different benzodiazepines are available in Canada. In addition to their use as anxiolytic agents and hypnotics, these drugs are also employed to treat alcohol withdrawal, as pre-operative sedatives, as muscle relaxants, and in the emergency management of severe seizures.

The effectiveness of the benzodiazepines in relieving anxiety over courses of treatment up to four weeks has been clearly established, although drug therapy alone does not provide the patient with techniques to cope with precipitating causes or other life problems. If these are left untreated, symptoms of anxiety will return when drug treatment is terminated. In recent controlled studies, therapeutic doses of these substances have proven safe and effective for as long as six months, but the use of these drugs in the long-term treatment of anxiety remains controversial.

Flurazepam and triazolam are the benzodiazepines most frequently used in the treatment of insomnia, although all of the drugs of this class are effective to some degree. Triazolam is very short acting, meaning that drowsiness the following day is unlikely. Flurazepam is longer acting, and more likely to cause hangover.

Diazepam is the benzodiazepine most likely to produce the pleasurable mood the illicit user wants, probably because of its fast absorption and onset of action. For this reason, it is popular among street users, who are known to self-administer doses far in excess of the usual therapeutic range, even up to several hundred milligrams per day. Benzodiazepines are also employed by heavy users of amphetamines or cocaine to relieve the anxiety and other negative moods produced by these agents.

The benzodiazepines may produce adverse reactions. Patients prescribed benzodiazepines initially complain of symptoms of acute intoxication such as drowsiness, poor co-ordination, emotional lability (i.e., mood swings), dizziness, impaired cognition and memory, visual disturbances, and slurred speech. These symptoms tend to disappear as tolerance develops. In some users, however, these symptoms may persist, leading to a state of chronic intoxication.

Benzodiazepine overdoses are common and account for a significant proportion of drug-related cases admitted to hospitals. High doses of benzodiazepines produce behavioural impairment that resembles intoxication induced by alcohol or other sedative-hypnotics. Unlike the case with alcohol or barbiturates, however, sedation is not accompanied by significant respiratory depression. Deaths due to consumption of benzodiazepines alone have never been reported.

Physical dependence is most likely to occur after long-term administration of high doses of benzodiazepines, but has also been reported in patients who have been treated with therapeutic doses for several months. Fortunately, however, severe withdrawal syndromes appear to be much less prevalent than sensationalist media accounts would have one believe. Commonly reported signs and symptoms include tremor; sweating; hypersensitivity to sensory stimuli; tingling sensations, ringing in the ears and other sensory distortions; insomnia; and headache. Rarely, severe symptoms such as seizures or psychosis may occur.

Psychological dependence, as reflected by a behavioural pattern of compulsive use of the benzodiazepines, can occur in both patients and non-medical users. Two major factors may contribute to compulsive use even when physical dependence is not present: on the one hand, a drug-induced positive mood experienced during intoxication; on the other, underlying symptoms of anxiety that may re-emerge when drug administration is discontinued.

Other Hypnotics

The barbiturates, a much older group of drugs, were first introduced in the early part of this century, but because of their potential toxicity, they are gradually falling into disuse as hypnotic agents. However, the ultra-short-acting thiopental is still used in the induction of anesthesia, while the long-acting drugs such as phenobarbital are employed in the treatment of epilepsy. Non-medical users prefer barbiturates that accumulate rapidly in the CNS, such as secobarbital, since they produce the most immediate and intense intoxication.

When given at low doses, the barbiturates produce effects resembling those of alcohol: that is, relaxation; relief of anxiety; enhancement of mood; drowsiness; dizziness; mild disinhibition; and other alterations of CNS function including prolonged reaction time and impaired psychomotor ability, cognitive processes, and short-term memory. There is further resemblance to alcohol in that the disinhibiting effects are heightened when the user is in a situation conducive to behavioural arousal. For example, a user at a party might appear excited and boisterous rather than drowsy.

Deaths due to barbiturate overdose (both accidental and deliberate) were very common until the 1970s. Many of these fatalities involved the administration of other depressant drugs (most commonly alcohol) at the same time as the barbiturate. Because barbiturates are less frequently pre-scribed now than they were in previous years, the incidence of overdose deaths is decreasing.

Because barbiturates are eliminated from the system relatively slowly, chronic administration can result in a state of chronic intoxication. Impaired CNS function, mood swings, and sleep disturbances are commonly reported.

High doses and longer duration of exposure are associated with an intense withdrawal syndrome. The user shows marked signs and symptoms of CNS hyperexcitability, which resemble those of the alcohol-induced delir-ium tremens (the "DTS"). Seizures, delirium, visual hallucinations and severe autonomic disturbances are common. Symptoms begin within 3 days of the last dose and peak between 3 and 10 days, during which period the sufferer may die from cardiovascular collapse or seizures. The withdrawal syndrome is more severe after discontinuation of short-acting barbiturates such as seco-barbital than after stopping one of the long-acting barbiturates such as phenobarbital.

The non-barbiturate sedative-hypnotics such as the bromides, chloral hydrate, ethchlorvynol, methyprylon, paraldehyde, glutethimide, and metha-qualone are a group of drugs with actions very similar to those of the bar-biturates. Although some were in use before the advent of the barbiturates, most were introduced later in the hopes that they would be safer and would have a lower dependence liability. Unfortunately, this turned out not to be the case. All have produced deaths due to respiratory depression, and, like the barbiturates, are especially dangerous when taken in combination with other CNS depressants such as alcohol. Their dependence liability is similar to that of the barbiturates. Heavy daily users may demonstrate signs of chronic intoxication, including psychomotor impairment, slurred speech, tremor, irritability, apathy, and difficulty with cognitive processes. For all the above reasons, these drugs have largely been replaced by the benzodiazepines. Of this whole group of drugs, methaqualone and glutethimide are the only two that are now being used illicitly by a significant number of people.

The antihistamines have been used since the 1940s in the treatment of allergies, motion sickness, and insomnia. Although some of the newer drugs of this class have negligible sedative effects, the older ones that do produce drowsiness are still used as non-prescription hypnotic agents. For example, diphenhydramine is the active ingredient in Nytol® and Sominex®. Antihis-tamines have also been used on the street in combination with other drugs (e.g. tripelennamine with pentazocine as "Ts and blues").

The hypnotic antihistamines produce sedation, dizziness, mild impairment of CNS function, mild mood enhancement, and a variety of autonomic effects. High doses can cause hallucinations, seizures, and severe cardiovascular disturbances. Deaths have been reported.

Tolerance to the sedative effects of the antihistamines develops with regular use. Their dependence liability is unknown. Antihistamines do not appear to be drugs of choice among street users. However, they are readily available without prescription and street users sometimes purchase them if other drugs are in short supply.

Inhalants

Inhalants provide a cheap, widely available means of achieving intoxication and are often the first group of drugs that young people experiment with. Most use is experimental, and involves a simple attempt to enhance mood. However, heavier users often seek a decrease in the intensity of negative feelings such as anxiety, depression, inferiority, or boredom. Use of inhalants is a problem among certain ethnic and age groups in Canada, but, as legally available industrial products, they are outside the purview of this book. Interested readers should refer to Fornazarri et al. or Jacobs and Fehr (see Further Readings).

Opioid Analgesics

Opioid analgesics are often classified with the CNS depressants, but, in addition to their sedative actions, they also have specific analgesic (pain relieving) and antitussive (cough suppressant) effects. Their pharmacology differs sufficiently from that of the other depressants to justify classifying them separately. Table 2.2 gives examples of this class of drugs.

Table 2.2
Opioid Analgesics

Agonists	heroin
	hydromorphone
	morphine
	meperidine (e.g., Demerol®)
	codeine
	methadone
	oxycodone (e.g., in Percodan®)
	hydrocodone (e.g., in Novahistex DH®)
Agonist/antagonists	pentazocine (Talwin®)
	butorphanol
Antagonists	naloxone (Narcan®)
	naltrexone

Opium first arrived in Europe during the Renaissance, and by the sixteenth century alcoholic extracts of the drug were being prepared for use in the treatment of both mental and physical ailments. Morphine was isolated in the early nineteenth century, but this drug was not fully effective until the invention of the hypodermic syringe in 1853. Since then many new opioids have been synthesized in an attempt to find an effective analgesic devoid of dependence liability. However, the search remains largely unsuccessful.

Opium, or dried poppy juice, is a tar-like substance which oozes from cuts made in the unripe pods of *Papaver somniferum*. The juice contains over 20 alkaloids, but only two—morphine and codeine—have analgesic properties. These are known as the naturally occurring opioids. Codeine and morphine can be modified chemically to produce "semisynthetic" opioids that are more potent than the parent drugs (e.g., hydrocodone, heroin). Drugs that mimic the effects of the opioids and are manufactured completely in the laboratory (e.g., methadone, meperidine) are known as "synthetic" opioids.

Opioids exert their effects by interacting with specific receptors located on certain cells both in the CNS and in other organs of the body. The normal function of these receptors is the modulation of the activity of the family of endogenous compounds called endorphins (see Chapter 1). There are many types of opioid receptors, differing in location, function, and binding properties. The spectrum of effects of the various opioids can be explained by the fact that they bind preferentially to different types of receptors. The differences in intensity of effects can be explained by differing affinities of the various drugs for these receptors. For example, morphine has a much higher affinity for a certain type of receptor than codeine and is therefore more potent.

Some opioids can be given orally (e.g., codeine, hydromorphone, hydrocodone, oxycodone) but many others fall victim to first-pass metabolism when given by this route, and therefore produce relatively little effect. When injected, these drugs by-pass the liver, and thus retain their potency for a longer period of time. Opioids reach the brain most quickly when injected intravenously, because this route delivers a high concentration to the brain all at once.

Analgesia occurs at low doses of opioids without marked CNS depression. The effect is specific in that the perception of pain is much more affected than other sensory modalities. The opioid-treated patient still recognizes the pain as such, but it is no longer a source of concern. These drugs relieve all types of pain to some extent, but are more effective for continuous dull pain than for sharp intermittent pain.

Drowsiness and mental clouding occur at doses higher than those required for analgesia. Lethargy and impaired concentration and cognition are reported. Mood changes occur that can be perceived by naive users as unpleasant or dysphoric. However, when the drug is given i.v., experienced users usually achieve a highly pleasurable subjective state that is likened to a sexual orgasm and lasts about 45 seconds.

Opioids also produce a number of physiological effects mediated by the autonomic nervous system. These include constriction of the pupil, respiratory depression (which can be life-threatening at high doses), suppression of the cough reflex, increased body temperature and sweating, nausea and vomiting, and a decrease in gastrointestinal motility and function. In addition, histamine release may produce intense itching and skin flushing.

There are many opioid analgesics subject to non-medical use. The properties of the most common ones are summarized briefly here.

Heroin is diacetylmorphine, which is rapidly metabolized to its intermediate product monoacetylmorphine and then to morphine in the blood and CNS. Heroin itself does not appear to bind with the opioid receptor. Rather, the binding of monoacetylmorphine and morphine accounts for its effects. However, non-medical users often claim a faster and more intense "rush" with heroin than with morphine, although under blind conditions they cannot always discriminate between the two drugs. The greater lipid solubility of heroin in the body may account for more rapid entry to the CNS and therefore a greater intensity of the initial effect.

Codeine is an opioid of relatively low potency found in cough syrups, and in preparations containing non-opioid analgesics (e.g., ASA, acetaminophen). It is sometimes used non-medically because it is readily available in Canada without prescription.

Meperidine (e.g., Demerol®) is a short-acting opioid used for the relief of moderate to severe pain. This drug can cause CNS excitement at high doses, manifested by muscle twitches, tremor, and agitation. It is not a drug of choice among street users because the "high" is less intense than that of heroin. However, it is the drug most commonly selected by medical personnel because it is widely available and does not produce telltale constriction of the pupils.

Hydromorphone is a potent analgesic used to treat severe pain and to suppress the cough reflex. This drug produces less nausea, vomiting, and drowsiness than morphine, but more intense respiratory depression. When given orally, it produces significantly less mood enhancement than injected heroin, but is easily available for non-medical use in the form of Dilaudid® cough syrup.

Oxycodone is used to treat moderate to severe pain. It has powerful mood-enhancing, analgesic, and sedative effects. It is available alone, or in combination with non-opioid analgesics such as ASA (e.g., in Percodan®) or acetaminophen (e.g., in Percocet®). This drug is widely accepted by drug users as an inexpensive drug that can be taken orally and is readily available on prescription.

Hydrocodone (contained in Novahistex DH®) is used mainly as a cough suppressant in combination with antihistamines. Non-medical drug users take it for the same reasons as they do oxycodone.

Methadone is a long-acting analgesic with properties similar to those of morphine. Unlike morphine, however, it is effective when administered orally, and works for up to 24 hours. Since it can be given once a day by mouth, and does not produce a "high" when taken in this manner, methadone is used primarily in substitution therapy for opioid-dependent individuals.

Pentazocine (Talwin®) is both an agonist and an antagonist. If given alone, it produces a mild analgesic effect, but if administered together with morphine, it blocks the effects of the more potent drug. In parts of the United States, non-medical users have crushed tablets of pentazocine and injected it with antihistamines such as tripelennamine ("Ts and blues"). A combination of pentazocine and methylphenidate ("Ts and Rs") has appeared in Western Canada. Intravenous injection of Talwin® tablets has recently been discouraged in the U.S. with the addition of the antagonist naloxone to the tablets. However, Talwin® has not been reformulated in Canada.

Antagonists such as naloxone and naltrexone have no agonistic action, and therefore cannot be used as analgesics. They produce few effects when given alone, but they block the effects of agonists. They are therefore useful in the treatment of opioid overdoses. Since they precipitate an immediate withdrawal reaction in opioid users, they can be used to diagnose opioid dependence, and they are also administered to users in treatment because they block the effects of street heroin.

Chronic effects of the opioids per se are relatively minor and tend to be manifestations of acute effects to which the user does not fully develop tolerance. They include constipation, apathy, reduced libido, reduced testosterone levels and sperm synthesis, and menstrual irregularities.

Most sickness and death in chronic opioid users results from factors related to intravenous administration or to lifestyle. Infections (such as septicemia, abscesses, hepatitis, endocarditis, and AIDS) resulting from non-sterile injection techniques are common. Emboli composed of small undissolved particles or air bubbles may block small blood vessels in the lungs, brain, heart, or other organs.

With continuous use, tolerance develops within days to many effects of the opioid agonists including respiratory depression, analgesia, sedation, nausea, and enhancement of mood. If administration is intermittent, however, the user experiences little change in drug sensitivity. The development of tolerance to the analgesic and mood-elevating effects can lead the user to escalate the administered dose to several times the initial amount. Tolerance develops more slowly or not at all to other effects such as constipation, constriction of the pupils, and altered levels of sex hormones.

Some signs and symptoms of physical dependence show up after withdrawal from all agonists and agonist/antagonists. With heroin and morphine the first symptoms appear 8–12 hours after the last drug administration and consist of tears in the eyes, runny nose, yawning, and sweating. At 12–14 hours post-drug the user may fall into a restless, fitful sleep. This is followed by additional signs including dilated pupils, anorexia (lack of appetite), gooseflesh, irritability, and tremor. The discomfort peaks between 42 and 72 hours post-drug. In addition, nausea, diarrhea, and abdominal discomfort are common. Heart rate and blood pressure are elevated. Chills and gooseflesh alternate with flushed skin and profuse sweating. Signs of CNS stimulation include muscle spasm, kicking movements, and orgasm in both men and women. Other rebound changes occur in the endocrine and other physiological systems. Dehydration can result in secondary physiological symptoms. Most symptoms disappear within 7–10 days, but some subtle changes (especially behavioural ones) may persist for several weeks post-drug.

CENTRAL NERVOUS SYSTEM (CNS) STIMULANTS

The CNS stimulants produce a general increase in the activity of the cerebral cortex and effects characterized by mood elevation, increased vigilance, and postponement of fatigue. Some stimulants are also used as anorexiants (appetite suppressants) and decongestants, and to treat attention deficit disorder with hyperactivity (ADDH). A list of stimulants can be found in Table 2.3. At the doses commonly employed, nicotine and caffeine are considerably less potent than cocaine and the members of the amphetamine family. For information about the legal CNS stimulants see Jacobs and Fehr, and other works in Further Readings.

Table 2.3
CNS Stimulants

Amphetamines	
Stimulant amphetamines	amphetamine dextroamphetamine (Dexedrine®) methamphetamine
Drugs to treat ADDH	methylphenidate (e.g., Ritalin®) pemoline (e.g., Cylert®)
Anorexiants	fenfluramine (e.g., Ponderal®) diethylpropion (e.g., Tenuate®)
Decongestants	phenylpropanolamine (PPA) and ephedrine (also found in "look-alike" stimulants) propylhexedrine (Benzedrex®)

Cocaine	hydrochloride and free base (also
	    produces depressant effects at high
	    doses)

Caffeine	in coffee, tea, cola drinks, chocolate, non- prescription and "look-alike" stimulants
Nicotine	in tobacco and some insecticides (also produces some depressant effects)

Amphetamines and Related Drugs

Although the first synthesis of amphetamines occurred in 1887, the physiological effects of these compounds were not recognized until 1927. At that time it was reported that these compounds could constrict blood vessels, increase blood pressure, and dilate the bronchial tubes. Benzedrine® was marketed in the early 1930s as a bronchodilator and nasal decongestant. Shortly thereafter, experts recognized the stimulant properties, and amphetamines have been used to treat depression and narcolepsy, as well as obesity and hyperactivity in children.

Because of their high dependence liability and potential toxicity, Canada limited medical use of amphetamine and some related drugs severely in 1972. Several anorexiants are no longer available, and Benzedrine® is now being taken off the Canadian market. However, non-medical users continue to have access to illicitly manufactured methamphetamine.

Amphetamines and related drugs are products of chemical synthesis. Those available on the street are either diverted from licit pharmaceutical firms or produced in illicit laboratories. When sold as white powders, amphetamines are almost always diluted with inert materials or weaker stimulants. "Look-alike" stimulants (which usually contain caffeine, and the decongestants ephedrine and phenylpropanolamine) can look surprisingly like amphetamine pills or capsules manufactured by the pharmaceutical industry.

Amphetamines produce their acute behavioural effects by stimulation of the CNS. Most of the physiological actions result from increased activity of the autonomic nervous system.

The most reinforcing effect of the amphetamines is a powerful enhancement of mood, accompanied by feelings of omnipotence and heightened self-confidence. These feelings are most intense during the brief "rush" (often described in sexual terms) that follows i.v. administration. Amphetamine intoxication is characterized by rapid flow of ideas, feelings of great strength and ability, and excitation. Concentration span is increased, fatigue is postponed, and there is a delay in the need for sleep. There may be an increase in libido, but appetite is suppressed.

Sometimes the effects of amphetamines are perceived as unpleasant. The user may experience dysphoria, anxiety, and agitation. Occasionally, a panic state may develop. At high doses, symptoms of an acute psychosis may appear.

The acute physiological effects of the amphetamines are characterized by increased heart rate and blood pressure, the latter sometimes associated with hypertensive headache. Sensitive users may experience irregularities in heartbeat (cardiac arrhythmias). Other effects include an increase in body temperature, dry mouth, and respiratory disturbances.

Doctors may now prescribe dextroamphetamine for a limited number of disorders that include narcolepsy and Parkinson's disease, and for the relief of sedation caused by some anti-epileptic drugs. Methylphenidate, a less potent drug, is used to treat attention deficit disorder with hyperactivity in children. Diethylpropion and fenfluramine are now prescribed over short periods of time for weight reduction, replacing the more potent amphetamines that were used as anorexiants prior to 1972.

Non-medical users take stimulants primarily to enhance mood and self-esteem. These drugs have also been used by athletes who believe they increase strength, endurance, and aggression, and by long-distance truck drivers who seek greater alertness and vigilance and a postponement of the need for sleep. The anorexiants are not drugs of choice among illicit users, but these users may take large doses as a last resort if more potent stimulants are unavailable.

The drugs used as decongestants have chemical structures similar to those of the amphetamines. Like the amphetamines, they constrict blood vessels, and thereby relieve nasal and sinus congestion. For this reason, they are found in many cold and allergy medications, often in combination with an antihistamine. However, their central stimulant effects are weak, and therefore they have been widely available without prescription. Recently, a number of these agents, primarily ephedrine and phenylpropanolamine (PPA), have been combined with caffeine and sold on the street, misrepresented as amphetamine preparations.

Another decongestant, propylhexedrine, has been extracted from nasal inhalers and injected intravenously. Such a solution is very acidic and causes severe local irritation, infections, and scarring. In addition, severe toxic effects including stroke have been reported in Toronto and other areas where i.v. use of this substance has occurred.

Heavy use of the amphetamines and related drugs can produce a clearly defined picture of paranoid psychosis. Methamphetamine users tend to self-administer the drug in a pattern of alternating "runs" and "crashes." A run is a series of repeated injections that may last for several days. Initially, users report euphoria and feelings of omnipotence and sexual arousal. By the second day, paranoid symptoms begin to appear, although they are usually recognized as being drug-induced. By the third or fourth day, the user experiences increased paranoid delusions and hallucinations (visual, auditory, olfactory, or tactile), and exhibits aggression or compulsively repeated bizarre behaviour. Unlike the schizophrenic, he or she remains oriented with regard to time, place, and self; consciousness is clear; and accurate memory of the period is retained. The paranoid symptoms usually clear within a few days of withdrawal.

Chronic users often show signs of malnutrition from long-term suppression of appetite. Their resistance to disease is decreased and they are subject to many infections, some of which may be caused by non-sterile injection techniques.

Tolerance to most amphetamine-induced effects occurs when the drug is administered chronically, and tolerance to the mood-enhancing effects develops particularly rapidly. Toward the end of a "run," it is not uncommon for a user to take a gram or more of methamphetamine per day. The "crash" phase (actually a manifestation of physical dependence) rapidly follows the discontinuation of amphetamine administration and is characterized by fatigue, ravenous hunger, irritability, and severe mood depression. These symptoms can persist for several days after a long run of use.

Cocaine

Cocaine is one of at least 17 alkaloids contained in the coca bush, *Erythroxylum coca*, which grows in the Andes region of South America. Its concentration in crude plant material is about one percent. Doctors still use the drug clinically as an anesthetic of the upper respiratory tract.

Cocaine is usually sold on the street in the form of its hydrochloride salt (cocaine HCl). Street cocaine is commonly diluted ("cut") with inert white crystalline powders (e.g., mannitol, inositol) to increase its bulk, local anesthetics (to mimic the numbing effects of cocaine in the nose), or cheaper stimulants (e.g., amphetamine). Illicit cocaine may also contain toxic by-products of extraction (e.g., acids), or other contaminants.

Cocaine HCl can be converted to cocaine free base by means of a simple chemical manipulation that involves the use of a weak base such as baking soda followed by extraction with an inflammable organic solvent such as ether. In its free-base form, the drug is more volatile than cocaine HCl, and less susceptible to decomposition when heat is applied. Therefore, it can be vaporized ("smoked") in a free-base pipe much more efficiently than its parent compound. A new smokable free-base preparation has recently become available in many large North American cities. This product, called "crack," is made by adding baking soda to a solution of cocaine HCl and heating the mixture. There is no ether extraction step. The dried residue is sold in the form of small pea-sized lumps.

Cocaine HCl crystals are absorbed efficiently from the nasal mucosa after "snorting." The user feels the effects within a few minutes of administration. For a very rapid and intense onset of effects, however, cocaine HCl can also be injected intravenously. Oral administration is inefficient, since the drug is broken down so quickly after absorption that most of it never reaches the brain. Smoking is a highly efficient method, allowing large quantities of the drug to be absorbed almost instantaneously. A user will experience intense effects of "crack" vapour seconds after inhaling it.

Cocaine users tend to readminister constantly until the supply runs out. Unlike heroin dependents who tend to take the drug at intervals of several hours, cocaine users often use at intervals of 15–60 minutes. Smokers may repeat their administration even more often than those who snort the drug. These factors account for the doses totalling several grams per day that may be consumed by heavy users.

With the exception of the local anesthetic action, the acute effects of cocaine are very similar to those of the more potent amphetamines. Cocaine typically elicits a dose-related enhancement of mood accompanied by a sense of well-being. Self-confidence increases, thoughts seem to flow rapidly, and the user experiences a feeling of boundless energy. Cocaine also produces a feeling of increased alertness and sensory awareness. It postpones feelings of fatigue, and may delay the onset of sleep. It also suppresses sensations of hunger and thirst. These effects are intensified when the drug is smoked or injected.

The period of mood enhancement is typically followed by a dysphoric phase. Depending on the dose, the initial symptoms may include anxiety and irritability. At this point, users may take a CNS depressant drug such as diazepam or alcohol in order to suppress their mounting agitation, or take more cocaine to re-establish the drug effect.

The physiological effects of cocaine result mainly from its stimulatory effects on the sympathetic nervous system. Heart rate is increased, reflexes are enhanced, and the pupils are dilated. At high doses, the user may experience hyperthermia, sweating, pallor, headache, nausea, tremors, and vertigo. Paradoxically, however, the drug suppresses respiration, an effect that the amphetamines do not share.

Symptoms of toxic psychosis (which resembles amphetamine psychosis) frequently occur toward the end of a cocaine "spree" when a user has taken the drug several times over the course of many hours or several days. This state is characterized by agitation, anxiety, paranoia, visual and tactile hallucinations ("coke lights" and "coke bugs" respectively), and sometimes by bizarre or violent behaviour.

High doses of the drug can induce severe respiratory depression, especially if it is taken together with another respiratory depressant (e.g., with heroin, in the form of a "speedball"). Anoxia (lack of oxygen due to respiratory depression) sometimes causes cocaine-related death. Fatalities can also result from seizures, cardiovascular collapse, or hyperthermia. Deaths can occur with any route of administration, often at surprisingly low doses.

The chronic cocaine user is likely to show the same sort of deterioration as the chronic methamphetamine user. He or she may also suffer from localized toxicity related to the route of administration. For example, free-basers show signs of respiratory toxicity, while snorters may develop nasal irritation, runny nose, and localized eczema around the nostrils.

Tolerance to the mood-enhancing effects of cocaine does appear to develop under conditions of heavy use, and the dose often escalates markedly during a "spree." If the user abruptly discontinues drug administration, abstinence symptoms similar to those associated with amphetamine withdrawal set in. These symptoms include fatigue, severe mood depression, and irritability and are commonly referred to as the "crash."

The powerfully reinforcing effects of cocaine (both as a euphoriant and as a treatment for post-drug "craving") overwhelm many users. Cocaine dependence can have devastating effects on a person's life, not only because of its pharmacological effects, but also because of its high cost.

HALLUCINOGENS

Approximately 100 species of plants contain hallucinogenic substances. Their use has been recorded in many ancient and modern cultures, for religious purposes and as medicines or poisons. The hallucinogens produce generalized disruption in many parts of the brain, with profound effects on perception, cognition, and mood. Examples of this group of drugs appear in table 2.4. In addition to their hallucinogenic effects, many of these agents also produce CNS depression and/or stimulation, and a wide range of autonomic effects. This section summarizes briefly the pharmacology of the hallucinogens most commonly found in Canada.

Table 2.4
Hallucinogens

LSD-like	lysergic acid diethylamide (LSD)
	psilocybin
	dimethyltryptamine (DMT)
	lysergic acid amide (derived from several species of morning glory)
Mescaline-like	mescaline
	paramethoxyamphetamine (PMA)
	methylenedioxyamphetamine (MDA)
	methylenedioxymethamphetamine (MDMA)
Dissociative anesthetics	phencyclidine (PCP)
	ketamine
Cannabis	marijuana
	hashish
	cannabis oil

Cannabis

Cannabis products originate from *Cannabis sativa*, the hemp plant, which has been used for thousands of years. The constituent of cannabis mainly responsible for the psychoactive effect is called delta-9-tetrahydrocannabinol (THC). The potency of a given preparation is largely determined by its concentration of THC, although the presence of other cannabinoids, notably cannabidiol (CBD) and cannabinol (CBN), may influence the effects to a small extent. These compounds belong to the cannabinoids, a family of over 60 chemicals found only in the cannabis plant.

The most common preparation, marijuana, consists mainly of the leaves of the cannabis plant. Recently, producers in California have developed methods of breeding and growing high-potency cannabis plants. Their seedless marijuana ("sinsemilla") contains a high proportion of the more potent buds and flowers, and tends to have a relatively high THC content.

Hashish, a more potent form of cannabis, consists mainly of the resin secreted on the upper leaves, buds, and flowers of plants grown in warm climates. The compressed chunks of dark resin may contain flowers and leaves as well.

Cannabis oils are made by extracting crude marijuana or hashish with an organic solvent. "Hash" oil, derived from the highly concentrated resin, is usually more potent than the "weed" oils extracted from marijuana.

In North America, cannabis is usually smoked. Marijuana leaves may be smoked either in a pipe or as a "joint" (i.e., in rolled cigarette form with twisted or folded ends). Hashish is smoked in a pipe, either alone or in combination with tobacco. Hand-rolled cigarettes with tobacco and cannabis are called "spliffs." Cannabis oils can be mixed with marijuana or tobacco and smoked in a pipe, wiped onto a cigarette paper and rolled into a joint, or vaporized on the heated tip of a knife. Cannabis products may also be consumed orally.

THC is a highly lipid-soluble molecule. This property is a major determinant of how the drug is handled by the body. When someone smokes cannabis, THC is absorbed rapidly from the lungs. The user feels the effects within a few seconds, and they peak within the first half-hour of smoking. If the drug is taken orally, absorption is slow and erratic. The user does not usually experience the effects for at least an hour after consumption, and they may not peak for three to four hours. Within hours of its administration, THC and the more lipid-soluble metabolites are redistributed to body fats. For this reason, excretion of cannabinoid metabolites in urine and feces is slow and may continue for several days after the administration of a single joint. A user smoking several joints per day may excrete detectable amounts of metabolites for several weeks after discontinuing drug use.

To a large extent, the effects of cannabis depend on the dose. However, the magnitude of the effects as well as their nature (i.e., whether they are experienced as pleasant or unpleasant) will also depend on the personality, the experience, and the expectations of the user. Naive cannabis users often report that they feel no effects at all, most likely because they do not know how to smoke a joint efficiently or because they have not learned what to expect from the drug. However, other factors may also be important. The effects of a few puffs ("tokes") of low-potency cannabis are subtle, and may not be recognized as such by the first-time smoker. In most experienced users, the cannabis "high" includes mild perceptual distortions, laughter and gaiety, a feeling of relaxation, difficulty with attention and short-term memory, and some drowsiness.

Anxiety reactions are particularly likely in naive smokers, but they also occur from time to time in experienced users, especially those who have taken a higher dose than usual. The symptoms, which may include panic, fear of losing control, and paranoia, almost always disappear rapidly as the effects of the drug begin to wear off, and no treatment other than simple reassurance is required.

Occasionally, an acute psychosis will result from cannabis use. Such a reaction, usually characterized by confusion, disorientation, depersonalization (an out-of-body experience), and visual and auditory hallucinations, can be precipitated in anyone if the dose of THC is large enough. However, if psychotic symptoms appear at low to moderate doses, it is very likely that the user has a pre-existing psychiatric condition that enhanced sensitivity to the drug. Except in the latter case, psychotic reactions disappear quickly once cannabis use is discontinued.

The most prominent acute physiological effects of cannabis are a some-times dramatic increase in heart rate and a reddening of the conjunctivae (the whites of the eyes). Other acute effects include dry mouth, a feeling of faintness when rising suddenly from a seated to a standing position (postural hypotension), slight respiratory depression, and changes in the regulation of some hormones.

Chronic, heavy cannabis users have been reported to exhibit cognitive difficulties and emotional lability even when not using the drug. This so-called chronic intoxication syndrome is not to be confused with "flashbacks" that appear spontaneously after a symptom-free period. Clinicians often describe a picture of apathy, slovenliness, and difficulties with concentration, memory, and abstract thought. It is often difficult to determine whether these symptoms preceded drug use or resulted from it. Many studies of healthy, well-functioning cannabis smokers have failed to reveal evidence of cannabis-induced cognitive dysfunction.

The question of whether cannabis may cause permanent brain damage is still unanswered. So too is the question of whether heavy cannabis use can precipitate a chronic psychosis in previously stable users. The use of this drug tends to occur in an age group (late teens and early twenties) where chronic schizophrenia is first emerging, and it is often difficult to determine exactly what role, if any, the drug played in the development of symptoms. However, it has now been established clearly that in previously diagnosed schizophrenics even infrequent use of cannabis can cause an acute exacerbation of psychotic symptoms.

Heavy cannabis use may adversely affect other organ systems. Chronic toxicity has been most clearly defined in the respiratory system, where the effects are related mainly to the non-cannabinoid constituents of the smoke and the factors that govern their retention in the lungs. In heavy users, it is common to find chronic bronchitis and similar signs of inflammation in other parts of the respiratory system. Biopsies of bronchial tissue from young cannabis smokers have suggested that these changes are much more severe than those seen in tobacco smokers of the same age. Sensitive testing has also revealed a chronic narrowing of the airways of daily users, contributing to less than optimal respiratory function.

There has been considerable debate about whether endocrine changes observed in animals are clinically significant in humans. There have also been inconsistent reports of a decrease in serum testosterone levels in men who smoke marijuana. Experts now generally agree that a drop in the testosterone level does occur, but that the decrease is temporary and the level remains within normal limits. In heavy chronic smokers, however, they have observed a decrease in sperm count, accompanied by abnormalities in sperm morphology and biochemistry. It is not known if these changes affect the fertility of the cannabis smoker. However, it has been demonstrated that the sperm counts return to normal within three months of abstaining from the drug. Very little is known about the effects of cannabis smoking on the reproductive function of the human female. Although there has been a report of disrupted menstrual cycles in heavy users, this effect has not been clearly established.

Animal-based evidence suggests that, at high levels of exposure, certain components of the immune system are impaired. This could be reflected as a decreased resistance to viral, bacterial, or fungal disease, or as an impaired ability to kill malignant cells. Thus far, little is known about the functional significance of these changes in human users.

A user can develop considerable tolerance to most of the acute effects of cannabis within a week if the drug is administered several times a day. Less frequent smokers report a loss of sensitivity to the desired effects of the drug over the course of several months of regular administration. The development of physical dependence has also been demonstrated in volunteers given the drug several times a day for two to three weeks. Mild symptoms appeared four to eight hours after abrupt termination of drug administration and consisted of irritability, insomnia, anorexia, weight loss, sweating, and intestinal cramps. Similar symptoms have recently been reported as occurring among heavy daily users of illicit cannabis.

There was a tendency in the past to regard cannabis as non-addicting, since even heavy users did not exhibit a well-defined withdrawal syndrome of the alcohol type. However, it is now well recognized that compulsive use of cannabis occurs in a small proportion of regular users regardless of whether they display physical symptoms when they try to stop. Clinical intervention may be required in these cases.

LSD

Lysergic acid diethylamide (LSD) is a synthetic drug that was discovered in the 1940s. Originally, this drug was commonly taken in therapeutic and non-therapeutic contexts to produce a feeling of expanded consciousness, a state of increased creativity, and religious or mystical insights. As non-medical use became more widespread, however, people began to take LSD and other hallucinogens, often in combination with other psychoactive drugs, simply to "get high."

LSD is usually taken orally. The effects of a typical street "hit" (which can range in amount from 40 to 500 μg) are felt within 15 to 45 minutes after administration. The intoxication reaches a peak about 1 to 2 hours later, and by 12 hours after ingestion the effects have largely dissipated.

Behavioural effects include perceptual distortions of visual and auditory stimuli and of the senses of time, space, and body image. Sensory stimuli seem more intense, and there is often a melding of the senses (synesthesia). For example, sounds may be perceived as visual objects. Thoughts are formed rapidly, often in a disorganized or uncontrolled manner, and concentration is impaired. Trivial objects may suddenly take on profound importance, and the meaning of the universe suddenly seems clear. The mind may seem detached from the body (depersonalization). Conflicting emotions (such as joy and sadness) can coexist or alternate rapidly. Physiological effects are generally mild, and may consist of numbness, difficulty with muscle control, cardiovascular and respiratory stimulation, or nausea.

Adverse reactions ("bad trips") can occur in any user at any time. The rapid and seemingly endless flight of ideas contributes to a fear of insanity. Users may also become severely depressed or exhibit symptoms of an acute toxic psychosis. The paranoia, hallucinations, delusions, confusion, and dis-orientation usually last for a limited time and respond to reassurance. Cases of longer-lasting symptoms have been reported; these are thought to arise from the unmasking of a latent schizophrenia.

"Flashbacks" (spontaneous recurrences of either affective symptoms or perceptual distortions) can occur days, weeks, or even months after the original experience. The cause is unknown.

Daily use of LSD is rare, since virtually complete tolerance to the effects of the drug develops within three to four consecutive days of administration. Once this happens, the effects are barely evident, no matter how high a dose is used. Physical dependence on LSD has never been described, but a small proportion of users do appear to become psychologically dependent.

PCP

Phencyclidine (PCP) is a synthetic drug known on the street as "dust" or "horse tranquillizer" (the latter term reflecting the drug's former use as a veterinary anesthetic). Sometimes it is misrepresented on the street as other substances, such as THC.

PCP is effective when given orally, but can also be snorted, smoked, or injected i.v. for a faster onset of effects. The effects (especially at low doses) are influenced by the mood, expectations, and personality of the user as well as the social situation in which the drug use occurs.

A low dose of PCP produces an enhancement of mood, relaxation, and sedation. Perceptual distortions (of time, space, body image, and visual or auditory stimuli) are common. The user often feels dissociated from the environment—totally isolated. Impairment of a number of higher cortical functions such as attention, concentration, judgment, motor co-ordination, and speech also occurs. Physiological effects include constriction of the pupils, blurred vision, an increase in body temperature, and mild stimulation of the cardiovascular system.

Higher doses of PCP can induce an acute toxic psychosis including paranoia, confusion, disorientation, restlessness, hallucinations, delusions, and preoccupation with trivia. Bizarre and sometimes violent behaviour has been reported in some users. When given in large amounts, PCP also has an analgesic effect that prevents a user from experiencing pain if injured. This tends to increase the severity of injuries, because the user fails to take protective action. High doses may also precipitate phsyiological changes that may be life-threatening, such as hypertension, hyperthermia, respiratory depression, and seizures.

Experts know little about the effects of long-term PCP administration. Users report impairment of memory and the ability to think abstractly, speech problems, chronic anxiety, and depression. These symptoms take several months to clear after terminaton of use. Chronic users of PCP with no history of psychiatric disorder prior to drug use have also developed a toxic psychosis, but the exact role of PCP in the etiology of these symptoms is unclear.

The available evidence—including unconfirmed reports of the administration of doses as high as 1,000 mg/day—suggests that users develop tolerance to the effects of PCP. Tolerance and physical dependence have been reported in animals, but the occurrence of withdrawal symptoms has not been confirmed in humans. Some users appear to become psychologically dependent.

Psilocybin

Psilocybin is found in Psilocybe and Conocybe mushrooms. This drug is usually sold in the form of dried intact or powdered mushrooms ("magic mushrooms" or "shrooms") and is taken orally. The user first perceives the effects 15–45 minutes after administration, and they persist from 3–6 hours.

The effects of psilocybin, similar to those of LSD, include an increase in blood pressure, heart rate, and body temperature. Initially, the user may experience nausea, vomiting, and intestinal cramping. Later, distortions of visual stimuli and "pseudohallucinations" (known to be drug-induced) are likely to occur. They are accompanied by distortions of time, space, and body image; heightened sensory awareness; synesthesiae; mystical thoughts; and a loss of boundaries between self and environment. Concentration, attention, cognition, and memory are impaired. As with LSD, users may have "bad trips," but these generally last for a limited time.

MDA

Methylenedioxyamphetamine (MDA) produces a combination of hallucino-genic and stimulant effects. This drug is usually administered orally, but can be sniffed or injected. A user taking MDA by mouth first perceives the effects after about 30 minutes. Low doses produce a sense of peacefulness and emotional closeness to others. For this reason it has been called the "love drug." The user also experiences a subjective feeling of increased insight and a heightened level of consciousness. However, perceptual distortions and hallucinations are rare. Adverse reactions to low doses of MDA include anxiety, confusion, and hyperactivity.

At higher doses, MDA produces significant amphetamine-like toxic effects. These include dilated pupils, hyperactive reflexes, heightened responses to sensory stimuli, hyperthermia, and agitation. Hallucinations, seizures, and respiratory insufficiency due to spasm of the chest muscles may also occur.

Recently an analogue of MDA, called methylenedioxymethamphetamine (or MDMA), became available in some parts of the U.S. This drug has been called "Ecstasy," and is reputed to produce more pleasurable effects than its parent drug. Some psychotherapists believe it could be therapeutically bene-ficial because it reputedly increases the ability to work out problems and personal conflicts. However, recent animal studies have suggested that admin-istration of this drug may be associated with significant damage to the central nervous system.

THE DEALER'S CHOICE:
SOME CONCLUDING REMARKS

The wide variety of licit and illicit drugs available to drug users is truly amazing, and the choice will, in all likelihood, continue to increase. What developments, in terms of drugs and their related problems, can be antici-pated over the next few years?

Clearly, non-medical drug use is an enduring phenomenon. In any given society, the extent of use of a particular substance is determined not only by its range of pharmacological effects, but also by factors such as its cost, availability, and social acceptability, and by the perceived degree of toxic effects. Although individual drugs may move in and out of fashion, the illicit drug user may basically select an agent from a limited number of themes: the depressants (and the opioid analgesics), the stimulants, and the hallucin-ogens. Over the last 25 years, virtually all new drugs entering the market have been variations on existing ones, with a few minor differences in pharmacology and with chemical structures altered enough to qualify them as new products for marketing purposes or (in the case of illicit substances) to avoid existing drug legislation. Therefore it is unlikely that any radically new and different drugs will appear on the illicit market in the near future, although choice and availability may be altered by changes in social attitudes, prescribing practices, law enforcement, and the skill of local underground chemists.

Public health problems will also vary somewhat in accordance with current drug fashions. For example, as cocaine becomes cheaper and more available, we can expect to see the number of users rise. This will almost certainly increase the incidence of adverse consequences such as lethal overdoses, medical and psychological problems, social dysfunction, and dependence requiring treatment. On the other hand, the prevalence of cocaine use may drop as its risks become more widely known.

We must remember, however, that we are talking about risk, not certainty. Drug effects are generally related directly to the degree of exposure, which is determined by both the dose and the duration of administration. In addition, users differ so much in their individual sensitivity to mood-altering drugs that any given person may not experience any of the possible effects—either desirable or toxic—at levels of exposure that would affect most others. The degree of toxicity in any particular case is, therefore, impossible to predict. Users are often overly optimistic in assuming that they will be among the lucky ones who escape adverse consequences.

Illicit drug users and the underground chemists who supply them are a remarkably creative group. It will be interesting indeed to monitor the scene over the next few years for new drugs and combinations, novel preparations of existing agents, and different methods of administration.

FURTHER READINGS

Clouet, D. H. *Phencyclidine: An Update*. NIDA Research Monograph 64. Rockville, Md.: Department of Health and Human Services, 1986.

Fehr, K. O., and Kalant, H. *Cannabis and Health Hazards: Proceedings of an ARF/WHO Scientific Meeting on Adverse Health and Behavioral Consequences of Cannabis Use*. Toronto: Addiction Research Foundation, 1983.

Fornazarri, L., Wilkinson, D. A., Kapur, B. M., and Carlen, P. L. Cerebellar cortical and functional impairment in toluene abusers. *Acta Neurologica Scandinavica*, 67:319–29 (1983).

Greenblatt, D. J., Shader, R. I., and Abernathy, D. R. Current status of benzodiazepines (First and second of two parts). *New England Journal of Medicine*, 309:354–58 and 410–16 (1983).

Harvey, S. C. Hypnotics and sedatives. In: Gilman, A. G., Goodman, L. S., Rall,

T. W., and Murad, F. (eds.). *Goodman and Gilman's The Pharmacological Basis of Therapeutics.* 7th ed. New York: Macmillan, 1985.

Jacobs, M. R., and Fehr, K. O. *Drugs and Drug Abuse: A Reference Text.* 2d ed. Toronto: Addiction Research Foundation, 1987.

Jaffe, J. H. Drug addiction and drug abuse. In: Gilman, A. G., Goodman, L. S., Rall, T. W., and Murad, F. (eds.). *Goodman and Gilman's The Pharmacological Basis of Therapeutics.* 7th ed. New York: Macmillan, 1985.

Jaffe, J. H., and Martin, W. R. Opioid analgesics and antagonists. In: Gilman, A. G., Goodman, L. S., Rall, T. W., and Murad, F. (eds.). *Goodman and Gilman's The Pharmacological Basis of Therapeutics.* 7th ed. New York: Macmillan, 1985.

Julien, R. M. *A Primer of Drug Action.* 4th ed. San Francisco: W. H. Freeman, 1985.

Kalant, H., and Kalant, O. J. *Drugs, Society and Personal Choice.* Toronto: PaperJacks, 1971.

Kalant, O. J. *The Amphetamines: Toxicity and Addiction.* 2d ed. Toronto: University of Toronto Press, 1973.

Kozel, N. J., and Adams, E. H. *Cocaine Use in America: Epidemiologic and Clinical Perspectives.* NIDA Research Monograph 61. Rockville, Md.: Department of Health and Human Services, 1986.

Montagne, M. Drug taking paraphernalia. *Journal of Psychoactive Drugs,* 15:159–75 (1983).

Nahas, G. G. A Pharmacological Classification of Drugs of Abuse. *Bulletin on Narcotics,* 33(2): 1–19 (1981).

Siegal, R. K. New trends in drug use among youth in California. *Bulletin on Narcotics,* 37(2 & 3): 7–17 (1985).

3

Toxicity Associated with Long-Term Intravenous Heroin and Cocaine Self-Administration in the Rat*

Michael A. Bozarth and Roy A. Wise

Opiate addiction has traditionally been associated with a moderate fatality rate (1, 7). Cocaine use, on the other hand, is considered by many to be a relatively safe habit. Reported cases of death directly attributable to cocaine use seem to be less frequent (6). With the current rise in cocaine use (2), it is appropriate to estimate the mortality rate from addiction to this compound relative to that of heroin, which is widely recognized as a moderately dangerous addiction. The possibility exists that factors limiting availability and use are responsible for the apparent safety of cocaine and that, given the availability of large quantities of high-grade drug, cocaine toxicity has been underestimated.

Studies involving intravenous (iv) drug self-administration in laboratory animals have typically limited access to the drug during the experimental session. One reason for this is that early tests of cocaine self-administration with unlimited access resulted in a high subject fatality rate (4, 8, 9). While this observation is sufficient to prompt investigators to limit periods of drug access during experimental testing of stimulant drugs, there has not been a systematic comparison of the toxicity of cocaine and heroin during continuous access. The present study reports tests where animals were allowed continuous access to either iv cocaine hydrochloride or heroin hydrochloride for 30 days. The hourly drug intake was measured for each 24-hour period of testing, and observations were made regarding the general health of the animals.

METHODS

Male Long-Evans rats were anesthetized with pentobarbital sodium, 60 mg/kg intraperitoneally, and long-term iv catheters (Silastic tubing; outside diameter, 1.194 mm) implanted in the right external jugular vein. Penicillin G procaine, 60,000 units intramuscularly, was administered prophylactically, and the subjects were allowed seven to ten days to recover from the surgical procedure.

The rats were randomly divided into two groups and placed in standard operant test chambers with food and water available ad libitum. One group of subjects (n = 12) had access to cocaine hydrochloride, 1 mg/kg per infusion, while the other group (n = 11) had access to heroin hydrochloride, 100 μg/kg (0.1 mg/kg) per infusion. Both drugs were dissolved in physiological saline containing 0.3 per cent sodium metabisulfite and sterilized by filtration. Each IV catheter was connected to a 50-mL syringe by polyethylene tubing, and a fluid commutator located between the subject and the infusion pump permitted unrestricted movement of the animal during testing. Pressing a lever activated a motor-driven syringe pump that delivered 0.25 mL of drug solution over 10 s. Pressing the lever during the infusion interval had no scheduled effect, but rats could self-administer another infusion of drug immediately after completion of an injection. Testing for drug self-administration continued 24 hours a day for a maximum of 30 days. The hourly drug intake was measured for each rat.

RESULTS

Both groups of rats quickly learned to self-administer the drugs. Rates of learning for the two groups were comparable, although the dose of cocaine tested produced a somewhat higher rate of lever pressing than the dose of heroin tested. All 11 rats tested for heroin self-administration reliably self-administered drug with approximately the same hourly intake of heroin as rats tested for two- and six-hour sessions. Ten (83%) of the 12 rats tested for cocaine self-administration showed reliable responding for cocaine. Two animals in the cocaine group did not learn to self-administer significant quantities of drug (i.e., took less than 10% of the normal hourly intake of subjects tested during two- and six-hour sessions[1]), and their data were omitted from subsequent analyses.

Animals self-administering heroin showed a gradual increase in 24-hour drug intake during the first two weeks of testing (Figure 3.1). After this time, the mean daily intake of heroin remained constant through the remaining weeks of testing, with no evidence of further learning or tolerance to the rewarding effects of the drug injections. Rats in the heroin group tended to take approximately the same number of injections each day and to distribute their responding evenly throughout the 24 hours of testing. Body weights of these subjects remained stable and grooming behaviour was maintained during the 30 days of testing.

The group tested for cocaine self-administration demonstrated erratic patterns of drug intake across days of testing. Many rats would take large amounts of drug during one 24-hour period and much less drug during the next period (Figure 3.2). The episodic pattern of responding developed early and continued throughout the 30 days of testing. Cocaine self-administration

Figure 3.1

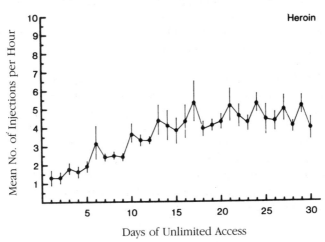

Daily intake of drug for typical subject self-administering heroin hydrochloride, 100 μg/kg per infusion. Note gradual increase in drug intake across first two weeks of testing and stable level of self-administration through termination of testing. Data are expressed as mean number of infusions per hour of testing, and error bars represent SEM.

was associated with a reduction in body weight (mean loss, 29%), and several animals lost around 40 per cent of their pretesting body weight. Grooming behaviour diminished over days of testing, and there was an obvious deterioration in the animals' general health. Several animals displayed full, clonicotonic seizures during testing but would reinitiate drug self-administration as soon as the convulsions subsided. The pattern of drug self-administration and the behavioural effects of chronic cocaine intake have been reported in detail elsewhere (4, 8, 9).

One of the most striking differences in the effects of continuous drug access in animals self-administering cocaine or heroin was the mortality rate (Figure 3.3). By the end of the second week of testing, 60 per cent of the subjects self-administering cocaine had died, while only 9 per cent of those self-administering heroin had died ($x^2[1] = 37.7$, p<.005). At the completion of the 30-day test protocol, the mortality rate for the cocaine group was 90 per cent and the mortality rate for the heroin group was 36 per cent ($x^2[1] = 23.1$, p<.005). Animals in the heroin group surviving the full 30 days of testing were still in good health, while the surviving animal in the cocaine group showed marked deterioration (32% weight loss).

Figure 3.2

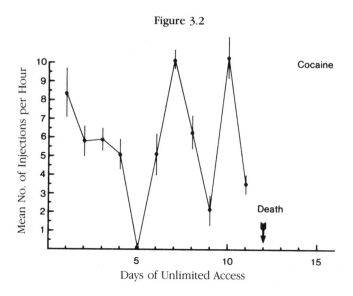

Daily intake of drug for typical subject self-administering cocaine hydrochloride, 1 mg/kg per infusion. Note erratic pattern of responding across days. Data are expressed as mean number of infusions per hour of testing, and error bars represent SEM.

COMMENT

Cocaine self-administration was accompanied by a substantially higher incidence of mortality than was heroin self-administration. This is reflected both by the number of days necessary to produce a 50 per cent mortality rate and by the number of animals surviving the 30-day testing protocol. Rats terminally deprived of food have been reported to die after a loss of around 40 per cent of their pretreatment body weight (3). In the present study, 56 per cent of the subjects responding for cocaine died after a loss of less than 30 per cent of their pretesting body weight. This suggests that the mortality associated with long-term cocaine use was not merely the result of a reduction of body weight; the high mortality rate is likely to be related to other factors, possibly the toxic effects of cocaine and its depression of medullary function (5, 10).

The fact that the number of fatalities following unlimited access to cocaine was over twice that following unlimited access to heroin has obvious implications for human drug abuse. While many drug users recognize the inherent danger of opiate addiction, they fail to recognize the potential danger of long-term cocaine use. The facts that cocaine is usually not available to humans in unlimited quantities and that the available cocaine tends to be of low purity probably account for the relatively few deaths associated with its use. As the

Figure 3.3

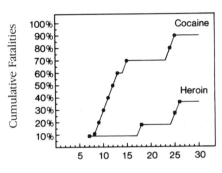

Days of Unlimited Access

Cumulative number of fatalities from intravenous cocaine hydrochloride and heroin hydrochloride self-administration during unlimited access to drug. Percentage of animals lost is depicted as function of days of continuous testing. Subject attrition due to catheter failure is not shown. Solid circles indicate deaths in cocaine group; solid squares, deaths in heroin group.

intake of cocaine increases and the concentration of this compound becomes greater (through the availability of higher-purity drug, by IV injections, or by "free-basing") the number of fatalities associated with cocaine abuse is likely to increase.

NOTES

1. M.A.B. unpublished data.

REFERENCES

1. Abelson, P. H. Death from heroin. *Science, 168*:1289 (1970).
2. Adams, E. H., and Durell, J. Cocaine: A growing public health problem. In: Grabowski, J. (ed.). *Cocaine: Pharmacology, Effects and Treatment of Abuse*. Washington, D.C.: National Institute on Drug Abuse, 1984. pp. 9–14.
3. Campbell, B. A., Teghtsoonian, R., and Williams, R. A. Activity, weight loss, and survival time of food-deprived rats as a function of age. *Journal of Comparative Physiology and Psychology, 54*:216–19 (1961).
4. Deneau, G. W., Yanagita, T., and Seevers, M. H. Self-administration of

psychoactive substances by the monkey: A measure of psychological dependence. *Psychopharmacology, 16*:30–48 (1969).

5. Evans, M. A., Dwivedi, C., and Harbison, R. D. Enhancement of cocaine-induced lethality by phenobarbital. In: Ellenwood, E. H. and Kilbery, M. M. (eds.). *Cocaine and Other Stimulants.* New York: Plenum, 1977. pp. 253–67.

6. Finkle, B. S. and McCloskey, K. L. The forensic toxicology of cocaine. In: Petersen, R. C. and Stillman, R. C. (eds.). *Cocaine: 1977.* Washington, D.C.: National Institute on Drug Abuse, 1977. pp. 153–78.

7. Jaffe, J. H. Drug addiction and drug abuse. In: Goodman, L. S. and Gilman, A. (eds.). *The Pharmacological Basis of Therapeutics.* New York: Macmillan, 1975. pp. 284–324.

8. Johanson, C. E., Balster, R. L., and Bonese, K. Self-administration of psychomotor stimulant drugs: The effects of unlimited access. *Pharmacological and Biochemical Behavior, 4*:45–51 (1976).

9. Pickens, R. and Thompson, T. Characteristics of stimulant reinforcement. In: Thompson, T. and Pickens, R. (eds.). *Stimulus Properties of Drugs.* New York: Appleton-Century-Crofts, 1971. pp. 177–92.

10. Richie, J. M., and Cohen, P. J. Local anesthetics. In: Goodman, L. S., and Gilman, A. (eds.). *The Pharmacological Basis of Therapeutics.* New York: Macmillan, 1975. pp. 379–403.

4

Heroin "Overdose" Death: Contribution of Drug-associated Environmental Cues*

SHEPARD SIEGEL, RILEY E. HINSON, MARVIN D. KRANK, AND JANE McCULLY

Substantial tolerance generally develops to the effects of opiates; the drug-experienced individual can survive a dose many times greater than that which would kill the drug-inexperienced individual (13). Despite such tolerance, about one per cent of U.S. heroin addicts die each year, mostly from the so-called overdose (17, 19). In urban areas with substantial numbers of addicts, drug overdose is among the leading causes of death in people aged 15 to 35 (1, 11). Postmortem examination of these victims routinely reveals pulmonary edema (14), which usually is attributed to hypoxia resulting from drug-induced respiratory depression (6).

Although mortality attributed to drug overdose is a major public health problem, its mechanisms are unclear. Some fatalities result from pharmacological overdose (8, 9, 12), but many experienced drug users die after a dose that should not be fatal in view of their tolerance (3, 5, 23). Indeed, some die following a heroin dose that was well-tolerated the previous day (5). Some fatalities may result from a synergism between the opiate and other drugs concomitantly administered or from adulterants (especially quinine) in the heroin, but many do not result from such drug interactions (3, 5, 23).

We suggest that drug "overdose" may frequently result from a failure of tolerance. That is, the opiate addict, who can usually tolerate extraordinarily high doses (14, 16), is not tolerant on the occasion of the overdose. A recently proposed model of tolerance based on the principles of Pavlovian conditioning (26, 27, 28) suggests conditions that favour such a failure of tolerance. The model is based on Pavlov's suggestion (22) that drug administration constitutes a conditioning trial, with the conditioned stimulus consisting of environmental cues present at the time of administration and the unconditioned stimulus consisting of the systemic effects of the drug. According to this interpretation of tolerance, as the drug is administered with increasing frequency, with the same environmental cues signaling each pharmacological stimulation, an association is established between these cues and the central effects of the drug. This association may be revealed in a subject with a history

---

*Reprinted from *Science, 216*, no. 4544 (April 1982): 436–37. Copyright 1982, The American Association for the Advancement of Science.

of drug abuse by administering a placebo in the drug administration environment. Conditioned pharmacological responses revealed in this manner are often the converse of the unconditioned drug effects (21, 26, 27, 28, 32). Such anticipatory responses attenuate the drug effects and contribute to tolerance. Accordingly, environmental signals of impending pharmacological stimulation are important because they enable the organism to make compensatory conditioned responses in anticipation of the unconditioned effects.

On the basis of this model, a failure of tolerance should occur if the drug is administered in an environment that has not, in the past, been associated with the drug. Indeed, several studies have demonstrated such dependence of opiate tolerance on environmental cues. For example, if the last of a series of morphine injections is given in the presence of cues that have not previously signaled the drug, rats and humans display less tolerance than if this injection were given in the presence of the usual drug-associated cues (2, 7, 15, 20, 24, 25, 29, 31). Although these studies establish a role for learning in morphine tolerance, primarily small drug doses were used. There is evidence, however, that the conditioning model of tolerance applies to the pernicious effects of very high doses of opiate (30). Thus, one contributing factor in death from the so-called opiate overdose might be the absence of a conditioned compensatory pharmacological response.

The results of the study described below indicate that heroin-induced mortality in heroin-experienced rats is higher when the drug is injected in an environment not previously associated with the drug than when it is injected in the usual drug-administration environment. The experimental design used provided a methodologically rigorous demonstration of the contribution of contextual stimuli to tolerance (10, 26, 27, 28).

Opiate-inexperienced male rats (Wistar-derived, 90 to 110 days old) with permanent jugular cannulas[1] were intravenously injected with diacetylmorphine hydrochloride (heroin) 15 times, one injection every other day. The dose was increased according to the following schedule: first injection, 1 mg/kg; second and third injections, 2 mg/kg; fourth through seventh injections, 4 mg/kg; and eighth through fifteenth injections, 8 mg/kg. Each rat also received one volumetrically equated injection of the vehicle (5% dextrose solution) on days when it was not injected with heroin.

The injections were given in two different environments. One was the colony, where the rats were individually housed. The animal was removed from its cage, injected, and returned to its cage. The other environment was a different room with constant white noise (60 dB SPL). Rats were injected 15 minutes after being transferred to this room and were kept there for an additional 2 hours. One group of rats received heroin in the distinctive room and dextrose in the colony; a second group received heroin in the colony and dextrose in the distinctive room. Finally, the subjects in each group were placed in one of the two environments and injected with 15 mg of heroin per kilogram. This procedure permitted evaluation of the effects of a high

Table 4.1
Rat mortality after the injection of heroin at 15 mg/kg

Group	Number of rats	Mortality (%)
ST	37	32.4
DT	42	64.3
Control	28	96.4

dose of heroin in the context of cues that had previously signaled lower doses of the drug (similarly tested [ST] rats) and in the context of cues not previously associated with the drug (differently tested [DT] rats). It should be emphasized that, throughout the study, both experimental groups were injected an equal number of times with the same doses of heroin at the same intervals between injections. (Results obtained from the two counterbalanced conditions were not significantly different.)[2] A third group received 30 daily injections of dextrose in each of the two environments on an alternating schedule and then an injection of heroin (15 mg/kg) in one of the two environments. Thus the control rats had no experience with the opiate before the final session.

Chi-square analysis indicates that mortality differed significantly among groups ($p < .001$).[3] Both groups with pretest experience with sublethal doses of heroin were more likely to survive the highest dose than control animals ($p < .002$), suggesting that tolerance resulted from the sublethal heroin injections independent of the environment associated with those injections. However, mortality was significantly higher in DT than in ST rats ($p < .001$), indicating that identical pretest pharmacological histories do not necessarily result in the display of equivalent tolerance to the lethal effect of heroin. The experiment was conducted in six replications (three involving testing in each of the two environments), and in every replication a greater proportion of DT than ST rats died ($p < .02$, binomial test). The combined results for all replications are summarized in Table 4.1.

In conclusion, groups of rats with the same pharmacological history of heroin administration can differ in mortality following administration of a high dose of the drug: rats that received the potentially lethal dose in the context of cues previously associated with sublethal doses were more likely to survive than animals that received the dose in the context of cues not previously associated with the drug.

NOTES

1. The cannula was a modified version of that described by R. J. Brown and C. B. Breckenridge (4). Subjects were cannulated 1 week before the exper-

iment. The rate of injection was controlled by infusing the injected substance at a rate of 0.005 ml/sec through the intravenous cannula with a Harvard model 902 infusion pump. The concentration of heroin (in sterile 5% dextrose) was 3.125, 6.250, 12.500, 25.000, and 50.000 mg/ml for the doses of 1, 2, 4, 8, and 15 mg/kg, respectively. Thus the duration of the infusion for all rats at all dose levels was equivalent (about 1 min/kg).

2. Of the 37 ST rats, 17 were injected with heroin in the distinctive room and 20 were injected with heroin in the colony. Half of the 42 DT rats were injected with heroin in each of the environments.

3. For subjects that died as a result of the injection of heroin at 15 mg/kg, the median times for the start of the injection until death (as determined by lack of heartbeat) in ST, DT, and control groups were 187, 174, and 164 seconds, respectively. Thus these animals died soon after the start of the lethal injection (differences between groups were insignificant), as is frequently the case with human victims of drug overdose (3).

REFERENCES

1. Abelson, P. H. Death from heroin. *Science, 168*:1289 (1970).
2. Advokat, C. Evidence for conditioned tolerance of the tail flick reflex. *Behavioral and Neural Biology, 29*:385–89 (1980).
3. Brecher, E. M., and the Editors of Consumer Reports. *Licit and Illicit Drugs*. Boston: Little, Brown, 1972.
4. Brown, R. J., and Breckenridge, C. B. A technique for long-term blood sampling or intravenous infusion in the freely moving rat. *Biochemical Medicine, 13*:280–86 (1975).
5. Canada. Commission of Inquiry into the Non-Medical Use of Drugs. *Final Report*. Ottawa: Information Canada, 1973.
6. Duberstein, J. L., and Kaufman, D. M. A clinical study of an epidemic of heroin intoxication and heroin-induced pulmonary edema. *American Journal of Medicine, 51*:704–14 (1971).
7. Ferguson, R. K., and Mitchell, C. L. Pain as a factor in the development of tolerance to morphine analgesia in man. *Clinical Pharmacology and Therapeutics, 10*:372–82 (1969).
8. Fraser, D. W. Methadone overdose: Illicit use of pharmaceutically prepared parenteral narcotics. *Journal of the American Medical Association, 217*:1387–89 (1971).
9. Garriott, J. C., and Sturner, W. Q. Morphine concentrations and survival periods in acute heroin fatalities. *New England Journal of Medicine, 289*:1276–78 (1973).

10. Hayes, R. L., and Mayer, D. J. Morphine tolerance: Is there evidence for a conditioning model? *Science, 200*:343–44 (1978).
11. Helpern, M. Fatalities from narcotic addiction in New York City: Incidence, circumstances, and pathological findings. *Human Pathology, 3*:13–21 (1972).
12. Huber, D. H. Heroin deaths—mystery or overdose? *Journal of the American Medical Association, 229*:689 (1974).
13. Hug, C. C. Characteristics and theories related to acute and chronic tolerance development. In: Mule, S. J., and Brule, H. (eds.). *Chemical and Biological Aspects of Drug Dependence*. Cleveland: CRC Press, 1972.
14. Jaffe, J. H., and Martin, W. R. Narcotic analgesics and antagonists. In: Goodman, A. G., Goodman, L. S., and Gilman, A. (eds.). *Goodman and Gilman's The Pharmacological Basis of Therapeutics*. 6th ed. New York: Macmillan, 1980.
15. LaHoste, G. J., Olson, R. D., Olson, G. A., and Kastin, A. J. Effects of Pavlovian conditioning and MIF-I on the development of morphine tolerance in rats. *Pharmacology, Biochemistry and Behavior, 13*:799–804 (1980).
16. Light, A. B., and Torrance, E. B. Opium addiction IV: The effects of abrupt withdrawal followed by readministration of morphine in human addicts, with special reference to the composition of the blood, the circulation and the metabolism. *Archives of Internal Medicine, 44*:1–16 (1929).
17. Louria, D. B., Hensle, T., and Rose, J. The major medical complications of heroin addiction. *Annals of Internal Medicine, 67*:1–22 (1967).
18. Mason, P. Mortality among young narcotic addicts. *Mount Sinai Hospital Journal, 34*:4–10 (1967).
19. Maurer, D. W. and Vogel, V. H. *Narcotics and Narcotic Addiction*. Springfield, Ill.: Charles C Thomas, 1973.
20. Mucha, R. F., Volkovskis, C., and Kalant, H. Conditioned increases in locomotor activity produced with morphine as an unconditioned stimulus, and the relation of conditioning to acute morphine effect and tolerance. *Journal of Comparative and Physiological Psychology, 95*:351–62 (1981).
21. Obál, F. The fundamentals of the central nervous control of vegetative homeostasis. *Acta Physiologica Academiae Scientiarium Hungaricae, 30*:15–29 (1966).
22. Pavlov, I. P. *Conditioned Reflexes*. London: Oxford University Press, 1927.
23. Reed, T. Challenging some "common wisdom" on drug abuse. *International Journal of the Addictions, 15*:359–73 (1980).
24. Siegel, S. Morphine analgesic tolerance: Its situation specificity supports a Pavlovian conditioning model. *Science, 193*:323–25 (1976).
25. Siegel, S. Tolerance to the hyperthermic effect of morphine in the rat is a learned response. *Journal of Comparative and Physiological Psychology, 92*:1137–49 (1978).
26. Siegel, S. The role of conditioning in drug tolerance and addiction. In:

Keehn, J. D. (ed.). *Psychopathology in Animals: Research and Clinical Applications*. New York: Academic Press, 1979.

27. Siegel, S. Opioid expectation modifies opioid effects. *Federation Proceedings, 41*:2339–43 (1982).

28. Siegel, S. Classical conditioning, drug tolerance, and drug dependence. In: Smart, R. G., Glaser, F. B., Israel, Y., Kalant, H., Popham, R. E., and Schmidt, W. (eds.). *Research Advances in Alcohol and Drug Problems*, Vol. 7. New York: Plenum, 1983.

29. Siegel, S., Hinson, R. E., and Krank, M. D. The role of predrug signals in morphine analgesic tolerance: Support for a Pavlovian conditioning model of tolerance. *Journal of Experimental Psychology: Animal Behavior Processes, 4*:188–96 (1978).

30. Siegel, S., Hinson, R. E., and Krank, M. D. Modulation of tolerance to the lethal effect of morphine by extinction. *Behavioral and Neural Biology, 25*:257–62 (1979).

31. Tiffany, S. T., and Baker, T. B. Morphine tolerance in rats: Congruence with a Pavlovian paradigm. *Journal of Comparative and Physiological Psychology, 95*:747–62 (1981).

32. Wikler, A. Conditioning of successive adaptive responses to the initial effects of drugs. *Conditioned Reflex, 8*:193–210 (1973).

5

Rat Park Chronicle*

BRUCE K. ALEXANDER, PATRICIA HADAWAY,
AND ROBERT COAMBS

The opiate drugs, especially heroin, have a demonic reputation. "Junkies" have been viewed as fools who toyed with irresistible pleasure and became enslaved, much as earlier unfortunates were thought to be possessed by demons for their sins. Fortunately, Isidor Chein, Stanton Peele, Norman Zinberg, and others are dispelling the devil-drug imagery and advocating a more human understanding of opiate addicts as people who need the powerful analgesic and tranquilizing effects of narcotics to cope with the stress of life (3, 8). The new understanding makes it possible to respond to heroin addiction more productively and to view the larger problem of addiction to alcohol, pills, work, gambling, love, etc., more clearly.

Curiously, there is a scientific roadblock to this progress. We first encountered it about four years ago during a university seminar on addiction. The class was organized around the "coping" concept of addiction, which was acceptable to almost all the students. One dissenter, however, insisted on the importance of the fact that rats and monkeys consume large amounts of opiate drugs, including heroin, in experimental settings. Does this not prove that coping problems are irrelevant? After all, how much coping is required of a laboratory animal living alone in a perfectly controlled environment? Isn't the craving for heroin and other opiate drugs more simply a natural affinity for the pleasure the drugs produce, a weakness of the flesh which *Homo sapiens* shares with its mammalian cousins?

It has to be admitted that many psychologists and psychiatrists (perhaps most) accept this interpretation of the biomedical research that it seems to justify extreme measures which have been applied to the heroin addiction problem. If opiate addiction is caused by a powerful natural affinity, then it cannot be cured or even prevented, any more than the sex or hunger drives can. It follows that the most reasonable defence against the threat of opiate addiction is effective prohibition—Drug Squads must be bolstered, borders guarded, and junkies kept out of circulation, lest they spread the habit.

Two of us protested this interpretation, but we were not able to carry the day. Our class rat expert had hard data, but we only had the suspicion that the animals' affinity for opiate drugs existed precisely because they were

---

*Reprinted from the *British Columbia Medical Journal, 22*, no. 2 (1980): 54–56. "1987 Update" contributed by the senior author.

isolated in laboratory cages. Who wouldn't want to be stoned during a life of solitary confinement? The "natural affinity" interpretation of the animal data has been questioned by other psychologists, including Stanton Peele and Edward Khantzian, but they have not provided direct evidence which refutes it (5).

Finding ourselves unable to win the argument in the seminar, we decided to bring the case to the laboratory. The crucial test, we decided, would be to compare the opiate consumption of rats in radically different environments. One environment would be the "normal" housing for laboratory animals in psychopharmacology experiments, i.e., individual cages mounted on steel racks, constructed so that the animals could not see or touch each other. The second environment was the most natural habitat we could contrive in the laboratory, so we named it "Rat Park." Rat Park is open and spacious, with about 200 times the square footage of a standard cage. It is also scenic (with a peaceful, British Columbia forest painted on the plywood walls), comfortable (with empty tin cans and other desiderata strewn about the floor), and friendly (we ran coed groups of 16–20 rats).

Would the opiate consumption in the two environments differ? In order to find out, we had to develop a means of measuring each individual's opiate consumption. This was accomplished by allowing the rats to drink solutions containing precisely measured amounts of opiate drugs. Oral consumption of opiate drugs has the same effect as injection except, of course, that the injection takes effect faster, producing the famous "rush," so renowned in junkie lore. Regardless of the romance of the "rush" and the needle, injection is not essential to addiction. Opiate addiction was widespread in North America before syringes were available and many present day opiate addicts never inject their opiates unless a drug shortage makes the more efficient injection technique necessary (2). This was especially true in Viet Nam during the war when heroin was, for a time, very cheap, and a majority of the soldier-addicts preferred to smoke, snort, or drink their heroin.

In the cages, opiate consumption was measured simply enough by fastening drinking bottles containing narcotic and inert solutions on each cage and weighing them daily. In Rat Park it was more difficult to measure individual consumption, especially since we didn't want to disrupt life in what we hoped would become an idyllic community. We built a short tunnel opening into Rat Park which was just large enough to accommodate one rat at a time. At the end of the tunnel, the rats could release a fluid from either of two drop dispensers and drink it. A video camera recorded how much each rat drank of each solution.

We obtained a small supply of morphine through the Health and Welfare Ministry of the federal government. Heroin is a form of morphine (diacetyl-morphine), and the psychoactive effects of the two drugs are very similar, provided the doses are equivalent. This is widely recognized both by professionals and by narcotics addicts.

Now we were ready for the experiments. It occurred to us that there are at least three ways of offering narcotics to rats, analogous to the ways they become available to people. The first, which we call the "Easy Access" procedure, is a situation where the drugs are freely available and very cheap. We made two solutions available around the clock both in the cages and in Rat Park. One solution contained morphine, dissolved in sugar water to mask its bitter taste. The alternative solution was also bitter-sweet (in fact we concocted it to taste exactly the same to us), but the bitterness came from a non-narcotic, quinine. Thus, as far as we could arrange it, the narcotic solution was just as available and palatable to the rats as the inert alternative and they had no other source of fluids. In hedonic cost, the drug was precisely as "cheap as water."

We called our second mode of presentation the "Seduction" procedure, based on the idea that people are sometimes lured into heroin use by an extraneous pay-off, like group acceptance or a feeling of successful rebellion. In our rodent microcosm, the "seduction" involved, again, a constantly available choice of water and morphine solution. This time the water in both environments was pure tap-water, but the morphine solution was sweetened. Every five days the sweetness was progressively (and diabolically) increased toward levels which should be irresistible even to the most strait-laced rat, since all rats have a powerful "sweet tooth."

Finally, we had a "Kicking-the-habit" procedure, simulating the dilemma faced by a person who is physically dependent on heroin and then has either to maintain the habit or endure the effects of withdrawal. In our version, the rat junkies were given nothing but morphine solution to drink for 57 days, long enough by far, according to current research findings, to produce tolerance and physical dependence. They were then given free choice between water and morphine solution under three different experimental regimes.

We first ran the "Easy Access" experiment. To our complete surprise, after the first day, rats in both environments drank the quinine solution almost exclusively, so the possibility of an environmental effect could not even be tested. Undaunted (almost), we proceeded to the "Seduction" and "Kicking-the-habit" experiments. In them, the environmental effects were crystal clear. No matter how much we induced, seduced, or tempted them, the Rat Park rats resisted drinking the narcotic solution. The caged rats drank plenty, however, ranging up to sixteen times as much as the Rat Park residents in one experimental phase, and measuring ten times as much in some other phases. The females, curiously, drank more morphine in both environments, but the Rat Park rats always drank far less than the caged rats. These data were duly transformed and statistically analysed and proved to be statistically significant, at an extremely high level of confidence (1, 4).

We think these results are socially as well as statistically significant. If rats in a reasonably normal environment consistently resist opiate drugs, then the "natural affinity" idea is wrong, an overgeneralization of experiments on isolated animals.

These animal findings are compatible with the new "coping" interpretation of human opiate addiction if one keeps in mind that rats are by nature extremely gregarious, active, curious animals. Solitary confinement causes extraordinary psychic distress in human beings and it is likely to be just as stressful to other sociable species, and therefore to elicit extreme forms of coping behaviour such as the use of powerful analgesics and tranquilizers, in this case, morphine.

It may also be that socially housed rats resist morphine because it is such a powerful anesthetic and tranquilizer. As such, it interferes with a rat's (or a person's) ability to play, eat, mate, and engage in all the other active behaviours which make life rewarding. We presently are guessing that this second possibility is the primary cause of the environmental effect because of the fact that neither group consumed more morphine in the "Easy Access" procedure.

The Rat Park results seem to fit with the most careful observations of opiate addiction in our own species. For example, Chein has shown that in the city neighborhoods where heroin is most freely available, most people simply ignore it, and those that don't suffer unusually severe family problems and have the most painful self-concepts (3). Robins has shown that over 90 per cent of heroin-addicted soldiers returning from Viet Nam kicked that habit, stateside, with little problem (7). Numerous observers have reported that more than 90 per cent of those made physically dependent by hospital medication have no hint of a craving for opiates upon recovery from their illness and release from the hospital.

Rats in Rat Park, ghetto dwellers, soldiers home from Viet Nam, patients released from the hospital all seem to be telling us the same story. Namely that, contrary to the "natural affinity" view, individuals are vulunerable to opiate drugs under some circumstances, but not others. Solitary confinement puts rats in a state of vulnerability. We are investigating whether it is the solitude, absence of sensory input, lack of activity, or some other aspect of the rats' housing which makes them vulnerable, but we believe that the more vital task is to determine the conditions in which people are vulnerable. Alienation, loneliness, self-hate, and helplessness, are terms which suggest themselves, but they are too vague, in current usage, to be a basis for action. The state of vulnerability must be described well enough so that we can identify its causes and reduce them as we guide the evolution of our society.

We have now spent four years in the gloom of our rat laboratory and we believe our faithful rodents have graciously told us something new and important. Our problem now is to perceive the dimensions of our own cages as clearly as we see those which house the rats.

1987 UPDATE

After this article was published in 1980 we spent a number of years trying to isolate environmental factors that stimulate and inhibit opiate consumption in rats. The answer eluded us because we ran into a completely unexpected phenomenon.

The original difference between socially housed and isolated animals, which was found in Wistar rats, could not be replicated with "new colony Wistar rats" that were introduced by the supplier, Charles River Inc., around 1980. Neither isolated nor socially housed rats of the new substrain would consume much morphine. A number of other psychopharmacological researchers in Canada and the U.S. could not reproduce their earlier drug and alcohol data with "new colony Wistars" either (6). We could not determine conclusively whether this was because of subtle genetic, immunological, or behavioural differences between the substrains. The original findings *could* be reproduced with a completely new strain of rats (Sprague-Dawley), however.

At this point, it seems that the genetic-immunological-behavioural complexities of morphine consumption in rats are remote from the factors that affect human addiction and that environmental influences must be investigated in our own species, with its own unique complexities.

Rat Park served its original purpose of dispelling the myth of a universal mammalian craving for opiate drugs that was proclaimed so uncritically in the literature of the late 1970s. In a more general sense, the Rat Park research showed us the limits of animal research in psychopathology. There probably is a strain of rats or a species of monkeys that will provide support for *any* hypothesis under the right experimental conditions. It is important for social scientists not to be dazzled by the high technology of the laboratory, but to treat such research with the same intense skepticism that is due any pronouncement that affects human welfare.

REFERENCES

1. Alexander, B. K., Coambs, R. B., and Hadaway, P. F. The effect of housing and gender on morphine self-administration in rats. *Psychopharmacology*, 58:175–79 (1978).
2. Brecher, E. M., and the Editors of Consumer Reports. *Licit and Illicit Drugs*. Boston: Little, Brown, 1972.
3. Chein, I., Gerrard, D. L., Lee, R. S., and Rosenfeld, E. *The Road to H*. New York: Basic Books, 1964.
4. Hadaway, P. F., Alexander, B. K., Coambs, R. B., and Beyerstein, B. The effect of housing and gender on preference for morphine-sucrose solutions in rats. *Psychopharmacology*, 66:87–91 (1979).
5. Khantzian, E. J. Opiate addiction: a critique of theory and some implications for treatment. *American Journal of Psychotherapy*, 28:59–70 (1974).

6. Petrie, B. F. Failure to replicate an environmental effect of morphine hydrochloride consumption: A possible psychopharmacogenetic link. Unpublished doctoral diss., Simon Fraser University, 1985.

7. Robins, L. N., Davis, D. H., and Nurco, D. N. How permanent was Viet Nam drug addiction? In: Greene, M. H., and Dupont, E. L. (eds.). *The Epidemiology of Drug Abuse.* NIDA Journal Supplement, Part 2, Vol. 64. Washington, D.C.: U.S. Government Printing Office, 1974.

8. Zinberg, N. E., Harding, W. M., Stelmack, S. M., and Marblestone, R. A. Patterns of heroin use. *Annals of the New York Academy of Science,* 3:10–24 (1978).

CANADA'S RESPONSE TO DRUGS: HISTORY AND LEGISLATION

In this section of the book, we turn to Canada's drug laws and the way in which they evolved. If our legislation had been created in a single sweeping policy initiative and if it had been based on a clearly articulated definition of the problem, the historical record might have been of less importance. However, our drug laws have proliferated in a piecemeal fashion, as crisis management rather than as comprehensive policy planning. Further, drug lawmaking has traditionally been an expression of essentially moral concerns. A newcomer to Canada's drug laws may discern some anomalies in the *Narcotic Control Act* and the *Food and Drugs Act*. For example, it may seem strange that phencyclidine (PCP) is in one Act, while the other hallucinogenic drugs are in another. One might also ask why cannabis is subject to the same penalties as heroin, or why sharing a marijuana cigarette with a friend is equivalent under the law to selling many kilos to a stranger. Because those provisions appeared at different times in response to differing circumstances, these questions can best be answered by reviewing the evolution of our laws.

Stepping back to compare the drug laws to other criminal legislation, one asks whether the penalties to which illicit drug users are subject and the enforcement powers of the police to arrest them seem reasonable when compared to other criminal offences. Stepping back even further, one also might ask whether it is appropriate to use the federal criminal law to control some drugs when other drugs are regulated but legally available. For over 15 years, scholars from a number of different disciplines have been examining these issues; they have concluded that the time is overdue to identify our essential concerns and develop laws and regulations that are guided by principles of consistency and fairness. There is widespread consensus that changes are called for, but little consensus on what these changes should be. Meanwhile, the present legislation has its own inertia; it seems that laws are more easily passed than amended or repealed.

As the history unfolds in this section, we shall see that the motive force for Canada's drug lawmaking has been either international pressure (particularly from the United States) or lobbying by interested parties (professional groups, law enforcement agencies, bureaucrats or moral entrepreneurs). As Parliament only rarely takes the initiative in moral matters, this should come as no surprise. As a rule, drug law reform initiatives were accompanied by articles in the popular press bringing the current concerns to the attention of the public, often in a most sensational fashion. Thus, lobbying buttressed by a scandalized public provided the foundation for legislative action.

Glenn Murray opens this section with a lively social history of the gentlemanly professional rivalry that led to legislation controlling the patent medicine trade. In this case, social reform came about because pharmacists and physicians were determined that controls should be placed on the industry. Their demands won out over the interests of the patent medicine manufacturers. In this debate, professional interests were at stake, and comparatively little attention was paid to the possible risks that consumers were running by dosing themselves with over-the-counter preparations containing opium, morphine, cocaine, alcohol, and any number of secret ingredients.

In contrast to this legislation, the precursors of our present *Narcotic Control Act* were enacted in an atmosphere of righteous indignation aroused by perceived threats to the prevailing moral order. Again, the debates were notable for the absence of concern about the true extent of the problem or its public health implications. As Robert Solomon and Melvyn Green trace this history, it proceeds from one moral crisis to the next; accordingly, each new legislative package was more Draconian than its predecessor. This progression continued as long as drug users could be branded as outsiders, and as long as they continued to have no voice because of their status as moral inferiors. The process stopped and showed evidence of reversing itself once otherwise conventional young Canadians began using illicit drugs and when significant numbers of them were subjected to the measures that the legislators had intended for an outcast class.

The result of this history is clearly and concisely described by Robert Solomon, who has contributed another chapter that could have been entitled: "Everything you ever wanted to know about Canada's drug laws . . . but might well have been afraid to ask." This chapter may serve as a reference for readers who are unfamiliar with Canadian legislation; the charts summarizing the offences and penalties under the *Narcotic Control Act* and the *Food and Drugs Act* should be particularly useful. As Professor Solomon notes, the maximum penalties permitted under these statutes have rarely been imposed in recent years. Conviction statistics indicating the range of sentences handed down appear in the Appendix at the end of this book.

Although Canada has traditionally shown little interest in developing a coherent and inclusive drug policy, evidence in the late 1960s of increases in the use of cannabis, LSD, methamphetamine, and volatile solvents prompted the appointment of a Commission of Inquiry into the Non-Medical Use of Drugs. It became known as the "Le Dain Commission," after its chairperson, Gerald Le Dain, a respected legal scholar and professor of law.

In fact, the order-in-council that appointed the Commission did not call for a comprehensive review of all non-medical drug use. However, the Commissioners chose to interpret their mandate broadly. They defined the scope of the inquiry as including drugs not specifically mentioned in the terms of reference, including alcohol and tobacco. This was a pivotal decision, because the exclusion of legal drugs would have created a false impression of the extent and patterns of non-medical drug use in Canada. It was also important as a point of public education, because at the time many alcohol and tobacco users were under the illusion that they were not drug users.

Between 1970 and 1973, the Commission published four reports. Even 15 years later, this body of work is widely cited and internationally respected. Because they were published in French as well as English, the reports had a more diverse readership and a wider international influence than similar efforts from other countries. Canadians tend to remember only that the Commissioners were divided on their recommendations and, in any case, that the policy proposals were ignored. Thus, it is worth noting here that the research chapters still remain a valuable reference source, and that the legal and philosophical discussions represent a unique and scholarly contribution to the debate surrounding drug use in Canada.

As suggested above, there are several levels from which an analysis of Canada's response to drugs can proceed. The most overarching perspective addresses the appropriateness of using criminal prohibition to control "vice," whether it be prostitution, gambling, or drug use. The Le Dain Commission considered not only the effectiveness of the criminal law as a policy, but also the suitability of applying it against drug users in a free and democratic society.

We intended to include the Le Dain argument on this issue as the closing chapter of this section, but space limitations prevented it. The Commission concluded that society does have the right to use the criminal law to restrict the availability of harmful substances in the interest of protecting its citizens. However, there is a crucial caveat: that the law should not be used without regard for its own potential for harm to the individual or society. We urge readers to refer to the Le Dain Commission's *Final Report* (Ottawa: Information Canada, 1973), especially Appendix F.2, "Whether in Principle, the Criminal Law Should Be Used in the Field of Non-Medical Drug Use." This elegant discussion guides us through the reasoning behind the Commission's unique approach to policy analysis, the fundamental principles being that the relative costs and benefits of policies must be considered in every case, and that the ultimate sanction should not be applied unless arguably more good than harm is likely to result.

6

The Road to Regulation:
Patent Medicines in Canada
in Historical Perspective

GLENN F. MURRAY

This chapter describes an important and previously neglected feature of the history of drug use in Canada: the use, trade, and regulation of patent medicines. Non-medical and quasi-medical use of these nostrums accounted for the bulk of the drug problem in Canada from the latter part of the nineteenth century through the early twentieth (29, 38). The "great patent-medicine craze" (33, p. 291) at that time was a boon to the pharmaceutical trade, one that left a mark of success on the future of this now enormous industry.

The social history of the origins of drug control in Canada has largely been concerned with legislation that would ultimately evolve into our present *Narcotic Control Act* (3, 10, 17, 39). A principal conclusion of these studies is that legislation became possible because of hostility toward the Chinese, whose opium smoking became a focus of racial prejudice (see Chapters 7 and 14). However, widespread use of proprietary and patent medicines was a much larger problem, cutting across the whole Canadian population. This chapter examines the way in which patent medicine use came to be defined as a social problem in this country, and discusses the origins of our first legislation to bring the trade under control, the *Proprietary or Patent Medicine Act* of 1908.

THEORETICAL FRAMEWORK

The existing literature on the origins of law tends to reflect a dichotomy of consensus and conflict theories (19, 21, 27). The notion that there is a consensus in society on important values, and that these shared sentiments are formalized in law for the common good, has been variously stated (2, 13, 14, 20, 22, 32). In contrast to this perspective is the position that conflict is endemic and inevitable. Hence, laws are an expression of particular interests rather than collective ones. That is, because there are competing interests and values in society, laws reflect the interests and values of those who have the power to shape them (4, 11, 40, 44, 45, 46).

Rather than describing these two perspectives as consensus and conflict theories, Hagan (19, p. 622) uses the terms "moral functionalism" and "moral

Marxism," respectively. He argues that both tend to view social phenomena from a normative standpoint rather than an empirical one—"moral functionalism" sees law as a good thing and "moral Marxism" sees it as a bad one. Thus, neither perspective approaches the study of law objectively. In consequence, little empirical progress has been made in the study of the origins of law.

A preferable approach for the sociology of law is to identify the factors operating in a specific socio-historical context, and how they are related to one another. In this approach, the sociology of social problems has application to the sociology of law. The dominant perspective in that line of inquiry hypothesizes that the course of a social problem involves overlapping stages of development. Using this hypothesis, the earliest indication of a troublesome condition (one defined as such by one or more groups within society) can be linked to eventual, though not inevitable, legislative action (15, 25, 31, 34, 36). Those who successfully impose their definitions, and create a social problem/law, will be those who have a vested interest in a particular issue and those who have more power than their opposition (46, p. 180).

From this point of view, law does not reflect collective values (as Durkheim believed). But neither does it reflect the interests of one particular, all-powerful group over a powerless one (as Marx argued). What it does represent is a plurality of interests. As we will see in the present analysis of the use, trade, and regulation of patent medicines, social reform came about because of some groups' demands, and in spite of other groups' interests. It was not a victory for the capitalists over the labourers. The central groups in the debate—pharmacists, physicians, and the patent medicine men—shared the same class position. Indeed, some pharmacists and physicians were patent medicine men as well.

THE GOLDEN AGE OF PATENT MEDICINES

The Favoured Source of Treatment

The term "patent medicine" originated in Great Britain in the eighteenth century when some proprietary remedies gained royal favour (47). Although such nostrums reached Canada in the baggage of eighteenth-century British immigrants, the patent medicine industry in Canada was not established until the beginning of the nineteenth century (18). A wide range of patent medicines was soon promoted as a cure for every ailment known to humanity.

The early history of advertising was synonymous with the growth of the patent medicine industry. One of the earliest English newspaper advertisements, in 1652, was for tea, a beverage imported from China which "owed its initial popularity to claims that it was a remedy or preventive against a long list of common human ills" (33, p. 289). Later, many newspapers and periodicals were supported, in large measure, by the high revenue from patent medicine ads. By the latter part of the nineteenth century in Canada, "patent medicine advertising accounted for a very large percentage of the total in print media of all kinds" (43, p. 235).

Patent medicines were a widely available source of treatment throughout the nineteenth century. They could be obtained from medical doctors and local drug stores. But, more importantly, they were available at the corner store, through the mail, and door-to-door. They were popularly perceived as an innocuous and inexpensive form of treatment, less threatening and extreme than some forms employed by physicians. Of course, the patent medicine trade was partly responsible for this perception. Their advertisements drew vivid contrasts between physicians and themselves: "Doctors wanted to cut people up or give prolonged treatment, while their 'sure cure' would instantly provide relief. Physicians charged high fees; their remedies were cheap" (41, pp. 127–28).

Although there were far more physicians in the latter part of the nineteenth century than at the beginning, they tended to be scarce in a vast and rural Canada. In 1881, for example, the 2,792 physicians in Canada provided a ratio of 1,249 people to each medical doctor. Although there were 4,448 physicians a decade later, the concurrent and rapid increase in the general population left a ratio of 1,069 to 1 (9, p. 413). By comparison, the trade in patent medicines was growing by leaps and bounds. Indeed, Canadian census data for that period show a dramatic increase in the number of patent medicine manufacturers—from 29 in 1880–81 to 116 in 1890–91 (6, 7).

The Emergence of a Social Problem

> The claims of some of the proprietary medicines on the market to-day are preposterous; some are little short of criminal in the assertions they make. And yet people in other respects normal will swallow both the advertisement and the medicine. (30, p. 114)

While some patent medicines were safe, few lived up to the miraculous healing claims made by their manufacturers. Moreover, many contained potentially dangerous substances, including cocaine, morphine, opium, and excessive amounts of alcohol (18, 47). However, most consumers would have been unaware of the contents of these nostrums. As the term "nostrum" implies, they were secret formula medicines.

A gullible public was bombarded with sensational and fraudulent advertisements, ones that were nevertheless quite believable because most consumers did not have the experience and information to question the appealing claims. Thus, people sometimes unwittingly "doped" themselves. The following case of a Montreal woman illustrates the insidious nature of the problem:

> A woman was received recently at a *Montreal hospital* with the trembling hands, staggering gait, insomnia, dyspepsia, loss of appetite, etc., of alcoholism, also

visual hallucinations, dilatation of the pupils, mental dullness and pronounced moral depravity. She had always been a person of quiet, modest tastes, and her husband asserted that she never took liquor. Asked whether she took any drug, he went home to investigate and returned with a bottle of Agnew's catarrh powder, a patent remedy which she had been using as a snuff for four or five months, consuming three bottles a week. The bottle held 80 grains and contained 1.75 per cent cocain [sic]. The therapeutic dose is 1/4 to 1 grain—*Un. Med. du Canada*, April. (24, p. 1092)

Patent medicines were often taken for non-medical purposes as well. The euphoric effects of cocaine, opium, and other drugs contained in these nostrums appealed to some users.

The Interests and Claims-making Activities of Competing Groups

Editorials in Canadian journals of pharmacy and medicine suggest that pharmacists and physicians were more concerned about curtailing the trade in patent medicines than about the dangers posed by their use. For some time, pharmacists had been engaged in activities to bring the "itinerant quack" (5a, p. 368) into disrepute and his wares under strict control. In 1871, pharmacists obtained professional status in law (8). That same year, "they sought to force patent medicine manufacturers to register their formulae" (8, p. 8). Two years later, a lengthy critique of the patent medicine trade appeared in the *Canadian Pharmaceutical Journal*. The following passage is taken from that editorial:

> From [the schemes of patent medicine men] arise the mighty houses, wrapped in the impenetrable armour of wealth, which promulgate with impunity millions of lies, deceiving the ignorant, deluding the unwary, and preying on the lives of suffering humanity. (5a, p. 368)

The trade in patent medicines left little market for the medicine-compounding business of pharmacists. Indeed, Clark (8, p. 7) argues that in nineteenth-century Ontario, "[d]ruggists were caught in a veritable commercial and professional maelstrom over patent medicines." Nevertheless, some pharmacists benefited from the patent medicine boom. Those who owned the stores in which they operated their compounding businesses profited by selling the more popular patent medicines. Some even patented their own medicines and found that enterprise to be more fruitful than their compounding businesses (8). These pharmacists would lobby against particular aspects of proposed patent medicine legislation. For most pharmacists, however, the trade in patent medicines represented a liability (8). All pharmacists, of course, fought to distinguish themselves professionally from the patent medicine men (5f).

Some pharmacists felt that the response to the sale of patent medicines should be radical (5b). It was suggested that pharmacists tell their customers to use the remedies they had prepared rather than the more popular patent medicines. The pharmacist was encouraged to stand by his product. He should say "I made it of the best materials, and it contains just what I claim it does" (5b, p. 180). He could not say the same for patent medicines. He knew they often contained dangerous substances, but he had no specific knowledge of the formulae. Yet he was expected to know, and be at least professionally responsible for, the medicines he sold. Many questions put to him by his customers would go unanswered (5c).

In 1892 pharmacists attempted to control patent medicines in Ontario through an amendment to the *Pharmacy Act*. It was not the first endeavour of this kind. Such measures had been attempted as early as 1869 (5d). None was successful.

The lucrative and growing trade in patent medicines was also a threat to the medical profession. Indeed, Starr (41, p. 127) argues that in the United States "the nostrum makers were the nemesis of the physicians. They mimicked, distorted, derided, and undercut the authority of the profession." The same situation existed in Canada. At first physicians responded by questioning the use of these medicines, but soon they were castigating them. In medical journals, patent medicines were often referred to as "quack medicines." Their use, it was stated, became a habit for the user which "eventually leads to the ruin of his mental, moral and physical nature" (28d, p. 274). Finally, they began to mount an organized campaign to regulate the trade.

Initially, medical opposition focused on the claims made in advertisements (28a, p. 359, 28b, pp. 362–64). Clearly, most were fraudulent. In 1903 a call to regulate such advertisements appeared in the *Montreal Medical Journal*. In a subsequent issue of that journal, physicians were encouraged to attend a meeting of the Proprietary Association (the patent medicine men). By attending these meetings, it was said, physicians would have an excellent opportunity to advise the opposition against employing excessive levels of alcohol in their preparations. They could also inform them about the "pharmacological effects of large doses of opium when given to children, upon the use of cocaine in catarrhal conditions, and upon the employment of abortifacients." It was further suggested that they vividly draw attention to "the methods of advertising which some owners of patent medicines employ" (28c, p. 656).

Within a few years, provincial and municipal medical associations began to make resolutions calling for controls on the sale of patent medicines. On March 12, 1906, for example, the Vancouver Medical Association unanimously supported a resolution that concluded as follows: "Be it resolved that the Dominion House of Commons, now in session, be petitioned to appoint a commission to investigate this whole matter [the sale of patent medicines] with a view to enacting laws which will eradicate these evils" (28d, p. 275). This resolution was sent to Sir Wilfrid Laurier, Prime Minister of Canada, in a letter dated March 19, 1906 (26a). The letter pointed out the dangers of opium in soothing syrup, cocaine in catarrh mixtures, and so on, and indicated the fraudulent nature of advertisements for patent medicines. Laurier's private secretary responded in a letter dated March 28, 1906, stating that "all due consideration will be given to your representations" (26b).

The effort to seek legislative change was not confined to Vancouver's physicians. Several provincial medical associations were concurrently attempting to have controls placed on patent medicines. The Government of Ontario was convinced enough to prepare a bill entitled "An Act regulating the manufacture and sale of proprietary and patent medicines" and to put it before the provincial legislature in 1906 (12). The bill did not pass three readings, however.

Clearly, pharmacists and physicians played a central role in defining the problem of patent medicines.[1] The professional status and economic interests of these two groups were in conflict with those of the patent medicine industry. Their inability to effect change after so many attempts, over so many years, may seem surprising. It isn't, however, when one considers that the trade in patent medicines was a boost to the economy. Moreover, the public had not joined in the debate to any great extent. Pharmacists and physicians failed to create a moral issue for the public. One would have thought that such an assignment would have been easy. The period from the late nineteenth century to the early twentieth was influenced by a movement known as the "social gospel." Revivalism in churches went hand in hand with the revival of society (1). It was an era of moral and social reform, leading one historian to conclude that "no aspect of the community's life, from the home to Parliament, was unaffected" by the tide (35, p. 171).

Legislation for patent medicines would be forthcoming, in 1908. But while pharmacists and physicians continued to seek such a measure, the legislation would not be what some pharmacists and most physicians had in mind.

Discussions and Activities of the Government of Canada, 1904–1908

The long and arduous official road to regulation of patent medicines began with a motion in the Senate. On July 28, 1904, a senator by the name of Sullivan, who happened to be a medical doctor as well, gave notice of a motion he would move the following Tuesday. He would ask the Governor General to have a statement prepared

> showing the names of all liquid mixtures known as patent or proprietary medicines . . . showing also the amount of money, if any, paid by importer, maker, mixer or vendor to the government as special tax or license . . . Showing likewise if the government has any knowledge of the ingredients. (37a, p. 869)

Sullivan said that the purpose of his motion was "to induce the House to take some action to prevent the sale and use of noxious medicine compounds." He expounded the problem at length, explaining that many patent medicines were "injurious instead of . . . beneficial" and that they "cultivate[d] an appetite for alcohol, opium and other injurious drugs." He went on to say that not one of these remedies "can possibly do what is claimed for it in the advertisements" (37a, p. 869).

One cannot say for certain whether Sullivan's notice of motion induced the Postmaster General, Sir William Mulock, to add the following section to a seemingly unrelated bill, An Act to Further Amend the Post Office Act. Yet a few days later (August 1, 1904), "out of the blue" as it were, the following amendment was proposed by the Postmaster General:

> It shall not be lawful to transmit by mail any books, magazines, periodicals, circulars, newspapers or other publications which contain advertisements representing marvellous, extravagant, or grossly improbable cures, or creative or healing powers by means of medicines, appliances or devices referred to in such advertisements. (23a, p. 8045)

To say the least, the section was not well received. It was seen as a drastic measure, one that gave too much power to the Government to censor these media. One member of the House suggested that the "medical men" must have been behind this proposal. He accused the Postmaster General of being in "combine" with them (23a, p. 8045). Two days later the section was struck from the Bill (23b).

When Sullivan made his expected motion on August 5, 1904 he said: "The reason I brought this up was because Dr. Bray [an eminent and experienced surgeon] introduced it at the meeting of the Ontario Medical Council." The council had recommended "that the drugs of which these patent medicines are composed, and the quantities of them, should be printed on the bottle or label" (37b, p. 1059). Sullivan was simply doing his duty to the profession of medicine. He followed up on the council's recommendation by making use of his influence and position as a senator. All the while, of course, he was cautious, even defensive. He suggested, for example, that the idea that "the medical profession had some feeling of envy or jealousy towards these medicines . . . is beneath contempt" (37b, p. 1057).

Sullivan's motion to look into the matter of patent medicines was agreed to by the Senate. And in a letter of the same date to the Minister of Inland Revenue, the Secretary of State, R. W. Scott, requested a statement along the lines suggested by Sullivan. It would take 8 months for the Minister of Inland Revenue to move to obtain such a report. On April 5, 1905, he instructed A. E. DuBerger, a pharmacist, to prepare one (38, p. 1). Scott and Sullivan waited another 12 months before receiving DuBerger's report on the "Drug and Proprietary Medicine Trade in Canada" (38).

There was little discussion of patent medicines, in the House or Senate, between the summer of 1904 and the spring of 1906. When the issue was raised, it was not given much consideration. It was enough to say that the matter was a "difficult" one (23c, pp. 1725–26) or that it was already "under consideration" (23d, p. 183; 37c, p. 70). One member of the House, Mr. Bergeron, raised the issue a few times, twice introducing a private member's bill "to force those who sell patent medicine[s] to have attached to the package the formula of the medicine they offer for sale" (23e, p. 213). Finally, on March 15, 1906, Bergeron said that it was his understanding that the Minister of Inland Revenue had "intended to bring in [such] a Bill" during the previous session. "The new Minister [he said] is not in, and I do not know what is his intention in the matter" (23e, p. 213). Bergeron made a motion to have his bill read. The motion was agreed to and his bill was given first reading. It received no further discussion, however, as there were related developments soon after.

One week after Bergeron's bill received a first reading in the House, Sullivan was back at it in the Senate (37d, pp. 153–54). Referring to his remarks on patent medicines 20 months earlier, Sullivan said:

> I was very nearly being made a martyr of in that patent medicines affair. I was threatened with sundry and dire punishments if I did not make a written retraction at once . . . However, I intend to go into this question thoroughly and with the aid of my confreres of the medical profession—I am simply acting as a spokesman of theirs. (37d, pp. 153–54)

A copy of A. E. DuBerger's report on patent medicines was formally accepted by the House on April 23, 1906. There was no discussion of it (23f). A couple of weeks later, however, a Mr. Stockton moved:

> That a committee . . . be appointed to inquire into and report upon the sale of fraudulent or deleterious medicines in Canada, and the advertisement thereof through the public press or otherwise; and to consider and report upon any enactments necessary to remedy any evils which may be found to exist. (23g, p. 2952)

Stockton mentioned three times that he had the public's interest in mind in making this motion. He felt that Parliament "should see to it that the proprietary medicines . . . sold in Canada should be of such a character as not to injure the public health" (23g, p. 2952). Although there is no record showing that Stockton's motion was a response to public complaints, including those of his own constituents, it might very well have been. Probably, articles in *Collier's Weekly* and the *Ladies' Home Journal* would have been brought to his attention. Certainly, pharmacists were aware of them (5f). These popular American journals, much read by Canadians, became the vehicle for a vigorous campaign against patent medicines that began late in 1905 and continued into 1906. For example, *Collier's* published a series entitled "The Great American Fraud" (41, p. 131). Samuel Hopkins Adams, the muckraking reporter for *Collier's,* "explored the cynical deceptions of medicine makers . . . who sold dangerous and addictive drugs. . . . The message underlying the exposés was that commercial interests were dangerous to health and that physicians had to be trusted" (41, p. 130). Patent medicine men were called "quacks" and their wares were described as "nostrum evils." The campaign did not create a moral issue, but the American Medical Association seemed to be successful in making the public aware of the fraudulent nature of the patent medicine trade. That is, they provided the material for Adams to write his (their) articles. They were also responsible for distributing "over 150,000 copies" of Adams' series on "The Great American Fraud" (41, p. 131).

It is not known whether this increased public awareness and concern gave Stockton and other members of the House a sense of responsibility to do something about patent medicines. In any event, his motion was agreed to. The following day a committee was appointed. It did not include Bergeron (23h), though he was appointed to replace one of its members the next day (23i).

The committee considered the matter for nine months before reporting to the House, on February 21, 1907, that a law to regulate the manufacture and sale of patent medicines was warranted (23j). Meanwhile, a bill had been prepared by the Government, not the committee (23j, 26c). However, the minister responsible for the bill's preparation, Mr. Templeman, the Minister of Inland Revenue, was a member of the committee. In introducing the bill, Templeman said:

> [It] has met with the approval of the public, so far as the public have cognizance of its contents, and it certainly has met with the approval of the interests concerned, the retail trade of the country and the proprietary manufacturers, except only those clauses which provide for the imposition of a stamp tax. It is a matter for further consideration to what extent the Bill will go in imposing a registration fee or stamp duty upon proprietary medicines. (23j, p. 3464)

Templeman requested that discussion of the bill take place on the second reading. It was read for the first time without discussion (23j).

There would be no discussion of the bill in that session of Parliament. On the 11th of March and again on the 4th of April, Bergeron requested that the Minister proceed with the matter (23k, 23l). But Templeman said the delay was necessary because they had been receiving the views of those interested in the trade, and would be meeting several delegations that week (23k). The patent medicine manufacturers and the retail druggists were unanimous in their distaste for the clause that imposed a revenue tax and registry fee. It seems that this was responsible for the delay. Thus, Templeman said that "a Bill along similar lines, with some amendments to meet the objections raised, should be submitted to parliament next session" (23l, p. 5863).

Between 1906 and 1908 numerous editorials and other comments on patent medicine legislation appeared in the *Canadian Pharmaceutical Journal*. Pharmacists wanted the trade in these medicines to be regulated. However, they were very annoyed by some of the proposed measures. When they learned that there would be both a registration fee and an Inland Revenue tax, the following accusation appeared: "The patent medicine men are with the Government to place a burden on the retail druggist" (5e, p. 308). Several editorials in the *Canadian Pharmaceutical Journal* strongly encouraged pharmacists to petition the Government with their concerns. Essentially, pharmacists were told to inform the Government that while they were "in favour of regulating medicines and protecting the public," retail druggists should not be taxed (5e, p. 308).

According to an editorial in the *Canadian Pharmaceutical Journal* in March 1907 (5f, p. 360), the bill that had been introduced in Parliament on February 21, 1907 afforded "no protection to the public." It was "clumsy and unworkable." By imposing an "obnoxious" tax it committed a gross injustice against the retail druggist. Moreover, "one of the most damning features" was that it made "no distinction . . . between the skilled, trained and educated pharmacist and the nostrum manufacturer. . . . The learned profession [of pharmacy was] . . . a safeguard to life and health. . . . Nostrum manufacturers [were] a menace to health and life."

Two months later, the tone of editorials in the journal was an optimistic one. It seems that Mr. Templeman had intimated to pharmacists that "no injustice should be done the pharmacists and that their professional and financial interests should be conserved" (5g, p. 459). When a new bill was finally introduced in the House on April 3, 1908, it was described by Templeman in the following way:

> The Bill of last session was of a rather drastic character, and after numerous interviews with representatives of the wholesale and retail trade and the manufacturers of proprietary medicines, it was found very difficult to frame legislation which would safeguard the public interests without at the same time committing injustice to the business interests. (23m, p. 6215)

There was little discussion on the bill in the House at this time.

On the 15th of June the bill was presented for second reading. Templeman suggested that the bill be sent to a special committee to consider amendments:

> [several months ago] I intimated to the Pharmaceutical Association of Canada [the pharmacists] that when the Bill was read a second time I would ask the House to send it to a small special committee and that if they had any views to express or suggestions of change to make, the committee would be glad to hear them. (23n, p. 10552)

Templeman must not have expected this committee to do very much, however, because he also said: "I have before me some amendments which [retail druggists] have suggested; . . . with these made it will meet with [their] absolute approval" (23n, p. 10552).[2] Templeman went on to admit that the proposed legislation was "not far-reaching" (23n, p. 10553). There was no subsequent reference in the House to the work of the special committee, and on the 10th of July the bill passed third reading (23o).

The bill was then taken up by the Senate the following week. Sullivan, Scott, and others were very dissatisfied with it (37e), but there was little they could do. Sullivan repeatedly protested that third reading of the bill in the Senate should be delayed. He argued that it was "a great shame and disgrace to the Senate" (37f, p. 1672). The bill passed in spite of his pleas. On July 20, 1908, it received royal assent and became law. On April 1, 1909, the *Proprietary or Patent Medicine Act* came into force.

The Act was a very weak instrument. All drugs listed in the Schedule to the Act simply had to be indicated on the patent medicine container. Thus, heroin, morphine, opium, and other dangerous drugs were deemed appropriate for use in patent medicines. Section 7 of the Act describes its prohibitive powers and reads as follows:

> No proprietary or patent medicine shall be manufactured, imported, exposed, sold or offered for sale
> (a) if it contains cocaine or any of its salts or preparations; [3]
> (b) if it contains alcohol in excess of the amount required as a solvent or preservative, or does not contain sufficient medication to prevent its use as an alcoholic beverage;
> (c) if it contains any drug which is included in the schedule to this Act but the name of which is not conspicuously printed on, and an inseparable part of, the label and wrapper of the bottle, box or other container. (42)

Clearly, any amount of heroin, morphine, opium, and other dangerous substances could be included in patent medicines, as long as these drugs were indicated on the label. Moreover, in acceptable doses (as judged by the Minister of Inland Revenue), these drugs did not even need to appear on the label. The Act's weakness is further illustrated by the fact that no restrictions were placed on the fraudulent claims that appeared in advertisements. As well, the penalties set out in the Act were far from harsh. Depending on what provisions were contravened, the maximum penalties ranged from a fine of $100 to 12 months' imprisonment. Most importantly, someone who contravened section 7 could receive, at the maximum, a $100 fine and loss of registration of the particular product in question. By way of comparison, the *Opium Act* of that same year provided maximum penalties of up to three years' imprisonment and/or a fine of $1,000.

SUMMARY AND CONCLUSIONS

This chapter has described the early social history of patent medicine use in Canada. Self-medication with patent medicines was the favoured form of treatment of late nineteenth- and early twentieth-century Canadians. Use of these secret-formula cure-alls was widespread, yet very few of them fulfilled the exaggerated and sometimes fraudulent claims made in promoting them. Furthermore, many were unsafe. Some contained high doses of cocaine, heroin, morphine, opium, or excessive amounts of alcohol. Since the contents of these medicines were generally unknown, some Canadians unwittingly doped themselves. Others knowingly took these nostrums for the non-medicinal effects they produced.

Clearly, a plurality of interests interacted to create this social problem and the eventual legislation. There was no identifiable victor and no consensus about the deviant status of patent medicines. The popular and rapidly growing trade in patent medicines was a threat to the neophyte professions of pharmacy and medicine. Self-medication with patent medicines—substances that offered an inexpensive and deceptively innocuous form of treatment, available door-to-door, through the mail, and at the corner store—diverted revenue from the hands of pharmacists and physicians. These two groups worked independently to make an issue out of patent medicine use. The problem was defined for their members through repeated editorials in their respective professional journals, and by discussions at their annual meetings.

Both pharmacists and physicians took their concerns to Ottawa in an attempt to regulate the trade in patent medicines. The road was long and arduous and the outcome was not satisfactory to some pharmacists and most physicians. Those pharmacists who made a profit from the sale of patent medicines were happy that they could continue to sell them without a burdensome tax. Others, along with the physicians, were unhappy because the trade in patent medicines would continue to take up a large portion of the market for health care services. In any event, there is no doubt that the claims made by pharmacists and physicians forged an important path along the road to regulation.

To say, as the Minister of Inland Revenue did, that the legislation was not far-reaching understates the case. It was an extremely weak instrument. The trade in patent medicines would remain virtually unrestricted for another decade. The Act did not mean the end of an era, though it did mark the end of the first cycle in the history of the use, trade, and regulation of patent medicines.

NOTES

1. Giffen, Small, and Lambert (16) found that pharmacists and physicians did not have much to do with the developments leading to the *Opium Act*, 1908, however.
2. Indeed, in the August 1908 issue of the *Canadian Pharmaceutical Journal* (5h, p. 23) an editorial would state that the bill as passed in Parliament "is

practically the recommendation of the C.Ph.A. [Canadian Pharmaceutical Association]."

3. For an explanation of why cocaine was absolutely prohibited, see Murray (29).

REFERENCES

1. Allen, R. *The Social Gospel in Canada*. Ottawa: National Museum of Man, History Division. Mercury Series, Paper no. 9, 1975.
2. Bohannan, P. The differing realms of the law. *American Anthropologist, 67*:33–42 (1965).
3. Boyd, N. The origins of Canadian narcotics legislation: The process of criminalization in historical context. *Dalhousie Law Journal, 8*:102–36 (1984).
4. Cain, M., and Hunt, A. *Marx and Engels on Law*. London: Academic Press, 1979.
5. *Canadian Pharmaceutical Journal* (Editorials)
   a. Patent medicines, 7:367–71 (1873–4).
   b. What is the duty of the professional pharmacist regarding patent medicines? *24*:180 (1891).
   c. Sale of patent medicines in dry good stores, *26*:17–18 (1892).
   d. Sale of poisonous patent medicines, *26*:50 (1892).
   e. Hustle that petition, *40*:308 (1907).
   f. The patent medicine Bill, *40*:359–60 (1907).
   g. The situation, *40*:459 (1907).
   h. The patent medicine Act, *42*:23 (1908).
6. *Census of Canada, 1880–81.* Vol. 3. Ottawa: Maclean, Roger & Co., 1882.
7. *Census of Canada, 1890–91.* Vol. 3. Ottawa: Queen's Printer, 1894.
8. Clark, R. J. The nether world of professionalization: Druggists in nineteenth-century Ontario. Paper presented to the History Workshop on Education in Modern Societies, University of Waterloo, March 11–13, 1983.
9. Coburn, D., Torrance, G. M., and Kaufert, J. M. Medical dominance in Canada in historical perspective: The rise and fall of medicine? *International Journal of Health Services, 13*:407–32 (1983).
10. Cook, S. J. Ideology and Canadian narcotics legislation, 1908–1923. M.A. diss., Department of Sociology, University of Toronto, 1964.
11. Dahrendorf, R. *Essays in the Theory of Society*. Stanford, Calif.: Stanford University Press, 1968.
12. Dominion Medical Monthly. An Act regulating the manufacture and sale of proprietary and patent medicines. Ontario. *Dominion Medical Monthly, 26*:240–44 (1906).

13. Durkheim, E. *The Division of Labor in Society.* New York: The Free Press, 1965.

14. Friedmann, W. *Law in a Changing Society.* London: Stevens & Sons, 1959.

15. Fuller, R. C., and Myers, R. R. The natural history of a social problem. *American Sociological Review, 6:*320–29 (1941).

16. Giffen, P. J., Small, S., and Lambert, S. Politics of Canadian narcotic drug control. Unpublished ms. Addiction Research Foundation, Toronto, 1982.

17. Green, M. A history of Canadian narcotics control: The formative years. *University of Toronto Faculty of Law Review, 37:*42–79 (1979).

18. Guest, R. G. The great patent medicine fraud. *Applied Therapeutics, 8:*449–57 (1966).

19. Hagan, J. The legislation of crime and delinquency: A review of theory, method, and research. *Law and Society Review, 14:*603–28 (1980).

20. Hall, J. *General Principles of Criminal Law.* Indianapolis: Bobbs-Merrill, 1947.

21. Hills, S. L. The formulation of criminal laws. In: Boydell, C. L., Grindstaff, C. F., and Whitehead, P. C. (eds.). *The Administration of Criminal Justice in Canada.* Toronto: Holt, Rinehart and Winston, 1974.

22. Holmes, O. W. The path of the law. In: Simon, R. James (ed.). *The Sociology of Law.* San Francisco: Chandler, 1968.

23. House of Commons. Canada. *Debates.*
    a. August 1, 1904: 8045–48.
    b. August 3, 1904: 8265–66.
    c. February 24, 1905: 1725–26.
    d. March 14, 1906: 183.
    e. March 15, 1906: 213–14.
    f. April 23, 1906: 1871.
    g. May 9, 1906: 2951–52.
    h. May 10, 1906: 3065.
    i. May 11, 1906: 3150.
    j. February 21, 1907: 3464–65.
    k. March 11, 1907: 4441.
    l. April 4, 1907: 5863.
    m. April 3, 1908: 6215–18.
    n. June 15, 1908: 10551–53.
    o. July 10, 1908: 12622–28.

24. Journal of the American Medical Association. [Excerpt from *Université Médical du Canada.*] Chronic cocainism from catarrh snuff. *Journal of the American Medical Association, 28:*1092 (1897).

25. Kitsuse, J. I., and Spector, M. Toward a sociology of social problems: Social conditions, value-judgements, and social problems. *Social Problems, 20:*407–19 (1973).

26. Laurier Papers, Ottawa: Public Archives of Canada.
    a. 1906, MG 26 G, Vol. 407:108297–99.

    b. 1906, MG 26 G, Vol. 407:108300.

    c. 1906, MG 26 G, Vol. 436:116397–405.

27. McDonald, L. *The Sociology of Law and Order.* Montreal: Book Center, 1976.

28. *Montreal Medical Journal.* (Editorials)

    a. Proprietary preparations, *32*:359–62 (1903).

    b. Medical advertising, *32*:362–64 (1903).

    c. Patent medicines, *33*:656 (1904).

    d. Patent medicines, *35*:274–75 (1906).

29. Murray, G. F. Cocaine use in the era of social reform: The natural history of a social problem in Canada, 1880–1911. *Canadian Journal of Law and Society, 2.* Forthcoming (1987).

30. Nasmith, G. G. Patent medicines and drug foods. *Annual Reports of the Ontario Provincial Board of Health, 23*:113–17 (1904).

31. Peyrot, M. Cycles of social problem development: The case of drug abuse. *Sociological Quarterly, 25*:83–95 (1984).

32. Pound, R. The need of a sociological jurisprudence. In: Simon, R. James (ed.). *The Sociology of Law.* San Francisco: Chandler, 1968.

33. Presbrey, F. *The History and Development of Advertising.* New York: Greenwood Press, 1968.

34. Reasons, C. The politics of drugs: An inquiry in the sociology of social problems. *Sociological Quarterly, 15*:381–404 (1974).

35. Rutherford, P. *A Victorian Authority: The Daily Press in Late Nineteenth-century Canada.* Toronto: University of Toronto Press, 1982.

36. Schneider, J. W. Social problems theory: The constructionist view. *Annual Review of Sociology, 11*:209–29 (1985).

37. Senate. Canada. *Debates.*

    a. July 28, 1904: 869–70.

    b. August 5, 1904: 1056–61.

    c. March 15, 1906: 70.

    d. March 22, 1906: 153–54.

    e. July 15, 1908: 1564–73.

    f. July 17, 1908: 1640–72.

38. *Sessional Papers.* Canada. To an order of the House of Commons, dated April 23, 1906, for a copy of the report of A. E. DuBerger, on the drug and proprietary medicine trade of Canada. *Sessional Papers, 40,* no. 125, 1906.

39. Solomon, R., and Madison, T. The evolution of non-medical opiate use in Canada: Part I, 1870–1929. *Drug Forum, 5*:237–65 (1976–77).

40. Spitzer, S. Marxist perspectives in the sociology of law. *Annual Review of Sociology, 9*:103–24 (1983).

41. Starr, P. *The Social Transformation of American Medicine.* New York: Basic Books, 1982.

42. *Statutes of Canada.* An Act respecting proprietary or patent medicines, S.C. 1908, c. 56.
43. Stephenson, H. E., and McNaught, C. *The Story of Advertising in Canada: A Chronicle of Fifty Years.* Toronto: Ryerson Press, 1940.
44. Taylor, I., Walton, P., and Young, J. *The New Criminology: For a Social Theory of Deviance.* London: Routledge and Kegan Paul, 1973.
45. Turk, A. T. Law as a weapon in social conflict. *Social Problems, 23*:276–91 (1976).
46. Weber, M. *From Max Weber: Essays in Sociology.* Ed. Gerth, H. H., and Mills, C. Wright. New York: Oxford University Press, 1946.
47. Young, J. H. *The Toadstool Millionaires: A Social History of Patent Medicines in America before Federal Regulation.* Princeton, N.J.: Princeton University Press, 1961.

7

The First Century: The History of Non-medical Opiate Use and Control Policies in Canada, 1870–1970*

ROBERT R. SOLOMON AND MELVYN GREEN

AN INTRODUCTORY REVIEW
OF THE FIRST CENTURY

Prior to 1908, few restrictions were imposed on the distribution or consumption of opiates, whether for medical or pleasurable purposes. Canada annually imported tons of raw opium and large quantities of processed opiates. Various low-cost opium preparations were freely distributed by doctors, travelling medicine shows, patent medicine companies, pharmacies, general stores, and Chinese opium shops. Although viewed as an individual medical misfortune or personal vice, opiate dependence was free from serious moral stigma. Indeed, in many circles, cigarette smoking and alcohol consumption were considered graver threats to public health and morals.

The decision to prohibit non-medical opiate use stemmed not from concern about its addictive properties, but rather from a redefinition of its moral impact by some vocal reformers. They came to perceive opiates as a menace that destroyed Christian inhibitions, thus exposing man's natural tendency to depravity. While similar campaigns against alcohol, tobacco, and other vices had only minor temporary effects, the anti-opium crusade fundamentally altered both public attitudes and the criminal law. This crusade succeeded because it was directed against Chinese opium smokers and Chinese opium factories, but at the same time posed no threat to the larger number of predominantly middle-class and middle-aged Caucasian users who were addicted to the products of the established pharmaceutical industry.

The events following the passage of the first criminal drug law in 1908 reinforced alarmist views of drug use and users. This prohibition spawned a prosperous illicit trade, inflated the cost of opium use, and created a new class of criminals. Parliament and the public were presented with stereotypical drug villains, who were primarily non-Christian and non-white, and who more than deserved the progressively harsher laws that were passed. The federal police and government drug bureaucracies, which were established in the

---

*Reprinted from *The University of Western Ontario Law Review*, 20, no. 2 (1982): 307–36. By permission.

early 1920s, aligned themselves with the moral reformers and anti-Asiatic forces in calling for stricter laws. In a series of near-annual amendments, Canada's drug statute was transformed during the 1920s into one of the country's most stringent pieces of criminal legislation.

By the early 1930s, federal police and drug officials emerged as Canada's only drug experts. Neither their perception of non-medical drug use as a law enforcement problem, nor the legislation itself, was seriously questioned during the next twenty years. As law enforcement efforts increased, distribution patterns, the drug of choice, and the manner of consumption changed. After World War II, intravenous use of heroin, the most potent opium derivative, began to replace intravenous use of morphine, which had previously replaced the smoking of opium.

It was not until the early 1950s that the concept of treating rather than punishing addicts was first forcefully proposed. Relying heavily on their American counterparts, Canadian enforcement officials attempted to discredit the suggested treatment programmes, and instead argued for heavier sentences, more vigorous enforcement, and custodial treatment. Parliament tried to accommodate these divergent views, but ultimately adopted the enforcement community's recommendations in the 1961 legislation. Nevertheless, at least some of the more Draconian features of the early drug law were repealed at this time.

Canada's addict population grew slowly after World War II, and there was even a sustained heroin shortage in the early 1960s. A restructuring of the illicit heroin trade in the mid-1960s soon provided abundant supplies for the domestic market and also for trans-shipment to the United States. By the end of the decade, heroin was more readily available in Canada than ever before, and the addict population, which already had exceeded previous levels, was still increasing sharply.

THE CHINESE OPIUM QUESTION, 1870–1908

Chinese Immigration and British Columbia's Anti-Asiatic Campaign

The first Chinese immigrants came to British Columbia in the 1850s (64, p. 508). Both the Chinese arriving directly from the Orient and those escaping from mounting racial discrimination in California were welcomed as a source of cheap labour for the railroads, mines, and other expanding industries. The Caucasian population viewed the Chinese as conscientious, thrifty, and law-abiding. Their smoking of opium was not considered to be physically harmful or socially degenerate. Yet, the public strongly disapproved of opium smoking among whites, because it involved mixing of the races—a matter considered far more serious than the drug's effects (39; 64, pp. 491–94, 508–9).

At the time, the various levels of government were concerned about opium smoking only for financial reasons. When British Columbia joined Confederation in 1871, the colonial duty on opium was replaced by the federal import tax (62a, Schedule B). The Chinese opium factories established in Victoria and later in Vancouver and New Westminster were subject to an annual $500 municipal licensing fee (67, p. 275).

The tolerant attitude to both the Chinese and opium smoking prevailed until the 1880s, when the decline in railroad construction and the gold rush restricted job opportunities in British Columbia. White labour felt it could not compete with the frugal, unmarried Chinese workers. Caucasian businessmen were not blamed. Rather, it was their Chinese employees who became targets of public resentment, for they accepted wages on which a white man's family could not live. As economic conditions worsened, complaints against the Chinese increased. They were criticized as being clannish, heathen, unsanitary, immoral, and disloyal to Canada[1] (13, p. 64; 36, pp. 58–63; 39; 57, pp. 163–68; 64, pp. 489–94, 508–9; 68, pp. 119–20).

In response to the wave of anti-Asiatic sentiment, the British Columbia Legislature enacted a series of measures designed to end Chinese immigration and to drive the Chinese out of the economic mainstream. For example, the Chinese were specifically denied the right to vote in provincial, municipal, and school board elections (3b, s. 24; 3c, s. 3; 3f, s. 33), to own crown lands (3e, s. 122), or to establish a registered company or association in the province. Although many discriminatory provisions did come into force, the federal government twice disallowed provincial legislation banning Chinese immigration to British Columbia (9, 10). The courts struck down a number of provincial statutes as unconstitutional (see for examples 49, 51, 65), including the *Chinese Regulation Act* (3a, 50, 52), which imposed an annual tax on all Chinese residents over fourteen years of age and a special certificate fee on Chinese miners. The Act also prohibited non-medical opium use and possession. This provision, however, appears to have been included as an afterthought, intended as merely another means of harassing the Chinese. Undaunted by these setbacks, the Legislature and British Columbia's members of Parliament urged the federal government to end Chinese immigration (64, pp. 489–90; 67, p. 275), as the United States in effect had done in the early 1880s.[2]

These demands were temporarily forestalled by the establishment of the 1885 Royal Commission on Chinese Immigration.[3] In testimony before the Commission, the Chinese were praised by employers and condemned by Caucasian labour spokesmen. The Commission spoke highly of the Chinese, acknowledging that many complaints about them were grossly exaggerated. Nevertheless, it recommended that Chinese immigration be regulated to meet the country's labour needs. Shortly thereafter, Parliament passed the *Chinese Immigration Act, 1885* (62b, s. 14), which imposed a $50 tax on Chinese immigrants entering British Columbia. The Commission also heard considerable testimony about opium smoking, much of which was neutral or even positive, compared to the views expressed about alcohol. The Commission's failure to make opium-related proposals suggests that the issue was not considered serious.

Continued public hostility prompted Parliament to double the tax on Chinese immigrants in 1901 (62c, s. 6) and to establish the 1902 Royal Commission on Chinese and Japanese Immigration. The Commission concluded that all Chinese immigration should be prohibited and that, in the interim, the tax should be increased to $500. Again, no opium-related proposals were made. Parliament raised the tax to $500 in 1904 (62d, s. 6), but did not prohibit Chinese immigration until 1923 (62n).

The 1904 tax, unlike the two previous measures, apparently contributed to a temporary reduction in Chinese immigration[4] (11, p. 116). However, a sharp increase in Japanese immigration in the mid-1900s (29, pp. 247–60) stirred another wave of public hostility. As in the past, the anti-Asiatic crusade in California served as a model. In September 1907, a leader of the Exclusion League of San Francisco came to Vancouver for the express purpose of encouraging anti-Japanese sentiment. On September 7, a labour demonstration against the Japanese erupted into rioting (29, p. 252). The federal government dispatched Mackenzie King, then Deputy Minister of Labour, to investigate the incident and to compensate Asians who had suffered losses (21, pp. 150–51). King was confronted during his investigation with claims from two Chinese opium merchants. Startled by the existence of an established Chinese opium industry, King strongly recommended in his official report that Parliament immediately eliminate the evil (17, p. 9; 31; 64, Appendix G).

Canada's First Criminal Opium Prohibition

King pursued the opium issue during his visit to Vancouver and undertook a second unofficial investigation in his capacity as a concerned citizen (32). His private report contained four dominant themes. The first three related to the increasing popularity of opium smoking among white men and women, the size of and profits from the Chinese opium trade, and the fact that it operated in open violation of the provincial pharmacy legislation. The fourth and perhaps most important point was that Canada, as a Christian nation, had to set an example in the international campaign against opium (32).

King did not discuss the physiological effects of opium. Instead, he emphasized the drug's deleterious social and moral impact. The following newspaper article which he quoted illustrates the tenor of his study:

Awful Effects of Opium Habit
In the police court this morning, while Vancouver lay in the beauty and brightness of early sunshine, there emerged into the light, ugly and horrible evidence of the dire influence which the opium traffic is exercising among the ranks of British Columbia womanhood. May Edwards, pretty and young, had been found

in a Chinese den. She said she had a husband in Victoria, and if allowed to go would return to him. She was allowed to go.

Much the sadder of the cases, however, was that of Belle Walker. A terrible record of the effects of indulgence in opium was written upon her appearance this morning. She was found by the police in an opium den. She had been there for three weeks. Magistrate Williams sent her to prison for six months. (32, pp. 7–8)

Less than three weeks after King submitted his private study, Parliament enacted the country's first criminal opium prohibition. The 1908 bill moved through the House of Commons without discussion. However, several senators complained that the bill would impose economic hardship on opium manufacturers, and they succeeded in adding a provision allowing manufacturers six months to dispose of their existing stocks (17, p. 15). The Hon. Mr. Sullivan, the only physician in the Senate, questioned whether opium smoking was harmful and expressed concern about the fate of addicted Chinese smokers. His views were ignored (53a). The 1908 *Opium Act* made it an indictable offence to import, manufacture, offer to sell, sell, or possess to sell opium for non-medical purposes, but prohibited neither simple possession nor use (62f). Violation of the statute was punishable by incarceration for up to three years and/or a $1,000 fine.

A comparison of the *Opium Act* with the other drug-related legislation introduced in the same year suggests that racial and economic factors were largely responsible for the success of the campaign against opium smoking. After prolonged discussions with industry representatives, the government enacted the *Proprietary or Patent Medicine Act* (17, pp. 15–16; 62h) of 1908. The legislation, which had been revised to take into account the Pharmaceutical Association's views, basically regulated, rather than prohibited, the non-medical use of patent medicines. The Act banned the use of cocaine and excessive amounts of alcohol in patent medicines. It also required manufacturers to register with the government and to label products containing any scheduled drug. While heroin was included in the schedule, opium and morphine were not. The maximum penalty for violation of this section was a $50 fine for a first offence and a $100 fine for subsequent offences (62h, ss. 7, 12). In the words of the Minister of Revenue, the legislation sought to "safeguard the public interests without at the same time committing injustice to the business interests" (27a, p. 6215). The accommodating attitude to the industry is noteworthy considering that far more people were probably addicted to opiates through the use of patent medicines than through the smoking of opium[5] (13; 17, pp. 7, 16; 22, pp. 7–8; 67, p. 275).

Shortly before the *Opium Act* was passed, a private member's bill to prohibit tobacco smoking was introduced. Despite heated debate about the pernicious moral, medical, and intellectual effects of tobacco smoking on Canada's youth, the bill was defeated.[6] Only two minor tobacco-related measures were enacted that session (17, pp. 16–19). The first was intended to assist the domestic tobacco industry in competing with foreign producers (62e, ss. 11, 12), and the second provided a maximum fine of $10 for those convicted of supplying tobacco to minors (62g).

Parliament's relatively aggressive response to opium smoking appears to have been due more to racial and political factors, than to concerns about its physiological effects. The 1908 drug reform legislation left Caucasian interests in the patent medicine and tobacco industries relatively unscathed, while it criminalized Chinese opium distributors and sacrificed Chinese business interests. The Chinese, a politically powerless and, at least in the west, a despised alien minority, were ideal targets for Canada's moral reformers and politicians.

THE EXPANSION OF THE CRIMINAL PROHIBITION, 1909–1929

The Opium and Drug Act of 1911

The passage of the 1908 *Opium Act* enhanced King's reputation as a social reformer and opium expert, furthered his political career, and led to his appointment to the 1909 Shanghai Opium Commission—the first international conference which was called for the purpose of suppressing the trade. King won a seat in the 1908 federal election and was appointed Labour Minister the next year (17, pp. 9–10). Following his return from Shanghai in 1909, he introduced a drug bill dealing exclusively with opium, only to withdraw it in favour of broader legislation after being warned of Montreal's growing "cocaine curse" (14, p. 96; 17, pp. 26–29).

The 1911 Act was most heavily influenced by the Royal Commission to Investigate Alleged Chinese Frauds and Opium Smoking on the Pacific Coast (54a). The Commission had been appointed in 1910 to investigate charges that customs officials and British Columbia Liberal Party members were engaged in corrupt practices. While these allegations proved to be groundless, the Commission reported that the illicit opium trade was flourishing. The 1908 *Opium Act* had inflated opium prices, creating a lucrative black market for smugglers. The Customs Department was unable to stem the traffic, and the municipal police believed that they had no jurisdiction in the drug field. The Commission, rather than reconsidering the initial opium ban, called for drastic legislation aimed at opium users. It recommended that Parliament prohibit opium possession and use, and expand enforcement powers. In an effort to deter offenders, the Commission also urged judges to impose imprisonment as well as fines (14, pp. 95–97; 17, pp. 25–26; 64, pp. 503–4).

Unlike the 1908 legislation, the 1911 *Opium and Drug Act* (62i) was discussed at length. King set the tone of the debate, quoting extensively from newspaper accounts of Montreal's cocaine wave (27c), and speaking of Canada's leadership role in the international drug suppression campaign.[7] In the words of one author, the Parliamentary debates on the issue:

> were characterized by vagueness on the one hand and by panic on the other hand. Although there was a paucity of specific details about the extent of the traffic or actual effects of the drugs, the moral epithets were vigorous. The legislators agreed to pass stern control measures over a problem about which they had very little real information. (17, p. 29)

The 1911 *Opium and Drug Act* clearly embodied the Royal Commission's and Parliament's paramount interest in effective drug enforcement. The 1908 statute was repealed; morphine, cocaine, and eucaine were added to the drug schedule; and new user-oriented offences were created. The importation, manufacture, sale, transportation, and possession of scheduled drugs were prohibited, except for medical or scientific purposes. The smoking of opium and merely being present in an opium "resort" without lawful excuse were also made offences. The Act placed restrictions on wholesale and retail distributors, physicians, and other health-care professionals. Police powers of search and seizure were expanded, and a special search warrant was created for drug cases (62i). The Act gave magistrates discretion to award half of an offender's fine to the person who had provided the information leading to conviction (62i, s. 11).

Although the provincial and municipal police lacked an explicit enforcement mandate, there was an average of over 900 convictions a year between 1912 and 1920 (54c, pp. 245–300; d, pp. 286–347; e, pp. 270–333; f, pp. 178–242; g, pp. 185–249). The courts apparently did not view drug offenders as serious criminals—about 90 per cent of drug convictions resulted in fines, a trend consistent across Canada during this period. The conviction statistics suggest that the illicit trade was confined almost exclusively to the cities in Quebec, Ontario, and British Columbia. In the east, Caucasians controlled the traffic, dealing primarily in morphine and cocaine smuggled into Canada from Europe. In British Columbia, Chinese opium distributors with contacts in the Orient dominated the trade (54c, pp. 245–300; d, pp. 286–347; e, pp. 270–333; f, pp. 178–242; g, pp. 185–249).

International Drug Control Efforts

There were no changes in federal drug law between 1911 and 1919. The Liberal Party was defeated in the 1911 election, and the Borden government was preoccupied with World War I and economic issues. Nevertheless, developments which occurred abroad during this period had profound effects on the subsequent development of Canada's drug law and the illicit trade.

The Shanghai Opium Commission was followed by a second international conference at which the 1912 Hague Opium Convention was formulated. The Convention was appended to the Versailles Treaty ending World War I and, as a result, did not come into general effect until the treaty was ratified in the 1920s (69, pp. 20–40). However, American complaints that opiates were being diverted from Canada's licit trade to the United States' black market (17, p. 36) prompted Canada to adopt the Convention's import and export provisions in 1919 (62j). The Canadian government fulfilled the Convention's remaining requirements in the 1920 drug amendment and also strengthened record-keeping procedures, increased some penalties, and renamed the statute the *Opium and Narcotic Drug Act* (62k). Debate on this bill lacked the moral fervour that had characterized earlier Parliamentary discussions. Instead, the debate reflected a reasoned attempt to eliminate diversion of licit supplies, easy access to potent opiate-based medicines, and the indiscriminate distribution of opiates by health-care professionals (17, pp. 64–66).

The international drug control movement had also contributed to the enactment of the 1914 Harrison Act, the first American federal prohibition against non-medical drug use (42, pp. 24–68). American law enforcement officials broadly interpreted the statute's modest provisions, claiming that physicians could not prescribe maintenance doses to addicts. Doctors who challenged this view were prosecuted. Denied access to licit sources, thousands of previously law-abiding addicts resorted to purchasing drugs on the black market at exorbitant prices, without the benefits of medical supervision or quality control (2, pp. 50–52; 42, pp. 121–50; 43, pp. 22–25). American east-coast racketeers with contacts in the Ontario and Quebec underworlds soon exploited the market. As law enforcement efforts increased the risks of arrest and financial loss, major traffickers switched from opium and morphine to heroin distribution. Heroin is several times more potent than morphine and is easier to dilute, thus providing traffickers with a greater profit potential. During the early 1920s, heroin began to replace morphine as the drug of choice in the United States and first appeared in eastern Canada (20, pp. 232–238; 26, pp. 34–68; 35, p. 65; 37, pp. 17–19).

In response to the plight of addicts, several American cities and states established clinics to provide low-cost opiates under medical supervision. Many clinics proved promising, but the New York City clinic, the most crowded, poorly managed and least successful, was given the greatest publicity. The press ran stories of the dispensing of drugs to non-addicts, prostitutes, and criminals, and carried reports of startling increases in addiction. All the clinics were forced to close and their failure was blamed on the addicts' dishonesty. The collapse of the clinical programmes, coupled with accounts of escalating rates of addiction, heightened public resentment of addicts, discredited drug treatment programmes, and strengthened the law enforcement agencies' control over the drug problem in Canada as well as in the United States (42, pp. 151–82; 43, pp. 24–31; 57, pp. 168–75).

The Resurgence of the Moral Reform Movement and Anti-Asiatic Sentiment

Many of the forces that prompted the enactment of the 1908 *Opium Act* re-emerged in 1920. That year saw the launching of a well-publicized moral crusade against drugs, the revival of anti-Asiatic hostility in British Columbia, and the establishment of a federal drug agency which, like King, served as a political catalyst for the enactment of legislation.

In 1920, *Maclean's Magazine* initiated a series of articles for the express purpose of arousing public demands for stricter drug legislation. The articles provided the first detailed coverage of the issue in any popular Canadian magazine, and it later formed part of Canada's first drug book, *The Black Candle* (41). Mrs. Emily Murphy, a magistrate and a judge of the Edmonton Juvenile Court, authored both the book and the articles. She approached the drug problem with a combination of genuine concern and strict Protestant morality. Her writing contained social, medical, and statistical information drawn from Canada and abroad, but it was interwoven with anecdotes, popular racial biases, and moral fables.

Murphy warned that drug use was increasing throughout Canada, especially among the young. The effects of the various drugs were not clearly distinguished. Yet, it hardly mattered since she was convinced that they all produced moral degeneration, crime, physical illness, mental disease, and intellectual and spiritual ruin. The reader was provided with two images of drug users—victim and villain. The victim was invariably white and usually young. The list of villains included: Chinese and black pushers who were motivated by greed and lust for white women; "aliens of colour" who were unwitting cogs in an international drug conspiracy designed "to injure the bright-browed races of the world" (41, p. 188); "script doctors" who prescribed drugs for profit; and "the 'ring," a mysterious and ruthless drug syndicate (41, pp. 165–89). Two characteristics shared by victim and villain alike were their overwhelming desire to infect others, particularly the young, and their need to commit crime. The appearance of all drug users was described in the most colourful language, complete with pictures. For example, the Chinese opium smoker was an "ashy-faced, half-witted drooler" who had "no more blood in his body than a shrimp" (41, p. 16). Even though the drug was virtually unknown in Canada, Murphy warned of the dangers of "marihuana" addicts. Quoting American police officials, she reported that these addicts were rendered raving maniacs capable of savage killings while under the drug's influence.

The first step in the fight against drugs was to arouse the apathetic public. Murphy advocated rigorous drug education programmes for youth and strict parental supervision. Police and customs resources had to be strengthened, and both agencies required far greater powers of arrest, search, and seizure. Critical of the sentences imposed by her fellow judges, Murphy called for mandatory minimum sentences, whipping, deportation of convicted aliens, and the establishment of a drug treatment prison on a remote island.

Her delineation of the scourge-like effects of drug use soon came to characterize Canadian narcotics policy, and most of her more punitive recommendations were eventually incorporated into the law.

The renewal of the anti-Asiatic campaign in British Columbia during the early 1920s fuelled public demands for drastic action against drug offenders. Service clubs, church organizations, civic groups, and the Anti-Asiatic Exclusion League pressed for immediate legislative action. British Columbia's members of Parliament were the major force in the enactment of the 1923 *Chinese Immigration Act*, which in essence prohibited Chinese immigration[8] (62n). They also led demands for longer sentences, hanging, whipping, deportation of convicted aliens, broader police powers, and reduced rights for drug suspects (17, pp. 81–91). The Chinese were publicly identified as the primary villains in the drug trade; their prey was Canada's unsuspecting youth. One Vancouver Member of Parliament, quoting the secretary of the Anti-Asiatic Exclusion League, bluntly informed Parliament that:

> Here we have a disease, one of many directly traceable to the Asiatic. Do away with the Asiatic and you have more than saved the souls and bodies of thousands of young men and women who are yearly being sent to a living hell and to the grave through their presence in Canada (27d, p. 1530).

As in 1908, the fact that the proposed drug legislation would be used against the Chinese, rather than ordinary citizens, apparently reassured some Parliamentarians who otherwise might have objected (17, pp. 88–89).

The Federal Drug Bureaucracy

International and American developments, Mrs. Murphy's writings, and intensified anti-Asiatic hostility all affected Canadian narcotics legislation. However, it was the creation of a centralized federal drug bureaucracy that was responsible for shaping Canadian drug policy and for drafting legislation to meet these policy objectives. Like King, the bureaucracy was a catalyst, translating domestic pressures, external influences, and its own interests into legislation.

In 1920, the newly created federal Department of Health was given responsibility for supervising Canada's drug law and international treaty obligations. An agency, later named the Narcotic Division, was established within the department to discharge these duties (17, p. 59; 54h, p. 16). In the same year, the Royal Canadian Mounted Police (RCMP) force was founded and given a mandate to enforce all federal law. The new force was not uniformly welcomed, and it relied heavily on rigorous drug enforcement as one means of justifying its existence. The drug squad's valiant, but nonetheless distasteful, battles against traffickers were detailed in the RCMP's first annual reports (54i, pp. 5–6; 54j; 54l, pp. 16–17). For example, in the 1922 report, the Commissioner commented:

> Reference was made in the last annual report to the calamitous nature of this traffic; I regret to be obliged to state that the evil persists, and I fear has grown in some parts of the country. To check it will require the united efforts of this force and the provincial and municipal authorities, and also drastic punishment of the agents, such as the peddlers who deliberately create addicts. . . .
>
> The difficulties of repression are exceedingly great, for several reasons. One is the ease with which these drugs, which are small in bulk, can be imported; numerous and very cunning devices are resorted to for the purpose of smuggling them, instances being known of their being most artfully concealed in shipments by apparently reputable firms from abroad. . . . Another difficulty is that the traffic is so remunerative that those who take part in it have abundance of money at their command and use it to counter our measures, and to fight cases stubbornly in the courts. Yet another obstacle is the repulsive nature of the work of repression, entailing as it does contact with peculiarly loathsome dregs of humanity; our men greatly dislike it, and it is undertaken only in accordance with duty, and because of the knowledge that while unpleasant it is a service to humanity. (54l, pp. 16–17)

The RCMP became a staunch ally of the Narcotic Division, serving as its enforcement arm. When its officers encountered difficulties, the RCMP turned to the Division, which acted as its spokesman in proposing remedial legislation. In the early 1920s, the federal government began to employ special prosecutors to handle all drug cases and to provide advice to local drug enforcement units. The Division encouraged federal prosecutors to appeal unfavourable court decisions and, in turn, drafted legislation to assist these prosecutors in obtaining convictions and stiff sentences (25, pp. 62–65).

Given its statutory mandate, its allies in enforcement and prosecution, and its direct access to the responsible cabinet minister, the Narcotic Division usually secured quick passage of its legislative proposals. Accounts of the failure of the American clinics, warnings about spiralling rates of addiction, the renewal of the anti-Asiatic campaign, Mrs. Murphy's writings, the RCMP's and Department of Health's own annual reports (54k, p. 33; 54l, pp. 16–17), and the absence of a vocal opposition all created an image of the addict that ensured public support for even the most drastic measures. In a near-annual series of amendments, the federal drug bureaucracy transformed Canada's drug statute into one of the country's most punitive pieces of criminal legislation. The six legislative revisions between 1921 and 1927 (62l, m, o, p, q, r) were consolidated in the *Opium and Narcotic Drug Act*, 1929 (62s), the major features of which are outlined below.

Health-care professionals were required by the Act to maintain detailed records of their drug transactions and were prohibited from prescribing or supplying drugs, except for medical purposes (62s, ss. 5, 6). As a result of the Narcotic Division's interpretation of what constituted "medical purposes," doctors were prosecuted for providing maintenance doses to addicts (4, pp. 12–13; 17, pp. 120–23). Violations of these provisions were punishable by up to five years' imprisonment.

Cannabis was added to the drug schedule in 1923, presumably as a result of Mrs. Murphy's warning. Illicit importing, exporting, manufacturing, selling, or possession of any scheduled drug were made serious offences. Any person occupying a premise or vehicle in which drugs were found was deemed to be in possession, unless he could prove that the drugs were there without his authority, knowledge, or consent (62s, s. 17). These offences carried a mandatory minimum sentence of six months' imprisonment and a $200 fine, and a maximum of seven years' imprisonment and a $1,000 fine. In certain cases, the judge could also order whipping and hard labour (62s, s. 4). Convicted offenders forfeited the article in which the drug was contained, the vehicle in which it was transported, and the money used in the transaction (62s, ss. 20–21). Aliens convicted of the more serious offences were subject to mandatory deportation at the end of their prison sentence (62s, s. 26). The right to appeal a drug conviction was severely curtailed (62s, s. 25).

Any officer who had reasonable cause to suspect that illicit drugs were kept in any place, other than a dwelling house, was authorized to enter that place without a warrant, day or night, and to search the premises and its occupants (62s, s. 19(1)). The statute also provided for the issuance of writs of assistance to RCMP drug officers. Basically the writ is a continuing blanket search warrant, which empowers the officer to whom it is issued to search any dwelling house, at any time, if he reasonably believes that the place contains illicit drugs[9] (25, pp. 64–65; 62s, s. 22). In order to prevent possible destruction of evidence, the officer may break in using whatever force is reasonably necessary. Once an application is made on behalf of an officer, a judge is required to issue a writ of assistance to that officer. The writ is not limited as to time or place and is valid for the officer's entire career. The judge who issues a writ has no control whatsoever over when, where, how often, or in what circumstances the writ is invoked (see 30, 44, 46, 47, 56). These sweeping powers represent a fundamental departure from the general principles of law that govern arrest, search, and seizure (60).*

Despite greater police powers, the annual number of drug convictions, which had peaked in the early 1920s, fell rapidly by the end of the decade to about 200 (38, p. 584). Probably the most important factor in this decline was the dying out of the older generations of Chinese opium smokers, which had provided the majority of offenders. The prohibition against Chinese immigration, the deportation of more than 500 convicted Chinese offenders during the 1920s (55, p. 538), and reduced public interest also contributed to this trend.

It is difficult to assess what, if any, deterrent effect the drug amendments

---

*The writs of assistance were abolished in December 1985. See Chapter 16.

of the 1920s had on the illicit trade. The patterns of smuggling and distribution remained unchanged, and there was no evidence of shortages (28; 59, pp. 28–32). The restrictions imposed on the licit distribution system probably had a greater impact on non-medical opiate use because they dramatically lessened the risk of addiction inherent in self-medication and medical treatment.

By 1929 the drug user's image had been changed from that of a morally weak, but otherwise benign, individual to that of a fiendish criminal, obsessed with the need to addict others and motivated by lust and greed. Moral reformers, prominent citizens, the RCMP, the Narcotic Division, and legislators were all clamouring for stern action against these "peculiarly loathsome dregs of humanity" (54l, p. 17). The addict, at least in the public mind, more than deserved a full measure of fear, hatred, and punishment. Public acceptance of this dope-fiend mythology permitted the virtually unchallenged passage of legislation that defined addiction as a law enforcement problem, extended the range of the criminal sanctions, increased the punitive consequences of conviction, and encroached on traditional civil liberties.

THE CONTINUATION OF THE
LAW ENFORCEMENT APPROACH, 1930–1952

There were no challenges to federal drug policy and only minor changes in the law during this period. The public was preoccupied with the Depression, World War II, and the post-war boom. The illicit drug trade was simply not an important public issue. Parliament had expressed its views through the comprehensive amendments of the 1920s and was content to let the Department of Health and the RCMP handle the problem.

The drug law underwent only three substantive changes between 1930 and 1952: the offences of cultivating opium and cannabis were added in 1938 (62t, s. 3); the deportation provisions were transferred to the new immigration legislation in 1952 (62u, ss. 19(1)(d), 19(2), 73); and the Schedule was expanded to include new compounds and synthetic narcotics.

During the 1930s, the federal drug bureaucracy consolidated its control over drug policy. The Narcotic Division established a permanent file of all known drug addicts in Canada which became a crude official census of the addict population (28, p. 9). The rivalry between the RCMP and various municipal police forces in the 1920s gave way to greater co-operation in the 1930s. The local police concentrated on users, leaving the RCMP free to deal with traffickers, major distributors, and importers. This division of labour was designed to maximize the value of the RCMP's expertise and nationwide information system. The Narcotic Division and the RCMP developed a close working relationship with their American counterparts, co-operating in joint investigations of the traffic between the two countries (26; 53b, p. 21).

Canada's illicit drug trade changed far more profoundly than did its drug policy. The war severed Pacific shipping lines, halted the flow of opium from the Orient, and crippled the Chinese opium distribution system (53b, pp. 23–25). North America's Chinese syndicates were unable to re-establish this system after the war because China, previously their largest source, was torn by civil war. When the Communist government finally came to power in 1949, they eliminated the traffic (61, pp. 56–58). The focus of the international trade shifted to the Middle East, where the export markets were controlled by French-Corsicans and other Europeans. North America's Chinese distributors had no contacts with these suppliers and, in any event, their traditional market within the Chinese community was rapidly disappearing (59). By 1945, offenders of Chinese origin accounted for only 10 per cent of Canada's drug convictions (28). Chinese narcotics syndicates would not again play a significant role in Canada until the early 1970s, when the Vietnam War and upheavals in the Middle Eastern and European traffic reshaped international distribution patterns (59).

Developments abroad also influenced Canada's east-coast traffic during this period. The repeal of alcohol prohibition in 1932 largely eliminated the illicit alcohol trade, prompting New York Mafia syndicates to expand their illicit drug activities. They obtained heroin from the French-Corsican laboratories of Paris and Marseilles and smuggled it into both American and Canadian east-coast ports aboard commercial ships (15, pp. 19–27; 20, pp. 236–42; 37, pp. 18–19). As in the west, the war disrupted smuggling operations and caused widespread shortages. Once the war ended, however, the east-coast distribution system was restored and strengthened. Several prominent French-Corsican racketeers, who had fled France to avoid prosecution for war crimes and for other offences, settled in Montreal. In conjunction with local and New York Mafia leaders, these expatriate French-Corsicans contributed to Montreal's emergence as a major trans-shipment centre for heroin en route to the United States. Mafia figures in Toronto and Hamilton established a parallel trans-shipment network, in some cases using unsuspecting Italian immigrants as drug couriers (15, pp. 29–89; 37, pp. 20–29). With the collapse of the Chinese trade and their own reliable sources of European heroin, Canada's east-coast Mafia soon completely dominated the domestic trade and played a major role in supplying the even more lucrative American market (8, Appendix B.2, pp. 570–72). There were sharp increases in American rates of heroin use after the war, whereas Canada's addict population apparently continued to fall.[10]

THE EMERGENCE OF A
TREATMENT ALTERNATIVE, 1952–1961

It was not until the early 1950s that the policy of criminalizing, rather than treating, addicts was first seriously questioned. Canadian enforcement officials responded to this challenge by raising the spectre of organized crime, and continued pressing for more stringent laws. Parliament made some attempt to accommodate the opposing views, but ultimately retained an enforcement perspective. Despite the lack of strong legislative support, some modest treatment programmes were initiated.

Discontent with the Law Enforcement Approach

Reports of spiralling rates of addiction among American ghetto youth and the televised American Senate hearings on organized crime sparked media accounts of similar issues in Canada (18, p. 75). Even though official statistics indicated that Canada's addict population had been decreasing (64, p. 420), these highly publicized events could not be ignored. Concern was expressed in Parliament, and by the Vancouver Community Chest, an association of social welfare agencies, which established a committee to study the local problem.

Relying on recent arrest and conviction statistics, the Committee concluded that heroin addiction was a growing problem in Canada, particularly among the young (45; 64, Appendix A). The Committee, which was chaired by a psychiatrist and dominated by physicians and social welfare officials, was disenchanted with the enforcement community's exclusive control over the addiction problem. Not surprisingly, the Committee's basic premise was that addiction should be regarded as a social and medical problem, not as a crime. With the support of the British Columbia Medical Association, the Committee called for the establishment of comprehensive drug education programmes, private experimental treatment centres, and narcotics clinics to dispense maintenance doses to registered addicts within a general rehabilitative programme. While favouring treatment for addicts, the Committee advocated more severe penalties for major traffickers (45). The Committee submitted its report to Mr. Martin, the federal Minister of Health and Welfare, in December 1952.

Although the report was not generally well received by the government and had no impact on the 1954 drug amendments, at least it forced the government to address the treatment issue (18, pp. 77–80; 64, Appendix G, pp. 16–18). Dr. Roberts, a senior official in the federal Department of Health and Welfare, basically rejected the Committee's treatment proposals in an article published in the February 1953 issue of the *Canadian Medical Association Journal*. Nevertheless, Dr. Roberts indicated that contrary to what was generally believed, the federal drug law did not prohibit physicians from treating addicts (48). Mr. Martin expressed the same view during the House of Commons debates on the 1954 drug amendments (27e, pp. 5308, 5311).

Despite considerable support in the House of Commons for treating addicts (27e, pp. 5304–5311, 5313), the government only paid lip-service to this issue in the 1954 drug amendments. The 1954 statute (62v), like previous drug legislation, was largely shaped by the enforcement needs of the RCMP drug squads. The police had complained that usually they were only able to

arrest traffickers for possession, because it was extremely difficult to appre-
hend them in the act of selling drugs. A new offence, possession for the
purpose of trafficking, was created to alleviate this problem. Once the prosecutor established unlawful possession, the accused was required to prove
that he had no intention of trafficking in the drug. If the accused failed to
satisfy this onus of proof, he would be convicted of possession for the purpose
of trafficking—an offence that carried the same penalties as trafficking. The
maximum sentence for trafficking was doubled to fourteen years' imprisonment, the related fine provisions were deleted, but whipping was retained
as a discretionary punishment (62v, s. 3). Possession was made a separate
offence, no longer subject to either fine or whipping (62v). The Minister of
Health claimed that the six-month mandatory minimum sentence for possession had been retained to ensure that addicts could be adequately treated
(27e, p. 5319). There were, however, no correctional drug treatment institutions, units, or even programmes in Canada at the time (27e, pp. 5308–9).

The Vancouver Community Chest persisted in lobbying the federal and
provincial governments (64, Appendices B, C, D). As a result of the Committee's efforts, British Columbia introduced the country's first correctional
drug treatment programme and founded the province's Narcotic Addiction
Foundation, a research, public education, and treatment facility centred in
Vancouver. In conjunction with the University of British Columbia, the Community Chest obtained federal and provincial funding for a comprehensive
scientific study of drug addiction in British Columbia (64).

The treatment approach continued to find little favour within the federal
Department of Health. The Department's hostility to the Community Chest's
proposals was perhaps best exemplified by R. Curran, the Department's chief
legal counsel. Referring to narcotics clinics, Curran wrote in a 1955 article,
"I feel it to be one of the most dangerous but specious solutions that can be
advanced. Unfortunately, like sin, it is attractively garbed" (19, p. 858; see also
48). Regardless of its view, the federal government could not publicly ignore
the Community Chest, if for no other reason than that it had mobilized a
cross section of British Columbia's legal, medical, academic, and social leaders.

The 1955 Senate Special Committee

In 1955, the federal government established the Senate Special Committee
on the Traffic in Narcotic Drugs in Canada under the chairmanship of a
Vancouver senator. No doubt the Canadian Senate Committee was partially
inspired by the widely publicized Kefauver Senate Committee on Organized
Crime, which had toured the United States in the early 1950s. The Senate
Special Committee held hearings in the major Canadian cities, receiving
testimony from physicians, drug researchers, the Vancouver Community Chest,
social welfare agencies, private citizens, federal officials, police representa-

tives, and H. Anslinger, the Commissioner of the American Bureau of Narcotics (18, pp. 80–81).

The law enforcement witnesses emphasized four major themes. First, the police outlined the difficulties inherent in convicting major traffickers. They testified that, despite their best efforts, it was impossible to stop the flow of drugs into the country (53b, pp. 25–26, 465–67). Second, they depicted the addict as a criminal and a complete social failure who "has no morals, no principles, and very seldom tells the truth" (53b, p. 66). The addict was not to be pitied as an unfortunate victim of circumstances. Third, any attempt to establish narcotics clinics would be doomed to failure. Some registered addicts would continue their criminal activities in order to buy additional drugs, and others would sell their licit supply on the black market. Young people would have nothing to lose by becoming addicts and consequently domestic addiction would rise sharply. Moreover, American addicts would flock to the Canadian clinics, turning them into centres of crime (53b, pp. 69–70, 229–32). Finally, the enforcement officials urged that a concerted effort be made to eliminate demand by aggressively enforcing the possession offence. Instead of addicts being supplied with drugs in the community, the addict would be removed from society for long periods of time. Chief Mulligan of the Vancouver Police suggested that since addicts were not rehabilitated by sentences of up to five years, they might be rehabilitated by sentences of ten or fifteen years. In a statement reminiscent of the views of Mrs. Murphy, Mulligan proposed that a drug treatment prison should be established on a remote island (53b, p. 71). Three senators immediately voiced support for the idea.

The testimony of the law enforcement officials was accepted almost without question. Ultimately, the Senate Special Committee advocated heavier trafficking penalties, and more aggressive enforcement of the possession offence and drug-related crimes, such as prostitution and theft (18, pp. 84–87). Advocates of a social or medical approach to addiction were generally viewed as being well-meaning, but misguided. The Committee apparently considered drug treatment as simply another means of assisting the police in their fight against the illicit trade (see 18, pp. 87–92). The Committee's recommendations were not incorporated into the federal drug law until 1961 (62w).

In the interim, North American academics, researchers, and enforcement officials continued debating the drug treatment issue (19, 33, 48, 63, 64, 66). At least some of the opinions expressed were based on questionable assessments of the American clinics of the late 1910s and of opiate maintenance in the United Kingdom. The most prominent and influential opponent of the British approach was Commissioner Anslinger of the American Federal Bureau of Narcotics. He successfully advocated long-term custodial treatment as an alternative to maintenance clinics, and his views had considerable influence in Canada.[11] In 1956, Ontario opened its first custodial drug treatment programme at the Alex Brown Memorial Clinic in Toronto. In the late 1950s, the federal government started developing plans for Matsqui, a drug-treatment penitentiary at Abbotsford, British Columbia (40, pp. 29–31). Like their American predecessors (see 2), the Canadian correctional treatment programmes proved to have little positive impact on the prisoners' subsequent rates of addiction[12] (see 7, pp. 10–13; 8, Appendix I).

The Present Law: The 1961 Narcotic Control Act

The 1961 *Narcotic Control Act* clearly reflected the Senate Committee's enforcement priorities and preference for custodial treatment. The maximum penalty for trafficking, possession for the purpose of trafficking, importing, and exporting was raised from fourteen years to life. A mandatory minimum sentence of seven years' imprisonment was enacted for importing and exporting (62w, ss. 4–5). Except for murder and treason no criminal offence carries as great a minimum term. The option of proceeding by way of summary conviction in possession cases was repealed (62w, s. 3). Nevertheless, the Act did eliminate some of the most severe features of the earlier legislation including: whipping, restrictions on appeals, the six-month minimum sentence for possession, and the provision deeming an occupant of a dwelling to be in possession of any drugs found therein. The restrictions on physicians' rights to prescribe drugs were removed from the Act and redefined in the regulations. The Minister of Health explained in the House that this change was intended to leave "to professional interpretation what is or is not a proper use of a narcotic. Actually, we hope to encourage doctors to take more responsibility for and interest in the health and well-being of the addict" (27f, p. 6001). Shortly thereafter, the Addiction Research Foundations of British Columbia and Ontario initiated methadone maintenance programmes, and the Canadian Medical Association established a committee to report on what constituted good medical practice in the care of narcotics addicts (18, pp. 101–4).

Part II of the Narcotic Control Act provided for "custody for treatment and preventive detention" of convicted addicts, akin to the proposals of Mrs. Murphy, Police Chief Mulligan, and Commissioner Anslinger. Once convicted of a single drug offence, an addict could be subject to a custodial sentence for treatment of an indeterminate length, and even if paroled was subject to supervision for a period not exceeding ten years. Upon a subsequent conviction, an addict could be imprisoned for life, subject to being paroled (62w, ss. 16, 17(1), 18). No special provisions were made for treatment. Prisoners governed by these provisions were to be confined to federal penitentiaries. Those convicted of a second trafficking offence of any kind were subject to preventive detention and could also be incarcerated for life, subject to being paroled (62w, s. 15). Part II of the Act was not proclaimed and thus never became law. Nevertheless, these provisions illustrate Parliament's disdain for traffickers and its concept of correctional treatment. In the name of treatment,

Parliament was willing to impose upon addicts sentences that had previously been reserved for the country's most violent and hardened criminals.

THE DECLINE AND SUBSEQUENT EXPANSION OF THE ILLICIT HEROIN TRADE, 1961–1970

During the Senate Special Committee hearings, Canadian police officials had acknowledged their inability to stem heroin smuggling or to seriously disrupt the major syndicates. However, in the late 1950s the American Bureau of Narcotics and the RCMP initiated a series of conspiracy prosecutions against the senior figures in the North American heroin trade. These men had been largely immune to traditional enforcement techniques because they did not personally handle, possess, or sell the drugs. Expendable employees bore these risks. In a conspiracy prosecution, the police only had to establish that there was an agreement to commit an unlawful act between the accused and any of his partners, suppliers, purchasers, or underlings. In essence, the offence was complete upon proof of an agreement; no other crime needed to have been committed or even attempted.

The syndicates were caught off guard (59, pp. 40–44; 8, Appendix B.2, pp. 571–72). Within a six-year period, North America's largest heroin operations were rocked by over 100 arrests and convictions. Those imprisoned included many of New York's most powerful Mafia leaders and their Montreal and Canadian contacts. In Canada, major domestic heroin distributors in Vancouver, Toronto, and Montreal were convicted and imprisoned.[13]

This unprecedented flurry of prosecutions contributed to a heroin shortage throughout North America. The scarcity was most apparent in Vancouver, the Canadian city with the largest addict population. The street price of a heroin capsule rose from five dollars in 1961 to fifteen dollars by the end of 1962. There were also corresponding increases in wholesale prices. According to the Vancouver RCMP, the purity of heroin decreased and the number of users fell sharply. It was suggested that many addicts turned to barbiturates or alcohol, registered in the Narcotic Addiction Foundation's methadone maintenance programme, reduced their consumption, or ceased use (58). During this period, about 100 Canadian addicts emigrated to the United Kingdom in order to lawfully obtain maintenance doses of narcotics. Most of the Canadians were deported or returned home voluntarily within several years, but some adjusted and remained (see 23, 24, 70). The heroin shortage in Canada lasted until 1965, abating when the Mafia re-established its importing and distributing networks (59, pp. 43–44).

The new syndicates were specifically organized to offset the advantages gained by the police in using the conspiracy charge. The chain of distribution was extended to insulate syndicate leaders from the activities of their lower-level employees. By operating only through trusted associates and by confining sales to known dealers, financiers could reduce the likelihood of a conspiracy prosecution. Even if a dealer was willing to risk testifying for the police, he could not directly implicate the financier. These and other precautions soon became standard operational features of the North American syndicates. Furthermore, the trade was not as tightly controlled or centralized as it had been in the late 1950s. With the increase in the number of sources, smuggling routes, importers, and distributors, the potential impact of any single prosecution decreased (58).

There was little public interest in the drug issue until the mid-1960s, when media attention was focussed on marijuana and LSD use. Grave concerns were expressed about the physiological and psychological effects of these drugs. Canadian police warned that the upsurge in hallucinogenic drug use was a prelude to a parallel rise in heroin addiction. The sordid details of life in Toronto's hippy community were given extensive media coverage, reinforcing public fears about the counterculture. Ominous statements were made about the future of Canada's youth. As in the past, Canadian perceptions were influenced by the American media and enforcement agencies (18, pp. 141–152).

The number of cannabis convictions rose sharply in the late 1960s and, by the beginning of the 1970s, accounted for well over 90 per cent of total convictions (1, p. 46). Unlike the typical heroin addict, many cannabis users were young, had no criminal record, and were largely indistinguishable from their contemporaries. The *Narcotic Control Act*'s penalty provisions were criticized as being unduly severe given the cannabis offender's age and social background. Sweeping changes in federal cannabis law were discussed (see 18, pp. 153–180). Ultimately, the government enacted very modest legislation in 1969, which gave the prosecutor the option of proceeding by way of summary conviction in possession cases (62x, s. 12)—a discretion that had only been withdrawn in 1961. Although this provision was intended for young, middle-class cannabis offenders, it was also invoked in some cases involving heroin users.

Public concern over the drug issue continued throughout the late 1960s, fuelled in large part by extensive media coverage. Academics, social welfare leaders, police officials, and prominent political figures all called for legislative action. The federal government responded to these diverse pressures by appointing a Royal Commission of Inquiry into the Non-Medical Use of Drugs, under the chairmanship of Gerald Le Dain, the Dean of Osgoode Hall Law School (18, pp. 153–180). The Commission issued its interim report in May 1970, reports on treatment and cannabis in 1972, and a final report in 1973 (5, 6, 7, 8). Despite these comprehensive reports, there has not been a significant change in the *Narcotic Control Act* since 1969.

Although there was a marked increase in the Canadian addict population during the late 1960s, the heroin trade changed far less dramatically than the hallucinogenic drug market. The epidemic increases in heroin use that swept the United States simply did nòt materialize in Canada. Nonetheless, there were significant developments in the domestic heroin traffic. In the early

1960s, heroin use was confined to Montreal, Toronto, Hamilton, Winnipeg, and Vancouver. During the late 1960s, small pockets of heroin trafficking and use developed, albeit temporarily in some cases, in Halifax, Kingston, London, Windsor, Calgary, Edmonton, Victoria, and a number of small cities and towns in British Columbia. Once prevalent only within the downtown core of the major cities, the trade spread outwards as additional suburban outlets opened. By the end of the 1960s, heroin was more readily available than it had ever been (59, pp. 43–45).

CONCLUSION

Canadian narcotics control policy has been shaped by various factors, the least significant of which have been the physiological effects of the opiates themselves. The early laws were the product of moral reformers, racism, and the political manoeuvring of Mackenzie King and the federal drug bureaucracy. By 1930 the drug law had been transformed into an inordinately repressive statute, characterized by sweeping police powers, punitive sanctions, and severe encroachments on civil liberties. The addicts' image, the law, and the drug bureaucracy's control over drug policy went unchallenged during the next two decades.

When the policy of criminalizing addicts was first questioned in the 1950s, Parliament deferred to the views of the drug bureaucracy and re-affirmed its commitment to stringent enforcement. Nevertheless, some of the severe features of the early law were repealed, doctors were again permitted to treat addicts, and health issues were discussed. The upsurge in cannabis and hallucinogenic drug use in the late 1960s generated renewed public interest and demands for reforms. Except for the creation of the Le Dain Commission, these events had little impact on policy. There was, however, a moderation in the general tone of the drug debate. Members of the academic, legal, and medical communities began to question perceptions about drug use and users, the breadth of police powers, the effectiveness of enforcement, and the law's impact on offenders. These latest developments are, of course, the most difficult to assess because there has been no comprehensive government response to these concerns or to the Le Dain Commission reports. Aside from the government's almost annual discussion of cannabis reform, the drug law and policies of the 1960s have evidenced little change.

Throughout this 100-year period, Canada's illicit trade has evolved in step with domestic enforcement and international market forces. Regardless of internal policies, the Canadian heroin trade will continue to be profoundly affected by developments abroad, particularly those in the United States. The relatively uninterrupted success of the illicit traffic, in the face of concerted enforcement efforts, attests to its economic vitality.

NOTES

1. A parallel sequence of events occurred in California about a decade earlier, and this served as a model for the campaign in British Columbia (36, pp. 58–63; 39; 57, pp. 163–68).
2. In 1868, China and the United States signed the Burlingame Treaty. It provided that the American government could reasonably limit the immigration of Chinese labourers, but could not prohibit Chinese immigration altogether. In response to increasing anti-Asiatic sentiment in California, and despite the Burlingame Treaty provisions, the United States enacted the Chinese Exclusion Act of 1882 which prohibited Chinese immigration to California. This prohibition was renewed several times until 1944, when about 100 Chinese were allowed to enter the United States (34, pp. 85–89; 36, pp. 58–61).
3. It should be noted that the Chinese population of British Columbia was relatively small, accounting for less than 9 per cent of the provincial total in the 1881 census (12a, p. 10). Despite the influx of Chinese workers to meet the needs of the Canadian Pacific Railroad in the early 1880s, the Chinese accounted for only 15 per cent of British Columbia's population in the 1891 census (12b, p. 362–63). Canada's Chinese population grew slowly because the vast majority of Chinese immigrants were unmarried male labourers who eventually returned home. While over 78,600 Chinese emigrated to Canada between 1886 and 1915, over 61,100 left during the same period (11, p. 116).
4. Chinese immigration fell from 4,847 in 1904 to 77 in 1905. It increased significantly after 1908, peaking in 1913 at 7,455 (11) and earning the federal government $3,500,000—about half of which was paid to British Columbia.
5. There is no doubt that the opium smoking trade in Canada was dwarfed by the patent medicine industry. In 1908, King reported that there were at least seven factories producing smoking opium which together generated sales of between $600,000 and $650,000 (32, p. 7). Not all of this smoking opium was consumed domestically. Large quantities of legally produced Canadian smoking opium were smuggled into the lucrative American market (16, pp. 49–54). In comparison, Canada's 37 patent medicine companies alone manufactured over $3,200,000 worth of goods in 1910 and this total was augmented by imported patent medicines (12c; 54b, pp. 98–99).
6. The tenor of the House debates on the cigarette prohibition bill was very similar to that of King's report on the need to prohibit opium smoking. The following excerpt from Mr. Telford's speech illustrates the nature of the House debates: "There is scarcely a town or city in Canada where you will not find boys, the sons of respectable parents, who have dwarfed their bodies, ruined their intellects and damaged their moral perceptions

to such an extent that they do not know the difference between right and wrong, and consequently many of them have had to be sent to reformatories. The medical profession almost to a man affirm the same thing with regard to this insidious habit: and I believe a majority of the members of this House will admit that it is an unmitigated curse to the boys of this country without a single redeeming feature. Therefore something ought to be done, more than has been done in the past, to lessen this growing evil" (27b, p. 5103).

7. King's public posturing about Canada's moral leadership in the international anti-opium movement is ironic. As a member of the British delegation to the Shanghai Commission, King was hardly in the vanguard of this movement. Britain had largely created and consciously fostered the opium smoking trade in China, in blatant defiance of Chinese law. Britain only reluctantly agreed to co-operate in international suppression efforts after its profits from the opium trade had declined, and domestic and foreign criticism of its opium policies became impossible to ignore. King, for his part, arrived late to the Commission because he had stopped in Britain and India to discuss methods of limiting Asiatic emigration to Canada. He apparently had little faith in the Commission, was not particularly attentive, and misreported some of the proceedings (21, pp. 192–94; 34, pp. 123–25).

8. The Act limited immigration to members of the diplomatic corps, Chinese children born in Canada who had left temporarily for educational or other purposes, specified classes of Chinese merchants, and Chinese students attending Canadian universities or colleges. Even a lawful Chinese resident of Canada was required to register prior to leaving the country temporarily, in order to ensure re-entry. The Act also provided for the deportation of any Chinese resident, except for a Canadian citizen, who fell within one of fifteen prohibited classes. These classes included persons who were likely to become a public charge; drug addicts; illiterates; persons of "constitutional psychopathic inferiority"; and persons who were mentally and physically defective to the extent that it affected their ability to earn a living.

9. For a discussion of the origins of the writs in drug law see 25.

10. Stevenson *et al.* (64) list the official Canadian estimates from 1924 to 1955 which suggest that there was a steady decline throughout this period. See, however, 53b, p. 61, for an RCMP estimate of the post-war addict population.

11. For example, the Senate Special Committee adopted Anslinger's recommendation for heavier trafficking penalties, even though the Canadian enforcement witnesses had not uniformly called for stiffer sanctions. The Committee also paid special thanks to Commissioner Anslinger in their recommendation section (see 18, p. 85). Anslinger's influence on the

Canadian federal drug bureaucracy was likely as great: as illustrated by the deference shown to Anslinger by Curran in his article (19, p. 858).

12. The Matsqui treatment programme was carefully designed, generously funded and staffed, and vigorously evaluated. Yet, despite these close-to-ideal conditions, the results were extremely disappointing. Matsqui's research officer reported that "the rate of recidivism approached 100%." It is curious that the addicts in the more intensive treatment programme did worse than those in the other programme. The research officer suggested that the intensive programme, rather than curing addiction, helped the addicts to become better adjusted, self-assured addicts who were capable of committing more offences and thereby purchasing more heroin (40, pp. 29–31).

13. In the late 1950s, Vito Genovese, then North America's most powerful Mafia leader, and fourteen of his associates were convicted of conspiracy to import heroin. Early in 1960, Giuseppe Cotroni, Robert Rene of Montreal, and twenty-nine high-ranking Mafiosi in New York were arrested and charged with conspiracy to traffic in heroin. Later in 1960, three Canadian Mafia distributors centred in Toronto and another twenty Mafia members in New York were arrested and charged with conspiracy to import heroin. Several years later, Lucien Rivard of Montreal was extradited to the United States to stand trial for conspiracy to import heroin. In the early 1960s, one of Vancouver's largest heroin distributors retired to avoid the risk of a conspiracy prosecution, while the other major distributor was arrested for conspiracy to traffic. North America's four largest importing and distributing operations were destroyed and the principal distributors in Canada's three largest cities were serving long prison terms (15).

REFERENCES

1. Blackwell, J., Green, M., and Solomon, R. *Cannabis Control Policy: A Discussion Paper*. Unpublished research study. Health Protection Branch, Department of National Health and Welfare, Ottawa, 1979.
2. Brecher, E. M., and the Editors of Consumer Reports. *Licit and Illicit Drugs*. Boston: Little, Brown, 1972.
3. British Columbia. *Statutes*.
    a. *Chinese Regulation Act*, S.B.C. 1884, c. 4.
    b. *An Act Respecting Municipalities*, Cons. S.B.C. 1877, c. 129.
    c. *An Act to make better provision for the Qualification and Registration of Voters*, Cons. S.B.C. 1877, c. 66.
    d. *Companies Act*, Cons. S.B.C. 1888, c. 21, s. 78.

e. *Land Act*, Cons. s.b.c. 1888, c. 66.

f. *Public School Act*, Cons. s.b.c. 1888, c. 104.

4. Canada. *Report of the Department of Health for the Fiscal Year Ended March 31, 1928*. Ottawa, 1929.

5. Canada. Commission of Inquiry into the Non-Medical Use of Drugs. *Interim Report*. Ottawa: Queen's Printer, 1970.

6. Canada. Commission of Inquiry into the Non-Medical Use of Drugs. *Cannabis*. Ottawa: Information Canada, 1972.

7. Canada. Commission of Inquiry into the Non-Medical Use of Drugs. *Treatment*. Ottawa: Information Canada, 1972.

8. Canada. Commission of Inquiry into the Non-Medical Use of Drugs. *Final Report*. Ottawa: Information Canada, 1973.

9. *Canada Gazette 17*:1568, 1884.

10. *Canada Gazette 18*:1569, 1885.

11. *Canada Year Book, 1915*, 1916.

12. Census of Canada.

a. *Census of Canada 1880–81*. (1883).

b. *Census of Canada 1890–91*. Vol. 1 (1893).

c. Manufacturers for 1910 as enumerated in June 1911. In: *Fifth Census of Canada 1911*, Vol. 3. (1913).

13. Chapman, T. Drug usage and the *Victoria Daily Colonist:* The opium smokers of Western Canada. In: Knafla, L. (ed.). Canadian Society for Legal History. *Proceedings 1977*. pp. 60–75, 1977.

14. Chapman, T. The anti-drug crusade in Western Canada, 1885–1925. In: Bercuson, D., and Knafla, L. (eds.). *Law and Society in Canada in Historical Perspective*. Calgary: University of Calgary, 1979.

15. Charbonneau, J. *The Canadian Connection*. Ottawa: Optimum, 1976.

16. Clark, C. *Tales of the British Columbia Provincial Police*. Sidney, B.C.: Gray's Publishing, 1971.

17. Cook, S. *Ideology and Canadian Narcotics Legislation, 1908–1923*. M.A. thesis, University of Toronto, 1964.

18. Cook, S. *Variations in Response to Illegal Drug Use*. Unpublished research study. Alcoholism and Drug Addiction Research Foundation, Toronto, 1970.

19. Curran, R. E. Some aspects of Canada's narcotic-drug problem. *Food Drug Cosmetic Law Journal, 10*:850–60 (December 1955).

20. Cusak, J. T. Response of the government of France to the international heroin problem. In: Simmons, L. and Said, A. (eds.). *Drugs, Politics, and Diplomacy: The International Connections*. Beverly Hills, Calif.: Sage, 1974.

21. Dawson, R. M. *William Lyon Mackenzie King: A Political Biography*. Toronto: University of Toronto Press, 1958.

22. Duster, T. *The Legislation of Morality: Law, Drugs and Moral Judgment*. New York: Free Press, 1970.

23. Frankau, I. M. Treatment in England of Canadian patients addicted to narcotic drugs. *Canadian Medical Association Journal*, 90:421–24 (1964).

24. Glatt, M. M. and Spear, H. B. The influence of Canadian addicts on heroin addicts in the United Kingdom. *British Journal of Addiction*, 66:141–49 (1971).

25. Green, M. A history of Canadian narcotics control: The formative years. *University of Toronto Faculty of Law Review*, 37:42–79 (1979).

26. Harvison, C. *The Horsemen*. Toronto: McClelland and Stewart, 1967.

27. House of Commons. Canada. *Debates*.
    a. April 3, 1908.
    b. March 16, 1908.
    c. January 26, 1911.
    d. May 8, 1922.
    e. June 1, 1954.
    f. June 7, 1961.

28. Josie, G. *A Report on Drug Addiction in Canada*. Ottawa: Department of National Health and Welfare, 1948.

29. Kawakami, K. *Asia at the Door: A Study of the Japanese Question in the Continental United States, Hawaii and Canada*. New York: Fleming H. Ravell Publishing Co., 1914.

30. Ketchum, P. Writs of assistance. *Chitty's Law Journal* 19:90–92 (1971).

31. King, W. L. M. Losses sustained by the Chinese population of Vancouver, B.C. on the occasion of the riots in that city in September, 1907. *Sessional papers 1907–8*, no. 74f.

32. King, W. L. M. The need for the suppression of the opium traffic in Canada. *Sessional papers 1908*, no. 36b.

33. Kirkpatrick, A. M. New approach to drug problem suggested. *Canadian Bar Journal*, 2:427–41 (1959).

34. Lowes, P. *The Genesis of International Narcotics Control*. New York: Arno, 1981.

35. Lyle, D. The logistics of junk. *Esquire*, March 1966.

36. Mark, G. Racial, economic and political factors in the development of America's first drug laws. *Issues in Criminology*, 10:49–72 (1975).

37. McCoy, A., Reid, C., and Adams II, L. *The Politics of Heroin in Southeast Asia*. New York: Harper & Row, 1972.

38. MacFarlane, B. A. *Drug Offences in Canada*. 2d ed. Toronto: Canada Law Book, 1986.

39. Morgan, P. A. The legislation of drug law: Economic crises and social control. *Journal of Drug Issues*, 8:53–62 (1978).

40. Murphy, B. *A Quantitative Test of the Effectiveness of an Experimental Treatment Programme for Delinquent Opiate Addicts*. Ottawa: Department of the Solicitor General of Canada, 1972.

41. Murphy, E. F. *The Black Candle*. Toronto: Thomas Allen, 1922.

42. Musto, David F. *The American Disease: Origins of Narcotic Control.* New Haven: Yale University Press, 1973.
43. Nyswander, M. E. History of a nightmare. In: Wakefield, D. (ed.). *The Addict.* New York: Fawcett World Library, 1966.
44. Parker, G. The extraordinary power to search and seize and the writ of assistance. *University of British Columbia Law Review, 1*:688–728 (1963).
45. "Ranta Report." *Drug Addiction in Canada: The Problem and Its Solution.* Reprinted as "Here's program to fight drug menace," Vancouver *Province*, July 30, 1952.
46. *Re Writs of Assistance*, [1965] 2 Ex. C.R. 645.
47. *Re Writs of Assistance* (1975), 34 C.C.C. (2d) 62 (Fed. T.D.).
48. Roberts, C. A. The problem of drug addiction. *Canadian Medical Association Journal, 68*:112–15 (1953).
49. *R.* v. *Corporation of Victoria* (1888), 1 B.C.R. (Part II) 331.
50. *R.* v. *Gold Commissioner of Victoria District* (1886), 1 B.C.R. (Part II) 260.
51. *R.* v. *Mee Wah* (1886), 3 B.C.R. 403 (Co. Ct.).
52. *R.* v. *Wing Chong* (1885), 1 B.C.R. (Part II) 150.
53. Senate. Canada.
   a. *Debates*, 1908.
   b. Special Committee on the Traffic in Narcotic Drugs in Canada. *Proceedings*, 1955.
54. *Sessional Papers.* Canada.
   a. 1911, no. 207.
   b. 1912, no. 11, Report of the Department of Customs.
   c. Vol. 47, 1912–1913, no. 17, Criminal Statistics.
   d. Vol. 50, 1915, no. 17, Criminal Statistics.
   e. Vol. 52, 1917, no. 17, Criminal Statistics.
   f. Vol. 54, 1919, no. 10d, Criminal Statistics.
   g. Vol. 57, 1921, no. 10d, Criminal Statistics.
   h. 1921, no. 12, Report of the Department of Health for the fiscal year ending March 31, 1920.
   i. 1921, no. 28, Report of the Royal Canadian Mounted Police for the year ended September 30, 1920.
   j. 1922, no. 28, Report of the Royal Canadian Mounted Police for the year ended September 30, 1921.
   k. 1923, no. 19, Report of the Department of Health for the fiscal year ended March 31, 1922.
   l. 1923, no. 21, Report of the Royal Canadian Mounted Police for the year ended September 30, 1922.
55. Sharman, C. H. L. Narcotic control in Canada. *Police Journal, 3*:535–49 (1930).
56. Skinner, J. Writs of assistance. *University of Toronto Faculty of Law Review, 21*:26–44 (1963).

57. Smith, R. Status politics and the image of the addict. *Issues in Criminology*, 2:157–75 (1966).
58. Solomon, R. Interview with RCMP officials in Vancouver. Unpublished brief, Commission of Inquiry into the Non-medical Use of Drugs, 1970.
59. Solomon, R. The criminal prohibition of non-medical opiate use in Canada. Unpublished research study, Commission of Inquiry into the Non-medical Use of Drugs, 1972.
60. Solomon, R. The noble pursuit of evil: Arrest, search and seizure in Canadian drug law. Chapter 16 of this book.
61. Solomon, R., and Versteeg, H. *A review of the development and present state of the illicit international heroin trade*. Ottawa: Health and Welfare Canada. Non-medical Use of Drugs Directorate, 1978.
62. *Statutes of Canada*.
    a. *An Act Respecting the Customs*, S.C. 1867–8, c. 6.
    b. *The Chinese Immigration Act, 1885*, S.C. 1885, c. 71.
    c. *The Chinese Immigration Act, 1900*, S.C. 1900, c. 32.
    d. *The Chinese Immigration Act, 1903*, S.C. 1903, c. 8.
    e. *An Act to amend the Inland Review Act*, S.C. 1908, c. 34.
    f. *An Act to prohibit the importation, manufacture, and sale of Opium for other than medicinal purposes*, S.C. 1908, c. 50.
    g. *An Act to restrain the use of tobacco by young persons*, S.C. 1908, c. 73.
    h. *The Proprietary or Patent Medicine Act*, S.C. 1908, c. 56.
    i. *The Opium and Drug Act*, S.C. 1911, c. 17.
    j. *An Act to amend the Opium and Drug Act*, S.C. 1919 (2nd sess.), c. 25.
    k. *An Act to amend the Opium and Narcotic Drug Act*, S.C. 1920, c. 31.
    l. *An Act to amend the Opium and Narcotic Drug Act*, S.C. 1921, c. 42.
    m. *An Act to amend the Opium and Narcotic Drug Act*, S.C. 1922, c. 36.
    n. *The Chinese Immigration Act, 1923*, S.C. 1923, c. 38.
    o. *The Opium and Narcotic Drug Act, 1923*, S.C. 1923, c. 22.
    p. *An Act to amend the Opium and Narcotic Drug Act, 1923*, S.C. 1925, c. 20.
    q. *An Act to amend the Opium and Narcotic Drug Act, 1923*, S.C. 1926, c. 12.
    r. *Opium and Narcotic Drug Act*, R.S.C. 1927, c. 144.
    s. *The Opium and Narcotic Drug Act, 1929*, S.C. 1929, c. 49.
    t. *An Act to amend the Opium and Narcotic Drug Act, 1929*, S.C. 1938, c. 9.
    u. *The Immigration Act*, S.C. 1952, c. 42.
    v. *An Act to amend the Opium and Narcotic Drug Act*, S.C. 1954, c. 38.
    w. *Narcotic Control Act*, S.C. 1961, c. 35.
    x. *An Act to amend the Food and Drugs Act and the Narcotic Control Act and to make a consequential amendment to the Criminal Code*, S.C. 1969, c. 41.

63. Stevenson, G. Arguments for and against the legal sale of narcotics. *Bulletin of the Vancouver Medical Association*, *31*:3–12 (1955).
64. Stevenson, G. H., Lingley, L. P. A., Trasov, G. E., and Stanfield, H. *Drug Addiction in British Columbia*. Vancouver: The University of British Columbia, 1956.
65. *Tai Sing* v. *Maguire* (1878), 1 B.C.R. (Part I) 101.
66. Trasov, G. E. Narcotic dispensaries. *Criminal Law Quarterly*, *2*:334–41 (1960).
67. Trasov, G. E. History of the opium and narcotic drug legislation in Canada. *Criminal Law Quarterly*, *4*:274–82 (1962).
68. Williams, D. *"The Man for a New Country": Sir Matthew Baillie Begby*. 1977.
69. Willoughby, W. *Opium as an International Problem: The Geneva Conferences*. New York: Arnold Press, 1976.
70. Zacune, J. A comparison of Canadian narcotic addicts in Great Britain and in Canada. *Bulletin on Narcotics 23*(4): 41–49 (1971).

8

Canada's Federal Drug Legislation

Robert R. Solomon

INTRODUCTION

There are two major federal statutes in Canada dealing specifically with illegal drugs—the *Narcotic Control Act* (NCA) (4i) and the *Food and Drugs Act* (FDA) (4f). Although these are by far the most important federal drug *Act*s, other federal statutes also create crimes involving drugs. For example, section 237 of the *Criminal Code* (4c) makes it a crime to operate or have care or control of a motor vehicle, aircraft, or boat while one's ability to do so is impaired by alcohol or another drug.

The NCA and FDA each set out offences and penalties, and both contain special police powers of entry, search, seizure, and forfeiture. The *Act*s do not make any reference to police powers of arrest, investigation, or the many other rules of procedure that govern the apprehension and trial of a suspect. In this sense, the NCA and FDA may be viewed as incomplete criminal statutes. However, by virtue of the *Interpretation Act* (4h), the *Criminal Code*'s procedural provisions apply to any crime created by other federal statutes, unless those statutes provide otherwise. Consequently, many of the *Criminal Code* provisions apply to the investigation and prosecution of the offences created by the NCA and FDA.

Before we turn specifically to the federal drug *Act*s, it is necessary to understand the classification of federal offences. All federal offences are divided into one of three categories—summary conviction offences, indictable offences, and dual procedure offences. The prosecutor is given discretion in dual procedure offences (also referred to as "hybrid" or "crown electable" offences) to proceed either by summary conviction or by indictment. Generally, it is the seriousness of the case that determines whether the prosecutor will elect to proceed by indictment or summary conviction. Once this decision is made, the case is then treated as any other summary conviction or indictable offence. It is important to note that a suspect apparently has no legal right to challenge how prosecutors exercise their discretion in dual procedure offences (36; 42, pp. 188–89). With the enactment of the *Canadian Charter of Rights and Freedoms* (4b) in 1982, the Supreme Court of Canada may be required to reassess the validity of such an unfettered discretion.

The essential difference between indictable and summary conviction offences is the criminal procedures that govern them. The *Criminal Code* contains one set of procedures for summary conviction offences and another set for indictable offences. As a general rule, the more serious crimes are indictable, and this is reflected in the nature of the procedures. For example, police are given broader powers of arrest for indictable offences than for summary conviction offences (4c, s. 450). The trial procedures used for indictable offences are more formal and complex than those that apply to summary conviction offences. A person charged with an indictable offence generally has a right to a jury trial, whereas those charged with summary conviction offences do not (4c, ss. 429 and 736(c)).

The prosecutor's exercise of discretion in dual procedure offences may affect not only the procedure, but also the sentence. Dual procedure offences usually provide two maximum sentences—one if the case is tried by summary conviction, and a second, usually heavier, maximum if the case is tried by indictment. For example, cannabis possession is a dual procedure offence, which if tried by summary conviction carries a maximum sentence of six months' imprisonment and a $1,000 fine for a first offence. However, if tried by indictment, possession carries a maximum sentence of seven years' imprisonment (4i, s. 3(2)).

The history of the NCA has been described in the previous chapter. The first *Food and Drugs Act* (4e) was enacted in 1920 and replaced the *Adulteration Act* (4a) which can be traced back to 1885. However, the sections dealing with non-medical drug use are relatively new. Until the 1960s, the FDA was almost exclusively concerned with ensuring that foods, cosmetics, medicines, and medical devices were produced in sanitary conditions, were safe for consumption and use, and were honestly and accurately advertised. The federal government added new parts to the FDA in the 1960s to deal with the increased non-medical use of lysergic acid diethylamide (LSD), amphetamines, barbiturates, and other drugs.

THE NARCOTIC CONTROL ACT

There are now approximately 100 different substances listed in the Schedule to the NCA. Although many of these substances, such as cannabis, cocaine, and phencyclidine (PCP) are not pharmacologically classified as narcotics, every drug listed in the Schedule is defined as a narcotic for legal purposes and is subject to the provisions of the NCA. The *Act* empowers the federal government to add or delete substances from the Schedule by means of orders-in-council (4i, s. 14).

The *Act* contains six common offences which include: possession of a narcotic (often referred to as "simple possession"); trafficking in a narcotic; possession of a narcotic for the purpose of trafficking; importing or exporting a narcotic; cultivation of opium or cannabis; and an offence commonly referred to as "prescription shopping" or "double doctoring." As shall be discussed, these offences are very broadly defined and carry severe maximum sentences. Except for the offence of cultivation, which applies only to opium and cannabis, the *Act* does not distinguish among the drugs in the Schedule. For example, cannabis and heroin offenders are subject to identical police enforcement powers, processes of fingerprinting and photographing, penalty provisions, and criminal record consequences. Until the mid-1960s, heroin and other opiates accounted for the vast majority of arrests and convictions. Thereafter, cannabis offences began to predominate. Between 1977 and 1985, there were approximately 329,000 NCA convictions recorded, nearly 93 percent of which were for cannabis offences (2, 3). Cocaine, PCP, heroin, and codeine account for almost all of the remaining offences (2, 3).

Possession of a Narcotic

The NCA adopts the broad *Criminal Code* definition of "possession." In order to be convicted of possession, a suspect must know what the substance is and have some measure of control over it. Possession charges can be laid in three different kinds of situations (4i, s. 2 "possession," 4c, s. 3(4)).

The simplest type of case is that in which the police find a narcotic in the suspect's physical possession. This would arise if the police caught a suspect smoking a joint or found it in his or her wallet during a search. The physical contact with the narcotic or its container need only be brief (19, 29). However, the prosecutors must establish that the suspect knew what the drug was and willingly took possession of it. The suspect could not be convicted if he or she inadvertently picked up a joint, without realizing what it was (1).

Second, an individual may be convicted of possession of a narcotic without being in physical possession of the substance, provided he or she exercises control over it (17, 27, 35, 39). Assume that a male suspect hides some marijuana in a box of books that he stores at his girlfriend's apartment. Assume, as well, that he tells his girlfriend about the marijuana, but not her room-mate. If the police find the marijuana, the suspect could be convicted of possession because he had control of the drug even though it was not in his physical possession. His girlfriend could also be convicted because she knowingly possessed the marijuana. However, the room-mate could not be convicted, even though she may have been in physical possession of the box, because she did not know that it contained an illegal drug.

The third type of situation is the most complex. Drugs found in the possession of one member of a group are considered, for legal purposes, to be in the possession of the other members if they were aware of this fact, consented to it, and had some control over the situation. A suspect could not be convicted of possession simply because she was at a party where other people were smoking marijuana, or because she walked down the street with a friend who she knew had a joint in his pocket (26, 38). In these situations, she had knowledge of the illegal possession, but that did not mean that she consented to the illegal act or had the power to control the situation. The result might well be different if she permitted a friend to smoke a joint while they were both sitting in her car. As the owner of the car, she has the legal right to control what happens in it. Her failure to protest or otherwise attempt to stop her friend would indicate that she consented to the illegal act (10, 22, 28).

Possession of any amount of a narcotic is unlawful, and a suspect may be convicted of possession even if the police seize only a very small quantity of the drug. The Canadian courts have upheld possession charges if the quantity of drugs found was observable to the naked eye. Consequently, ashes from a joint, scrapings from a hash pipe, and droplets from a syringe may be sufficient to support a possession conviction. However, courts have shown greater reluctance to convict a suspect of possession in cases involving microscopic quantities that are not really visible or capable of normal physical handling (5, pp. 550–62). On the other hand, if the police seize a quantity of drugs larger than would normally be used by one person, the suspect may be charged with the more serious offence of possession of a narcotic for the purpose of trafficking.

As indicated, possession of a narcotic is a dual procedure offence. If it is tried by summary conviction, the maximum penalty is six months' imprisonment and a $1,000 fine for a first offence, and imprisonment for a year and a $2,000 fine for a subsequent offence. If, however, the prosecutor proceeds by indictment, the maximum penalty is seven years' imprisonment (4i, s. 3(2)(a) and (b)). Note that sentences of two years or more are generally served in federal penitentiaries, whereas shorter sentences are served in provincial jails or prisons.

Trafficking in a Narcotic

Contrary to the impression sometimes created by the media, the offence of trafficking encompasses an extremely broad range of activities. The NCA defines trafficking to include manufacturing, selling, giving, administering, transporting, sending, delivering, or distributing a narcotic. Offering or agreeing to do any of these acts also constitutes trafficking, even if the suspect has no intention or ability to fulfil this commitment (4i, s. 2 "traffic"). Consequently, distilling "weed oil" from marijuana solely for personal use or holding a heated knife while a friend inhales smoke from the oil both constitute trafficking. The first act is manufacturing a narcotic (11), and the second is administering a narcotic (15). Similarly, an individual who purchases even a small quantity of a narcotic and takes it over to a friend to give her some may be convicted of trafficking for having transported the drug (41). Note that to be convicted of trafficking based on transporting a narcotic, the suspect must have carried the drugs with a view to distributing them. Thus, an individual who moves his personal supply of drugs from one place to another could not be convicted of trafficking (21, 41). It is also important to note that trafficking includes the act of giving a narcotic to another person (23, 24, 37, 40). No exchange of money is necessary, and no distinction is made in terms of the quantity involved. A member of organized crime who sells heroin in 10-kg lots and an individual who shares a single joint with a friend are both trafficking. However, the drug involved, the quantity, and the offender's motives are factors that may be considered in sentencing.

An individual may also be charged with trafficking for selling a substance that is not a narcotic, if he or she has claimed that it is a narcotic. For example, an accused may be convicted of trafficking in heroin for having sold sugar which he or she alleged to be heroin. The main element of the offence is the holding out or representing of a substance as a narcotic (25, 32, 34).

Possession of a Narcotic for the Purpose of Trafficking

The police will usually charge a suspect with simple possession if they seize a quantity of drugs that they believe is for the suspect's own use. However, if the amount seized would not normally be used by one person, the suspect may be charged with the more serious offence of possession of a narcotic for the purpose of trafficking (6, 12).

The police will also consider other evidence of trafficking, such as scales, bags, lists of names, association with drug traffickers, a large quantity of small bills, a large quantity of cash, and the accused's own statements. This type of evidence may support a conviction for possession for the purpose of trafficking, even if only a very small amount of the drug is seized (7, 13, 29). The police do not have to prove that the drugs were intended for sale or that any minimum quantity was involved. For example, a suspect may be convicted of possession for the purpose of trafficking if he or she admits that a joint was to be shared, or given to a friend (31).

Trafficking and possession for the purpose of trafficking are both indictable offences that carry a maximum sentence of life imprisonment (4i, s. 4(3)).

Cultivation of Cannabis or Opium

Unless authorized by the government, it is a criminal offence to cultivate any quantity of cannabis or opium. Whether the suspect grows acres of cannabis as part of a large-scale trafficking scheme or grows a single plant under "grow lights" solely for personal use, he or she may be convicted of cultivation. The prosecutor must establish that the suspect knew what the plant was and did something to assist its growth. This includes the planting of seeds, hoeing, weeding, watering, fertilizing, or pruning the plants (9, 18, 30). It is not essential that the seeds germinate or that a plant emerge above the surface of the soil (16). Nor does the suspect have to be caught actually tending the plants. Thus, a suspect may be convicted if the police find fertilizer, seeds, potting soil, "grow lights," and growing marijuana plants in the suspect's possession (9). However, a person found in possession of cannabis seeds only may be charged with possession or possession for the purpose of trafficking, but not cultivation.

Cannabis grows wild in some parts of Canada and someone who is unaware of its presence on his or her land could not be convicted. Even farmers who are aware that marijuana is growing wild on their land could not be convicted of cultivation unless they took positive action to assist its growth.

Cultivation of cannabis or opium is an indictable offence that carries a maximum sentence of seven years' imprisonment (4i, s. 6(2)).

Importing and Exporting a Narcotic

The offences of importing and exporting a narcotic are among the most serious crimes in Canada. An individual may be charged with importing or exporting for transporting or arranging to transport any quantity of a narcotic across the Canadian border. The fact that the drugs were intended solely for personal use or that the quantity involved was small is no defence. The prosecutor must show that the suspect knew that the substance was a narcotic and intentionally brought it across the border. It does not matter that the suspect was unaware of the exact quantity, the specific type of narcotic, or the seriousness of the offence (8, 14).

Importing and exporting are indictable offences and carry a mandatory minimum sentence of seven years' imprisonment and a maximum of life imprisonment. Except for murder and treason, no other *Criminal Code* offence carries as great a mandatory minimum penalty (4i, s. 5(2)).

Prescription Shopping or "Double Doctoring"

Although narcotics used for medical purposes can be obtained by prescription, access to them is carefully controlled. The NCA makes it an offence to get or attempt to get narcotics from one doctor without disclosing that one has obtained a prescription for a narcotic from another doctor within the previous 30 days. The fact that the doctor did not ask the suspect about when he or she last obtained a prescription is no defence, because the NCA imposes a positive obligation on the suspect to disclose any prior prescriptions within the previous 30 days (4i, s. 3.1(1)).

Until the *Criminal Law Amendment Act* (4d) came into force on December 4, 1985, prescription shopping was classified in the *Narcotic Control Regulations* as a summary conviction offence that carried a maximum penalty of a $500 fine and six months' imprisonment. Prescription shopping was moved from the *Regulations* to the *Act* and was made a hybrid offence. If tried by summary conviction, it carries a maximum penalty of six months'

Table 8.1
The Narcotic Control Act: Offences, Definitions, and Penalties

Offence	Definitions	Maximum Penalty

Possession	—to knowingly have a narcotic on your person
	—to knowingly control a narcotic in another place or within another person's possession
	—to have knowledge, consent, and some control over a narcotic in the possession of a fellow group member
		Summary Conviction
		—First offence:
		   6 months &
		   $1,000 fine
		—Subsequent offence:
		   1 year & $2,000 fine
		Indictment
		—7 years

Trafficking	—to manufacture, sell, give, administer, transport, send, deliver, or distribute any narcotic or substance held out to be a narcotic —to offer to do any of these things	Indictment —life
Possession for the purpose of trafficking	—to possess any narcotic for the above-mentioned purposes	Indictment —life
Cultivation	—to knowingly grow or assist the growth of opium or cannabis	Indictment —7 years
Importing or exporting	—to knowingly transport or arrange for the transport of any narcotic across the Canadian border	Indictment —life (7 years mandatory minimum)

Prescription shopping	—to obtain or attempt to obtain a narcotic from one doctor, without disclosing a prescription for a narcotic obtained from another doctor within the previous 30 days	Summary conviction
		—First offence:
		   6 months or
		   $1,000 fine
		—Subsequent offence:
		   1 year or $2,000 fine
		Indictment
		—7 years

imprisonment or a $1,000 fine for a first offence, and one year's imprisonment or a $2,000 fine for a subsequent offence. If it is tried by indictment, the maximum penalty is seven years' imprisonment (4i, s. 3.1(2)).

THE FOOD AND DRUGS ACT

As explained earlier, the FDA is primarily concerned with ensuring that foods, cosmetics, medicines, and medical devices are safe for human consumption and use. Only a very small section of this complex *Act* and its 450 pages of *Regulations* are relevant to our purposes; namely, the two parts dealing with drugs that are used for non-medical purposes, and those *Regulations* governing the unauthorized sale of prescription drugs.

Part III of the FDA: "Controlled" Drugs

Part III of the *Act* governs what are known as the "controlled" drugs; a controlled drug is defined as any drug listed in Schedule G. In addition to amphetamines and barbiturates, this Schedule contains about a dozen less commonly used stimulants and depressants. The key factor in classifying a substance as a Schedule G drug appears to be that it is used for medical as well as non-medical purposes.

The FDA contains only two offences for Schedule G drugs—trafficking and possession for the purpose of trafficking. Although there is no offence of simple possession of a controlled drug, a person found in possession of a larger quantity than is normally associated with personal use may be charged with possession for the purpose of trafficking. In this part of the FDA, the offence of trafficking is defined so as to include only the unauthorized manufacturing, selling, exporting, importing, transporting, and delivery of a Schedule G drug (4f, s. 33 "traffic"). Unlike the definition of trafficking in the NCA, the FDA definition does not include giving, administering, or sending a drug or offering or agreeing to traffic (20, 33). The recent amendment to the FDA made it clear that an individual may be convicted of trafficking even if no money is exchanged (4f, s. 2 "sell"). The FDA does not contain separate offences for importing and exporting. Anyone caught bringing a controlled drug across a Canadian border is charged with trafficking.

Trafficking and possession of a controlled drug for the purpose of trafficking are dual procedure offences, punishable upon summary conviction by a maximum sentence of 18 months' imprisonment, and upon indictment by a maximum of 10 years (4f, s. 34(3)).

Like the NCA, the FDA has been amended to include the offence of prescription shopping. It is now an offence under the FDA to seek a controlled drug from one doctor without disclosing that one has obtained controlled drugs from another doctor within the past 30 days. Prescription shopping is a hybrid offence, which if tried by summary conviction carries a maximum penalty of six months' imprisonment or a $1,000 fine for a first offence, and a maximum of one year's imprisonment or a $2,000 fine for any subsequent offences. If the offence is tried by indictment, the maximum penalty is a $5,000 fine or three years' imprisonment (4f, s. 33.1).

Part IV of the FDA: "Restricted" Drugs

Part IV of the *Act* governs restricted drugs; a restricted drug is defined as any drug listed in Schedule H. Psilocybin, LSD, dimethyltryptamine (DMT), and methylenedioxyamphetamine (MDA) are the most commonly used of the approximately 25 drugs in this Schedule. Unlike controlled drugs, restricted drugs are not used for medical purposes.

There are three offences created for restricted drugs: possession, trafficking, and possession for the purpose of trafficking. This part of the *Act* adopts the *Criminal Code*'s broad definition of possession that was discussed earlier. Possession of a restricted drug is a dual procedure offence. If the prosecutor proceeds by way of summary conviction, the maximum penalty is six months' imprisonment and a $1,000 fine for a first offence, and one year's imprisonment and a $2,000 fine for a subsequent offence. However, if the prosecutor proceeds by indictment, the maximum sentence is three years' imprisonment and a $5,000 fine (4f, s. 41(2)).

The definitions of trafficking and possession for the purpose of trafficking are the same for both controlled and restricted drugs. Trafficking and possession for the purpose of trafficking in a restricted drug are also dual procedure offences, punishable on summary conviction by up to 18 months' imprisonment and on indictment by up to 10 years' imprisonment (4f, s. 42(3)).

Unauthorized Sale of Prescription Drugs

The FDA's *Regulations* contain very complex rules governing the manufacture, distribution, and sale of prescription drugs. Unless authorized, the drugs listed in Schedule F of the *Regulations* cannot be sold without the appropriate verbal or written prescription. Any unauthorized sale constitutes a dual procedure federal offence. If the offence is tried by summary conviction, the maximum penalty is three months' imprisonment and a $500 fine for a first conviction, and six months' imprisonment and a $1,000 fine for a subsequent offence. If the prosecutor proceeds by way of indictment, the maximum penalty is three years' imprisonment and a $5,000 fine (4g).

THE IMPACT OF DISCRETION

The preceding analysis of the NCA and FDA may create the impression that most drug offenders suffer an unduly harsh fate. As in many other areas of the Canadian criminal justice system, the severity of the law is lessened by police, prosecutorial, and judicial discretion. Those most likely to benefit from such discretion are young first offenders who are involved in the least serious offences.

For example, the police may take a teenager found in possession of a single joint home to be dealt with by his or her parents, rather than laying a charge. Possession charges may be brought against only one occupant of a car, even though the factual circumstances would support charging other occupants. Federal drug prosecutors usually charge those caught bringing small quantities of cannabis across the border with possession for the purpose of trafficking. By not laying importing charges, prosecutors protect these

Table 8.2
The Food and Drugs Act: Classifications, Offences, Definitions, and Penalties

Classifications	Drugs in Classification	Offences and Definitions	Maximum Penalty
Part III Controlled drugs: Schedule G	amphetamines barbiturates (other stimulants and depressants)	Trafficking —to manufacture, sell, export, import, transport, or deliver any Schedule G drug or any substance held out to be a Schedule G drug	Summary conviction —18 months Indictment —10 years
		Possession for the purpose of trafficking —to possess any Schedule G drug for the above-mentioned purposes	
		Prescription shopping —to obtain or attempt to obtain a Schedule G drug from one doctor without disclosing a prescription for a Schedule G drug obtained from another doctor within the previous 30 days.	Summary conviction —First offence: 6 months or $1,000 fine —Subsequent offence: 1 year or $2,000 fine Indictment —3 years or $5,000 fine

suspects from the mandatory minimum sentence of seven years that is required by the NCA. Although possession is a dual procedure offence, prosecutors rarely proceed by way of indictment. Similarly, judges rarely impose the maximum sentence or anything close to it in cannabis cases.

The existence of this broad discretion is not without its own problems. First, it is exercised on an ad hoc basis, by hundreds of different officials in tens of thousands of cases a year. Not surprisingly, there are major inconsistencies in the investigation and prosecution of drug cases, and in the sentencing of drug offenders. Second, while there are some general constraints imposed by local practice, administrative guidelines, and the limited possibility of legal challenge, those exercising discretion are not held publicly accountable for their decisions. Finally, suspects have no control over whether discretion will be exercised on their behalf, and no recourse if the full weight of the law is brought to bear against them.

Table 8.2 (continued)

The Food and Drugs Act: Classifications, Offences, Definitions, and Penalties

Classifications	Drugs in Classification	Offences and Definitions	Maximum Penalty
Part IV Restricted drugs: Schedule H	LSD MDA DMT psilocybin (other hallu- cinogens)	Possession —to knowingly have a Schedule H drug on your person —to knowingly control a Schedule H drug in another place or within another person's possession —to have knowledge, consent, and some control over a Schedule H drug in the possession of a fellow group member	Summary conviction —First offence: 6 months & $1,000 fine —Subsequent offence: 1 year & $2,000 fine Indictment —3 years & $5,000 fine
		Trafficking —see definition opposite	Summary conviction —18 months Indictment —10 years
		Possession for the purpose of trafficking —see definition opposite	
Prescription drugs	antibiotics tranquillizers birth control pills painkillers (many other prescription drugs)	Selling —unauthorized sale of a prescription drug without the appropriate verbal or written prescription	Summary conviction —First offence: 3 months & $500 fine —Subsequent offence: 6 months & $1,000 fine Indictment —3 years & $5,000 fine

CONCLUSION

As discussed in several other chapters in this book, Canadian drug law is largely the product of history, rather than any reasoned analysis of the harms posed by the drugs themselves. This is clearly reflected in the NCA's catego-rizations of the drugs, broad definitions of the offences, and severe penalty provisions. The racial and explicitly moralistic considerations that generated these features of the law have long since been abandoned. While the rationale for the law has changed dramatically, the legislation itself has remained virtually unchanged for the last 20 years. The enlightened exercise of discretion may lessen the severity of the law, but it is no substitute for comprehensive reform.

REFERENCES

1. *Beaver* v. *The Queen* (1957), 118 C.C.C. 129 (S.C.C.).
2. Canada. Bureau of Dangerous Drugs. *Canadian Drug Users and Conviction Statistics, 1981*. Ottawa: Department of Health and Welfare, 1982.
3. Canada. Bureau of Dangerous Drugs. *Narcotic, Controlled and Restricted Drug Statistics, 1985*. Ottawa: Department of Health and Welfare, 1986.
4. Canada. *Statutes of Canada*.
   a. *Adulteration Act*, R.S.C. 1915, c. 9.
   b. *Canadian Charter of Rights and Freedoms*, being Part I of the *Constitution Act, 1982*, being Schedule B to the *Canada Act, 1982* (U.K.), c. 11.
   c. *Criminal Code*, R.S.C. 1970, c. C-34.
   d. *Criminal Law Amendment Act 1985*, S.C. 1985, c. 19.
   e. *Food and Drugs Act*, R.S.C. 1920, c. 27.
   f. *Food and Drugs Act*, R.S.C. 1970, c. F-27, as amended.
   g. *Food and Drugs Act Regulations*, C.R.C. 1978, c. 870, s.c.01.041(1).
   h. *Interpretation Act*, R.S.C. 1970, c. I-23, s. 27.
   i. *Narcotic Control Act*, R.S.C. 1970, c. N-1, as amended.
5. MacFarlane, B. A. *Drug Offences in Canada*. 2d ed. Toronto: Canada Law Book, 1986.
6. *R.* v. *Barsikhian* (No. 1) (1984), 12 W.C.B. 153 (Que. C.A.).
7. *R.* v. *Blais* (1974), 19 C.C.C. (2d) 262 (Man. Q.B.).
8. *R.* v. *Blondin* (1970), 2 C.C.C. (2d) 118 (B.C. C.A.), aff'd. on other grounds (1971), 4 C.C.C. (2d) 566 (S.C.C.).
9. *R.* v. *Busby* (1972), 7 C.C.C. (2d) 234 (Y.T. C.A.).
10. *R.* v. *Colvin and Gladue* (1942), 78 C.C.C. 282 (B.C. C.A.).
11. *R.* v. *Daniel* (1982), 1 C.C.C. (3d) 101 (Ont. C.A.).
12. *R.* v. *Denholm* (1973), 13 C.C.C. (2d) 313 (Sask. C.A.).
13. *R.* v. *Douglas* (1977), 33 C.C.C. (2d) 395 (Ont. C.A.).
14. *R.* v. *Duffy* (1973), 11 C.C.C. (2d) 519 (Ont. C.A.).
15. *R.* v. *Eccleston and Gianiori* (1975), 24 C.C.C. (2d) 564 (B.C. C.A.).
16. *R.* v. *Fahlman* (1968), 5 C.R.N.S. 192 (B.C. Co. Ct.), aff'd. on other grounds [1970] 2 C.C.C. 273 (C.A.).
17. *R.* v. *Fuller* (1973), 14 C.C.C. (2d) 433 (S.C.C.).
18. *R.* v. *Gauvreau* (1983), 35 O.R. (2d) 388 (C.A.).
19. *R.* v. *Guiney* (1961), 130 C.C.C. 407 (B.C. C.A.).

20. *R.* v. *Hancock*, [1978] 2 W.W.R. 197 (B.C. C.A.).
21. *R.* v. *Harrington and Scosky*, [1964] C.C.C. 189 (B.C. C.A.).
22. *R.* v. *Kushman* (1948), 93 C.C.C. 231 (B.C. C.A.).
23. *R.* v. *Larson* (1972), 6 C.C.C. (2d) 145 (B.C. C.A.).
24. *R.* v. *Lauze* (1980), 60 C.C.C. (2d) 469 (Que. C.A.).
25. *R.* v. *Mamchur*, [1978] 4 W.W.R. 481 (Sask. C.A.).
26. *R.* v. *Marshall*, [1969] 3 C.C.C. 149 (Alta. C.A.).
27. *R.* v. *Martin* (1948), 92 C.C.C. 257 (Ont. C.A.).
28. *R.* v. *Maxwell* (1978), 39 C.C.C. (2d) 439 (B.C. C.A.).
29. *R.* v. *Miller* (1984), 12 C.C.C. (3d) 54 (B.C. C.A.).
30. *R.* v. *Munce* (1974), 15 C.C.C. (2d) 326 (Ont. Co. Ct.).
31. *R.* v. *O'Connor* (1975), 23 C.C.C. 110 (B.C. C.A.).
32. *R.* v. *Petrie*, [1947] O.W.N. 601 (C.A.).
33. *R.* v. *Santa* (1978), 42 C.C.C. (2d) 471 (Ont. Prov. Ct.).
34. *R.* v. *Sherman* (1977), 36 C.C.C. (2d) 207 (B.C. C.A.).
35. *R.* v. *Smith* (1973), 10 C.C.C. (2d) 384 (B.C. C.A.).
36. *R.* v. *Smythe*, [1971] S.C.R. 680.
37. *R.* v. *Taylor* (1974), 17 C.C.C. (2d) 36 (B.C. C.A.).
38. *R.* v. *Terrence* (1983), 4 C.C.C. (3d) 193 (S.C.C.).
39. *R.* v. *Tokarek*, [1967] 3 C.C.C. 114 (B.C. C.A.).
40. *R.* v. *Verge* (1971), 3 C.C.C. (2d) 398 (B.C. C.A.).
41. *R.* v. *Young*, [1971] 3 W.W.R. 195 (B.C. C.A.).
42. Salhany, R.E. *Canadian Criminal Procedure.* 4th ed. Toronto: Canada Law Book, 1984.

DRUGS, DEVIANCE, AND DEFINITIONS: THEORETICAL PERSPECTIVES

The way we conceptualize or define a problem dictates the measures we take to solve it. This observation may be a truism, but it is an important starting point when its corollary is considered: that faulty definitions of problems lead to inadequate solutions. Because the theoretical track record is poor when it comes to drugs, we have devoted this section of the book to the problem of defining the problem, and to the kinds of policy responses that flow from different theories about drug use.

Scientists who set out to explore the meaning and nature of drug use find that the subject is shrouded in romantic myths and false beliefs. Much energy must be devoted to debunking these ideas before serious research can begin. Because drug use can be approached as a medical, psychological, sociological, economic, legal, criminological, pharmacological, or philosophical problem, academics from many disciplines become involved, and each discipline imposes its own conceptual framework. The public meanwhile interpret the arguments of the experts through the haze of traditional beliefs and attitudes, and drug users themselves enter the fray by promulgating their ideologies and inventing new myths about who they are and what they are doing. In the end we are left with competing definitions leading singly or in combination to unsatisfactory and unsuccessful social responses.

Why does so much mythology surround illegal drug use? Part of the reason may be that these substances have been underground for the better part of a century and their deviant status may render them larger than life. This cannot be the whole explanation, however, because we have also been known to entertain mythological and sometimes downright silly ideas about the legal drug alcohol—for example, the one that says becoming leglessly drunk is a manly act. Nevertheless, the fact that some drugs have been prohibited and their users criminalized means that they are necessarily hidden from public and scientific view, thus becoming even more mysterious.

The drugs we take, like other consumer goods, are symbolic of the kinds of people we are. Being a "wine lover" carries a different symbolic message from being a "beer drinker"; these epithets convey not only beverage of choice, but information about status and lifestyle. Similarly, becoming an LSD, or heroin, or cannabis user can have diverse impacts on self-image and representation of self. In some cases, the symbolic power of drugs may be as harmless as similar beliefs about what it means to drive a certain car or wear a certain style of clothes. However, myths about drugs can also encourage harmful drug-related behaviour and help to initiate drug-related problems. As long as we continue to hold beliefs about the ways in which drugs manipulate us and represent us as certain kinds of people, we must be very careful about the content of our mythology.

All of the authors in this section have tried to take a fresh look at illicit drug use, its meaning, its nature, and the way we might respond to it if we could step back and reflect on our essential concerns. To clear the path for these papers, a critical analysis of some of the more enduring myths is in order.

Two related concepts underlie the popular misconceptions to be discussed here. The first attributes extraordinary powers to drugs, suggesting that they overwhelm users or compel them to behave in certain ways. The second falsely characterizes human beings as helpless and lacking volition when confronted with drugs. There is no doubt that the ability to avoid drug-related problems is not evenly distributed in the population and that youth, psychological instability, and other factors may increase the probability of their occurrence. However, the mythology attributes etiology to pharmacology, painting a picture of the powerless individual in the grip of the all-powerful drug.

Ideas about the effects of drugs on users have traditionally come from observation of a biased sample. Most users of prohibited substances do not advertise themselves, and when they do surface it is usually because of problems: arrest, dependence, overdose, drug-related criminal activity, and so on. As a result, conclusions are drawn from the worst cases, while users with more benign patterns of use remain out of sight.

For example, a school principal or child psychologist may encounter many young cannabis users whose grades are falling, who are in trouble with their teachers and parents, or who have drawn attention to themselves because of other problem behaviour. The well-behaved cannabis users, by virtue of the fact that they can use drugs while continuing to be successful in the other areas of their lives, may go about their business unobserved. Similarly, if all the heroin or cocaine users seen by professionals are hopelessly enmeshed in a life of crime, addiction, or both, it is tempting to conclude that this is the inevitable result of using the drug.

Let us consider this scenario. Imagine a situation in which all information about alcohol and its effects came from patients in alcoholism treatment programmes or prisoners drying out in "drunk tanks." Then it would be common knowledge that, although most people start by taking a few drinks out of curiosity and sociability, the frequency of drinking gradually increases until users cannot feel comfortable without alcohol. We would understand it to be an extremely powerful drug which radically changes the way people feel about themselves and the way in which they conduct their relationships with others. Looking at their struggles with alcohol and their reports of intense craving or loss of self-control, we would conclude that alcohol drinkers are bound to end up addicted, with their lives in ruins around them. Lacking knowledge of "ordinary" drinkers who have not encountered problems, we would assume that the seductive and destructive powers of alcohol were derived largely from its pharmacology.

People tend to believe that the pharmacological properties of drugs are far more overwhelming and behaviourally specific than they are in reality. This error arises partly from fear and ignorance, but it also comes from the confusion of correlation with causation. Observations of drug users with other social problems have led to the assumption that drug use caused these problems, although there is no logical reason why the reverse might not be true, or why no causal relationship might exist. We will now turn to an analysis of some of the more persistent myths that have arisen from such faulty reasoning.

"MARIJUANA MADE ME DO IT": PROGRESSION MYTHOLOGY AND "GATEWAY" DRUGS

The notion that the use of one drug "causes" people to move on to other and stronger drugs has been around since the early part of this century, but it really came into its own in the United States after World War II. Originally, it was thought that this so-called progression, usually from marijuana to heroin, had a pharmacological basis. Once this was debunked, the focus shifted to psychiatric factors, but that argument did not stand up to scrutiny either. Nowadays, progression is rarely mentioned, but there is a good deal of talk about cannabis as a "gateway" to other drugs.

The gateway idea is based on a respectable body of research into patterns of multiple drug use. However, for those who are not aware of the scientific underpinnings of the idea, substitution of "gateway" for "progression" probably does not make much difference. Both words imply that by taking one kind of drug the individual increases his or her risk of taking another, and that perhaps some mysterious drug-related forces are at work that will lure users along against their better judgment.

Research has shown that cannabis smokers are more likely to report use of other drugs than are non-users. Furthermore, multiple illicit drug users are more likely to have been heavier, rather than light, cannabis users. They are also more likely to have been involved in the buying and selling of cannabis. However, none of these facts can be attributed to special properties of cannabis per se.

The processes involved are very human, and therefore also very social. They reflect involvement in friendship networks that at first include those who use only cannabis, but widen to include users of other drugs. That most people have never tried a drug like LSD or heroin should come as no surprise, since most people have never been given the opportunity to accept or refuse. These are relatively rare illegal commodities that even cannabis users may not encounter. One needs using friends before a decision can be made for or against personal use.

Other research has widened the scope of the investigation to take in a full range of unconventional adolescent activities, including illicit drug use. These studies have found that drug use of any kind, legal or illegal, tends to be part of a larger behavioural syndrome for a given age cohort. Thus, the same factors that predict cannabis use also predict precocious initiation into alcohol and into sexual intercourse, and they are also associated with other indicators of reluctance to conform strictly to the norm. In sum, there is nothing magical about "gateway" drugs. Rather, there seems to be a con- stellation of social and psychological factors that place some people at risk to dabbling in naughtiness and others to running the gamut from naughtiness to full-blown deviance. Illicit drugs are only part of this story.

ENSLAVING DRUGS: THE MYTH OF INEVITABLE AND IRREVERSIBLE ADDICTION

Just as taking one illicit drug does not necessarily lead to taking others, the use of dependence-producing substances does not necessarily lead to depen- dence. This is self-evident for a drug like alcohol, but in the popular mind is less obvious in the case of illicit drugs.

As discussed above, when we only see the worst cases, we assume the worst of drugs. In recent years, however, researchers have begun to study users of cocaine, heroin, or other potentially addicting drugs who do not experience compulsiveness or loss of control over consumption. This is an important line of research, because it promises to lead to a better under- standing of dependence. If we can discover how and why some people avoid running into trouble, we potentially can learn more about how and why others come to grief. These studies are also valuable because they lead to a wider concept of drug use in a socio-cultural context.

Our culture provides us with alcohol consumption norms for appropriate and inappropriate drinking behaviour. Most of us have the opportunity to learn about the rules of drinking well before we have our first drink. Illicit drug users, on the other hand, must rely on personal innovation or rules espoused by their own group of drug-using friends to keep their use within certain limits.

Nevertheless, rule-making is only part of the story. Research into non- addictive use of drugs is also a lesson in why substance use should not be viewed in isolation from all the social and psychological characteristics that make up human individuals. As a general rule, considerable effort has to be put into becoming dependent on a drug, especially one that is illegal, expensive, and scarce. Drug users who are also occupied with work or education, with nurturing personal relationships, or with recreational interests other than drug use will be hard pressed to find the time to develop a habit. But even more important are the beliefs individuals hold about the place of drug use in their lives as a whole, their self-image, self-respect, and their future ambitions. Drug use decisions are quality-of-life decisions.

These factors also come into play in recovery from dependence. Although conventional wisdom held that "once an addict, always an addict," it is becoming increasingly evident that this is just another myth. People can and often do leave dependence behind and a significant number do so without the aid of formal treatment. Further, the factors that encourage recovery are very similar to those that work against the development of dependence. Thus, the chances of recovery are better when users find new hope and meaning in a drug-free life, change their self-image, and acquire good reasons for having an investment in conformity, reasons such as stable family ties, religious conversion, or improved occupational prospects, for example. So once again, although the drug is an important player, it acts within the confines of the social and psychological strengths and weaknesses of the drug user, and only in this arena can its power over the individual be limited or amplified.

THE "CRIMINAL ADDICT":
THE CRIMINOGENIC MYTH

The common theme that runs through all the myths discussed so far is the exaggerated conception of an all-powerful drug manipulating the innocently vulnerable human being. The "drugs cause people to become criminals" myth is firmly within this tradition.

It is self-evident that one cannot use an illicit drug without committing a criminal act. In addition, criminal organizations thrive on the profitable illegal markets that support all the activities called "vices" or "victimless crimes," whether they be gambling, bootlegging, prostitution, or drugs. But does taking a drug inevitably cause one to adopt a criminal lifestyle? Clearly, the answer is "no," but the drugs-crime connection is a tenacious idea that arises frequently in discussions of drug use.

One of the best reasons to dismiss the criminogenic myth comes from research on former illicit drug users, which has revealed that some people *stop* because they are unwilling or unable to become involved in acquisitive crimes to support a drug habit. In addition, now that researchers have begun to look beyond the hard-core heroin or cocaine users, they have found both dependent and non-dependent users who pay for their heroin with their own legitimate earnings.

Heroin is the drug most commonly believed to be criminogenic. It is a highly expensive illegal commodity and some members of the "junkie" subculture do commit predatory acquisitive crimes to finance their consumption. However, the cost to society of such activity tends to be exaggerated. The usual calculus is as follows: an estimate (dubious) of the number of users is multiplied by an estimate (doubtful) of the daily cost of their drugs and then increased by a predetermined factor to account for value lost by using fences to dispose of stolen goods. This calculus displays ignorance of the research that has been done on the economics of the heroin subculture. Apparently, a large part of the subcultural economy is self-generated within the using community, through users buying and selling drugs, doing favours and errands, and so on. Much of the money that comes from outside is derived from prostitution or legal income sources—part-time work or "borrowing" from relatives, for example.

Having determined these inflated daily cost estimates, their authors then compound them into annual estimates, multiplying by a factor that assumes every user is active in the market every day of the year. In fact, chronic users have been found to report their consumption at the level they would ideally use every day if they could; in everyday life they often make do with much less. They also go through cycles of enforced or voluntary abstinence. Most estimates of the costs of "addict crime," therefore, are gross overestimates.

If heroin were made legally available, would crime be reduced? Yes, but addict crime would be unlikely to disappear. Participants in the heroin sub-culture often have a history of delinquency, arrests, and incarceration before their involvement with the drug. Part of the reason they opt for the life of the junkie is that they perceive it to be a desirable outlaw role to play. Satisfying their need for drugs would relieve some of the financial burden and might well permit some to live normal lives. For the remainder, however, the legal drug could no more transform them into model citizens than the illegal one can be blamed for "causing" their criminality in the first place.

MYTHS ABOUT PUSHERS AND PEERS

The classical image of the "pusher" is that of a man in a slouch hat and trench coat who haunts school playgrounds dispensing free samples to youngsters he hopes to addict. Mercifully, this depiction is fading into history. Yet, concerned parents and neighbourhood groups still tend to blame the drug dealers for all the problems surrounding illicit drug use.

Blaming the dealer is probably satisfying on an emotional level, but it misses the point on two counts: it displays ignorance of the way people become illicit drug users and it is blind to the characteristics of drugs as commodities. For the most part, drug users initiate their friends and siblings, and the practice spreads through existing informal social networks, like any other fad or recreational activity. Furthermore, an unknown but significant number of dealing networks are also friendship networks. As a general rule, people do not have to be persuaded to buy drugs; drugs sell themselves. In the illicit marketplace, more time is spent by users seeking a connection than by dealers looking for customers.

This brings us to another issue, that of characterizing the peer group as another kind of pusher. Discussions of youthful drug use tediously reiterate the notion of "peer pressure," leaving the impression that the country is filled with pliable innocents who are at the mercy of a multitude of threatening friends whose imprecations they cannot resist. That young people choose their friends does not seem to be taken into account, nor is it mentioned that logically there can only be a limited number of innocents among the pressurers. Substituting the peer group for the evil pusher does not lead to any useful social policies and, worse, shifts the focus away from the important issue of demand, how it is generated, and how it can be reduced.

THEORETICAL PERSPECTIVES ON DRUG USE

Leaps in logic such as false attribution of causation are not uncommon in the population at large. However, they are a cause of special concern when they infiltrate scientific thought. In the first chapter of this section, Bruce Alexander takes to task the disciplines of psychology and pharmacology for their commitment to an "exposure orientation," that is, the assumption that drugs are so potent that simple exposure to them will inevitably ensnare the user into addiction. Rallying empirical evidence, he argues the case against this orientation and speculates about why academics have been so attracted to "dramatic popular stereotypes" at the expense of their objectivity.

Judith Blackwell is also concerned with the interplay between popular beliefs and academic theories about the nature of drug dependence. Her paper traces the development of two conflicting models of drug dependence: the moral failure concept and the disease concept. She analyzes both critically and finds them to be inadequate. Although they are fundamentally in conflict, both persist in popular and scientific thought, with grave social consequences. Dr. Blackwell argues that humane and effective social responses to the problem of dependence await the development of more adequate and comprehensive theories.

Why are some kinds of drug use deemed desirable while others are defined as disreputable? John Hagan critically analyzes this problem within a framework of six different sociological definitions of deviance. He uses elements of these definitions to develop a model for evaluating the seriousness of drug-related activities. The criteria by which seriousness is determined are: the perceived harmfulness of a given drug-using behaviour, the degree of societal consensus about the norm that is violated by it, and the severity of social response.

The first element, harmfulness, is the focus of Melvyn Green's paper. He proposes that a rational legal classification of drugs should reflect the hierarchy of risks or the potential for harm of various drug-related behaviours.

Having described and criticized the current prohibition model, he recodifies it into a semi-prohibition model based on the scientifically known hazards of drugs, not on the moral properties that have traditionally been attached to them. Mr. Green discusses in detail the issues surrounding such a theoretical model and considers the methodologies needed in the development of an empirically sound, risk-based index of potential for harm.

9

When Experimental Psychology
Is Not Empirical Enough:
The Case of the "Exposure Orientation"*

BRUCE K. ALEXANDER

Most psychologists and psychopharmacologists accept the familiar assumption that exposure to an opiate drug, especially heroin, engenders a powerful tendency to subsequent addictive use. This view of opiate addiction has elsewhere been labelled the "exposure orientation" (23). It appeared in the 19th century (18), and was popularized in Canada by police magistrate Emily F. Murphy of Edmonton, who wrote a series of articles in *Maclean's Magazine* and a highly influential book, *The Black Candle*, in 1922 (52). The exposure orientation is expressed throughout her book: for example,

> In many instances, these unfortunates ... have become addicted to the use of narcotics, not through their own desire, but through the carelessness of their family physician in prescribing narcotics, for such a patient as might have been afflicted with some bronchial, rheumatic or neuralgic affection. The patient having received relief from the narcotic, unwittingly becomes addicted to its use. ...
> ... The youth, curious as to its effects, is offered a pinch of heroin, morphine or cocaine and, with incredible rapidity, he finds himself in the clutches of a habit, and held as stubbornly as a devil-fish envelops its victim with its tentacles. (52, pp. 119, 120)

The most developed alternative to the exposure orientation can be labelled "the adaptive orientation"—the view that opiate addiction is not created by exposure to the drug, but rather is a desperate attempt to adapt to previously existing distress through habitual drug use. Although this view violates the popular wisdom of the exposure orientation, it often appears in the psychological and psychiatric literature (17, 40, 70, 71, 97, 99).

In previous articles, Hadaway and I argued that the exposure and adaptive orientations cannot be accepted simultaneously without logical contradiction, that the exposure orientation is contradicted by much recent research, and that research should now be concentrated on critical evaluation of the adaptive orientation as the most likely successor to the exposure orientation (3, 4).

The present article was inspired by vigorous and (usually) good-natured

---

*Reprinted from *Canadian Psychology, 25,* no. 2 (1984): 84–95. By permission.

critics of our earlier work who rose to the defence of the exposure orientation. Studying the data they offered in support of the exposure orientation prompted a complete review and expansion of the case against it and, ultimately, an attempt to understand how such a thoroughly disproven view could be so tenaciously held.

The first aim of this article is to present the evidence against the exposure orientation in enough detail to convey a sense of its comprehensiveness. Doing this may put a worn-out idea finally to rest, thereby clearing a path for investigation of more useful alternatives. The value of such an endeavour has been stated eloquently by George Albee:

> Frequently a revolution in scientific thinking occurs when some widely accepted premise, some "historical truth," is seen finally as inaccurate or incorrect. Our minds explore the crowded spaces created by the walls of fixed ideas until eventually we question why the walls are there at all. With the expanse of space that comes into view as the old conceptual walls are torn down, completely new kinds of explorations are possible. (1, p. 213)

The second aim of this article is to propose an explanation for the paradox of an empirical discipline's consistently accepting a principle that is strongly contradicted by the empirical evidence.

This article makes frequent use of the term "addiction," a word sometimes disdained by empirical psychologists and psychopharmacologists because it has often been used loosely. However, addiction describes an important and ubiquitous human affliction and the term cannot be expunged from the language by fiat (see 30, p. 11). "Drug addiction" is defined in Goodman and Gilman's authoritative pharmacology text as follows:

> A behavioral pattern of drug use, characterized by overwhelming involvement with the use of a drug (compulsive use), the securing of its supply, and a high tendency to relapse after withdrawal. (37, p. 536)

This general definition fits well with contemporary research on addiction and proves helpful in analysing some arguments to be discussed in this article.

AN EMPIRICAL CRITIQUE OF THE EXPOSURE ORIENTATION

I will first present evidence relevant to the exposure orientation in its broad, traditional form and then evidence related to two more specific variations and their putative experimental support.

In direct contradiction to the exposure orientation, it is now established that most people who are exposed to opiate drugs do not continue to use them, and many of those who do continue, stop later on. This has been shown in several ways. First, less than one per cent of patients exposed to regular doses of opiates in American hospitals became addicted after release (45, 100).

In 19th-century America, when large quantities of opiate drugs were used without restriction as cure-alls in medical practice and in home medicine, there was no significant problem of opiate addiction. The best estimates are that the number of addicts in the 19th-century United States never reached one-half of one per cent of the population and was declining at the end of the century (12, 18).

Contrary to popular opinion, even the unregulated and over-enthusiastic medical use of morphine in the American Civil War did not precipitate a measurable outbreak of opiate addiction (53). The historian Courtwright has tried to assemble a case for the contrary view, but it is not impressive (18, see pp. 54–56).

More recently, extraordinary amounts of high-quality heroin were available to American soldiers in Vietnam. Nonetheless, only 12 per cent of regular heroin users among American soldiers relapsed to addiction within three years after returning to the U.S. (67, 68; see also 56). The low re-addiction rate could result from a relative paucity of domestic opiates, as suggested by Goldstein (29), but if exposure really creates an irresistible craving, returnees could have found a supply, as do the half-million American "junkies" and 3.5 million casual users (82). Moreover, the veterans reported finding heroin readily available in the United States, and many reported occasional, but not addictive, heroin use (68).

In the United Kingdom, heroin is widely used as a medication for cough, diarrhoea, and other illnesses. For example, in 1972 British physicians prescribed 29 kilograms of heroin to the organically ill (equivalent to 2.9 million 10 mg doses) (82). Trebach summarized British statistics on heroin prescriptions and iatrogenic addiction as follows:

> It must be accepted that despite the use of heroin for decades in treating the organically ill, there is a virtual absence of addicts created by this singular medical practice. (82, p. 83)

Twycross (83) reported that cancer patients kept on heroin, often in very high doses, came off the drug easily if their cancer symptoms went into remission. Twycross stated that "none of the patients reviewed became addicted" (p. 197).

Berridge and Edwards (10) reviewed 19th-century medical practice in England and found that hypodermic morphine was regarded for decades as a panacea for literally dozens of common illnesses. Prescriptions were unregulated and patients were frequently given syringes for *ad libitum* self-administration. In addition, opium preparations were universally available outside medical practice through grocers and other merchants. Between 1830 and 1860, at the height of this flood of opiates, Berridge and Edwards estimate that enough opiates were used each year to provide an average of 127 therapeutic doses for each man, woman, and child in Britain. The authors summarized a review of addiction treatment admissions data as follows:

> Even quite limited administration of the drug ... in unwise quantities or on an extended basis could have resulted in a serious escalation of addict numbers. But there is little evidence that there were large numbers of morphine addicts in the late nineteenth century. The quite small numbers of addicts who happened to be obvious to the [medical] profession assumed the dimensions of a pressing problem—at a time when, as general consumption and mortality data indicate, usage and addiction to opium in general was tending to decline, not increase. (10, pp. 3–4)

The exposure orientation is also contradicted by the existence of large numbers of casual heroin users, who use heroin irregularly, over long periods, without becoming addicted (11, 17, 63, 101, 103). Recent estimates suggest there are a half-million regular heroin users in the U.S. and as many as 3.5 million occasional users (82).

The exposure orientation can be shored up by an assertion that only some people are constitutionally vulnerable to exposure (22). This "metabolic disease" concept, however, reduces the exposure orientation to no more than a restatement of the fact that some users become addicts—that is, it offers no means of telling who have the "disease" except by whether or not they become addicted. Because only 12 per cent of addicted Vietnam soldiers became re-addicted following repatriation, at least 88 per cent of those addicts did not have the "metabolic disease." Because well under one per cent of patients treated with opiates in medical settings become addicted, the incidence of the "metabolic disease" in the general population must be minuscule, if it exists at all.

Spontaneous termination of opiate addiction provides another difficult problem for the exposure orientation since, according to its central assumption, each exposure should increase the drug-consuming habit. Yet as many as half of American heroin addicts permanently stop using heroin, often without treatment (66, 84, 85, 86, 95, 96) or shift from addictive to casual use (33).

Animal psychopharmacology appears to provide the only real evidence for the exposure orientation. Laboratory animals self-administer opiates in some free-choice situations, both orally (42, 54) and via implanted catheters (88, 89). Goldstein (26, 27, 29) has inferred a fundamental opiate avidity in mammals (including *Homo sapiens*) from this research, and others have used it to support different forms of the exposure orientation (7, 20, 37, 50, 94). Such generalizations, however, are dubious.

In the first place, the animals do not seem to seek the drugs with the desperate avidity of human addicts. In an authoritative review of the data on self-injection of opiates, Kumar and Stolerman (44) pointed out:

> When the morphine dose per intravenous infusion was reduced or the response requirement raised, the small increases in response rate were insufficient to prevent substantial decreases in the hourly dose. (p. 332)

This casual self-administration does not seem similar to the relentless drug-seeking behaviour of human addicts.

Moreover, human beings in "self-injection" situations do not consume opiates at all avidly. Bennett *et al.* (9) maintained post-operative patients on a self-medication device that delivered about 1 mg of morphine sulphate intravenously when the patient pressed a bedside button. The machine limited infusions to one every six minutes (i.e., a fixed interval schedule). Fifty patients were kept on this regimen between one and six days. In each, the self-administered dosage was moderate and *progressively declined*. Although the regimen allowed up to 10 mg/hr of morphine sulphate, patients averaged 1.4 mg/hr (range 0.0–4.2 mg/hr). Using the same self-administration technology, Bennett *et al.* (8) found that patients self-administering morphine, by contrast with controls on a standard post-operative dose administered by nurses, were more able to maintain pain control, but were less often asleep during the day, and were more physically active. There has been no problem of addiction following this regimen even in a small number of cases that were allowed larger doses over longer times (Graves, personal communication).

Perhaps the difference in self-injection behaviour between laboratory animals and human beings receiving medical care arises because the barren, isolated laboratory environment may itself stimulate opiate consumption, an idea suggested by Khantzian (41) and Peele and Brodsky (62). Studies in the Simon Fraser Drug Addiction Laboratory have, in fact, demonstrated much lower levels of oral consumption of morphine hydrochloride solution in rats housed in a quasi-natural environment compared to those isolated in traditional metal cages (5, 6, 32). Recent, still-unpublished studies indicate that the difference in morphine consumption between the two environments may not be as robust as first thought, but reinforce the finding that rats housed in quasi-normal conditions have very little appetite for opiates.

A final set of facts that contradict the exposure orientation concerns regular users of opiate drugs who are not addicted in the sense of Jaffe's definition—that is, who are not "overwhelmingly involved" with opiates. Some are doctors who use opiates as part of their daily routine but function effectively in both their work and other community activities (10, 12, 102, 103). There are also non-professional workers who are regular users of opiates without being "overwhelmingly involved" (14, especially the discussion of "hidden addicts," pp. 7–8; 58). It might be argued that these regular users must be considered addicts because many are subject to withdrawal symptoms (although not all are: see, e.g., 103). However, it will become clear in the discussion of withdrawal symptoms that this familiar equation of withdrawal symptoms with addiction is untenable in the light of recent evidence.

Withdrawal Symptoms as the Cause of Addiction

Two variations on the exposure orientation have been couched in more scientific language and can claim some experimental support. One variation attributes opiate addiction to avoidance of withdrawal symptoms and the other to metabolic needs induced by exposure to opiates. Because these formulations assume the exposure orientation, explicitly or implicitly, they are contradicted by the evidence above. However, because they appear to lend modern experimental support to the exposure orientation, they warrant additional consideration.

It is a familiar concept that repeated doses of opiates produce "physical dependence," a state in which abstinence results in agonizing withdrawal symptoms that produce an almost irresistible compulsion to resume the narcotic habit. This dramatic conception is so compelling that, in this century, addiction and withdrawal symptoms are often considered synonymous. However, this equation is invalid, in spite of its recent reformulations in conditioning terminology.

Withdrawal symptoms are not what maintains opiate addiction. A careful interview study by Cummings, Gordon, and Marlatt (19) found that "relapses involving opiates do not occur primarily in response to somatic discomfort" (p. 305), including withdrawal symptoms. Chaney, Roszell, and Cummings (16) found that only 16 per cent of the relapses of methadone patients "involved coping with physiological states associated with prior substance use" (p. 294).

Every addict who wishes to withdraw knows ways to control withdrawal symptoms, and so there is no need for withdrawal symptoms to be a barrier to abstinence. Bothersome withdrawal symptoms can be suppressed by gradually declining doses of any opiate supplemented with clonidine (37), or they can be substantially ameliorated with alcohol and other licit and illicit sedatives available to drug addicts. Anecdotal reports suggest that hypnosis, acupuncture, and group pressure can largely or completely suppress withdrawal symptoms as well. In addition, it is now widely accepted that opiate withdrawal symptoms are far milder than their over-dramatized media portrayals (13, 38, 103).

Perhaps the strongest evidence against the withdrawal concept of addiction comes from the countless thousands of junkies who have gone through compulsory "detoxification," either gradually or "cold turkey." They almost invariably revert to addiction, in spite of the fact that their withdrawal symptoms are over (12).

Another major flaw in the withdrawal symptom position is that profound addictions can occur without withdrawal symptoms. Many people who present for treatment as opiate addicts do not have withdrawal symptoms even when tested by naloxone challenge (23, 24, 50, 55, 65). Perhaps many would have developed withdrawal symptoms if they had been able to afford more drugs. Nevertheless, withdrawal symptoms cannot be maintaining their existing addiction; and yet their addiction is powerful enough that they may steal, prostitute themselves, ruin their families, and spend years in jail.

Addictions to tobacco, cocaine, and the amphetamines can be as profound as addiction to opiates (12, 36, 69, 90), but these drugs do not produce serious withdrawal symptoms (37). R. K. Siegel (72) has recently reported dramatic withdrawal symptoms following cocaine "freebasing," but cocaine addiction was known long before the emergence of "freebasing."

There is good evidence that withdrawal symptoms increase the likelihood of opiate self-administration in laboratory animals (reviewed by Cappell and LeBlanc (15)), but these isolated laboratory animals do not have the multitude of behavioural options in their barren cages that are available to human beings. The human data reviewed above show unequivocally that withdrawal symptoms are neither sufficient to maintain addiction to opiate drugs nor necessary to produce it. Therefore, withdrawal symptoms must be regarded as of relatively minor importance in human opiate addiction.

The withdrawal-symptom conception of addiction has been given new life by its restatement in classical conditioning terminology. In this formulation, cravings for opiates in abstinent addicts are said to be caused by stimuli that have been linked by classical conditioning to withdrawal symptoms (74, 92). Thus, relapse that occurs long after "withdrawal symptoms" in the usual sense of the term have subsided can be attributed to *conditioned* withdrawal symptoms. Although this is an ingenious application of conditioning theory to a difficult problem, the experimental data do not support it.

Although withdrawal responses have been successfully conditioned to previously neutral stimuli in some (not all) human subjects by O'Brien (55) and O'Brien *et al.* (57), these conditioned responses were extinguished in the first three non-reinforced trials. Therefore, they cannot account for relapses that often occur after long periods of abstinence in the environment where relapse eventually takes place, since the conditioned responses must have had more than ample opportunity to extinguish. Self-reports confirm this. McAuliffe and Gordon found, among 60 interviewed addicts, "only one who had ever responded to conditioned withdrawal symptoms by relapsing" (49, p. 803).

Teasdale (80) successfully extinguished conditioned withdrawal symptoms in three subjects, but two of them quickly resumed heroin use after leaving treatment, and the third entered a therapeutic community. Teasdale suggested:

> Conditioned abstinence symptoms were only one of a number of factors leading to resumption of drug use, and even if the treatment had successfully eliminated abstinence symptoms conditioned to a whole range of environmental stimuli these other factors might still be operative and lead to resumption of drug use. (80, p. 281)

Similar reports have been made by O'Brien (55) and Wolpe, Groves, and

Fischer (98). On purely logical grounds, it is hard to imagine that conditioned withdrawal symptoms would be strong enough to reinstate an addiction when, as shown above, *unconditioned* withdrawal symptoms do not appear powerful enough to do so.

Siegel's influential application of classical conditioning theory to addiction (74) holds that relapse following detoxification is caused by environmental stimuli that were present when the drug was initially administered rather than stimuli present at the time of withdrawal symptoms. These stimuli are said to elicit "compensatory conditioned pharmacological responses" that cause withdrawal symptoms, craving, and relapse when they occur without simultaneous administration of the drug. This model is more powerful than earlier withdrawal-symptoms conceptions. It can account for the failure of relapse to occur in returning addicted American Vietnam veterans, if it is assumed that the stimuli associated with heroin use in Vietnam were left behind and the veterans therefore did not experience withdrawal at home (74, 93).

As with the previous conditioning model, however, it is hard to imagine that conditioned responses of this sort are sufficiently resistant to extinction to produce relapse in human beings. Siegel (73) reported conditioned compensatory responses in rats two weeks after the last morphine injection, but these extinguished by the third presentation of the conditioned stimuli.

In addition, these explanations are based on a definition of the stimuli associated with original opiate administration that is strict enough to rule out similar stimuli that might elicit the conditioned pharmacological responses, for example in Vietnam addicts after return to the United States. By the same strict specifications of what constitutes the conditioned stimulus, Siegel's model predicts that detoxified addicts would not be attracted by opiates on entering jail or hospital for the first time or on being sent to Vietnam. This is obviously not the case. In fact, the theory implies that addiction can be cured simply by relocating following withdrawal. This is not true either; although many physically dependent people facilitate withdrawal by relocation, others overcome their addictions without relocating, and others move and take their addictions with them (11, 47, 86, 95).

These objections can be circumvented if the stimuli associated with drug taking are defined more loosely, as Siegel seems to prefer. In recent papers the "stimuli" that can precipitate relapse are said to include "internal states such as stress and depression" (75, p. 50), "talking about drugs and 'works,' " and "imagining themselves injecting drugs in the customary settings" (74, p. 158). But "stimuli" of this sort are as available to Vietnam veterans in the United States as they were in Vietnam, and the theory in this form could not predict their abstinence following repatriation. Thus, the theory seems caught in a logical dilemma. If the conditioned stimuli are defined strictly, the theory fails to explain one set of observations; but if they are defined loosely, it fails to explain another.

Experimental support for Siegel's model has been drawn from Thompson and Ostlund's (81) study of rats forced to consume morphine solution and then withdrawn for 30 days. Such rats "relapsed" more to drinking morphine solution when the choice test was given in the original environment than when it was given in a different environment. But this experiment is far from compelling. The consumption of morphine in the "re-addiction" phase was low in both groups, reaching a maximum of about 5 mg/rat/day in the familiar environment compared to about 2½ mg/rat/day in the novel environment. It seems strained to compare this 2:1 difference to the huge differences in consumption between a relapsed addict and a former addict who remains abstinent. Moreover, the experiment was not counterbalanced: since all rats were initially administered morphine in a single room, the same and different "re-addiction" environments were perfectly confounded with whatever effects might be due to the rooms *per se*.

It is possible that withdrawal symptoms, while not necessary to addiction, still contribute to it, at least in some cases. Careful consideration of the facts collected here, however, makes even this reduced contribution look dubious. There seems to be a consensus among both clinicians and drug addicts that cocaine, the amphetamines, and tobacco, with no conspicuous withdrawal symptoms, are at least as addicting as the opiate drugs (12, 69, 90). If withdrawal symptoms added substantially to a drug's addictivity, it would be unlikely that such drugs would be as addictive as opiates. Moreover, treatments that effectively relieve or eliminate withdrawal symptoms have had no measurable success in curing addiction.

One of the major obstacles to clear thinking about opiate addiction, over the years, has been the tendency to equate physical dependence (i.e., vulnerability to withdrawal symptoms when drug use ceases) with addiction (overwhelming involvement in the use of drugs). It is now amply established that these two phenomena are neither equivalent nor causally linked even when withdrawal symptoms are classically conditioned. Jaffe, in Goodman and Gilman's text, has stated this point succinctly:

> It is possible to be physically dependent on drugs without being addicted and, in some special circumstances, to be addicted without being physically dependent. (37, p. 536)

Induced Metabolic Change as the Cause of Addiction

Another widespread variant of the exposure orientation is the view that opiate drugs alter the metabolism in some way, making subsequent opiate ingestion physiologically necessary (12, 20, 22, 38, 48, 91, 94). Different biochemical models of the process have been advanced throughout the late 19th and 20th centuries (18, 53), and it has been proposed most recently that repeated exposure to opiates might create a long-term incapacity of the body to synthesize endogenous opiates and thus motivate opiate-seeking behaviour (28, 43, 76).

All the evidence above that contradicts the exposure orientation, just as clearly contradicts its metabolic variations. There are several more specifically relevant considerations, however.

First, no metabolic basis for addiction to opiates (or any other drug) has been demonstrated, in spite of decades of hopeful experimentation. Way (87) has chronicled the unforeseen complications that have bedevilled the still unsuccessful attempts to prove that addiction results from an induced incapacity to produce endorphins. Often the popular media have seized on fragments of evidence supporting this attractive hypothesis as if they were a full demonstration. The fact that endogenous opiate levels are somewhat lower in human beings and animals that have been given exogenous opiates (25, 34) is far from proof of the hypothesis. Are these lower endogenous opiate levels long-lived? Do they induce an irresistible craving for self-administration of opiates? These questions have not been answered.

Second, even the best methadone maintenance programmes cannot keep more than a minority of addicts in any locality in treatment, and most who leave treatment revert to use of an illegal opiate (21). If addiction were merely an induced chemical deficiency, a heroin addict would be no more likely to refuse medically provided opiates than a diabetic would be to refuse insulin.

Third, addiction to opiates seems behaviourally indistinguishable not only from addictions to non-opiate drugs, such as cocaine, amphetamines, alcohol, and tobacco, but also from involvements with food, gambling, television, "placebos," obsessive love relationships, jogging, etc. (e.g. 39, 51, 62). It is hard to believe that evolution is either malevolent or prescient enough to have produced specific chemical vulnerabilities to dozens of substances and practices that were unknown during the development of *Homo sapiens*, as the specific metabolic vulnerability conception would imply.

It is conceivable that one general metabolic addictive mechanism underlies all human addictions as suggested, perhaps, by indications that high levels of endorphins might be found during a "runner's high" (60). Although this common mechanism has not been found, its existence cannot be disproved empirically because there will always be a new place to look for it. Logically, however, if the mechanism exists, it cannot be activated simply by exposure. If it were, virtually all human beings would be addicted, since there are few people who do not at least occasionally engage in practices to which other people have become addicted.

Two other interrelated variations on the exposure orientation are the hedonic view ("it's so good, don't even try it once") and Solomon and Corbit's (77, 78, 79) opponent process theory of acquired motivation. These were discussed by Alexander and Hadaway (4) and, with one exception, we have seen no need to revise that earlier discussion.

The single exception is that Stewart, de Wit, and Eikelboom[1] have elaborated the hedonic model in a positive reinforcement framework by asserting that stimuli associated with drug administration come to produce conditioned responses similar to the drug. Such stimuli later serve a "priming" function to reinstate lapsed drug-taking behaviour in the same way as a gratuitous pellet of food reinstates extinguished food-reinforced bar pressing. This addition of a classically conditioned factor to the hedonic model would explain how positive reinforcement can account for recurrence of addictive behaviours long after the last experience of the drug effect, and thus support the exposure orientation. However, this interpretation seems inadequate to explain drug addiction because its authors have not as yet demonstrated that conditioned stimuli can serve as primers. Nor have they shown why, if they have correctly identified the mechanism of drug addiction, all people are not addicted to all reinforcing stimuli to which they have ever been exposed.

In sum, the variations on the exposure orientation are no more supportable than the overarching exposure orientation. Rather than shoring it up, they only obscure its weakness.

WHY HAS THE EXPOSURE ORIENTATION PERSISTED?

The case against the exposure orientation seems as complete as any in psychology. Why then is it still so widely held? The evidence against it is found in readily available sources. Moreover, the exposure orientation has not persisted for lack of a plausible alternative. The late Isidor Chein and his colleagues eloquently stated an alternative view two decades ago in *The Road to H*, a book based on several lines of social psychological research (17). Psychologists Stanton Peele and Archie Brodsky have expanded the alternative view in more recent books based on research studies and case reports (61, 62). Many other psychologists have discussed alternatives to the exposure orientation (40, 70, 71, 97, 99). Since most of those alternatives share a common underlying assumption, Alexander and Hadaway (4) proposed labelling them collectively as the "adaptive orientation."

The adaptive orientation has by no means been proven correct. In fact, there has been very little systematic research on it. It is, however, clearly the most widely held alternative to the exposure orientation, and it is compatible with the evidence that discredits the exposure orientation. Therefore, its critical evaluation seems to be the issue on which research energies should now be focused.

Rather than argue for the adaptive orientation, as Hadaway and I (3, 4) have attempted elsewhere, the intention here is to suggest an answer to the question of why so many psychologists, psychopharmacologists, and other biomedical professionals hold tenaciously to the exposure orientation.

I believe, in spite of scientific psychology's dedication to objectivity, that our scholarly deliberations, in this instance, have been overwhelmed by dramatic popular stereotypes.

The 20th century has seen the discovery that the "absolute" facts proclaimed by 19th-century science are heavily influenced by cultural themes, myths, and prejudices. In experimental psychology this is exemplified in Hodos and Campbell's (35) demonstration that the "phylogenetic scale" concept that was a cornerstone of research in comparative psychology until the middle of this century was not an evolutionary or even scientific concept, but an expression of the ancient notion of the "great chain of being" (46).

A more dramatic example is Gould's (31) startling re-analysis of the 19th-century empirical proofs of innate inferiority of blacks and women. Gould showed that the most eminent brain scientists of that era, including Broca himself, erred outrageously in collecting, analysing, and selecting data, and always in the direction of the popular conclusion. Moreover, Gould presented evidence that the errors were not conscious:

> we can be fairly certain that biases—though often expressed as egregiously as in cases of conscious fraud—were unknowingly influential and that scientists believed they were pursuing unsullied truth. (31, p. 27)

In the present case, psychologists' views on addiction are at odds with existing data at a time when powerfully dramatic stereotypes of hapless junkies being "hooked" by vicious pushers have proliferated in popular media for a half-century. It would seem unrealistic to maintain that psychologists concerned with addiction, functioning as imperturbable practitioners of pure science, have transcended the cultural influences. Berridge and Edwards (10) have suggested a slightly more diabolical view:

> Images of addiction are in fact consistently and relentlessly marketed—in the nineteenth century to make opium the property of the medical profession, in the twentieth century to justify the position of enforcement agencies or the international control apparatus, or to win tomorrow's research budget. Images compete, and in the process the marketing becomes even more aggressive. The medical and scientific images feed and change the public, administrative and political view, and in return these perceptions give the doctors and scientists the needed support. (10, p. 250)

Whatever the origin, I believe psychologists have acquiesced in the presently dominant "image" of opiate addiction, which includes the exposure orientation, in two ways. First, most psychologists prefer to ignore the issue of opiate addiction, leaving the lurid media dramatizations unchallenged. This seems an abdication of responsibility in an area of psychopathology where undisciplined thinking can lead to harmful myths and cruel, ineffective legal practices.

Second, many psychopharmacologists acquiesce in the popular image by uncritically repeating and refining the insubstantial psychopharmacological support for the exposure orientation and ignoring the mass of historical, clinical, and experimental observations that invalidate it. Surely the unique virtue of empirical psychology is lost if conclusions are based on a few narrowly defined, albeit experimental, procedures and the broader context of empirical fact is ignored. In this case the threat to the proper, authoritative role of empirical science does not come from anti-intellectual forces. Rather it comes from the temptation to be narrowly experimental rather than truly empirical. I believe it is now time for empirical psychology to assert its licence to lead, rather than follow, popular culture.

NOTES

1. This model was elaborated in a paper by J. Stewart, W. de Wit, and R. Eikelboom entitled, "The role of unconditioned and conditioned drug effects in the self administration of opiates and stimulants," presented at the Canadian Psychological Association Meetings, Winnipeg, June 1983.

REFERENCES

1. Albee, G. A competency model to replace the defect model. In: Gibbs, M. S., Lachenmeyer, J. R., and Sigal, J. (eds.). *Community Psychology: Theoretical and Empirical Approaches*. New York: Gardner Press, 1980.
2. Alexander, B. K. James M. Barrie and the expanding definition of addiction. *Journal of Drug Issues, 12*:397–413 (1982).
3. Alexander, B. K., and Hadaway, P. F. Theories of opiate addiction: Time for pruning. *Journal of Drug Issues, 11*:77–91 (1981).
4. Alexander, B. K., and Hadaway, P. F. Opiate addiction: The case for an adaptive orientation. *Psychological Bulletin, 92*:367–81 (1982).
5. Alexander, B. K., Coambs, R. B., and Hadaway, P. F. The effect of housing and gender on morphine self-administration in rats. *Psychopharmacology, 58*:175–79 (1978).
6. Alexander, B. K., Beyerstein, B. L., Hadaway, P. F., and Coambs, R. B. The effect of early and later colony housing on oral ingestion of morphine in rats. *Pharmacology, Biochemistry, and Behavior, 15*:571–76 (1981).
7. Bejerot, N. Addiction to pleasure: A biological and social-psychological theory of addiction. In: Lettieri, D. J., Sayers, M., and Pearson, H. W. (eds.). *Theories on Drug Abuse*. NIDA Research Monograph no. 30. Washington, D.C.: U.S. Government Printing Office, 1980.
8. Bennett, R. L., Batenhorst, R. L., Bivins, B. A., Bell, R. B., Graves, D. A., Foster, T. S., Wright, B. D., and Griffen, W. O. Patient-controlled analgesia:

A new concept of postoperative pain relief. *Annals of Surgery*, *195*:700–705 (1982).

9. Bennett, R. L., Batenhorst, R. L., Graves, D. A., Foster, T. S., Bauman, T., Griffen, W. O. and Wright, B. D. Morphine titration in postoperative laparotomy patients using patient-controlled analgesia. *Current Therapeutic Research*, *32*:45–51 (1982).

10. Berridge, V., and Edwards, G. *Opium and the People: Opiate Use in Nineteenth-century England*. London: Allen Lane, 1981.

11. Blackwell, J. Drifting, controlling, and overcoming: Opiate users who avoid becoming chronically dependent. *Journal of Drug Issues*, *13*:219–35 (1983).

12. Brecher, E.M., and the Editors of Consumer Reports. *Licit and Illicit Drugs*. Boston: Little, Brown, 1972.

13. Canada. Commission of Inquiry into the Non-Medical Use of Drugs. *Final Report*. Ottawa: Information Canada, 1973.

14. Caplovitz, D. *The Working Addict*. White Plains, N.Y.: M. E. Sharpe, 1976.

15. Cappell, H., and LeBlanc, A. E. Tolerance and physical dependence: Do they play a role in alcohol and drug self-administration? In: Israel, Y., Glaser, F. B., Kalant, H., Popham, R. E., Schmidt, W., and Smart, R. G. (eds.). *Research Advances in Alcohol and Drug Problems*, Vol. 6. New York: Plenum, 1981.

16. Chaney, E. F., Roszell, D. K., and Cummings, C. Relapse in opiate addicts: A behavioral analysis. *Addictive Behaviors*, *7*:291–97 (1982).

17. Chein, I., Gerard, D. L., Lee, R. S., and Rosenfeld, E. *The Road to H*. New York: Basic Books, 1964.

18. Courtwright, D. T. *Dark Paradise: Opiate Addiction in America before 1940*. Cambridge, Mass.: Harvard University Press, 1982.

19. Cummings, C., Gordon, J. R., and Marlatt, G. A. Relapse: prevention and prediction. In: Miller, W. R. (ed.). *The Addictive Behaviors*. Oxford and New York: Pergamon, 1980.

20. Dole, V. P. Narcotic addiction, physical dependence and relapse. *New England Journal of Medicine*, *286*:988–92 (1972).

21. Dole, V. P. Addictive behavior. *Scientific American*, *243*(6):138–54 (1980).

22. Dole, V. P., and Nyswander, M. E. Heroin addiction—A metabolic disease. *Archives of Internal Medicine*, *120*:19–24 (1967).

23. Gay, G. R., Senay, E. C., and Newmeyer, J. A. The pseudo-junkie: Evolution of the heroin lifestyle in the non-addicted individual. *Drug Forum*, *2*:279–90 (1973).

24. Glaser, F. B. Psychologic vs. pharmacologic heroin dependence. *New England Journal of Medicine*, *290*:231 (1974).

25. Gold, M. S., Pottash, A. L. C., Extein, I., and Kleber, H. D. Anti-endorphin effects of methadone. *Lancet*, *2*(8201):972–73 (1980).

26. Goldstein, A. Heroin addiction and the role of methadone in its treatment. *Archives of General Psychiatry*, *26*:291–97 (1972).

27. Goldstein, A. Heroin addiction: Sequential treatment employing pharmacologic supports. *Archives of General Psychiatry, 33*:353–58 (1976).
28. Goldstein, A. Opioid peptides (endorphins) in pituitary and brain. *Science, 193*:1081–86 (1976).
29. Goldstein, A. Heroin maintenance: A medical view. A conversation between a physician and a politician. *Journal of Drug Issues, 9*:341–47 (1979).
30. Goldstein, A. Some thoughts about endogenous opioids and addiction. *Drug and Alcohol Dependence, 11*:11–14 (1983).
31. Gould, S. J. *The Mismeasure of Man.* New York: Norton, 1981.
32. Hadaway, P. F., Alexander, B. K., Coambs, R. B., and Beyerstein, B. The effect of housing and gender on preference for morphine-sucrose solutions in rats. *Psychopharmacology, 66*:87–91 (1979).
33. Harding, W. M., Zinberg, N. E., Stelmack, S. M., and Barry, M. Formerly-addicted-now-controlled opiate users. *International Journal of the Addictions, 15*:47–60 (1980).
34. Herz, A. Role of endorphins in addiction. *Modern Problems in Pharmacopsychiatry, 17*:175–80 (1981).
35. Hodos, W., and Campbell, C. B. G. Scala Naturae: Why there is no theory in comparative psychology. *Psychological Review,* 76:337–50 (1969).
36. Hunt, W. A., Barnett, L. W., and Branch, L. G. Relapse rates in addiction programs. *Journal of Clinical Psychology, 27*:455–56 (1971).
37. Jaffe, J. H. Drug addiction and drug abuse. In: Gilman, A. G., Goodman, L. S., and Gilman, A. (eds.). *Goodman and Gilman's The Pharmacological Basis of Therapeutics.* 6th ed. New York: Macmillan, 1980.
38. Jones, H., and Jones, H. *Sensual Drugs.* Cambridge: Cambridge University Press, 1977.
39. Joyce, C. R. B. Quantitative estimates of dependence on the symbolic function of drugs. In: Steinberg, H. (ed.). *Scientific Basis of Drug Dependence: A Symposium.* New York: Grune & Stratton, 1969.
40. Kaplan, E. H., and Weider, H. *Drugs Don't Take People, People Take Drugs.* Secaucus, N.J.: Lyle Stuart, 1974.
41. Khantzian, E. J. Opiate addiction: A critique of theory and some implications for treatment. *American Journal of Psychotherapy, 28*:59–70 (1974).
42. Khavari, K. A., and Risner, M. E. Opiate dependence produced by ad libitum drinking of morphine in water, saline and sucrose vehicles. *Psychopharmacologia, 30*:291–302 (1973).
43. Kosterlitz, W. W., and Hughes, J. Biological significance of the endogenous opioid peptides and the opiate receptors. In: Israel, Y., Glaser, F. B., Kalant, H., Popham, R. E., Schmidt, W., and Smart, R. G. (eds.). *Research Advances in Alcohol and Drug Problems,* Vol. 4. New York: Plenum, 1978.
44. Kumar, R., and Stolerman, I. P. Experimental and clinical aspects of drug

dependence. In: Iverson, L. L., Iverson, S. D., and Snyder, S. H. (eds.). *Handbook of Psychopharmacology*, Vol. 7. New York: Plenum, 1977.

45. Lindesmith, A. *Addiction and Opiates*. 2d ed. Chicago: Aldine, 1968.

46. Lovejoy, A. O. *The Great Chain of Being*. Cambridge, Mass.: Harvard University Press, 1966. (Originally published, 1933).

47. Maddux, J. F., and Desmond, D. P. Residence relocation inhibits opioid dependence. *Archives of General Psychiatry, 39*:1313–17 (1982).

48. Martin, W. R. Emerging concepts concerning drug abuse. In: Lettieri, D. J., Sayers, M., and Pearson, H. W. (eds.). *Theories on Drug Abuse*. NIDA Research Monograph no. 30. Washington, D.C.: U.S. Government Printing Office, 1980.

49. McAuliffe, W. E., and Gordon, R. A. A test of Lindesmith's theory of addiction: The frequency of euphoria among long-term addicts. *American Journal of Sociology, 79*:795–840 (1974).

50. McAuliffe, W. E., and Gordon, R. A. Reinforcement and the combination of effects: Summary of a theory of opiate addiction. In: Lettieri, D. J., Sayers, M., and Pearson, H. W. (eds.). *Theories on Drug Abuse*. NIDA Research Monograph no. 30. Washington: U.S. Government Printing Office, 1980.

51. Morgan, W. Negative addiction in runners. *The Physician and Sportsmedicine, 7*:57–59 (1979).

52. Murphy, E. F. *The Black Candle*. Toronto: Thomas Allen, 1922. Facsimile ed. Toronto: Coles, 1973.

53. Musto, D. F. *The American Disease: Origins of Narcotic Control*. New Haven: Yale University Press, 1973.

54. Nichols, J. R. How opiates change behavior. *Scientific American, 212*(2): 80–88 (1965).

55. O'Brien, C. P. Experimental analysis of conditioning factors in human narcotic addiction. *Pharmacological Reviews, 27*:533–43 (1976).

56. O'Brien, C. P., Nace, E. P., Mintz, J., Meyers, A. L., and Ream, N. Follow-up of Vietnam veterans: I. Relapse to drug use after Vietnam service. *Drug and Alcohol Dependence, 5*:333–40 (1980).

57. O'Brien, C. P., Testa, R., O'Brien, T. J., Brady, J. P., and Wells, B. Conditional narcotic withdrawal in humans. *Science, 195*:1000–1002 (1977).

58. O'Donnell, J. A. *Narcotics Addicts in Kentucky*. Chevy Chase, Md.: National Institute of Mental Health, 1969.

59. Oswald, I. Personal view. *British Medical Journal, 3*:438 (1969).

60. Pargman, D., and Baker, M. C. Running high: Enkephalin indicated. *Journal of Drug Issues, 10*:341–49 (1980).

61. Peele, S. *How Much Is Too Much?* Englewood Cliffs, N.J.: Prentice-Hall, 1981.

62. Peele, S., and Brodsky, A. *Love and Addiction*. Scarborough, Ont.: New American Library of Canada, 1975.

63. Powell, D. H. A pilot study of occasional heroin users. *Archives of General Psychiatry, 28*:586–94 (1973).

64. Pradhan, S. N. and Dutta, S. N. Narcotic analgesics. In: Pradhan, S. N. and Dutta, S. N. (eds.). *Drug Abuse: Clinical and Basic Aspects*. St. Louis, Mo.: Mosby, 1977.

65. Primm, B. J. Pseudoheroinism. In: Pradhan, S. N. and Dutta, S. N. (eds.). *Drug Abuse: Clinical and Basic Aspects*. St. Louis, Mo.: Mosby, 1977.

66. Robins, L. N. and Murphy, G. E. Drug use in a normal population of young negro men. *American Journal of Public Health, 57*:1580–96 (1967).

67. Robins, L. N., Davis, D. H., and Nurco, D. N. How permanent was Viet Nam drug addiction? In: Greene, M. H., and DuPont, R. L. (eds.). *The Epidemiology of Drug Abuse*. NIDA Journal Supplement, Part 2, Vol. 64. Washington: U.S. Government Printing Office, 1974.

68. Robins, L. N., Helzer, J. E., and Davis, D. H. Narcotic use in Southeast Asia and afterwards. *Archives of General Psychiatry, 32*:955–61 (1975).

69. Russell, M. A. H. Tobacco smoking and nicotine dependence. In: Gibbins, R. J., Israel, Y., Kalant, H., Popham, R. E., Schmidt, W., and Smart, R. G. (eds.). *Research Advances in Alcohol and Drug Problems*, Vol. 3. New York: Wiley, 1976.

70. Satinder, K. P. *Drug Use: Criminal, Sick, or Cultural?* Roslyn Heights, N.J.: Libra, 1980.

71. Schaffer, H., and Burglass, M. E. Epilogue: Reflections and perspectives on the history and future of addictions. In: Schaffer, H., and Burglass, M. E. (eds.). *Classic Contributions in the Addictions*. New York: Brunner/Mazel, 1981.

72. Siegel, R. K. Cocaine and sexual dysfunction: The curse of mama coca. *Journal of Psychoactive Drugs, 14*(1–2): 71–74 (1982).

73. Siegel, S. Evidence from rats that morphine tolerance is a learned response. *Journal of Comparative and Physiological Psychology, 89*:498–506 (1975).

74. Siegel, S. The role of conditioning in drug tolerance and addiction. In: Keehn, J. D. (ed.). *Psychopathology in Animals: Research and Clinical Implications*. New York: Academic Press, 1979.

75. Siegel, S. Classical conditioning, drug tolerance and drug dependence. In: Smart, R. G., Glaser, F. B., Israel, Y., Kalant, H., Popham, R. E., and Schmidt, W. (eds.). *Research Advances in Alcohol and Drug Problems*, Vol. 7. New York: Plenum, 1983.

76. Snyder, S. H. Opiate receptors and internal opiates. *Scientific American, 236(3)*: 44–56 (1977).

77. Solomon, R. L. The opponent-process theory of acquired motivation: The cost of pleasure and the benefits of pain. *American Psychologist, 35*:691–712 (1980).

78. Solomon, R. L., and Corbit, J. D. An opponent-process theory of motivation: II. Cigarette addiction. *Journal of Abnormal Psychology, 81*:158–71 (1973).

79. Solomon, R. L. and Corbit, J. D. An opponent-process theory of motivation. I: Temporal dynamics of affect. *Psychological Bulletin, 81*:119–45 (1974).

80. Teasdale, J. D. Conditioned abstinence in narcotic addicts. *International Journal of the Addictions, 8*:273–92 (1973).

81. Thompson, T., and Ostlund, W. Susceptibility to readdiction as a function of the addiction and withdrawal environments. *Journal of Comparative and Physiological Psychology, 60*:388–92 (1965).

82. Trebach, A. S. *The Heroin Solution*. New Haven: Yale University Press, 1982.

83. Twycross, R. G. Clinical experience with diamorphine in advanced malignant disease. *International Journal of Clinical Pharmacology, Therapy and Toxicology, 9*:184–98 (1974).

84. Waldorf, D. Natural recovery from opiate addiction: Some social-psychological processes of untreated recovery. *Journal of Drug Issues, 9*:237–80 (1983).

85. Waldorf, D., and Biernacki, P. Natural recovery from heroin addiction. *Journal of Drug Issues, 9*:281–89 (1979).

86. Waldorf, D., and Biernacki, P. The natural recovery from opiate addiction: Some preliminary findings. *Journal of Drug Issues, 11*:61–74 (1981).

87. Way, E. L. Some thoughts about opiopeptins, peptides with opiate-like activity. *Drug and Alcohol Dependence, 11*:23–31 (1983).

88. Weeks, J. R., and Collins, R. J. Factors affecting voluntary morphine intake in self-maintained addicted rats: A review of the literature. *Psychopharmacologia, 6*:267–79 (1964).

89. Weeks, J. R. and Collins, R. J. Patterns of intravenous self-injection by morphine-addicted rats. In: Wikler, A. H. (ed.). *The Addictive States*. Baltimore, Md.: Williams & Wilkins, 1968.

90. Weil, A., and Rosen, W. *Chocolate to Morphine: Understanding Mind-active Drugs*. Boston: Houghton Mifflin, 1983.

91. Wikler, A. Some implications of conditioning theory for problems of drug abuse. *Behavioral Science, 16*:92–97 (1971).

92. Wikler, A. Dynamics of drug dependence. *Archives of General Psychiatry, 28*:611–16 (1973).

93. Wikler, A. *Opioid Dependence*. New York: Plenum, 1980.

94. Wikler, A., and Pescor, F. T. Classical conditioning of a morphine abstinence phenomenon, reinforcement of opioid-drinking behavior and "relapse" in morphine-addicted rats. *Psychopharmacologia, 10*:255–84 (1967).

95. Wille, R. Processes of recovery from heroin dependence: Relationship to treatment, social changes and drug use. *Journal of Drug Issues, 13*:333–42 (1983).

96. Winick, C. Maturing out of narcotic addiction. *Bulletin on Narcotics, 14*:1–7 (1962).

97. Wishnie, H. *The Impulsive Personality*. New York: Plenum, 1977.

98. Wolpe, J., Groves, G. A., and Fischer, S. Treatment of narcotic addiction

by inhibition of craving: Contending with a cherished habit. *Comprehensive Psychiatry, 21*:308–16 (1980).

99. Wurmser, L. *The Hidden Dimension: Psychodynamics in Compulsive Drug Use.* New York: Jason Aronson, 1978.
100. Zinberg, N. E. The search for rational approaches to heroin use. In: Bourne, P. G. (ed.). *Addiction.* New York: Academic Press, 1974.
101. Zinberg, N. E., and Jacobson, R. C. The natural history of "chipping." *American Journal of Psychiatry, 133*:37–40 (1976).
102. Zinberg, N. E., and Lewis, D. C. Narcotic usage: I. A spectrum of a difficult medical problem. *New England Journal of Medicine, 270*:989–93 (1964).
103. Zinberg, N. E., Harding, W. M., and Apsler, R. What is drug abuse? *Journal of Drug Issues, 8*:9–35 (1978).

10

Sin, Sickness, or Social Problem?
The Concept of Drug Dependence

JUDITH BLACKWELL

In everyday language, people talk of being "addicted," to pleasurable pastimes or to their favourite foods. Television addicts call themselves "couch potatoes," and we hear people refer to themselves as "chocoholics." Most of us have an intuitive understanding of what addiction means. Nevertheless, when drug experts try to analyze this concept and precisely define it, they find the task more difficult than might be expected. Indeed, after years of debate, there is still no accepted definition of "addiction" or "dependence" that all scientists can agree upon.

There is even controversy over which of these words to use. Canada's Le Dain Commission preferred the dependent/dependence terminology to addict/addiction, primarily because of the pejorative connotations of the latter. Recently, Alexander (1) has argued that, since "addiction" has been perfectly serviceable for four centuries, it should not be abandoned; he defines it to mean "compulsive involvement" which may or may not include physiological as well as psychological symptoms. Psychiatric experts also seem to be tending toward a broad conception of the phenomenon, but they prefer to call it "dependence" (30). Until this issue is finally resolved, it is probably safe to use either terminology.

Historically, two very different conceptions of the nature of dependence have been promulgated. One model characterizes drug dependence as largely a matter of moral failure, weakness of will, and self-indulgence. A more recent model represents dependence as a disease. The conflict between these two models accounts for a good deal of the confusion and debate over illicit drugs, among professionals as well as the public. As we shall see below, it has also produced social responses to drug use that incorporate the two models into uncomfortable and sometimes unholy unions.

That the sin model and the sickness model of drug dependence came to be accepted in a single historical period is, in itself, an interesting phenomenon. Despite the fact that these approaches to the problem are at odds, in recent years lay and professional observers have demonstrated the ability to adhere to both simultaneously. Here we will explore how attempts to combine the models have emphasized the most dubious aspects of each of them. Thus, we are embarking upon a case study illustrating the way in which inadequate intellectual formulations can have grave social ramifications.

Although it is premature to aspire to a satisfactory new model of drug dependence, we will see that, out of the crucible of conflicting theories, the process of redefinition is under way.

Two dependence-producing drugs, alcohol and heroin, have been chosen for analysis here. Although this book is concerned with illicit drugs, the legal drug alcohol has been brought into the discussion, because it helps to illustrate the bifurcation in our thinking that has hampered understanding of the problems surrounding drug dependence.

It is legal for adults to buy alcohol; drinkers, including alcohol dependents, can be found in every walk of life. Until recently, heroin could not be legally obtained in Canada; it was reintroduced for strictly limited medical uses late in 1985. Nevertheless, the lion's share of the heroin consumed in this country is imported by criminals and sold on the illicit black market. The junkie is the archetypal "addict" and carries an outlaw identity that is not comparable to any image we might hold of a problem drinker. Yet, the same questions arise when we try to understand the fundamental nature of either alcohol or opiate dependence.

DRUG DEPENDENCE AS SIN:
THE MORAL FAILURE MODEL

The moral failure model of drug dependence places the full responsibility for an individual's drug consumption squarely on his or her own shoulders. In the case of alcohol dependence, especially when it is associated with other serious problems, the response is moral condemnation. Dependence on a prohibited drug, such as heroin, evokes society's ultimate moral opprobrium, criminalization. Legally, heroin dependents are not punished for their dependence per se. The law simply prohibits them from possessing the drug, sharing it with their friends, and so on. Thus, it has been made virtually impossible to use it without committing a criminal offence. The moral failure model rests on the assumption that drug-dependent persons are individuals of free will, personally responsible for the choice between behaving morally or immorally, within or outside the law.

One of the most vexing problems with the moral failure model of drug dependence is the way in which it is so unevenly and inconsistently applied. The legal status and social acceptability of alcohol conspire to produce a moral advantage for those who become dependent on it. Its widespread use undoubtedly contributes to a generalized reluctance to condemn drinkers. In addition, the notion that drunkenness provides an alibi for otherwise unacceptable aggressive or sexual behaviour, although not accepted in every culture, is thoroughly ingrained in ours (21). Although drunkenness generally does not obviate blameworthiness in the courtroom, in society at large it seems to act as a relatively effective, all-purpose excuse for otherwise unacceptable behaviour (27).

There is abundant evidence relating alcohol use to homicide, rape, incest, and other crimes against the person. In the words of the Le Dain Commission: "Of all drugs used medically or non-medically, alcohol has the strongest and most consistent relationship to crime." (9, p. 402). Yet problem drinkers who commit these offences are not invested with a special deviant identity, such as "criminal drinker." On the other hand, heroin dependents who prostitute themselves, sell drugs to one another, shoplift, or commit other petty property crimes are considered to belong to a singular category, the "junkie" or the "criminal addict."

In the world of alcohol use, the only candidates who can lay claim to the kind of total deviant identity the junkie has are the homeless, jobless, chronic drunkenness offenders who live the life of skid row (35). Their deviant status derives from their public visibility, including their vulnerability to repeated arrests for public drunkenness or related infractions. Whether they are sent around the revolving door of the "drunk tank" or taken repeatedly to detoxification centres, no noticeable inroads seem to have been made into their deviant status.

The evident inequality in the way the moral failure model is applied has little, if any, relation to the pharmacology of alcohol or the opiates. Because alcohol is legal, widely available, relatively inexpensive, and normatively accepted, it is relatively easy to acquire. Heroin dependents must go to some trouble and expense, and they are generally understood to commit crimes in order to *obtain* the drug, when they are in need of it or under its declining influence. Drinkers, on the other hand, are more likely to become involved in offences committed *under the influence* of alcohol. Thus, our society attaches greater stigma to antisocial behaviour motivated by the onset or anticipation of withdrawal distress than to similar, and sometimes more serious, behaviour which occurs while the individual is in a state of self-induced intoxication. This overlooks a basic pharmacological fact: that the withdrawal syndrome is as much an effect of a drug as is acute intoxication.

Social class plays an important role in selective stigmatization of those dependent on alcohol or other drugs. For example, middle- or upper-class status provides a range of alternatives to and buffers against public identification as a problem drinker, including involvement with the criminal justice system. Similarly, an unknown, although probably considerable, number of heroin dependents are fortunate enough to manage their habits with little or no resort to criminal activities other than possession of illicit drugs (7, 10). They too have a degree of protection from public identification.

The selective attribution of moral failure to opiate dependents is reflected in our official record keeping. The Bureau of Dangerous Drugs in Ottawa maintains a separate statistical category for persons who have become dependent in the course of medical treatment, as well as one for the medical professionals who themselves become dependent on pharmaceutical supplies. The third category has been reserved for "known users of illicit narcotic drugs," formerly known as "criminal addicts."

In the case of patients who become dependent in the course of medical treatment and have played no active part in the development of their condition, distinctions of this order seem reasonable. On the level of personal responsibility, however, it is more difficult to understand the justification for placing doctors, nurses, and pharmacists in a less stigmatized category than those who buy their drugs on the black market. Indeed, it might be argued that medical professionals are even more culpable, for they have abused a position of trust and should have been better able than non-professionals to understand the risks they were taking.

In summary, moral condemnation of drug dependence is selectively applied according to the social status of the user and the drug involved. Legal status, availability, social acceptability, and popular beliefs about drug effects relegate pharmacological concerns to a subordinate position in this moral calculus. As a result, society is more eager to stigmatize a heroin-dependent prostitute than a spouse-battering problem drinker. It is neither the fact of dependence nor even the severity of antisocial behaviour which may be associated with it that ultimately determines whether an individual will be subjected to the full force of moral opprobrium.

DRUG DEPENDENCE AS SICKNESS: THE DISEASE MODEL

Our legal system assumes that individuals are able to choose between lawful and unlawful behaviour and, therefore, holds them personally responsible for any illegal acts they commit. An exception to this is made for the mentally ill, who are deemed not to be responsible for their actions. The sane are expected, if found guilty, to understand that any punishment meted out to them by the criminal justice system is deserved. Theoretically, willful wrongdoers are punished; the mad are treated.

The disease model of drug dependence does not go so far as to suggest that dependents have no moral responsibility for their behaviour, but it proceeds part way in that direction. An early example of this can be found in a nineteenth-century treatise which argues that both opiate and alcohol dependence are diseases (17). Here a distinction is drawn between drunkards who suffer from the "disease of inebriety" and the self-indulgent "who drink from sheer 'cussedness,' in whom ... the closest scrutiny has detected only moral obliquity" (p. 13). The characteristic by which the diseased drunkard may be recognized is asserted to be "an overpowering impulse to indulge in intoxication at all risks." Uncontrollable craving thus distinguishes the sick from the sinner, and to some degree relieves the former of moral accountability.

We have seen that the moral failure model is selectively applied. Theoretically, the disease model is more democratic. Any person who is dependent on any drug is presumed to be suffering from a disease, and thus to be within the province of medical treatment. Dependence is deemed to be a medical problem, whether the drugs used are licit or illicit, whether or not individual victims have been branded as deviants.

A more democratic model that advocates treatment over punishment is an appealing alternative to its predecessor. Unfortunately, experts have never been able to agree on a scientifically meaningful definition of the disease of dependence, nor have they attained consensus on the criteria by which a diagnosis should be made. Over the years, distinguished committees have been convened, have studied and debated, and have produced new definitions. Zinberg (36) has critically examined a series of these definitions, and found all of them to be wanting. Furthermore, the currency of the disease model is devalued not only by disagreement over diagnostic criteria, but also by the medical profession's inability to produce a reliable cure for the disease of dependence.

SIN OR SICKNESS? CRIME OR DISEASE?

The co-existence of competing models of dependence brings confusion to every attempt to understand and respond to the problem. On the one hand, dependents are seen as self-determining, self-indulgent individuals, responsible for their own behaviour and deserving of their fate. On the other, they are considered to be sick wretches who cannot help themselves and who are in need of medical treatment. To shed some light on how this unsatisfactory situation has come to pass, we must look to our recent history.

The notion that chronic drunkenness might be a disease is a relative newcomer, considering our long history of treating it as moral failure. Dependence as a disease can be traced back to eighteenth-century England, but it was largely applied to the elite in society; for the poor, chronic drunkenness remained a vice (25). This class distinction disappeared in the following century, when physicians began to write treatises articulating the disease model of alcohol and opiate addiction. Furthermore, the temperance movements in nineteenth-century Britain and America promulgated the ideas that alcohol paralyzed the will and that the victims of alcohol deserved sympathy, not denunciation (14, 18). This served as another foundation for the disease model. Thus, the sin and sickness conceptions have been juxtaposed for over two centuries.

In Britain, the disease concept was firmly entrenched by 1910. The reason for its success in that country can be found in the changing role and status of the medical profession in Victorian society, at a time when doctors were beginning to appropriate some of the functions of the clergy:

Physicians, the new guardians of morality, simply substituted new names for ancient evils: madness became mental illness; drunkenness became alcoholism; and the sin of Onan became masturbation. The old sins to be confronted and overcome were, by the late nineteenth century, diseases to be cured. (23, p. 292)

At the same time, physicians were tightening up their ranks and establishing themselves as a remarkably prestigious and influential profession.

In North America, however, similar professional solidarity was to come somewhat later. By the time the Canadian Medical Association (CMA) had become a viable organization, in the 1920s, a law-enforcement response to drug control was firmly entrenched (12). In the absence of advocates for the disease model, the moral failure model held sway.

Across the Atlantic, British doctors were playing an important role in the formulation of drug policy. They thus retained the right to prescribe regular doses of heroin or other opiates to their dependent patients, even when there was no physical illness or injury to justify the prescription (3). Unhindered by influences external to their profession, they jealously guarded their freedom to determine therapy in individual cases.

Meanwhile, North American law enforcement authorities held a trump card: they could define the boundaries of legitimate medical practice by arresting those doctors they deemed to have exceeded them. The onus was on the physician to prove that the therapy was justified. This effectively discouraged doctors from prescribing opiate maintenance and made them frightened even of prescribing for their patients in pain (34).

That the responsibility for supervision of the Canadian drug laws was lodged in the Narcotic Division of the Department of Health might be taken as evidence that the disease model had some currency. However, the Division worked closely with the Royal Canadian Mounted Police. Some of the interdepartmental correspondence between these two agencies in the 1920s is available in the Public Archives in Ottawa. Reading through these documents, one is struck by the active participation of the Department of Health in criminal cases, especially those that involved physicians who prescribed drugs for dependents. The Narcotic Division not only helped the RCMP to identify suspects, but also made strategic decisions during all the phases of investigation, arrest, and prosecution.

In the early decades of this century, American physicians showed reluctance to accept the disease concept of alcoholism. Nevertheless, a variety of conditions combined in the thirties and forties to revive the medical model (16, 29). After the Second World War, the law-enforcement hegemony over heroin policy received its first official challenge from the medical profession (2, 20). In Canada, a Senate Special Committee on the Traffic in Narcotic Drugs held hearings in 1955. Although this committee "cannot be said to have become wholly committed to the view that the addict should be treated as a patient rather than as a criminal" (12, p. 89), it is evident that medical testimony was taken into account. The 1961 *Narcotic Control Act* and *Reg-*

ulations encouraged the professions to take responsibility for articulating proper medical practice with regard to the treatment of drug dependents. In 1965, the Canadian Medical Association took up the challenge, producing guidelines which were considerably more permissive than those issued by its U.S. counterpart. By the mid-1980s, the CMA was urging the government to restore the physician's right to prescribe heroin for pain, a right the profession had been deprived of in the 1950s on the recommendation of the law enforcement authorities. Thus, as the disease model of drug dependence has gained ascendency, so has the voice of the medical profession gained influence in drug policy debates.

Both the medical profession and the public have gradually come around to the view that alcohol and other drug dependence is a disease. Room reports (29) that by the early 1960s about 65 percent of the U.S. public agreed that alcoholism was a disease, up from about 20 percent in the immediate post-war period. Nevertheless, the corollary that therefore the alcoholic was not responsible for his or her behaviour did not gain congruent public accep-tance. It seems that people paid lip-service to the disease concept. When presented with practical situations in which drinkers lost their jobs, neglected their families, or had other problems, the public continued to believe it was because the drinkers were "no good" and "weak-willed." Thus, the disease model became increasingly accepted, but there was no corresponding decline in the moral failure model.

That two very different definitions of drug dependence, each evoking different social responses, should co-exist for a time is not in itself surprising. In our intellectual history, we find a multitude of examples of competing definitions of reality, in the physical as well as the social sciences. It usually takes some time before the newer models are permitted to take the place of their less satisfactory predecessors. This process is generally accomplished after a period of controversy in which both competitors maintain some degree of currency.

What is odd in the present case is the apparent tenacity of both models.

COALITIONS AND MERGERS:
THE MODELS COMBINED

Perhaps if medical science had managed to discover a reasonably effective cure for the disease of dependence, the boundary between medical and law enforcement responsibility for dealing with dependence and drug-related behavioural problems would have been more clearly drawn by now. This has not, however, been the case.

No treatment modality can guarantee a satisfactory outcome for all drug-dependent patients who come for help. This applies whether the treatment setting is a general or a psychiatric hospital, a halfway house, a clinic or detoxification centre, and whether the treatment is conducted on an inpatient or outpatient basis. Limited success can be expected whether the treatment employs counselling, individual or group therapy, behavioural, chemical, physical, or occupational therapies. Certain modalities appear to be better suited to some patients than others; some require levels of verbal competence, education, or commitment to the program that cannot reasonably be expected from everyone. All can claim that some patients have benefited, although success rates vary. Different agencies measure treatment outcome in different ways, and their reports of success present problems of interpretation. The successful cases may have been better motivated to begin with, or they may have had more social resources and fewer life problems. Indeed, some treatment successes might have improved on their own, without professional assistance.

It has been suggested that our failure to develop reliably effective treatment for drug dependents may be the reason why the sickness model has not displaced the sin model. This is a tenable, if untestable, assumption, the converse of which also seems reasonable: that an uncomfortable association of the models has hampered the development of effective treatment.

Close analysis of the treatment modalities reveals that in practice the disease concept is frequently merged with or overlaid by essentially moral concerns. One of the goals of methadone maintenance, for example, is to control criminal and other antisocial behaviour in heroin dependents. Self-help groups, such as Alcoholics Anonymous, inculcate the notion that dependence is an unremitting disability, while mandating moral steadfastness to hold it at bay. When treatment fails, there is a tendency to blame the patient, to suggest that she or he did not try hard enough or was not sufficiently motivated. These examples illustrate the way in which both models impose their influence; they also suggest some of the difficulties that would be encountered if one were to try to design a treatment regime uncontaminated by moral overtones and concerns about social control.

Dependent persons who come to the attention of the medical profession, social agencies, or law enforcement authorities normally do so because of psychological, medical, or social disabilities. These may be associated with their drug use, but they cannot be guaranteed to disappear once the dependence is brought under control. Whether these problems are a cause of, caused by, or incidentally coincident with drug use, neither model seems capable of suggesting strategies that encompass them all. Neither do the models fare much better in combination.

We will return to this issue below, but first we will examine two institutional arrangements that clearly express the simultaneous acceptance of the two models in our society: drug treatment in penal settings and compulsory commitment for treatment. In the former case, where drug treatment is imposed on an already criminalized and incarcerated population, it can be characterized as a kind of "cohabitation" of the sin and sickness models. The true "marriage" of models occurs when free individuals are compelled to be institutionalized for treatment under compulsory treatment legislation.

COHABITATION: TREATMENT
IN A PENAL SETTING

Depending on the reigning penal policy, two of the goals of incarceration, punishment and rehabilitation, are given more or less emphasis relative to one another. When attention focuses on rehabilitation, more resources are made available for medical professionals, psychologists, teachers, and social workers in penal settings. Thus, special programs for alcohol and heroin dependents have been established, and the treatment model has come to be housed within prison walls, formerly the sole domain of the criminal model.

The most ambitious, sophisticated, and well-controlled Canadian experiment in the treatment of drug dependents in prison took place at the medium-security penitentiary at Matsqui, British Columbia (22). With a matched group of inmates serving as controls, an experimental group of heroin dependents in a special "pilot treatment unit" were offered intensive group therapy and educational upgrading. Briefly, the aim of the treatment was to enable them to function successfully in society without drugs.

Both groups were followed up after they left Matsqui. Paradoxically, the men who had gone through the treatment program spent more time committing crimes than did the controls, and they made more money doing so. They also used more heroin. Murphy, who was responsible for the design and execution of this study, concluded that the treatment had inadvertently produced a "well-adjusted, well-educated dope fiend" (22). The education, social skills, and self-understanding the program imparted might well have helped these men in "straight" society, but instead they used these acquisitions to transform themselves into more successful hustling junkies.

It would not seem unreasonable to hypothesize that the ironically disappointing results of the Matsqui experiment came about because it focused on men who were "doing time" and could not be considered in any real sense to be voluntary participants. Perhaps they had no strong desire to put their heroin use behind them and that was why the intent of the treatment became perverted. However, most so-called voluntary patients in both alcohol and other drug treatment have been compelled in some way to come forward: by family pressure, by probation order, or because some combination of circumstances has made their lives intolerable. For the Matsqui inmates, compulsion thus may have been simply a matter of degree.

Nevertheless, treatment in penal settings raises a fundamental ethical problem: if the patient is not wholly committed to and capable of change, what right do the helpers have to try to impose it? If society assumes that some degree of intervention for what is perceived to be the welfare of others is justified, it must determine the point at which such intervention becomes unacceptably coercive. In practice, however, such ethical concerns seem academic when one contemplates those that arise from the perfect marriage of the criminal and medical models: compulsory commitment for treatment. When incarceration is *imposed* in order to effect treatment, a situation of much graver ethical import arises.

MATRIMONY: COMPULSORY COMMITMENT FOR TREATMENT

Part II of Canada's *Narcotic Control Act* provides for a very controversial method of controlling drug users: preventive detention and custody for treatment. Although this part of the Act has not been put into force by proclamation, it does represent Parliamentary intention. If this policy were implemented, arrested or convicted drug users could be placed in preventive detention where they would be observed and examined by at least one "duly qualified medical practitioner." A decision would then be reached on whether the individual was a "narcotic addict," that is, dependent on any of the drugs in the Act. If so, the court could then send the individual for treatment in a penitentiary for an indeterminate period of time. This disposition would be in lieu of any other sentence that the person might have received· if the determination of addiction had not been made.

Why Part II has never been activated is a matter of some speculation. Part of the answer may lie in the problems surrounding provincial and federal responsibilities in this area. Nevertheless, in the absence of active federal legislation, several provinces have enacted their own compulsory treatment laws. Mental health comes under the jurisdiction of the provinces, all of which have laws that allow for compelling certain psychiatrically disabled persons to accept inpatient treatment. Wholeheartedly adopting the disease model of drug dependence, the provinces extended this power to encompass drug users.

In Section 6 of this book, Neil Boyd and his associates trace the history of compulsory treatment in British Columbia and discuss some of the problems concerning its efficacy and legality. Here we will briefly review some of the ethical issues that arise when the sin and disease models are wed at the alter of legislation of this type.

Compulsory treatment laws are not a Canadian innovation. The states of California and New York have experimented with this kind of legislation, and a U.S. federal program was instituted in 1966. The American models allow for self-commitment, commitment on petition by a third party, opting for treatment in lieu of criminal prosecution or accepting it as an alternative to imprisonment or other sentence.

Similar legislation drafted in the province of Prince Edward Island is even more ambitious in this regard. Unlike its counterparts elsewhere, it includes alcohol drinkers within the scope of the law. It also greatly expands the powers of police:

> A police constable may enter private premises to remove a person considered by him to be suffering from mental disorder caused by the use of alcohol or other chemical substance and may use such reasonable force as is necessary to take a person ... to an appropriate place. (Bill 37, s. 13 (b))

That a province should employ mental health legislation to extend the conditions under which police are permitted to invade the privacy of its citizens and remove them from their homes may seem curious. However, this is an excellent example of how marriage of the criminal and medical models is capable of amplifying the most dubious characteristics of either.

Psychiatrists cannot always agree in their diagnoses of mental illnesses. This legislation is asking police constables to do the diagnosing, ignoring the obvious fact that psychiatric experts could be hard pressed to specify whether psychiatric disorder in any given instance has been caused by drug use or not. Drug use may be symptomatic of a pre-existing mental problem, or the two may be randomly coincident, or some interaction may be taking place (9). That the P.E.I. police should be given right of entry into private dwellings on the basis of their presumed ability not only to diagnose mental disorder, but also to determine that the condition arose as a direct result of alcohol or other drug use, is highly questionable at best.

The American systems define the grounds for commitment for treatment on a more limited basis: "addiction" and, in some jurisdictions, "imminent danger of becoming addicted." The latter specification has been a cause of some concern, because of the discretion it gives the state doctors and the courts. Presumably, anyone who takes a drug with dependence potential is in *some* danger of becoming addicted. A broad interpretation of "imminent" would significantly increase the population vulnerable to commitment.

Advocates of compulsory treatment argue that its value lies in segregating dangerous drug users from society. From this, they say, will flow two major benefits: protecting the public from the predations of drug users and preventing the spread of drug dependence. The reader will note that the first is based on the moral failure model, the second on the medical.

The "quarantine" argument is interesting, as it is hard to imagine its application to alcohol. Although in reality some alcoholics undoubtedly encourage others to drink more heavily, most people would think it ludicrous to suggest that they should be locked up to prevent the spread of the disease. Similarly, heroin dependents have been known to be a bad influence on their friends. The spread of heroin use, however, is largely through relative newcomers to the drug, users who have not yet experienced problems with it. Thus, the "infectious" element is found most often amongst those least likely to have been identified as users by the authorities. Furthermore, just as one drink does not necessarily make an alcoholic, heroin users do not necessarily become dependent (4). In sum, the quarantine argument can be dismissed on the grounds that it is highly unlikely to fulfill its promise.

The crime-reduction argument has more validity, in so far as some drug dependents do indulge in acquisitive and predatory crimes, offences they would be constrained from committing if they were in custody. If this were the sole basis for compulsory commitment, it would hardly be fair also to lock up those who do not make a habit of preying on the public. Be that as it may, whatever the extent of crime committed by drug dependents, presumably the appropriate response would be through the criminal justice system, not mental health legislation.

Their technical inadequacies aside, the quarantine and crime-reduction justifications are essentially arguments for preventive detention, that is, holding individuals in custody in order to prevent them from committing acts we predict they are likely to commit. Under the cloak of the medical model, dependence per se is thus made grounds for deprivation of liberty, a criminal sanction.

If there were a magic bullet, a reliable cure for dependence that worked under conditions of involuntary confinement, a debate over whether the ends justified the means might be entertained. There is no evidence that compulsory treatment is any more effective than voluntary programs or, for that matter, straightforward incarceration (6, 8, 9). Thus, no argument can be made for suspending human rights on the grounds that compulsory treatment will wean a significant number of dependents from their destructive drug use habits (28).

Judging from previous experiments with compulsory treatment, the inmates of such programs have no illusions about whether or not they are patients or prisoners. To minimize the length of their incarceration, they must appear to be co-operating with the treatment. However, from their point of view, they are still just "doing time," with a few extra role requirements thrown in for good measure (33). It is not surprising that they lack enthusiasm for compulsory treatment, considering that they may well spend more time in commitment than if they had been incarcerated in the normal course of the criminal justice system.

The fundamental ethical concerns which stem from the marriage of the criminal and medical models were summed up by C. S. Lewis four decades ago:

> To be taken without consent from my home and friends; to lose my liberty; to undergo all those assaults on my personality which modern psychotherapy knows how to deliver; to be re-made after some pattern of 'normality' hatched in a Viennese laboratory to which I never professed allegiance; to know that this process will never end until either my captors have succeeded or I grown wise enough to cheat them with apparent success—who cares whether this is called Punishment or not? (19, p. 304)

TOWARD RE-DEFINITION

We have seen that two competing conceptions of alcohol and other drug dependence have been with us for some time. Translated into social policies, their co-existence has generated some disturbing ethical and practical problems. It can be argued that the moral failure model invests dependent persons with too much responsibility for their behaviour; the disease model, on the other hand, tends too far in the opposite direction by depriving people of personal responsibility for their condition.

Both models suffer from sociological myopia, because both fail to acknowledge that drug users are social creatures acting in social settings. The medical model especially can be criticized for ignoring the complex social interactions in which individuals make decisions about their drug use. The natural history of alcohol and other drug use is profoundly influenced by biographical contingencies and accidents of the social environment over which the individual often has little control (4, 32). Actors in social relationships, although free to improvise within them, are constrained by them.

A new understanding of drug dependence must encompass positive and negative external forces, as well as the strengths and weaknesses of drug users themselves. Indeed, the professional pride and personal sanity of those engaged in treating drug users may depend on their ability to allow the disease model of dependence to expand beyond the limits of a strict medical model. Furthermore, the success of treatment may be contingent on this ability to surmount purely medical and legal concerns, and take realistic account of social and cultural factors.

That treatment "failures" reflect unanticipated socio-cultural factors is well illustrated by the Matsqui study. Outsiders may find it difficult to appreciate that drug-centred, deviant lifestyles can hold strong attractions for their participants. The Matsqui inmates required more than lessons on how to function in conventional society. They also needed to believe that it was worth while to try to apply these skills in an unfamiliar environment, among people who would be unlikely to view their former lives with equanimity or understanding. They had to be convinced to change their identities, find new friends, turn their backs on a life which had its rewards as well as problems. Their situation was not dissimilar to that of the detoxified drinker who returns to skid row out of loneliness, because it is at least a familiar and sympathetic world, and from discouragement, because prospects of success in conventional society appear remote (13, 35).

Similarly, the early promise of methadone maintenance collided with the realities of the world of heroin use. When evidence began to appear of continuing criminal behaviour in methadone clients, it was received with some chagrin by those who had argued that drug maintenance would obviate the need for acquisitive crime. With hindsight, it may seem naive to have expected hustling "dope fiends" to be so effortlessly transformed into conventional citizens with middle-class values. However, the competing models are, to some degree, at fault. The pioneers of methadone maintenance were arguing *against* the law enforcement perspective, *for* a more humane medical approach. In this laudable effort, they acknowledged a limited sociological perspective, but failed to see that a very complex social system would work at cross-purposes to their intentions. A less adversarial setting might have encouraged a more realistic prediction of treatment outcome.

These experiences serve as cautionary examples. It is time to incorporate the insights derived from social scientific research into our understanding of the nature of drug dependence. This does not mean that a social scientific cabal is vying for hegemony in the drug arena, as some advocates of the disease model seem to fear (Keller, 1981, as cited in 29). A new synthesis is required, not a new vested interest.

In recent years, a number of research advances have influenced our understanding of drug dependence. Although much of this research has focused on alcohol, the prospect of its application to other addicting drugs is encouraging.

Both the sin and sickness models suggest that alcoholics constitute a distinct subgroup of the drinking population, those who possess certain qualities not shared by "normal" or "social" drinkers. However, analysis of the statistical distribution of alcohol consumption in the general population indicates that the distinction is largely a quantitative one. In any given population, most people drink very little. A few consume large quantities of alcohol and experience many problems associated with their drinking. Between these extremes, levels of use and related problems shade and blend into one another along a continuous curve. Thus, alcohol dependence is defined as an arbitrary cutting-off point on a continuum and, statistically, does not appear as a discrete pattern of consumption (24).

Accumulating evidence also indicates that there are many levels and styles of illicit drug use, including heroin use, between "experimentation" and "dependence" (4, 36). We do not have sufficient epidemiological data to plot the consumption curves of the illicit drugs, but the available information suggests that, like the situation with alcohol, a large proportion of users remains at non-addictive levels of use or exits from use before becoming chronically dependent. In the world of non-medical drug use, tobacco would appear to be the exception to this rule, because a large proportion of users rapidly progresses to the heavier levels of use that lead to dependence.

Under the influence of the disease model, the natural history of drug dependence was visualized as an inevitable slide down a slippery slope toward heavier consumption and more drug-related problems, until finally the addict hit bottom and appeared for treatment. Modern research challenges this conception. Over time, individuals move in and out of problem drinking and other drug use, attaining abstinence or returning to lower-risk levels of use, often without receiving formal treatment (4, 11, 31). Some of these findings have provoked considerable controversy, but such debates appear to be a product of conflicting models and opposing ideologies, rather than a reflection on the quality of the new research (15, 26).

Self-reports of drug users suggest that some of the problems encountered in conceptualizing dependence arise because its presumed symptoms or indicators are themselves variables. With regard to craving for drugs, users speak of feelings that range from mere speculation about the possibility of using to intense desire. Loss of control over consumption can manifest itself as a single incident of buying drugs with money that should have been saved to pay the rent, or feelings of helpless futility in the grip of a destructive drug use pattern. Withdrawal symptoms can be mild or severe. Finally, the relationships among these variables, or between any one of them and reported use patterns, cannot be reliably predicted except in extreme cases (5).

A more dynamic conception of drug dependence, rooted in a firm social scientific perspective, would lead to an increased appreciation of the individual differences among drug dependents, while highlighting similarities between users of different drugs. The rigid models of the past have allowed us to do things to people in the name of "treatment" which would never have been considered appropriate as "punishment." They have characterized drug-dependent persons as improbably self-indulgent or as unrealistically bereft of free will. Together, they created a situation where the helped did not know if they were criminals or patients, and helpers were confused as to whether their role was that of custodian or therapist. It is little wonder that we have had very few therapeutic success stories to tell.

Despite the awesome inertia of the old models, recent research efforts are helping to change ideas about the nature of dependence and the problems of persons who suffer from it. These developments promise more comprehensive, humane, and effective social policies for the future.

REFERENCES

1. Alexander, B. K. Drug use, dependence, and addiction at a British Columbia university: Good news and bad news. *Canadian Journal of Higher Education*, 15:13–29 (1985).
2. American Bar Association and American Medical Association. *Drug Addiction: Crime or Disease?* Bloomington, Ind.: Indiana University Press, 1963.
3. Berridge, V. War conditions and narcotics control: The passing of Defence of the Realm Act Regulation 40b. *Journal of Social Policy*, 7:285–304 (1978).
4. Blackwell, J. Drifting, controlling, and overcoming: Opiate users who

avoid becoming chronically dependent. *Journal of Drug Issues*, *13*:219–35 (1983).

5. Blackwell, J. Opiate dependence as a psychophysical event: Users' reports of subjective experiences. *Contemporary Drug Problems*, *12*:331–50 (1985).

6. Brecher, E. M., and the Editors of Consumer Reports. *Licit and Illicit Drugs*. Boston: Little, Brown, 1972.

7. Brotman, R., and Freedman, A. M. *A Community Mental Health Approach to Drug Addiction*. U.S. Department of Health, Education and Welfare, Social and Rehabilitation Service. Washington, D.C.: U.S. Government Printing Office, 1968.

8. Brown, J. W., Mazze, R., and Glaser, D. *Narcotics, Knowledge and Nonsense: Program Disaster versus a Scientific Model*. Cambridge, Mass.: Ballinger, 1974.

9. Canada. Commission of Inquiry into the Non-Medical Use of Drugs. *Final Report*. Ottawa: Information Canada, 1973.

10. Caplovitz, D. *The Working Addict*. White Plains, N.Y.: M. E. Sharpe, 1976.

11. Clark, N. B. Loss of control, heavy drinking and drinking problems in a longitudinal study. *Journal of Studies on Alcohol*, *37*:1256–90 (1976).

12. Cook, S. J. Variations in response to illegal drug use: A comparative study of official narcotic drug policies in Canada, Great Britain, and the United States from 1920 to 1970. Project H.139. Toronto: Addiction Research Foundation, 1970.

13. Giesbrecht, N. Stakes in conformity and the "normalization" of deviants: Accounts by former and current skid row inebriates. *Journal of Drug Issues*, *13*:299–322 (1983).

14. Harrison, B. *Drink and the Victorians: The Temperance Question in England, 1815–1872*. London: Faber & Faber, 1971.

15. Heather, N., and Robertson, I. *Controlled Drinking*. London: Methuen, 1981.

16. Jellinick, E. M. *The Disease Concept of Alcoholism*. New Haven, Conn.: Hillhouse Press, 1960.

17. Kerr, N. *Inebriety or Narcomania: Its Etiology, Pathology, Treatment and Jurisprudence*. 1894. Reprint. New York: Arno Press, 1981.

18. Levine, H. G. The alcohol problem in America: From temperance to alcoholism. *British Journal of Addiction* *79*:109–19 (1984).

19. Lewis, C. S. The humanitarian theory of punishment (1948–1949). In: Grupp, S. E. (ed.). *Theories of Punishment*. Bloomington, Ind.: Indiana University Press, 1971.

20. Lindesmith, A. R. *The Addict and the Law*. Bloomington, Ind.: University of Indiana Press, 1965.

21. MacAndrew, C., and Edgerton, R. B. *Drunken Comportment: A Social Explanation*. London: Thomas Nelson and Sons, 1970.

22. Murphy, B. C. *A Quantitative Test of the Effectiveness of an Experimental*

Treatment Programme for Delinquent Opiate Addicts. Ottawa: Department of the Solicitor General of Canada, 1972.

23. Parssinen, T. M., and Kerner, K. Development of the disease model of drug addiction in Britain, 1870–1926. *Medical History*, *24*:275–96 (1980).

24. Popham, R., Schmidt, W., and de Lint, J. Government control measures to prevent hazardous drinking. In: Ewing, J. A., and Rouse, B.A. (eds.). *Drinking: Alcohol in American Society—Issues and Current Research*. Chicago: Nelson-Hall, 1978.

25. Porter, R. The drinking man's disease: The pre-history of alcoholism in Georgian Britain. *British Journal of Addiction*, *80*:385–96 (1985).

26. Roizen, R. The great controlled drinking controversy. In: Galanter, M. (ed.). *Recent Developments in Alcoholism*, Vol. 5. New York: Plenum, 1986.

27. Room, R. How good an excuse is drunkenness? Seminar presentation sponsored by the Westermarck Society at the Institute of Law, University of Helsinki, May 10, 1984.

28. Room, R. New curves in the course: A comment on Polich, Armor and Braiker, "The course of alcoholism." *British Journal of Addiction*, *75*:351–60 (1980).

29. Room, R. Sociological aspects of the disease concept of alcoholism. In: Smart, R. G., Glaser, F. B., Israel, Y., Kalant, H., Popham, R. E., and Schmidt, W. (eds.). *Research Advances in Alcohol and Drug Problems*, Vol. 7. New York: Plenum, 1983.

30. Rounsaville, B. J., Spitzer, R. L., and Williams, J. B. Proposed changes in DSM-III substance use disorders: Description and rationale. *American Journal of Psychiatry*, *143*:463–68 (1986).

31. Stall, R., and Biernacki, P. Spontaneous remission from the problematic use of substances: An inductive model derived from a comparative analysis of the alcohol, opiate, tobacco, and food/obesity literatures. *International Journal of the Addictions*, *21*:1–23 (1986).

32. Vaillant, G. E. *The Natural History of Alcoholism*. Cambridge, Mass.: Harvard University Press, 1983.

33. Waldorf, D. *Careers in Dope*. Englewood Cliffs, N.J.: Prentice-Hall, 1973.

34. Waldorf, D., Orlick, M., and Reinarman, C. *Morphine Maintenance: The Shreveport Clinic, 1919–1923*. Washington, D.C.: Drug Abuse Council, 1974.

35. Wiseman, J. P. *Stations of the Lost*. Englewood Cliffs, N.J.: Prentice-Hall, 1970.

36. Zinberg, N. E. *Drug, Set, and Setting: The Basis for Controlled Intoxicant Use*. New Haven: Yale University Press, 1984.

11

Drugs and Disrepute:
The Thin Line

JOHN HAGAN

Drug use abounds in our society. It perhaps should not surprise us, then, that so many different meanings attach to drug use. Yet relatively little is known about these meanings, how they emerge, why they are applied, and with what consequences. For example, how is it that use of the same drug in the same quantity can be seen in one context as desirable and another as disreputable? This kind of definitional problem has plagued efforts to study and understand drug use as a form of social deviance. The question seems deceptively simple: a matter of determining when drug use is indeed deviant. Various sociological definitions of deviance attempt to resolve this problem, and thereby to establish the kinds of drug use we should study as deviance. As we will see, none of these approaches is without its own problems, although the problems themselves can usefully be made a focus of research.

SIX SOCIOLOGICAL APPROACHES TO THE DEFINITION OF DEVIANCE

This discussion first outlines the central points and problems of six socio-logical approaches to the definition of deviance. These approaches are (a) a legal-consensus definition, (b) a socio-legal definition, (c) a cross-cultural definition, (d) a statistical definition, (e) a labelling definition, and (f) a utopian-conflict definition. Following a critical review of the six approaches, elements of the definitions are combined to form a new approach to the problem. This paper argues that this last approach is best suited to the study of drug use as deviance.

The Legal-Consensus Approach

The hallmark of this approach is the use of the law as its guide. The most articulate advocate of a legalistic approach to the definition of deviance was the lawyer-sociologist Paul Tappan (21). Tappan insisted that we limit our study to what is legally defined as criminal. In Canada, this would include the *Narcotic Control Act* and the *Food and Drugs Act*. Using this approach, Tappan insisted that "Crime is an intentional act in violation of the criminal law ... committed without defence or excuse, and penalized by the state"

(21, p. 100). He insisted further that persons studied as criminals must be adjudicated (i.e., convicted) as such. Acknowledging that cultures vary in what they call criminal, Tappan argued that governing statutes provide the only clear and definitive indication of what any specific cultural group holds deviant: "Here we find *norms* of conduct, comparable to mores, but considerably more distinct, precise, and detailed" (21, p. 100). In short, Tappan suggests that the criminal law provides a reliable guide to what is consensually defined as deviant, including forms of drug use, in any given society. Armstrong and Turner adopt a similar position for the study of Canadian drug use when they state: "we are only concerned with those aspects . . . that result in actions prohibited by the criminal law" (1, p. 504).

The salient difficulty with Tappan's approach is that it systematically ignores much of what many analysts of deviance wish to study: the non-criminal but nonetheless disreputable pleasures of various deviant lifestyles, including those which involve, for example, the sniffing of glue and the excessive use of alcohol, barbiturates, and amphetamines. A related problem is that the legal-consensus approach neglects the basic issue of why some acts—including some kinds of drug use—are legislated as criminal, while others remain only informally the subject of disrepute. Further, this approach misinforms us in suggesting that legal definitions clearly reflect societal consensus about what is deviant. This is conspicuously not the case in Canada, where provisions of the *Narcotic Control Act* have lagged behind changing public attitudes, for example in the control of marijuana (10). Finally, being legally called a criminal depends on getting caught and convicted. This sampling process results in not only a narrowly defined, but also a non-representative, collection of subjects (more accurately called "captives") for study.

The Socio-Legal Approach

Edwin Sutherland (19) suggested a relaxation of the legal criteria to be used in defining our subject matter, a relaxation that permitted attention to a wider range of "anti-social behaviors." Retained, however, was an emphasis on criminality, as designated by two explicit criteria: "legal description of acts as socially injurious and legal provision of a penalty for the act" (p. 132). Sutherland (see also 6) demonstrated with the use of these criteria that it is possible to consider "criminal" many unethical business practices handled in civil courts. Recent examples involving drugs would include the efforts to obtain compensation for the health problems produced by prescription of thalidomide and DES to future mothers.

Sutherland's redefinition of the field of study facilitated a new and important emphasis on the crimes of "upperworld" offenders, who have exploited drugs as well as other sources of profit. However, reluctance to widen the scope of attention beyond statutory matters leaves this definition of deviance open to two earlier criticisms of the legalistic approach: first, non-criminal forms of deviance, including many kinds of drug use, continue unnoticed; second, like those of the criminal courts, civil court dockets undoubtedly provide a biased sample of illegal drug-related activity and enterprise.

The Cross-Cultural Approach

Thorsten Sellin (18) proposed a definition of deviance that extends attention beyond the realm of law. He argued that every group has its own standards of behaviour called "conduct norms," and that these standards are not necessarily embodied in law. "For every person, then, there is from the point of view of a given group of which he is a member, a normal (right) and abnormal (wrong) way of reacting, the norm depending upon the social values of the group which formulated it" (18, p. 30). Beyond this, however, Sellin argued that there are some conduct norms that are invariant across *all* cultural groups. Further, he insisted that these norms were the appropriate focus of research: "Such study would involve the isolation and classification of norms into *universal categories* transcending political and other boundaries, a necessity imposed by the logic of science" (18, p. 30).

Unfortunately, Sellin did not specify what the universal conduct norms might be, and it is unlikely in any case that drug use of any kind would qualify. The drug use that is criminal in one society may be sacred in another. The lesson of a large body of anthropological research is that norms of conduct are remarkably varied, with the universals of human behaviour, if any, limited primarily to the trivial necessities of everyday life. Universal *and* non-trivial conduct norms, especially relating to drug use, probably cannot be found.

The Statistical Approach

Wilkins (24) suggests a somewhat more plausible approach to our subject matter, while remaining attentive to the problem of cultural variation. He begins with the assumption that, "At some time or another, some form of society . . . has defined almost all forms of behaviour that we now call 'criminal' as desirable for the functioning of that form of society" (24, p. 46). Wilkins then suggests that the frequency with which various forms of behaviour occur in any particular society be used as the criterion of deviance. From this perspective, high-frequency behaviours are considered normal, and low-frequency behaviours deviant. The resulting definition of deviance is represented by a normal bell-shaped curve. "It may be supposed that the model given by the normal frequency distribution shown in this chart represents the ethical content of human action" (p. 47). Serious crimes and saintly acts form the two extremes in this definition. The range of additional acts to be considered deviant remains at the discretion of the researcher.

One weakness of this approach is easily recognized as it applies to the study of drug use: infrequent drug use is not necessarily designated deviant or criminal. Many drugs are used rarely because they are scarce or because users do not appreciate their effects. Beyond this, while infrequency of behaviour can sometimes be taken as one indicator of deviance, the statistical approach neglects the role of societal groups in selecting from infrequent acts those considered undesirable. What is required, then, is an addition of social content to the quantitative framework provided.

The Labelling Approach

While the statistical approach may minimize the importance of the societal response, this one does not. Howard Becker provides a concise statement of the labelling viewpoint: "The deviant is one to whom that label has successfully been applied; deviant behavior is behavior that people so label" (3, p. 9). The point Becker is making is that behaviours are not recognized as deviant unless others, as members of cultural groups, react to them as such. The importance of this approach lies in making us aware of the significance of the ways in which we respond to deviance. Nonetheless, this approach also presents some problems.

Bordua (5) notes that the labelling perspective tends to see deviance as "all societal response, and no deviant stimulus." In the context of drug research, it is as if to say that the drugs themselves play no role in eliciting responses from users as well as from those who react to them. Becker's classic discussion of becoming a marijuana user (2), and Lindesmith's writings on the process of becoming a heroin addict (14), are cases in point. This is not to deny the significance of the societal response, but rather to acknowledge the roles of drug, act, and actor-related variables as well.

The Utopian-Conflict Approach

The "new criminologists," Ian Taylor, Paul Walton, and Jock Young (22), offer a provocative approach to the definition of deviance as "human diversity." Deviance represents, according to the new criminologists, a normal and purposeful attempt to correct or protest social injustice. Society's response to such challenges is to repress the behaviour by criminalizing the actors involved. Thus deviance is seen here as conflict between the oppressed and the oppressors. The new criminologists propose a solution that reverses this conflict situation: "For us, ... deviance is normal ... the task is to create a society in which the facts of human diversity ... are not subject to the power to criminalize" (22, p. 282).

In the area of drug research, it is perhaps Thomas Szasz who comes closest to the utopian-conflict position. However, even Szasz (20) is sensitive to the problem that drug use, at least in some instances, may intrude on the rights of others, especially minors. The problem is that the kind of position the new criminologists take is both useful and utopian. On the one hand, it alerts us to the possibility that some behaviours, including some kinds of drug use, may be called deviant or criminal because they are offensive or threatening to privileged segments of society. On the other hand, to assume that many kinds of drug use are benign, or a part of a politically meaningful lifestyle, is utopian. Ultimately, the issue may be to determine how far we can go in the direction inspired by the utopian-conflict approach, while still wishing to live in the society of our design.

What, then, is the appropriate definition of deviance for the study of drug use? A proposed approach follows.

DEFINING DEVIANCE AS A CONTINUOUS VARIABLE

This definition begins with a simple premise: that deviance consists of variation from a social norm. Beyond this, it is proposed that the many varieties of deviance can be divided and subdivided into several categories, with these categories in turn conceived theoretically as ranging from those considered least to most serious in any given society. There is an obvious difference in the attention our society currently pays to heroin addiction and the attention it pays to the casual use of marijuana. Similarly, many forms of drug use can be located empirically on a continuum of seriousness. It is true that not all individuals or groups, in any given society, will agree, or have strong feelings about, the wrongfulness of each act. For example, most persons may have no strong feelings about whether it is "right" or "wrong" to smoke lettuce leaves or banana peels. However, this in itself is the first measure of seriousness: the degree of agreement about the wrongfulness of drug-related activity. This kind of assessment can range from confusion and apathy, through high levels of disagreement, to conditions of general agreement. Agreement about the norm is the first index of seriousness.

The severity of societal response an act elicits is the second measure of seriousness. Such penalties can vary from public execution to polite avoidance, with a range of responses in between. The more serious the societal evaluation of drug-related activity, the more severe the penalty prescribed and the support that it receives.

A societal evaluation of the harm inflicted by drug-related activity constitutes the third measure of seriousness. Some drug-related activities seem largely personal in their consequences, and the persons involved are frequently willing and anxious participants. Much of the debate that goes into an evaluation of harmfulness is concerned with the degree of victimization and the personal or social harm that a set of activities may involve.

It is suggested that the above three measures of seriousness are closely correlated. Thus more serious drug-related activities will involve (a) broad agreement about the wrongfulness of such activities, (b) a severe societal

Figure 11.1
The Varieties of Deviance

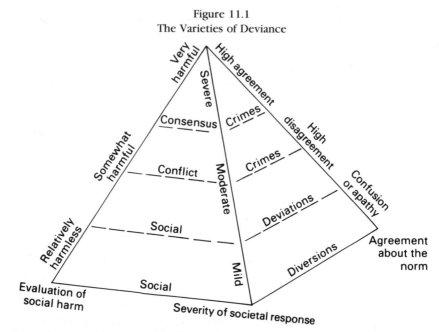

From John Hagan, *The Disreputable Pleasures* (Toronto: McGraw-Hill Ryerson, 1977), p. 14.

response, and (c) an evaluation as being very harmful. This situation can be visualized in the form of a pyramid (see Figure 11.1). The drug activities regarded as less serious are located at the base of this pyramid, the activities regarded as more serious at the peak, with each vertical axis representing one of the measures of seriousness. The pyramid shape implies that the most serious forms of drug activity in a society tend also to be less frequent, while less serious forms of drug activity may be considerably more common.

The acts included are separated into two general categories (criminal and non-criminal forms of deviance) and four subdivisions (consensual crimes and conflict crimes; social deviations and social diversions). Two points need to be made here about these divisions and categories. First, the division between these categories is purposefully imprecise, as represented by the broken lines in Figure 11.1. These divisions are permeable and subject to change, a point pursued below. Second, the designation of seriousness is empirically, rather than ethically, determined. Thus the object is not to create a universal scale of immorality, but rather to describe and explain the institutionalization and the violations of the norms of an existing social order. The results of such an exercise could be relevant to, but not sufficient for, the formation of moral judgments.

We turn now to a discussion of the categories in Figure 11.1. The forms of deviance regarded as most serious are defined by law as criminal, and are subdivided in the figure into *consensus* and *conflict* crimes. Legal philosophers at one time characterized consensus crimes as *mala in se*—"wrong in themselves." However, modern sociologists emphasize that few, if any, human behaviours are universal or timeless in their criminal character. Nonetheless, there have been times when some drugs were the subject of considerable consensus in their designation as criminal. Of such an earlier era in North America, Bonnie and Whitebread write that, "Increasingly associated with the slothful and immoral 'criminal classes' who degraded the nation's cities, narcotics use threatened to retard national growth with pauperism, moral degeneracy, and crime. A consensus had emerged: the nonmedical use of 'narcotics' was a cancer which had to be removed entirely from the social organism" (4, p. 17). There is evidence that the media played a significant role in building this consensus.

Research on the role of the media in the passing of drug laws and in the building of public consensus about these laws has focused chiefly on the U.S. Federal Bureau of Narcotics and its director, H. J. Anslinger. In various ways and with different emphases Becker (3), Lindesmith (14), Reasons (17), Musto (16), and Bonnie and Whitebread (4) all argue that the media moulded American public opinion about narcotics. Yet Galliher and Walker (11) have demonstrated that most of this media attention followed rather than preceded the passing of marijuana legislation. Still, Bonnie and Whitebread (4) are able to show that Anslinger and the Bureau used newspaper articles and editorials to their advantage in Congressional testimony. But we are not yet able to separate the influence of these media materials from that of factors which provoked their publication. What we know is that media attention correlates with the development and maintenance of public consensus about narcotics. Whether the influence is causal remains open to debate. How durable such consensus is, is also subject to debate.

Controversy currently surrounds the presence of many offences, including those involving narcotic drug use, in our criminal law. These crimes are sometimes referred to as *mala prohibita*, or "wrong by prohibition": for example, as proscribed and punished by statute. As one moves away from the statutes it becomes increasingly clear that public opinion is divided about the appropriate status of such offences. More importantly, class interests and racial bias are frequently cited as the roots of such conflict. We call these the conflict crimes.

There is little doubt that historically narcotics legislation was partly an expression of hostile attitudes toward minority groups associated with drug use. Musto observes that "in the nineteenth century addicts were identified with foreign groups and internal minorities who were already feared and the objects of elaborate and massive social and legal constraints" (16, p. 5). For example, the Chinese were associated with opium (7, 8, 16, 17), southern blacks with cocaine (16), and Mexicans with marijuana (4). Before becoming prime minister of Canada, Mackenzie King acquired much of his early reputation by lobbying for passage of Canada's first narcotics legislation in terms of the "threat" posed by Asian immigration. It made little difference in Canada or the United States that the "evidence clearly indicates that the upper and middle classes predominated among narcotic addicts in the period up to 1914" (9, p. 9). Only after the passage of the Harrison Act in the United States in 1914 did this picture seem to change, so that "by 1920, medical journals could speak of the 'overwhelming majority [of drug addicts]' from the 'unrespectable parts' of society" (9, p. 11). By persuading the public to associate narcotics use with disenfranchised minorities, lobbyists laid a foundation for legislative prohibition. The campaign was also advanced by the facts that, regardless of the class distribution of users, use was still a minority phenomenon (Musto cites estimates that 2 to 4 percent of the population was addicted in 1895), and that opiate use was known to produce pronounced physiological consequences within a fairly short period of time (i.e., the withdrawal effects were pronounced). However, we remain uncertain of the relative significance of these factors. Nor is it clear why the association between the Chinese and opium has been a much more transient stereotype than that between other minority groups and drugs. Finally, we do not know why a change in the class composition of marijuana users seems to be producing a relaxation of the marijuana prohibition (11), whereas a similar change in the composition of cocaine consumers has yet to have much effect. What we do know is that there is recurrent controversy about these drugs.

We turn now to the non-criminal forms of drug use, included in the conceptualization as the *social deviations* and *diversions* (Figure 11.1). The theme that unites the social deviations is that while they are not considered criminal, they are nonetheless disreputable. Of particular interest is the stigma that may follow from contact with non-criminal agencies of social control, such as alcohol treatment centres. Such agencies characteristically attempt to minimize their stigmatizing effects. However, their efforts vary in effectiveness, and sociologists are particularly interested in determining how access to personal resources affects this problem.

It is interesting to speculate about why alcohol abuse is today a non-criminal social deviation. Put differently, why did the prohibition of narcotics outlast the prohibition of alcohol? Bonnie and Whitebread (4) offer an interesting answer. As noted above, narcotics legislation had its roots in a moral consensus directed against isolated minority groups, particularly Chinese, blacks, and Mexican Americans. In contrast, the prohibition of alcohol never attained consensual support, largely because it was aimed at urban immigrants who, though poor, had access to power through urban machines and union politics. This argument is worth considering in more detail.

Alcohol prohibition in America followed from the well-organized lobbying activities of the Women's Christian Temperance Union and the Anti-Saloon League. Of course, this lobby did not work in a vacuum. Gusfield (13) explains that temperance legislation grew out of a variety of status-group conflicts between American-born and immigrant Americans, Protestants and non-Protestants, and rural and urban residents. This contrasts sharply with the finding of Bonnie and Whitebread that "narcotics policy . . . was supported by a latent popular consensus" (4, p. 13). Undoubtedly, a major portion of the difference derived from the widespread use of alcohol in America, which had developed over a considerable period of time. Therefore, although a concerted attempt was made to link alcohol with poverty, crime and insanity, organized resistance was possible.

Thus Timberlake (23) observes that although wage earners were unable to thwart the enactment of temperance legislation, they were strong enough to ensure its ultimate failure. "Many working men . . . opposed prohibition because it smacked of paternalism and class exploitation. To them it was a hypocritical and insulting attempt to control their personal habits in order to exact greater profits for their employers, who themselves had no intention of giving up liquor" (23, p. 93). As much as 81 percent of the American Federation of Labor (A.F. of L.) was wet (23), which is consistent with the claim of Samuel Gompers that the great majority of the membership opposed Prohibition.

Economic considerations may also have affected the rise and fall of Prohibition, but they were often in conflict. Some businessmen believed that temperance would increase industrial efficiency, redistribute money spent on liquor, decrease welfare expenditure on crime and poverty, and reduce threats of disorder during strikes. Others argued that Prohibition would diminish public revenues, increase unemployment in liquor and related industries, shift political power balances, and increase government regulation of business. World War I seemed to strengthen the former set of arguments, but this balance was to shift again during the depths of the Depression (23). The contradictory nature of these arguments does much to support Gusfield's assertion that symbolic considerations were more important than instrumental motives. The passing of the Prohibition Act appears to be explained by the perception that urban, immigrant alcohol use threatened the status of native, middle-class Protestants rather than the economic foundations of capitalism.

Some final mention should be made of the social diversions. Drug-related diversions are frequent and faddish, ranging from harmless acts (e.g., smoking lettuce leaves) to dangerous feats. The motivations for such diversions are probably universal: the search for personal stimulation and social reinforcement. However, our thresholds of boredom and isolation vary. These human traits assure that diversionary uses of drugs will persist and, of course, diversify.

CONCLUSIONS

This chapter has reviewed various definitions of deviance, all of which attempt to deal with the variations in cultural definitions of deviant behaviour, including drug use. It has been suggested that for the purposes of studying drug use, deviance is best conceptualized on a continuous scale that ranges from the most to the least serious acts in any given society. According to this definition, the more serious acts of deviance are likely to involve high agreement about what the norm is, a widespread perception of harmfulness, and a severe societal response. The continuum envisioned includes two general categories of deviance (criminal and non-criminal forms of deviance) and four subdivisions (consensual crimes and conflict crimes; social deviations and social diversions). A major sociological concern is to determine why at any given time in a society some acts are considered criminal while others are not. As we have seen, while marijuana use at one time approached the level of a consensus crime, today it is in some places a conflict crime, and in others a form of social deviation, if not simply a form of social diversion. Some of the most important drug research has sought to account for this variation. The conceptual framework presented here was intended to provide a definition of deviance that emphasizes the importance of such research, while at the same time allowing for the study of drug-using behaviour itself.

REFERENCES

1. Armstrong, J. D., and Turner, R. E. Special problem offenders: Alcoholics, drug abusers, sex offenders. In: McGrath, W. T. (ed.). *Crime and Its Treatment in Canada*. Toronto: Macmillan, 1976.
2. Becker, H. S. Becoming a marihuana user. *American Journal of Sociology, 59*:235–42 (1953).
3. Becker, H. S. *Outsiders: Studies in the Sociology of Deviance*. Glencoe, New York: Free Press, 1963.
4. Bonnie, R., and Whitebread, C. *The Marihuana Conviction*. Charlottesville, Va.: University of Virginia Press, 1974.
5. Bordua, D. Recent trends: Deviant behavior and social control. *The Annals of the American Academy of Political and Social Science, 369* (January): 149–63 (1967).
6. Clinard, M., and Yeager, P. *Corporate Crime*. New York: Free Press, 1980.
7. Cook, S. Canadian narcotics legislation, 1908–23: A conflict model interpretation. *Canadian Review of Sociology and Anthropology, 6*:36–46 (1969).
8. Cook, S. *Variations in Response to Illegal Drug Use*. Toronto: Alcoholism and Drug Addiction Research Foundation, 1970.
9. Duster, T. *The Legislation of Morality: Law, Drugs and Moral Judgment*. New York: Free Press, 1970.
10. Erickson, P. G. *Cannabis Criminals: The Social Effects of Punishment on Drug Users*. Toronto: ARF Books, 1980.

11. Galliher, J., and Walker, A. The puzzle of the origins of the Marihuana Act of 1937. *Social Problems, 24*:367–76 (1977).
12. Galliher, J., McCartney, J., and Baum, B. Nebraska's marijuana law: A case of unexpected legislative innovation. *Law & Society Review, 8*:441–55 (1974).
13. Gusfield, J. *Symbolic Crusade.* Urbana: University of Illinois Press, 1963.
14. Lindesmith, A. R. *Opiate Addiction.* Bloomington, Ind.: Principia Press, 1947.
15. Lindesmith, A. R. *The Addict and the Law.* Bloomington, Indiana: University of Indiana Press, 1965. New York: Vintage Press, 1967.
16. Musto, D. F. *The American Disease: Origins of Narcotic Control.* New Haven: Yale University Press, 1973.
17. Reasons, C. The politics of drugs: An inquiry in the sociology of social problems. *Sociological Quarterly, 15*:381–404 (1974).
18. Sellin, T. *Culture Conflict and Crime.* New York: Social Science Research Council, 1938.
19. Sutherland, E. *White Collar Crime.* New York: Dryden, 1949.
20. Szasz, T. The ethics of addiction. *American Journal of Psychiatry, 128*:541–46 (1971).
21. Tappan, P. Who is the criminal? *American Sociological Review, 12*:96–102 (1947).
22. Taylor, I., Walton, P., and Young, J. *The New Criminology.* London: Routledge and Kegan Paul, 1973.
23. Timberlake, J. H. *Prohibition and the Progressive Movement: 1900–1920.* Cambridge, Mass.: Harvard University Press, 1963.
24. Wilkins, Leslie. *Social Deviance.* London: Tavistock, 1964.

12

Towards Rational
Drug Scheduling*

MELVYN GREEN

INTRODUCTION

Much of human behaviour entails personal and social risks. The law, as a potent instrument of public policy, is often utilized to manage or mitigate the consequences of hazardous conduct. Psychoactive drug use, like many other social activities, involves serious risks. However, in the case of drugs (apart from alcohol and tobacco), the legal response is presently one of prohibition (enforced through severe sanctions) rather than a legal framework that addresses those specific risks that are appropriate objects of social concern. This absolutist posture itself entails identifiable risks or costs that, in some cases, may be greater or more deleterious than those represented by the prohibited activity. Given our culture's high valuation of self-determination, it would appear obvious that some distinction should be drawn between those drug-related risks that are socially acceptable and those that are not. Any legal classification of drug-using behaviour and related penal sanctions should, then, mirror this hierarchy of risks so as to maximize personal freedom while simultaneously minimizing the chances of truly hazardous consequences. Unfortunately, in Canada, such is not the case.

Although no legal system is characterized by perfect symmetry or consistency, many do attempt to classify and ascribe sanctions for prohibited acts, services, or substances according to some rational basis such as magnitude of threat to public or individual welfare. In the world of drugs, however, there appears to be little rhyme or reason (apart from historical accident or wholesale moral opprobrium) for much of the Canadian (or international) scheduling. The *Narcotic Control Act*, for example, includes opiates, cocaine, cannabis, and PCP—four drug-types which are so dissimilar in their pharmacological effects, chemical constitution, and potential for harm as to defy any attempt at a naturalistic rationalization of the identical penalties statutorily provided for their possession, importation, and sale.

The law, however, serves symbolic as well as penal functions, and the *Narcotic Control Act* thus serves to publicly communicate the monolithic gravity that Canadian legislators ascribe to the use of any of these substances.

---

*A revised version of a report prepared for the Research Bureau, Non-Medical Use of Drugs Directorate, Health and Welfare Canada.

The deterrent value of such a symbolic classification may have been partly responsible for inhibiting the diffusion of cannabis, cocaine, and opiate use[1] until the early 1960s.[2] Since then, however, the explosive increase in the use of drugs (particularly cannabis)—combined with the wealth of scientific research and personal experience that such use has generated—has fractured conventional stereotypes, impaired public confidence in the law generally, compromised drug education programmes, and converted much of drug law enforcement into an expensive, ineffectual, and often tragic perversion of the criminal justice enterprise.

Recognizing the problems inherent in a classificatory system that fails to appreciate the differences between, for example, heroin and marijuana, some jurisdictions have chosen to respond in a piecemeal, crisis-management fashion, by reclassifying cannabis "downwards" or, as has occurred in approximately a dozen American states, by decriminalizing the possession of cannabis. While this legislative approach reflects a persuasive analysis of the costs of cannabis law enforcement versus the potential liabilities associated with cannabis use, it still fails to provide a generalizable procedure for the legal classification of drugs used for non-medical purposes.

One generalizable—and rational—procedure that has often been suggested by those mandated to recommend policy alternatives in the field of drug control is a legal classification and penalty structure adjusted to the "potential for harm" (or "hazard potential" or, simply, "risk") associated with any given drug category. The notion that different drugs entail different risks is intrinsic to every nation's drug scheduling. While this underlying conception is explicit in some classifications (the United States *Controlled Substances Act* and the international *Convention on Psychotropic Substances*, for example) and implicit in others (such as the British *Misuse of Drugs Act*), no drug scheduling is, in fact, founded on a scientific, empirical appraisal of the relative hazards actually associated with various psychoactive substances.[3] However, this very orientation to the problem of legal classification of drugs has been expressly recommended in the reports of, for example, the Le Dain Commission, the (U.S.) Shafer Commission, the New Zealand Board of Health, the Netherlands Narcotics Working Party, and the Interdepartmental Committee on the Le Dain Commission.

Despite such international unanimity, the Canadian reality is that nothing has changed. Indeed Bill S–19, the only legislative initiative in twenty years, constituted an act of patent political expediency rather than the holistic legislative development that would seem to follow naturally from the considered recommendations of federally-funded commissions and committees.

Apart from political considerations, the major problems in developing a risk-based classification are methodological. What factors does one include in a risk appraisal? How does one measure these factors? Where is the epidemiological data base? What values should be assigned to which risks? How does one "trade off" therapeutic benefits or the "costs" of enforcement? What role do moral or ideological considerations play? While some of these questions defy contemporary knowledge and others involve politico-policy issues, the task of constructing an *approximate* risk-index—or at least itemizing those factors necessary for any cost-benefit accounting—appears feasible and has, in fact, been essayed by several research and policy analysts.

A META-RATIONALIZATION

While the idea of legally classifying drugs according to their empirically determined potential for harm is not novel, there appear to be few publicly available discussions of the macro-theoretical bases of such a reformulation. One means of providing this analytical foundation involves a "mapping" of the drug control model that presently obtains in Canada and most other Western nations.[4] This model may be conceived of as the "Prohibition Model" and, in the abstract, it can be seen as applying to all prohibited goods and services. Essentially, it assumes the structure graphically delineated in Figure 12.1.

Simply put, the Prohibition Model proscribes the possession and/or use of certain goods and services. This prohibition is legitimated by what anthro-

Figure 12.1
Prohibition Model

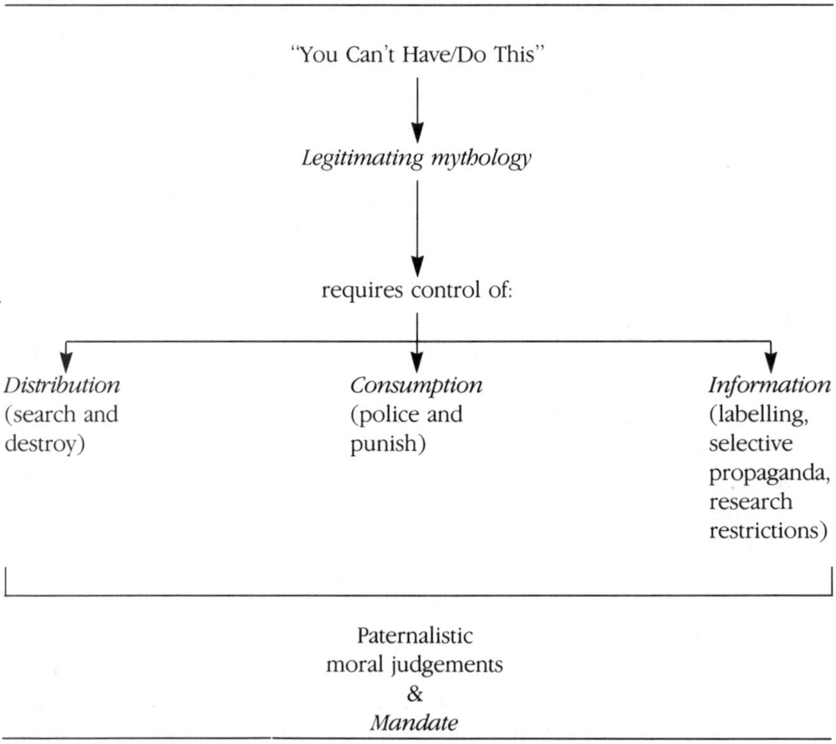

"You Can't Have/Do This"

Legitimating mythology

requires control of:

Distribution	*Consumption*	*Information*
(search and destroy)	(police and punish)	(labelling, selective propaganda, research restrictions)

Paternalistic
moral judgements
&
Mandate

pologists would call a mythology (selective facts and fiction) and perpetuated by legal and extra-legal control of distribution, consumption, and information. All of this leads to paternalistic (though often unconscious) moral judgments on the part of the authorities and a mandate that reinforces the initial proposition and mythology in a circulating feedback fashion. The Prohibition Model rests on the assumption that the state has a paternalistic obligation to protect its citizens from harm—and on the complementary assumption that a state's citizens trust its authorities to do what is best for them.

The problem with the Prohibition Model is that it is in radical conflict with human needs, interest and experience, individual differences, and the notion of self-determination. As a result of this reality conflict (captured in the statement: "I like it and I want it. So I'll do it anyway!"), we have witnessed the development of legitimating counter-mythologies (based on fact, fiction, and personal experience), alienated and criminalized lifestyles, and the evolution of an enormous illicit market system (because of the tremendous potential for tax-free profits in prohibited goods and services) that provides delivery without even the most rudimentary of quality controls.

The unfortunate reality of the Prohibition Model is not only that it is self-perpetuating, but that it routinely responds to such conflicts or challenges by simply "tightening up" its control apparatuses, without ever seriously questioning the assumptions on which it rests. The inevitable result is that the problems it is attempting to resolve are further aggravated in a continually spiraling fashion. Indeed, apart from institutional root-influences (such as economic and educational impoverishment, discrimination, and unemployment), the Prohibition Model is primarily responsible for the "abusive" use of drugs and the major adverse correlates of such "abuse." Some historical examples include the following: Operation Intercept temporarily reduced the importation of marijuana into the United States while increasing the use of substitute drugs such as barbiturates and heroin; tightened controls on marijuana importation inspired cannabis distributors to shift to hashish and then, with further restraints, to "hash oil"; increased penalization of heroin users has isolated this population from non-criminal prophylactic and treatment intervention and forced its members to develop evasive skills and criminal careers; the profits derived from the illicit marketplace (a direct product of the Prohibition Model) have enabled professional criminal organizations to subsidize non-drug criminal activities, to expand into non-criminal commercial ventures, and to corrupt police and elected officials. The Prohibition Model has not only failed to control the destructive use of drugs but, ironically, has unwittingly nurtured such developments.

Given such counterproductivity, it appears reasonable to attempt to construct alternative models of drug control that are more rationalistic and realistic, and less destructive of the individual and society. The alternative most extremely opposed to the Prohibition Model may be referred to as a libertarian, individualistic, or self-determination approach to drug use. The basic philosophical tenets of this model are best expressed by one of its leading proponents, the American psychiatrist Thomas Szasz (28, pp. 65, 68):

> In a free society, it is none of the government's business what idea a man puts into his mind; likewise, it should be none of its business what drug he puts into his body....
>
> We should regard freedom of self-medication just as we regard freedom of speech and religion, as a fundamental right....
>
> Like most rights, the right of self-medication should apply only to adults; and it should not be an unqualified right.... The limiting condition ... should be the inflicting of actual harm on others....
>
> In principle, the right to self-medication must entail unqualified responsibility for the effects of one's drug intoxicated behavior on others.

While this ethic has much to recommend it, it represents such a politically implausible leap from conventional drug attitudes and policies that a more detailed analysis is hardly justified. It is possible, however, to develop a less grandiose alternative control model that acknowledges both human nature and contemporary political realities, that rationally relates "controls" to the hazardous potential of various drugs, that discourages persons from using the more harmful substances while encouraging their use of safer drugs or, ideally, non-drug alternatives, and that is a politically feasible alternative to the Prohibition Model.

This "Vice," "Regulatory," or "Semi-Prohibition" Model begins with two assumptions: (1) that people want and need drugs, and (2) that psychoactive substances can be rationally located along a potential-for-harm continuum. Essentially, then, this approach recodifies the Prohibition Model on the basis of the scientifically known hazards associated with various drugs, rather than their moral properties. The paternalism, here, is rationalized, and the interests of self-determination and public security are more reasonably balanced. Structurally, the Semi-Prohibition Model can be mapped in the manner outlined in Figure 12.2.

The operational key to this model is the development of a practicable and valid means of discriminating between drugs according to their potential for harm. It is to this problem that the remainder of this paper is addressed.

PRIOR APPROACHES

Prior approaches to the problem of comparative risk appraisal can be divided into two major categories: first, those involving attempts to generate criteria of evaluation and, on occasion, *qualitative* assessments based on these criteria; and second, those studies that have actually developed some methodology for the *quantitative* determination of relative benefit or harm.

Figure 12.2
Semi-Prohibition Model

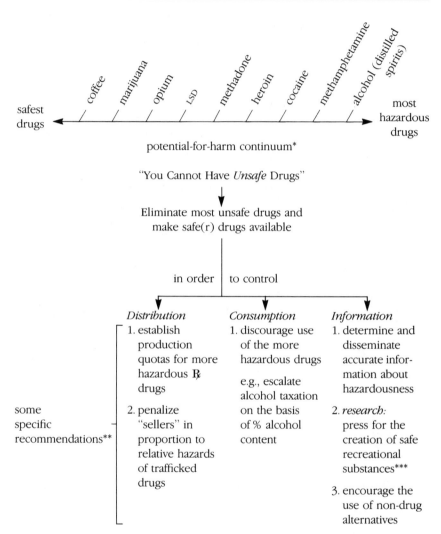

potential-for-harm continuum*

"You Cannot Have *Unsafe* Drugs"

↓

Eliminate most unsafe drugs and
make safe(r) drugs available

in order │ to control

Distribution	*Consumption*	*Information*
1. establish production quotas for more hazardous ℞ drugs	1. discourage use of the more hazardous drugs e.g., escalate alcohol taxation on the basis of % alcohol content	1. determine and disseminate accurate information about hazardousness
some specific recommendations** — 2. penalize "sellers" in proportion to relative hazards of trafficked drugs		2. *research:* press for the creation of safe recreational substances*** 3. encourage the use of non-drug alternatives

*Technical matters related to the development and structure of this particular potential-for-harm continuum are discussed in Irwin (12). The ordering of drugs along the continuum is Irwin's, and does not necessarily reflect the views of the author.

**A more comprehensive listing of specific recommendations appears in Irwin (12).

***The development of "safe" psychotropic substances allows the opportunity to "outcompete" alcohol (an extremely hazardous drug) and provides a mercenary "trade-off" incentive for both the pharmaceutical industry (facing some ℞ quotas) and the government (facing a reduction in alcohol taxation revenue).

Qualitative Appraisals

Qualitative appraisals of the risks associated with drug use are most characteristic of the reports of governmental departments, commissions, and task forces. Typically, a public—but semi-independent—agency will be charged with the duty of studying the "drug problem" and devising related policy and legislative recommendations. Not bearing any electoral responsibility for their proposals, these agencies have generally sought a rational (as opposed to tradition-bound or politically expedient) basis for distinguishing between drugs. The discriminating criteria (the specifics of which vary from report to report) have almost universally crystallized about the notion of "risk" or "potential for harm," and some investigating bodies have gone so far as to rank or index drugs accordingly. With few exceptions, however, these agencies have eschewed assigning quantitative values to any risk-indicators, preferring simply to catalogue these indices and, on occasion, make "expert" guesstimates as to their relative rank.

One illustration of this approach is provided by the Le Dain Commission, which subscribed to the proposition that the "*extent to which any particular drug use is to be deemed undesirable will depend upon its relative potential for harm, both personal and social*" (3, para. 390. See also 4, p. 265). In its *Cannabis* report, for example, the Commission majority applied this harmfulness test to cannabis in reaching its legislative recommendations. Having identified four major areas of "social concern" associated with the use of cannabis (adolescent maturation, driving, mental health, and the development of multiple-drug use), the Commission majority then proceeded to assess the "costs" of the criminal law prohibition of cannabis. The Commissioners' concerns included the effect of criminal convictions on the lives of young persons, encouraging the development of an illicit market, obliging people to engage in criminal involvements and exposing them to other more dangerous drugs, undermining the credibility of drug education programmes, creating disrespect for law and law enforcement generally, and diverting law enforcement resources from more important tasks. Impressionistically balancing these "costs" against the "benefits" flowing from retention of the simple possession offence for cannabis (i.e., some unspecified measure of protection from the "social concerns" earlier identified), the majority recommended the elimination of the offence and a relaxation of the definitions, penalties, and burden of proof in regard to trafficking, importation, and cultivation.[5]

One of the most thorough discussions of the importance of risk calculation in the establishment of realistic social objectives and the development of related governmental policy is that contained in the final report of the presidentially-appointed U.S. Shafer Commission, *Drug Use in America: Problems in Perspective* (24). Challenging the conventional wisdom that the goal of American drug policy should be the elimination of non-medical drug use, the Shafer Commission advised that

> policy makers must . . . develop rational distinctions between that which should be disapproved and that which should be tolerated, or even approved. Within the area of disapproval, policy makers should not consider all disapproved drug use to be of equal importance; priorities must be assigned on the basis of actual and potential social consequences and not just on the basis of numbers of users. (24, p. 21)

For the Shafer Commission, some drugs—at some patterns or levels of use (particularly that of dependence)—have certain effects on individual behaviour which generate social risks and, consequently, arouse public concern and justify public intervention. The broad areas of social risk identified as sources of legitimate concern were public safety (particularly in regard to criminal activity and driving), public health and welfare (with reference, primarily, to the utilization of health and social service resources), and, of lesser importance, the normative social order.

The Commission's primary policy goal was the minimization of "irresponsible drug-using behavior" (24, p. 205) by minimizing the incidence and consequences of intensified and compulsive use. The attainment of this objective involves what the Shafer Commission refers to as "the availability decision": determination of those conditions under which specific psychoactive substances should—or should not—be available. Hence, the calculus of availability (which is eventually translated into scheduling or classification decisions) depends, primarily, on a drug's "relative social cost": "what it is worth to society to prevent or reduce its use by means of control" (p. 210). This calculus is nowhere quantified in the Shafer Commission's report. However, its emphasis on social—as opposed to individual—risks in determining the relative cost of drug use and its concentration on the consequences of drug-induced behaviour rather than drugs themselves both constitute major contributions to a rational scaling approach.[6]

For the Dutch government, the use of the criminal law to restrict drug use is only indicated in those cases where the drug-related risks are considered "unacceptable" and alternative measures (such as education, treatment, and rehabilitation) do not produce satisfactory results. Governmental response to drug use must, therefore, involve consideration of its positive and negative characteristics, an understanding of the situations in which drugs are used, and a sense of proportion. In a Dutch policy committee's words:

> In any assessment of the risks, the pros and cons of use must be weighed against one another and the nature and scope of the measures taken must be in line with the magnitude of the risks involved and the conditions in which the drugs are used. (20, p. 2)

The 1972 Netherlands Narcotics Working Party defined "risk" as "the chance of one or more harmful effects" (19, p. 3). Among those risk-areas identified by the Narcotics Working Party are drug dependence, physical harm, "psychic" harm, and social or "community" harm. Upon assessing these risks for each drug it is then possible to construct a "danger scale" that allows empirically-based distinctions to be drawn between drugs of differing hazard-potential. Control measures, then, should be directed towards the mitigation of identifiable hazards and should be proportionate to a drug's risk as determined by *all* risk criteria.

Towards Quantification

While "official" studies of non-medical drug use consistently contain pronouncements about the need to determine the relative "cost," "risk," or "harm" of drugs in order to formulate appropriate control responses, there have been few attempts to actually measure the degree of risk associated with various psychotropes. Part of the problem, of course, is that some risk factors (those relating to the "normative order," for example) defy quantification while, for others, there are simply no data to permit comparative analysis. However, there are resourceful means of ascribing risk-values to drugs—even though conventional indexing or scaling methodologies may not be utilizable.

Probably the most sophisticated attempt at constructing an index of drug hazardousness is that developed by Dr. Samuel Irwin who, as a professor of pharmacology at the University of Oregon Medical School, devised a workable methodology by which to compare drugs *quantitatively* according to a series of risk-related factors (12).

Beginning with the reasonable assumption that "some drugs are more dangerous than others" (pp. 15–16), Irwin proposes a list of those "items considered of most concern for rating the hazard potential of drugs" (p. 16). These risk criteria are psychomotor impairment (which is subdivided into memory, judgment, vigilance, perception, coordination, and psychotic reaction), death (from overdosage, drug withdrawal, and tissue damage), health (including irreversible tissue damage and physical, mental, and social deterioration), "special hazards" (of which ease of overdosage, intravenous mode of administration, and combination effects are considered), and drug dependence (psychological and physical). Both individual and social hazards—at chronic abuse levels—were surveyed by asking a panel of seven doctors and scientists to assign scores to each item relative to fixed maximal scores for sudden acute death (individual risk) and violence (social risk) for each of twenty-one CNS drugs, as well as food.

Irwin's approach represents a significant advance over those that have simply proposed risk criteria or made qualitative assessments of drug hazardousness. The assigning of base-line scores to the most serious hazards and subsequent relative weighting of all other risk factors is a further demonstration of the methodological sophistication of this analysis. However, despite its value as a model for quantitative risk analysis, this index suffers from serious—but corrigible—defects related to such problems as scorer's bias, the failure to translate risk scores into their demographic correlates, and Irwin's concentration on "maximum chronic abuse" and his consequent failure to assign hazard potential scores to the much more common moderate levels and patterns of use.

Whatever problems may attend Irwin's methodology, it does have the unique distinction of being the first quantitative approach to hazard potential determination to directly influence the legislative process. Oregon's 1977 *Uniform Controlled Substances Act* incorporated many of Dr. Irwin's proposals.

CONFRONTING THE ISSUES

The preceding survey reveals both the feasibility of and problems associated with the construction of a drug risk scale or index. While refined completion of such an index is beyond the scope of this paper, some of the major hurdles can be identified, some solutions recommended, and the conceptual outlines of a more rational classificatory system finally delineated.

This process can be most systematically furthered through, first, a discussion of those assumptions that are critical to the formulation of any harm-based legal classification of drugs; second, a review—and, where possible, resolution—of those issues which constitute points of contention in the development of such a re-classification; and, finally, a consideration of some available scaling methodologies and how they can best be utilized to differentiate between drugs along a risk or harm continuum. This proposed survey of assumptions, issues, and methods is not exhaustively developed in this paper. However, it is hoped that the concerns discussed serve to focus attention on many of those matters that must be confronted in the construction of one rational alternative to what is, at present, an inconsistent and counter-productive drug control policy.

Common Assumptions

Any exercise in policy deliberation involves a series of assumptions. Often these operating premises are thought so common-sensical or seemingly natural that they are functionally invisible. As a result, complex programmes or legislation are often built on ideological foundations which, it may later be discovered, are not so shared as to provide consensual support. In order to forestall—or, at least, reduce the likelihood of—such an eventuality, it is probably worthwhile to attempt to articulate what is often taken for granted; in other words, to discuss those assumptions or premises which most likely underlie the development of any rationally-based scale or index of relative drug risk. Should these assumptions prove contentious, then it is clear that risk-index development is premature and that more attention should be paid to achieving a consensual definition of the problem.

One immediate assumption, shared by the authors of those inquiries and reports previously reviewed, is that there is a more rational basis for classifying or scheduling drugs than that presently extant, and that that more rational basis is risk or potential for harm—"the criterion which, in an ideal world, would be the determining factor as to the acceptable measure of legal control" (30, p. 119; cf. 3, p. 197). Rational, then, refers to a scientific or empirically-founded method for distinguishing between drugs according to their potential (and/or actual) harmfulness. Rational also implies the most efficient, cost-effective, and equitable means of achieving certain specified goals.

Another assumption, one that introduced this paper, is that all drug use, like many other varieties of human behaviour, is potentially risky or hazardous. Whether or not such risk is sufficient to justify any formal social control (and, if so, what type and degree of social control) depends on the precise *nature* of the identifiable hazards, the *chance* of impairment, injury, or loss, the severity or *gravity* of such loss, and the most likely *victims* (i.e., risk-assumers or others; the young and vulnerable or mature adults) of any adverse consequences.

There are at least two related premises. First, that "risk" can be most simply defined (subject to some refinement below) as in the report of the Dutch Narcotics Working Party (19): "the chance of one or more harmful effects" (19, p. 3). Second, that the risk associated with the use of drugs varies according to the pharmacological properties of each drug and the personal and social concomitants of its use. Thus, it is possible to determine the *relative* safety/hazardousness of various drugs along some hierarchy or continuum of risk. It is this possibility that permits the development of a "risk-index"— and related legislative reforms. As the Shafer Commission has noted, "the fact that all drug taking poses some risk does not mean that all use poses the same risks, and official policy should not pretend that it does" (24, p. 205).

Another important assumption is that we are certain enough of the physiological and psychological effects of drugs to begin developing a pharmacology-based index of potential harm. Of course what we do know of pharmacological effects is not necessarily definitive or exhaustive (and, additionally, is only one of several considerations relevant to any relative risk evaluation), but there is sufficient agreement to warrant comparative analysis of effects data. Even where pharmacological certitude has not been established, we can, as Teff notes, "at least introduce policies and legislation more consonant with what we *do* know, or have good grounds for believing" (30, p. 145).

Several characteristics of social control are also germane to this discussion of underlying premises. First, it must be recalled that social control is a continuous variable (2). This means not only that the sanctions for criminally

defined activities range, in Canada, from discharges and fines to life imprisonment but also that *types* of social control can be similarly located along a
severity-of-sanctions continuum. From this perspective the criminal law must
be seen as the most extreme type of social control (since its application may
result in deprivation of liberty, segregation from family and friends, public
degradation, considerable restrictions of future opportunities and mobility,
monetary loss, etc.), while other institutional measures (such as psychiatric
treatment, social work, and education) are usually more moderate (and less
financially and socially expensive) mechanisms for maintaining normative
order. Thus, the criminal sanction, in the words of the respected legal theorist
Herbert Packer, is the "ultimate threat . . . that should be reserved for what
really matters" (22, p. 250). Of course, what really matters is dependent on
our moral and social priorities and resources; but any deliberation on the
most appropriate and effective means of achieving particular socio-behavioural
ends must consider alternative types of social control to that represented by
the criminal law. As the Le Dain Commission has observed,

> an analysis of policy options requires consideration not merely of the balance
> of benefits and costs—the net yield, so to speak—but also [of] the ability of
> alternative policies to produce a desired result. (5, p. 21)

Apart from the provisions for alcohol and tobacco, alternatives to the
criminal sanction have not, as yet, been seriously entertained in the development of Canadian drug control policy. And, within the criminal law, the
distinctions drawn between prohibited drugs (as reflected in the schedules
to the *Narcotic Control Act* and *Food and Drugs Act*) fail to mirror the relative
harm scientifically or even popularly identified with each drug. Packer has
written of the importance of proportionality in distinguishing between offences,
but his words are just as applicable to the legal classification of drugs.

> The very idea of discriminating among offences necessarily implies proportion.
> . . . The starting point . . . is the idea that some offences are to be taken more
> seriously than others and that the severity of the available punishment should
> be proportioned to the seriousness with which the offence is viewed. (22, p. 143)

While these differences are not reflected in current scheduling, a rational,
harm-based method for distinguishing between drugs does exist from which
proportional control measures can be devised. The question of whether or
not these control measures *should* include criminal sanctions—and, if so,
for what conduct—is best left for the following survey of unsettled issues.
However, the principle of proportionality—both in type and degree of
sanction—remains a critical component in the design of any rational drug
control policy.

One further assumption deserves mention: that the criminalization of
particular forms of behaviour (including drug use) often results in social and
individual consequences of far greater public concern than those evils which

originally inspired the criminal sanctions. (See, generally, 1, 16, 17, 23, 29, and, as regards drug use specifically, 7, 15, 18.) Therefore, a critical appraisal of drug control measures necessarily involves an assessment of both the success attributable to those measures and those undesired concomitants that accompany any control programme. The comparison of these two assessments constitutes the cost-benefit analysis critical to the development of any drug control policy that does not create more disastrous problems than it sets out to solve.

The most reasonable and balanced Canadian discussion of the issues relevant to any cost-benefit analysis of drug risks is probably that of the Kalants in *Drugs, Society and Personal Choice* (14). Perhaps their most important conclusion is that "*the degree of risk is related not so much to the specific drug which is used as to the amount, frequency and manner of its use*" (p. 85). For example, the hazardousness associated with the occasional ingestion of a five-milligram capsule of pharmaceutical amphetamine is of a profoundly different order from that associated with the regular injection of large amounts of "speed"—and yet the identical drug is involved. Thus, in attempting to determine the harm related to the use of a particular drug, it is essential that the risks, individual and social, be seen as a function of dosage, mode of administration, and frequency and regularity of use—as well as any pharmacological properties of the drug itself (19, 24). In fact, in many cases—heroin being the classic example—it is the pattern of use or administration, rather than pharmacological effects, which accounts for most personal sequelae.

The Kalants also draw attention to the importance of epidemiological considerations in evaluating the harm or risk associated with the use of different drugs. It has been argued that the log-normal distribution curve that characterizes alcohol consumption may also describe the consumption of other drugs. If so, to take but one example, the decriminalization of cannabis possession may increase the total number of cannabis users and, concomitantly, the number of heavy users, and, consequently, the likelihood of cannabis-related liabilities. But even this simple social prognosis must be subject to qualifications if, for example, the government acts to limit the commercial distribution of cannabis to that of weak potency, or if there is a "natural" distribution of consumption that may already have been approximated in some populations, or if the log-normal hypothesis proves inapplicable to drugs other than alcohol. The point, simply, is that the *social* harm (such as driving accidents, acquisitive crime, and loss of productivity) related to the use of a particular drug is a function of the number of users of that drug and the distribution of their consumption—particularly at heavy levels of use. Thus, epidemiological data that both pertain to contemporary drug use prevalence and are likely to obtain under differing legal circumstances are critical to policy revisions founded on criteria of harmfulness.

An additional concern involves the common, but unfortunate, assumption of certainty. As the Kalants note, the "classification of any drug effect as either 'beneficial' or 'harmful' depends on the scale of values of the person who is making the classification" (14, p. 98). Pharmacological effects that, for example, relate to sexual interest or performance, emotional expression, or work motivation are likely to be interpreted differently by persons assuming different normative stances. It is for this reason that any scaling methodology must, as far as possible, insulate its itemization and scoring procedures from the risk of moral biases. (Some possibilities in this regard are discussed below.) But, despite such precautions, it remains clear that any cost-benefit analysis will ultimately involve consideration of scientific facts, probability estimates, and necessarily subjective—if "expert"—value judgments. Such value judgments are not, of course, antithetical to the rule of law, but it is to be hoped that evaluative standards will be articulated as such and not passed off as the collective wisdom of an unimpeachable scientific community (11, pp. 4, 7).

Issues

Any attempt to develop a rational alternative to our current system of drug classification and control minimally requires agreement as to the conceptual boundaries of the exercise. Less controversial considerations have been discussed as *assumptions* in the preceding section, while some of those concerns that are characterized by more controversy are surveyed here. These more contentious *issues* derive from various sources including differing moral or ideological perspectives, lack of definitional precision, oversimplification, and professional or disciplinary bias. In some cases, an issue can be stripped of its disputatious property by synthesizing varying viewpoints or providing lucid definitions. In other situations a reasoned and reasonable resolution will be proposed. And with some issues, particularly those of a moral-political character, the best that can be attempted is a clear expression of the problem and a survey of the positive and negative consequences of various decision alternatives.

Laws, law enforcement, and criminal dispositions are one set of formalized mechanisms for achieving certain ends in the realm of drug control. Whether or not such measures are effective—or even appropriate—depends to a large degree on the nature of the drug policy goals and objectives they are designed to achieve. Unfortunately, the goals of Canadian drug policy are nowhere publicly articulated and it is only by way of inference—through examination of the relevant legislation, law enforcement policy and activity, governmental expenditures, and international treaty obligations—that one can approach the apparent primary objective of national drug control: the elimination of all non-medical drug use, apart from alcohol and tobacco.

The hypocrisy of such an objective is patent, both in regard to the specious distinction between medical and non-medical drug use and the commercially convenient—but increasingly unconvincing—fiction that alcohol and tobacco are not drugs. More importantly, however, the elimination of drug use is both an unrealistic and an unfeasible goal. As the Le Dain Commission observed: "In the face of... widespread and persistent non-medical use of drugs a social policy of abstinence is not a feasible one. It is unrealistic to expect the majority of people to give up non-medical drug use altogether" (5, p. 19). The pursuit of such a social policy is thus doomed to failure. The abstinence objective is unachievable since it is at odds with contemporary North American social reality, the lessons gleaned from cross-cultural and anthropological research (10) and, perhaps, human nature itself (see 32).

To a large degree goals dictate the means used to achieve them. Extreme goals inspire extreme measures, but success remains distant when a goal is intrinsically unattainable. What is required is a *realistic, achievable* goal that reflects legitimate social concerns. Once such an objective is articulated, an appropriate strategy can be designed and its effectiveness assessed.

The Le Dain Commission states that Canada's drug policy objective

> should be to discourage the non-medical use of drugs as much as possible and to seek a general reduction in such use, but at the same time, to equip those who persist in use with sufficient knowledge to enable them to use drugs as wisely as possible. (5, p. 19)

The discouragement and reduction of the non-medical use of drugs are, of course, much more realistic and feasible goals than those that may be inferred from a survey of Canadian drug control measures. But such an objective, once again, implicates drugs rather than people and, most importantly, fails to directly address that one concern which justifies official intervention: harm—"the most useful criterion for social policy" (4, p. 265).

The elimination (or at least reduction) of drug-related harm—not drug use itself—is characteristic of those objectives enunciated by almost all other governmentally-appointed commissions, committees, and task-forces (11, 20, 24). Their various statements of drug policy objectives share a common under-standing: the use of some drugs, under some conditions of use, involves risks that are sufficiently grave to warrant resort to risk-directed social control measures for the protection of users, other members of the public, or society at large. What is to be deterred, then, is not drug use *per se*, but that *type* of drug use (as defined by drug, manner, level, circumstances, or population of use) that is empirically recognized as entailing an unacceptable chance of individual and/or social harm. This idea has been expressed by the Nether-lands Ministry of Public Health: "Social policy should be directed to the prevention of risks rather than to the prevention of drug use itself" (20, p. 3). At its simplest then, a realistic policy goal is the minimization of drug-related potential for harm.

Several questions—or issues—immediately arise. About which harm risks, or potential liabilities, should we be concerned? At what point do such risks become "unacceptable"? If official social control measures are, in fact, justified, what form should they take? Should such controls be drug-, user-, or situation-directed? And if criminal sanctions are to be adopted, how best are such sanctions to be adjusted to relative risk? While these are difficult and often divisive issues, some tentative resolutions can be assayed.

The risks associated with the use of drugs are almost universally divided into two types: those involving personal or individual harm and those involving social or community harm. (This subdivision is somewhat artificial since, as the Dutch Narcotics Working Party notes, "the interest of the individual and of the community are closely interwoven" [19, p. 3]; but for analytical purposes, the social or community rubric is meant to refer to drug-induced behaviour that threatens or endangers the health or safety of non-consenting persons *other* than the user himself, or that avoidably burdens the community at large.) Acute psychosis, embolisms, lung cancer, hepatitis, and malnutrition are illustrative of direct and indirect *individual* risks related to the use of certain drugs. Adverse *social* consequences (i.e., costs of drug use that are borne by individual others or the community as a whole) include such items as acquisitive and violent crime, driving accidents, loss of productivity, and the utilization of health and welfare resources.

One risk-factor about which there is considerable disagreement is what is sometimes called "dependence liability"—i.e., the notion that the ease with which one can become physically and/or psychologically dependent on a particular drug, or the strength of such dependence, is, *sui generis*, a measure of that drug's potential for harm. While it is true that persons who are dependent on a drug are likely to be involved in frequent, high-dosage levels of use, the dependence itself is immaterial unless there are *other* risks (beyond dependence liability) associated with the drug which a heavy using pattern is likely to exacerbate (24). The point, as the Kalants make clear, is that it "is not the presence of dependence itself which is the problem; it is the severity of consequences of that dependence which are important" (14, p. 80). These consequences may, of course, have individual *or* social implications, but unless they constitute significant hazards the chance of dependence itself appears irrelevant to any risk calculation.

A second risk area about which there is some controversy relates to the impact of drug use on the dominant social order or traditional value system. The exact dimensions or indices of this concern are rarely developed, but it is reasonable to assume that most Canadians desire social stability and continuity. It is less certain, however, whether the use of drugs represents any material threat to the social order or whether it is even popularly perceived as such. To a considerable degree, this debate may be properly viewed as an anachronism or historical residue of the cultural conflict that characterized much of the drug debate during the late 1960s and early 1970s. In any event, it is clear that the dominant value system will ultimately find expression in decisions regarding the levels at which certain risks become unacceptable and thus subject to social control initiatives.

Another and more problematic issue concerns those hazards that are undesired products of attempts to eliminate non-medical drug use: for example, the dysfunctions of our present control system. Unintended drug complications such as methyl alcohol–induced blindness during Prohibition and those pulmonary and circulatory disorders stemming from the use of unsterilized needles or the injection of insoluble materials are illustrative of individual health hazards generated by a legal framework. As regards social risks, the Shafer Commission notes that "much drug-related crime, particularly that associated with dependence on opiates such as heroin, is a function of prohibitory social policy toward availability rather than of drugs themselves" (24, p. 33). This consideration of dysfunctionality suggests that the prevalence and gravity of certain drug-related hazards (such as overdosage, the communication of immunological deficiencies, acquisitive crime, interpersonal violence, and some psychotic reactions) should properly be conceived of as risks flowing from our present drug control policy rather than the use of drugs *per se*. In any cost-benefit accounting, then, these risks must be seen as "costs" of a prohibitory strategy.

It must be recognized that many important potential hazards exist independently of any particular social policy, although they are exacerbated by present controls. Mode of administration is one such hazard variable. Intravenous injection, for example, entails certain risks irrespective of those further complications introduced by a prohibitory control policy. Similarly, while ease of overdosage and adverse drug combination effects may be aggravated by a policy which effectively inhibits quality and potency controls, these pharmacological risks would persist, at some level, under any control system. Thus, the extent to which current drug policies contribute to drug-related hazards must be carefully assessed in any cost-benefit accounting and in the formulation of new risk minimization policies.

Assuming that the drug-associated risks justifying official concern and intervention can be identified, the question remains as to what form of intervention or social control is most appropriate. The traditional Canadian response has been to normatively discount the drug-using conduct that is perceived to generate risk, and to impose criminal sanctions on those who persist in using the prohibited substance. Sociologist Austin Turk concluded his detailed survey of the application of legal sanctions (what he calls "legalization") with the following comment and advice:

> Before they assume the costs and risks of legalization, sensible authorities will require evidence that the problem is objective as well as perceptual, that it is necessary for them to deal with the problem, that legalization is the only or best control strategy, and that a particular degree of legalization is called for, knowing that legal sanctioning used blindly may well be the greatest of all threats to legal authority. (31, p. 75)

Turk's message is that legal sanctioning, and criminal law sanctioning particularly, should be reserved for as narrow and clearly justifiable a range of conduct as possible.[7] The question thus becomes: does the use of any drug engender such potential for harm that its criminalization is warranted? This, in turn, depends on the nature of the harm, the availability and effectiveness of other modes of social intervention or amelioration, and the proper scope of the criminal sanction.[8] Even where substantial social damage can be demonstrated, non–criminal justice mechanisms for effectively reducing the chance of harm are available, such as informational, educational, therapeutic, and social welfare programmes, and analytical and research facilities. In addition, as the Le Dain Commission has indicated,

> the fact that a drug has a significant potential for harm and does not lend itself to controlled use does not automatically lead to a policy of prohibition. We may decide for a number of reasons, as we do with other risks, to rely on people's judgment, wisdom, self-interest or learning capacity to avoid harm. (5, p. 16)

In light of these considerations, the application of scaling methodology to the potential for harm associated with various drugs suggests three broad control strategies. First, based on a standardized combination of risk factors (individual and social), each drug could be rated as to its potential for harm and subsequently located in a penalty-appropriate schedule among those appended to new or revised drug control legislation. This, essentially, is the approach adopted in Oregon's *Uniform Controlled Substances Act*. It is also akin to the "Semi-Prohibition" model discussed above.

A second approach—in line with the Shafer Commission's recommendations and the more general jurisprudential guidelines of the federally-appointed Ouimet Committee—is that only those drugs that generate substantial potential for *social* harm be subject to criminalization, the appropriate sanctions being a function of the indexing determination of relative social harm. Drug use identified as entailing substantial *individual* risks could then be dealt with through other, non-coercive modes of social control or intervention. Priorities in this regard could be partly determined by the relative values assessed for each drug at each risk factor.

A third approach allows that it is the *social consequences* of the manner and occasions in which drugs are used—and not the drugs themselves—that engender our real concerns. Consequently, the criminal sanction should only be employed to provide societal protection in those situations where, first, drug use entails a substantial risk of harm to others and, second, where the conduct that constitutes that harm is not already legally circumscribed. In such situations (driving soon after ingesting a psychomotor-impairing substance, for example), recklessness—the wanton disregard for the lives or safety of others—would likely serve as a more acceptable basis for criminal liability than those rationales offered for our present prohibitory system. An index of drug-related potential for harm could thus serve to identify empirically those drug-induced social risks requiring situational controls, while substantial individual risks could be reduced through modalities apart from the criminal law. It is this approach that probably best harmonizes our societal interest in public security with our equally important interest in self-determination.

Methods

While the development of a polished scaling methodology may be premature, some of the major considerations affecting this process can be presently surveyed. For analytical, comparative, and legislative purposes, it appears prudent to construct two separate potential-for-harm scales, one for personal/individual risks and one for social/community risks. While these two dimensions may be representable in a single composite score (see 12), separate risk-accountings will provide a substantive foundation for consideration of a variety of harm-based drug-control strategies. The construction of separate scales will also allow for complementary panels of "experts," one of which could, for example, be composed of doctors, psychologists, and pharmacologists while the second could chiefly contain sociologists, criminologists, and epidemiologists. In this manner, the problem of having professional authorities assess risk factors outside of their area of expertise or competence could be somewhat alleviated.

Should those responsible for developing drug policy wish to consider a cost-benefit accounting in addition to a comparative risk appraisal, then a third scale is required. While several cost-benefit "trade-offs" are possible (for example, individual and/or social costs associated with use of a drug vs. the drug's therapeutic or extra-therapeutic benefits), the one most relevant to the issue of whether or not persons should be subject to criminalization for the possession of a particular psychoactive substance involves a comparison of drug-induced harm and the harm that flows directly from the criminalization process itself.[9] While some aspects of this harm (such as creating generalized disrespect for the law and reduced police morale) may be difficult to evaluate, other costs of a prohibitory drug control policy (such as law enforcement and correctional services expenditures, productivity losses, and some proportion of welfare, medical, and property-crime costs) are readily quantifiable.

Quantification—if only the determination of relative rank—is a prerequisite to any useful scaling activity. Since there are few drug-related risks for which reliable data exist, the scoring of drugs for any inventory of risks must involve a process of informed extrapolation. The better informed the scorers, the greater the likelihood of reliable risk estimates. But since the drug phenomenon is of multi-disciplinary interest and since few authorities are critically familiar with the universe of drug literature, any panel of experts selected to assess the relative hazard potential of drugs must be representative of the full range of scientific drug expertise. To further reduce the possibility of rating bias, the scoring should be weighted according to their expertise. Any risk factor for which there is considerable intra-panel scoring variance should probably be reported as a liability range rather than reduced to a single mean.

While ordered scaling methodology may prove sufficient to identify risk priorities, the development of a rational, graduated scheduling framework founded on relative potential for harm probably depends on stronger techniques that permit measurement of inter-factor distance or the quantification of "relative" harm. Irwin (12) provides an example of this methodology and, while certain problems remain, the interval scaling of drug-related risks (through the assigning of a base-value to the gravest risk and the subsequent scoring of all other factors relative to this baseline) does appear technically feasible. For purposes of mundane grounding and perspective, it is important that any such scoring procedure include socially-accepted psychoactive substances such as alcohol, nicotine, and caffeine, and non-drug ingestives such as food.

One risk-related consideration which has often been neglected involves the epidemiological consequences of various hazards.[10] While some mortality data exist, there is little systematic information about the association of drug use and morbidity. In order to reliably estimate the incidence of harm likely to result from the use of any drug, it is necessary to have considerable data as to the extent of such use, the social characteristics of the using population (age and gender, for example), patterns and occasions of use, and modes of administration. The information would permit an epidemiological analysis of the distribution of drug-related risks under *present* legal circumstances. Epidemiological projections for *hypothesized* legal circumstances could then be compared to determine the likely results of legislative change and consequent social costs differentials. Irrespective of the exact methodology employed, the concern to obtain realistic social costs estimates dictates that present risks be assessed for "actual" use levels rather than those associated with maximum hazardousness.

CONCLUSION

Exercises such as those proposed in this paper would perform two important policy-related functions. First, they would allow for an informed discussion of realistic policy alternatives. And second, once policy objectives have been established, they would provide for the formulation of means of achieving those objectives—means that minimize demonstrable individual and social risks at acceptable levels of individual and social costs. Any effective drug control regime must have the capacity to address significant changes in such things as using patterns and drug availability (for example, the appearance of new "designer drugs"). This responsiveness in turn depends on a continual monitoring of the underlying phenomenon. Such monitoring is also critical to any assessment of the effectiveness of the policy itself. The starting point, however, remains the development of an empirically sound, risk-based index of potential for harm. Given the consequences of our present drug control policy, this initial undertaking would appear to be a very modest investment indeed in rational social planning and constructive legislative change.

NOTES

1. PCP was not added to the *Narcotic Control Act* until 1973.
2. For a discussion of the historical and current deterrent effect, or lack thereof, of Canadian cannabis legislation, see (8, 9).
3. One exception to this generalization appears to be the 1977 Oregon *Uniform Controlled Substances Act*.
4. This analysis is primarily derived from task-directed discussions among invited participants to a free-ranging "think tank"–type conference sponsored by Hoffman-LaRoche (U.S.A.) in 1972.
5. The minority "Conclusions and Recommendations" also employed cost-benefit analyses founded on the notion of potential for harm.
6. Further American expressions of the principle that drugs should be classified on the basis of their potential for harm and attempts to develop a rough methodology for such classification are found in various mid-seventies "White House" and "Federal Strategy" reports. (See 6, 25, 26, 27).
7. This attitude is echoed in the writings of major legal scholars who decry the "crisis of overcriminalization" (13) and the "trivialization" of the criminal sanction (22). See also the comment of the Ouimet Committee (21, pp. 12–13) that the designation of "certain conduct as criminal in an attempt to control anti-social behaviour should be a last step . . . to be employed only as an unavoidable necessity."
8. As to this last consideration, see the criteria set out in the Ouimet Committee's *Report* (21, p. 12).
9. The notion of therapeutic benefits as a counterweight to drug-related risks is more germane to the question of pharmaceutical licensing and regulation than to consideration of the proper scope of the criminal law sanction.
10. See the Introduction to Section 4, following, for an explanation of the epidemiological concepts discussed here.

REFERENCES

1. Becker, H. S. *Outsiders: Studies in the Sociology of Deviance*. Glencoe, New York: Free Press, 1963.
2. Black, D. *The Behavior of Law*. New York: Academic Press, 1976.

3. Canada. Commission of Inquiry into the Non-Medical Use of Drugs. *Interim Report*. Ottawa: Queen's Printer, 1970.
4. Canada. Commission of Inquiry into the Non-Medical Use of Drugs. *Cannabis*. Ottawa: Information Canada, 1972.
5. Canada. Commission of Inquiry into the Non-Medical Use of Drugs. *Final Report*. Ottawa: Information Canada, 1973.
6. Domestic Council Drug Abuse Task Force. *White Paper on Drug Abuse*. Washington, D.C.: U.S. Government Printing Office, 1975.
7. Duster, T. *The Legislation of Morality: Law, Drugs and Moral Judgment*. New York: Free Press, 1970.
8. Erickson, P. G. Deterrence and deviance: The example of cannabis prohibition. *Journal of Criminal Law and Criminology, 67*:222–32 (1976).
9. Erickson, P. G. *Cannabis Criminals: The Social Effects of Punishment of Drug Users*. Toronto: ARF Books, 1980.
10. Furst, P. T. *Hallucinogens and Culture*. San Francisco: Chandler & Sharpe, 1976.
11. Interdepartmental Committee on the Le Dain Commission. *Report*. Unpublished manuscript, Non-Medical Use of Drugs Directorate, Ottawa, 1975.
12. Irwin, S. A rational approach to drug abuse prevention. *Contemporary Drug Problems, 2*:3–46 (1973).
13. Kadish, S. H. The crisis of overcriminalization. *Annals of the American Academy of Political and Social Science, 374*:157–63 (1967).
14. Kalant, H., and Kalant, O. J. *Drugs, Society and Personal Choice*. Toronto: PaperJacks, 1971.
15. Kaplan, J. *Marijuana: The New Prohibition*. New York: World Publishing, 1970.
16. Lemert, E. M. *Social Pathology*. New York: McGraw-Hill, 1951.
17. Lemert, E. M. *Human Deviance, Social Problems, and Social Control*. Englewood Cliffs, N.J.: Prentice-Hall, 1967.
18. Lindesmith, A.R. *The Addict and the Law*. Bloomington, Indiana: University of Indiana Press, 1965. New York: Random House, 1965.
19. Netherlands. Narcotics Working Party. *Background and Risks of Drug Use*. The Hague: G.P.O., 1972.
20. Netherlands. Ministry of Public Health and the Environment: Interdepartmental Steering Group on Drug Misuse Policy. Non-medical drug use in the Netherlands: A summary of policy trends. Unpublished manuscript, Leideschendam, April 20, 1976.
21. Ouimet, R. *Report of the Canadian Committee on Corrections—Toward Unity: Criminal Justice and Corrections*. Ottawa: Queen's Printer, 1969.
22. Packer, H. L. *The Limits of the Criminal Sanction*. Stanford: Stanford University Press, 1968.
23. Schur, E. M. *Crimes Without Victims, Deviant Behavior and Public Policy:*

Abortion, Homosexuality, Drug Addiction. Englewood Cliffs, N.J.: Prentice-Hall, 1965.

24. Shafer, R. P. *Drug Use in America: Problems in Perspective.* Second report of the National Commission on Marijuana and Drug Abuse. New York: MSS Information Corporation, 1973.

25. Special Action Office for Drug Abuse Prevention. Social cost of drug abuse. Unpublished manuscript, Special Action Office for Drug Abuse Prevention, Washington, D.C., December 1974.

26. Strategy Council on Drug Abuse. *Federal Strategy for Drug Abuse and Drug Traffic Prevention 1975.* Washington, D.C.: U.S. Government Printing Office, 1975.

27. Strategy Council on Drug Abuse. *Federal Strategy for Drug Abuse and Drug Traffic Prevention 1976.* Washington, D.C.: U.S. Government Printing Office, November 1976.

28. Szasz, T. A different dose for different folks. *Skeptic,* 7:47–49 and 63–70 (1977).

29. Tannebaum, F. *Crime and the Community.* New York: Ginn & Co., 1938.

30. Teff, H. *Drugs, Society and The Law.* Lexington, Mass.: Lexington Books, 1975.

31. Turk, A. T. *Legal Sanctioning and Social Control.* Rockville, Md.: National Institute of Mental Health, 1972.

32. Weil, A. *The Natural Mind.* Boston: Houghton Mifflin, 1972.

SECTION 4

THE EPIDEMIOLOGY OF ILLICIT DRUGS IN CANADA: METHODS AND TRENDS

Epidemiology is the study of the source, distribution, and control of diseases or other health-related problems in society. Its root, "epidemic," derives from the word "epidemy." According to the Oxford English Dictionary (OED), this word comes from Old French, where it was used to refer to the plague. The OED cites the following from 1472: "Many of the sowders that went to hym into Bretayne been dede off the fflyxe, and other ipedemye."

Modern dictionaries define an *epidemic* as a communicable disease that spreads rapidly through a population during a given period of time, produced by some special factor that is not generally present in that population. In popular usage, the word sometimes refers to diseases that are not communicable, as in epidemics of back pain or heart disease; it has also been used for social phenomena that are not diseases, such as crime or illicit drug use. As we shall see, epidemiological methods have been used successfully in the study of such problems, even though they are not "epidemics" in the strictest sense of the word.

The common confusion between "epidemic" and "endemic" requires comment. The latter is an adjective describing any phenomenon that is constantly present to one degree or another in a society. For instance, death on the highways is endemic in our society. It would only become an *epi*demic phenomenon if new circumstances noticeably increased the rate of motoring mortality at a certain time.

To take an example from the world of illicit drug use, in the late 1960s and early 1970s the use of marijuana and hashish was introduced into certain strata of Canadian society where they had been unknown previously, and cannabis smoking spread rapidly in these groups. While use rates were rising steeply, we were witnessing an epidemic, at least on a metaphorical level. By the late 1970s, however, cannabis use rates began to level off. This is not to say that there were no new recruits to cannabis smoking, but rather that new users more or less numerically replaced those who stopped use. We can say, therefore, that we have moved out of a cannabis epidemic into an endemic phase.

Nevertheless, this does not mean that epidemiologists must bow out of the picture at this stage. Because cannabis use is a matter of some concern in our society, we still want to monitor the situation, to predict which direction use rates are likely to take in the future, and to continue to seek explanations for the distribution of cannabis use throughout the population. This kind of information is as important to an analysis of an endemic situation as to an epidemic one.

As a scientific discipline, epidemiology resides in faculties of medicine. Its practitioners, however, have much in common with sociologists who study the distribution of social problems in society and analyze the reasons for the distributions observed. The epidemiological enterprise is no longer confined to the study of diseases per se, but takes as its subject matter any social phenomenon in the population that results in morbidity (illness or injury) or mortality (death), whether epidemic or endemic.

Epidemiologists classify their subject matter in terms of three concepts: agent, host, and environment. The agent of a communicable disease would be a bacteria or a virus. As not everyone falls victim to any given disease, epidemiology must consider host factors that produce vulnerability in people—age or unhealthy lifestyles, for example. Environmental factors may also account for the distribution of diseases in the population—open sewers or industrial pollution would be two examples.

The concepts parallel to host, agent, and environment in drug use epidemiology are drug, set, and setting. The set factors reside within individuals who may be more or less vulnerable to drug use because of their social characteristics, their beliefs and attitudes, or certain psychological strengths or weaknesses. The setting is the environment in which drug-using decisions take place, and research into the setting may take into account societal values, influences of peers, and so on. Clearly, the analogy between communicable diseases and drug use is not perfect, but the epidemiological orientation is a useful one, from the viewpoints of both theory and methodology.

There are two basic aspects to epidemiological research:
1. The study of the distribution of a disease or other phenomenon in the population
2. An examination of the factors that account for its distribution.
These two activities are complementary in so far as the first can give insight into the second. For example, when acquired immune deficiency syndrome (AIDS) first came to be identified in North America, it was immediately apparent that homosexual men were greatly over-represented among its victims. Further observation of the spread of the disease indicated other high-risk groups, including intravenous drug users and hemophiliacs. This led to speculation about the transmission of the disease through sexual activity, needle sharing, and contaminated blood transfusions. Thus, research on the distribution of the disease provided clues to its nature. Furthermore, the research indicated ways in which the spread of the disease could be curbed.

Descriptive epidemiology is basically head counting: finding out how many individuals exhibit a phenomenon and describing their socio-demographic characteristics. At this preliminary stage, other information that might contribute to understanding the nature of the problem is collected. Epidemiologists may be interested in locating the entity in time (do psychiatric admissions increase in certain months of the year?), or geographically (does Parkinson's disease or heroin use occur more frequently in rural or urban areas?). They may also be required to estimate populations at risk, that is, to define the size and characteristics of the groups in society who are vulnerable to a given disease or who are likely to engage in the behaviour of interest. Armed with information on the size of the target population and their social characteristics, planners are better prepared to make policy decisions, to launch educational or preventive campaigns, and to predict potential demands on the health-care system.

Epidemiological methods include population surveys, criminal statistics, hospital or other institutional records, or appeals to attending physicians to report to a central registry any new cases they encounter. Each of these sources can include biases, and so one of the jobs of the epidemiologist is to explore ways of uncovering cases that have escaped identification, or to estimate the size of hidden populations.

There are three key concepts in descriptive epidemiology, and we will define them here with reference to illicit drug use:
1. *Prevalence* refers to the numbers of users of the various drugs at any given time, or use rates in the population as a whole.
2. *Incidence* indicates the rate at which illicit drug use is increasing, or the numbers entering the drug-using population.
3. *Attrition* tells about those who are leaving the population of drug users because of cessation of consumption, migration, or death.

Descriptive epidemiological research should generate hypotheses that can then be tested by analytical epidemiological methods. At this stage, studies are designed with the intention of discovering either the causes of the phenomenon under investigation or the factors that encourage its transmission through social groups. Because correlation does not necessarily imply causation, such studies are rarely definitive. Nevertheless, they are often a rich source of clues which may then be followed up in other research settings. Prevention initiatives need not necessarily await definitive proof of a causal connection: for example, once an inflated risk of lung cancer is repeatedly and consistently identified in tobacco smokers compared to non-smokers, it is in the interest of the public to be warned of this association, whether or not the precise causal mechanism has been established beyond doubt.

In this section, Judith Blackwell traces the ebb and flow of drug problems in Canada since our first drug legislation was enacted. Here we will see that, although drug consumption is endemic in our society, successive epidemics have changed the size and nature of the illicit-drug-using population, and have influenced the relative popularity of certain drugs in Canada.

Irving Rootman describes the various epidemiological methods in use and discusses their strengths and weaknesses. He shows why epidemiologists can estimate the numbers and characteristics of users of certain drugs with some confidence, but have much more difficulty with other drugs whose users are less available to the methodologies they employ.

Kenneth Stoddart's work provides an example of one of these methodological problems. His research shows how the official crime statistics on heroin users, one of the sources experts use to estimate their numbers and their social characteristics, are influenced by day-to-day interactions between users and police in the real world of the Vancouver heroin subculture.

13

Epidemiologic Methods and Indicators

IRVING ROOTMAN

INTRODUCTION

Methods used in the epidemiology of illicit drugs are the same as those used in the epidemiologic study of any other social or biological phenomenon. On the other hand, epidemiologists engaged in research on illicit drugs face unique problems in the application of these methods. This is mainly because the topic of study is by *definition* illegal, and people engaging in the behaviour therefore have a vested interest in keeping it hidden from authorities who may have the power to punish them for it. In addition, because of the nature of the trade in illicit drugs or the circumstances of their use, users may not always be aware of what drugs they are using or have used in the past. Thus, epidemiologic research on illicit drugs is particularly challenging and requires flexible and innovative use of the methods of epidemiology. This chapter will describe these methods and suggest how they might be adapted to the study of illicit drug use. In doing so, it will refer particularly to the Canadian context, although the approaches discussed are applicable in other countries as well, especially developed ones.

METHODS OF EPIDEMIOLOGIC RESEARCH

In general, there are six main approaches that may be applied to the epidemiologic study of illicit drugs. These are (1) analysis of existing data, (2) key informant studies, (3) observational studies, (4) population surveys, (5) recording and reporting systems, and (6) special studies. Each of these approaches has been used to some degree in Canada. They are described in turn along with Canadian examples of their use and discussion of their strengths and weaknesses.

Analysis of Existing Data

Canada has a variety of routinely collected data that bear on illicit drug use and that can be and have been used in its epidemiologic study. These include criminal offence data, involving charges and convictions under the drug laws as well as other laws violated by drug users; reports of thefts of controlled drugs; drug seizures; police exhibits identified as illicit drugs by drug analysis laboratories; admissions to penitentiaries and correctional institutions for drug-related offences; statistics on consumption of products secondarily related to drug use or drug-induced states; reports of drug involvement by poison control centres; hospital statistics on drug-related cases; reports of patients treated with methadone; statistics on conditions associated with various drugs or drug usage lifestyles; and drug-related deaths.

Each of these data sources has particular strengths and weaknesses from the point of view of the epidemiologic study of illicit drugs.

For example, drug-related criminal offences are useful as a reflection of some of the societal consequences of illicit drug use. They are, however, only a rough indicator of the use of certain kinds of drugs (e.g., opiates, amphetamines)—those that are likely to lead to fund-raising criminality or acting out. An unknown number of users may not resort to crime and an unknown number of such offences are not reported to the police, so arrest and conviction statistics do not give a complete picture. Furthermore, changes observed from one year to the next may reflect variations in law enforcement activity.

Similarly, statistics based on drug analyses are useful in that they give a rough indication of the sorts of drugs that are on the market, what the probable source of each is (e.g., hashish from different countries differs in colour and composition), and what drugs are being marketed in the guise of other drugs. However, they, as well as a number of other police-derived statistics, are subject to much variance because of differences in police efficiency and direction of focus from place to place and time to time. In addition, they give very little, if any, information about the patterns of illicit drug use or the characteristics of the drug users.

Poison control statistics give a useful indication of some medical consequences of illicit drug use and the characteristics of the people who experience these consequences. On the other hand many, if not the majority, of people who use illicit drugs do not experience toxic reactions; those who suffer such reactions may not tell the precise truth about the illegal drugs of which they were victims; the toxic content of drugs may vary depending on place and time, and the preciseness with which poison control statistics are kept depends on the motivation and vigilance of medical staff. Other treatment data such as hospital statistics also reflect the activities of program staff, but nevertheless provide some indication of the medical consequences of drug use, the characteristics of those who are misusing them, and the circumstances in which this happens.

As a final example, statistics on the consumption of products secondarily related to drug use or drug-induced states—such as underground publications on drug lore, tiny spoons for ladling out cocaine or crystal methamphetamine, hypodermic syringes, or empty gelatin capsules—can be helpful in indicating shifts in patterns of drug use in a locality. Bias is present, however, in that the public also uses these products in varying degrees for purposes other than illicit drug-taking and, even among drug users, consumption can take a "one-shot" rather than continuous form.

In general, the main strengths of the various data sources are that they reflect reasonably well one or more specific dimensions of illicit drug use and that they are relatively inexpensive and easily accessible. Their main weakness is that they each contain biases which result from the process by which the information comes to the attention of, and is recorded by, authorities—a point elaborated by Stoddart in Chapter 15 of this book and discussed elsewhere (47). In using these sources of data, therefore, it is extremely important to analyze and take into account these biases when interpreting the information. It is also important to use multiple sources of information wherever possible, as each sheds a different light on the phenomena of interest, thereby providing a more complete picture.

A Canadian example of using multiple sources to try to paint a complete picture is a Federal-Provincial Task Force on Heroin Epidemiology, established in 1977 to examine the extent of heroin use in British Columbia and to make recommendations regarding the future collection of epidemiologic data on heroin use in that province (26).

The Task Force examined all available indicators of heroin use in British Columbia and found that almost all of them showed increases until 1972 or 1973, followed by consistent, steady declines. Treatment data, law enforcement data, and data from miscellaneous sources all showed the same trends, suggesting that heroin use in British Columbia had been stable or even declining in the three or four years preceding the establishment of the Task Force. On the other hand, interviews with treatment and enforcement personnel suggested that heroin use had increased, but that the number of users becoming dependent on heroin had stabilized or decreased. In any case, the government of British Columbia decided to proceed with the "heroin treatment plan" which is discussed by Boyd, Millard, and Webster in Chapter 24 of this book.

Partly inspired by the work of the Task Force, the Non-Medical Use of Drugs Directorate of Health and Welfare Canada decided to produce a publication entitled *Canadian Drug Indicators* which collated existing statistics on alcohol, tobacco, and other drugs in Canada for convenient use by people in the drug field (11). This volume was updated in 1980 by the Health Promotion Directorate and subsequently discontinued, partly because the Addiction Research Foundation began to produce a volume of similar statistics as a supplement to their annual report (1). Subsequent reports increased the amount of statistical information on drugs (2). The Foundation continues to produce this volume regularly and it is widely used by people in the field as a convenient source of available statistics on illicit and licit drugs.

Thus, in spite of the limitations of existing data on illicit drugs, there continues to be a demand for their analysis and reporting in Canada. It is therefore not surprising that a recent Federal-Provincial Working Group on Drug Monitoring recommended that a national drug monitoring network, relying at least in part on the analysis and interpretation of existing statistics, be established in Canada (50). This group also prepared an inventory of available drug data sources, which includes an assessment of the serviceability of the data. It is available through the Health Promotion Directorate of Health and Welfare Canada.

Key Informant Studies

In addition to the analysis of existing data, the Working Group recommended the establishment of a community correspondents group, which is a network of observers of the local drug scene coming together from time to time to share their knowledge and perceptions. This is a form of *key informant study*, or an approach which entails asking selected individuals to report on the practices of groups familiar to them, rather than on their own practices as in the case of typical surveys (30, p. 19).

In spite of the fact that it is relatively inexpensive and easy to carry out, this approach has not been widely used in the illicit drug field in Canada. One example of a successful attempt to use it, however, was a study carried out in Calgary in 1972 (34). Among other things, the study interviewed personnel from a wide range of agencies (including specialized, crisis, educational, social, residential, and law enforcement) about the number and types of clients with drug-related problems they had seen over a three-month period. This allowed the investigators to estimate the relative demand for services for drug-related problems experienced by the various agencies, as well as the characteristics of the people coming to their attention. However, the reports may have been distorted due to faulty recall, lack of knowledge, exaggeration, or inappropriate choice of informants. Thus, it is very important when using this method to assess the validity of the information obtained by comparison with other methods. In the study under discussion, this was accomplished partly by obtaining data from records in one of the agencies and partly by establishing a system of recording contacts for a certain time period in others. Where comparisons were possible, the key informant reports proved to be generally consistent with the other data sources.

A more systematic attempt to examine the consistency among key informant and self-reported estimates of drug and alcohol use was made in a 1976 study in Southern Ontario (49). In this study, the estimates of teachers and administrators were compared to self-reports of drug use by students. Among other things, the investigators found that the teachers' and administrators' estimates were higher than the students' reports for all drugs with the exception of tobacco. Moreover, many teachers and administrators were unwilling and/or unable to answer questions regarding drug use among students. This led the investigators to conclude that "the use of teacher or administrator surveys to determine the prevalence of drug use among students ... cannot be recommended" (49, p. ii). On the other hand, it is at least conceivable that students under-reported their drug use, meaning that the "correct" estimate may have been somewhere between the student reports and the teacher/administrator estimates. It is also conceivable that other groups and individuals may be better estimators of illicit behaviour than teachers and administrators.

One should not abandon efforts to do key informant studies in the drug field, especially if they are done carefully and as part of a comprehensive attempt to assess illicit drug use. One example of an innovative key informant approach that might be applied to the drug field is a method developed by Liban and Smart to estimate alcohol use (20). Briefly, it consisted of gathering data from groups of informants who met for a few hours to discuss answers to questions about the drinking patterns of the members of a group to which they themselves belonged, namely their occupational group. The investigators found that this approach provided relatively good estimates of alcohol consumption. In fact, they argued that the estimates were more accurate than estimates obtained through population surveys (39). Whether or not this is true, it is clear that this approach has potential for the study of illicit drugs, and it would be desirable to try it. No doubt there are other innovative key informant methods, such as the one developed by Murphy for studying alcoholism (22), which could also be applied in the drug field, bearing in mind the limitations that have been discussed.

Observational Studies

Observational studies have the following distinguishing characteristics: the observer is the primary instrument of measurement; the observations tend to occur in settings that are natural to those who are being observed; the observers try to describe what appears to be happening in objective terms; usually they also attempt to understand the situations from the point of view of the participants; and those observed are often unaware that the information conveyed is considered to be important (30, p. 21). One of the key advantages of this approach over the others discussed in this chapter is that it allows the researcher to broaden his or her focus to include phenomena outside of the original conceptual framework. In other words, it has the potential to bring to light a broader range of information about behaviours and their context than other approaches can. It is also relatively inexpensive and can be done quickly.

On the other hand, this approach is limited in that its value depends on the skills and perceptiveness of the observers. In addition, the representativeness of the information obtained is difficult to determine. Perhaps for these reasons, it is not an approach which has been widely used by traditional epidemiologists.

Nevertheless, there are some examples of the use of observational methods in the study of illicit drug use in Canada. An early one comes from the Le Dain Commission, which conducted regular participant-observation studies in several "street-level" drug-using communities (4). These studies allowed the commissioners to develop an in-depth understanding of the nature of the drug scene in Canada which they would not have been able to obtain from any other source.

Since the Le Dain Commission completed its work, there have been a few other examples of the use of observational approaches to study illicit drug use in Canada. Perhaps most notable are studies by Stoddart in Vancouver (45) and by Delgaty in Niagara Falls (7). Both of these investigators used their considerable skills as observers to carry out systematic studies of illicit drug use in their respective communities of concern.

Stoddart's study, described in detail in Chapter 15, is particularly interesting because he assessed the potential influence of police and participant activities on official statistics. His work leads to the conclusion that we must interpret such statistics with caution, as they do in fact systematically reflect the activities of police and participants. Observational studies can help us to understand the nature of these influences on the statistics and are therefore a very useful tool in the armamentarium of the epidemiologist.

Unfortunately, as noted, they are a tool not used as much as they might be, perhaps because there is an element of danger in studying illegal behaviours this way. However, if an investigator takes the kinds of precautions exercised by both Stoddart and Delgaty, it is possible to carry out such studies successfully with minimal personal danger. In the future, this approach may be used more in Canada to study illicit drug use, perhaps adopting some of the techniques that have been developed in the alcohol field (37).

Population Surveys

Population surveys involve the systematic collection of information from a representative sample of people drawn from the population of concern. This might be the population as a whole, or certain segments of it such as high school or college students, residents of correctional institutions, or members of the armed forces (30).

In contrast to observational studies, population surveys have frequently been employed in Canada in the epidemiologic study of illicit drug use. This is not surprising, since such surveys are extremely useful in producing credible estimates of drug use in the population of concern. They are also valuable in providing information on the social and other characteristics of *representative* samples of the drug-using population—information that is difficult if not impossible to obtain from other sources. In addition, they are helpful in developing and testing explanations of illicit drug use.

On the other hand, population surveys are expensive to conduct and demand a considerable amount of technical expertise to do properly, although there are ways to reduce cost and requirements for this expertise. When applied to the study of illegal phenomena, they can also produce underestimates, because respondents are inclined to give socially desirable answers and surveys tend to miss those who are more likely to use illegal drugs (e.g., school dropouts or heavy users who are not often at home when interviewers call). Population surveys may also be limited in the sense that the opinions people express in such surveys are not necessarily good predictors of their actual behaviours in real situations. Nevertheless, as mentioned, such surveys have been used frequently and to good advantage in Canada in the study of illicit drug use.

An early example is a series of three surveys carried out by the Le Dain Commission (4). Specifically, the Commission conducted national surveys of the adult population, of school children, and of college students in order to obtain information on drug use unavailable from any other source. Although these surveys were relatively costly, they provided the Commission with a wealth of information which was well used in preparing its various reports.

Since then there have been a number of other Canadian population surveys of drug use. Regional surveys of school-aged populations have been especially popular. At least five continuing series of surveys in school populations have been carried out in Canada since the 1970s. Perhaps the best known of these is the Ontario school survey by the Addiction Research Foundation (43), but continuing surveys of in-school populations have also been conducted in Prince Edward Island (16), Halifax (21), Montreal (8), and Vancouver (13). A national survey of school children, although it did not focus entirely on drug use, contained a number of questions to assess the extent of both illicit and licit drug use among a nationally representative sample of students in grades 7 and 10 (17). In addition, Health and Welfare Canada commissioned surveys of school-aged children to assess, among other things, the use of marijuana in a nationally representative sample (9). A major methodological difference between this survey and others is that the Health and Welfare surveys were conducted at home rather than in school. Perhaps as a result, the estimates of marijuana use are somewhat lower than is the case with the school surveys (32). Nevertheless, the trends indicated in the two types of surveys are the same, as are the characteristics of users, suggesting that the two approaches are complementary.

Since the Le Dain Commission produced its report, there have also been some surveys of adult populations which provide information on illicit drug use, although fewer than there have been for school-aged populations. The Canadian Gallup poll carried out one such adult survey on behalf of Health and Welfare Canada in 1978. As part of an omnibus survey (i.e., a survey which obtains information on a variety of topics), this one asked questions about the use of cannabis of a sample of Canadians over the age of 17. It provided Health and Welfare with useful information about the extent and patterns of cannabis use for a relatively low cost (27). Similar surveys covering a wider range of drugs have been carried out on a provincial basis (42). A recent national survey of adults also used questions derived from the provincial surveys to inquire about use of marijuana and cocaine, as well as certain licit drugs, by a nationally representative sample of over 11,000 Canadian adults (18). In contrast to the provincial surveys, however, this one was conducted by telephone—using random-digit dialling to select the sample. There was some evidence from the pilot study for this research that telephone interviews resulted in slightly higher estimates of drug use than face-to-face interviews (23). Again, however, the patterns of drug use appeared to be similar to patterns observed in other kinds of surveys.

Finally, there are a limited number of examples of Canadian surveys of illicit drug use that have focused on special populations such as members of the armed forces (19). It is apparent that more such studies are needed to complete the picture of illicit drug use in this country. In general, however, population surveys have been used to considerable advantage in Canada in the study of illicit drug use and no doubt will continue to be so used in the future.

Recording and Reporting Systems

Recording systems are established by agencies to gather pertinent information about contacts with clients or about client characteristics. Such systems have been established in Canada by agencies providing services to those who may be experiencing problems related to the use of illicit drugs. These systems enable the agencies to systematically describe their clientele and workload on an ongoing basis. They also enable researchers to study the magnitude of problems associated with the illicit use of drugs, as well as the social and demographic characteristics of people seeking help for such problems. On the other hand, such systems provide no information on the characteristics of people with drug-related problems who do not come to the attention of agencies or those users who have not had problems. This makes extrapolation to the larger population of illicit drug users questionable. In addition, the validity of such systems depends very much on the ability and willingness of agency staff to record information consistently and accurately.

One Canadian system designed to record contacts with people having problems related to the non-medical use of drugs, including illicit ones, was established in the early 1970s at the Calgary Drug Information Crisis Centre. This system, described in detail in a number of published papers (5, 6, 28), was based on a brief, computerized contact card completed by agency staff and volunteers for all contacts. Although the system did not record the names of clients, it did permit identification of the drugs which they might have been using, and therefore provided an extremely useful means of monitoring trends in illicit drug use in the population coming to the attention of the agency. However, as suggested above, it gave no information about people who were not in contact with the centre and, because names were not recorded, it was impossible to know for sure how many contacts a given individual had with the centre over a particular period of time. Nevertheless, the system proved extremely useful to the agency and to researchers studying trends in problems related to the use of illicit drugs. Consequently, it was maintained for as long as the agency existed. Similarly, a number of provincial drug commissions or foundations established recording systems in the mid- to late seventies and have continued to maintain them.

Some of these latter systems are not only *recording* systems but *reporting* systems as well, in that reports are "submitted to a central body using systematic reporting procedures" (29). An example is the British Columbia client/agency monitoring system which was established in the mid-seventies by the Alcohol and Drug Commission of British Columbia (12). In addition to recording contacts with individual agencies, the system required these agencies to submit their reports to a central unit at the Alcohol and Drug Commission. The unit compiled the reports using a computer and produced a variety of conglomerate reports, allowing the Commission to study the nature of clientele coming to the attention of the entire treatment system rather than to single agencies. At the same time, the system permitted reports on single agencies to be prepared. Thus, the reporting system expanded the scope of the individual recording systems by collating the information in a coherent way. In other words, reporting systems have all the advantages of recording systems with an additional advantage of a wider scope. They also have all of the limitations of recording systems, with the possible additional limitations of increased cost and the need for highly trained personnel.

As described in a 1980 World Health Organization publication (29), there are three types of reporting systems: event reporting systems; case reporting systems; and case registers. Examples of each type of system as it pertains to illicit drug use exist in Canada. The British Columbia system is an example of a *case* reporting system which is capable of linking different events involving the same individual in the same reporting institution (12). An example of an *event* reporting system is the Uniform Crime Reporting System which is based on monthly reports submitted to Statistics Canada by police forces using a standard form (29). In addition to other information, these forms request information on violations of federal drug statutes reported or known to the police. This permits calculation of rates of reported drug offences although, as is the case with any event reporting system, it is impossible to eliminate multiple reports on the same individual.

An example of a case register is the Bureau of Dangerous Drugs Drug Users Index. Established in the 1950s, it is based on reports from the police, treatment centres, and pharmacists. Operated as a McBee card system for over 20 years, it converted to a computerized system in 1976. It has provided useful information on the numbers and characteristics of illicit drug users in

Canada coming to the attention of authorities. A number of scientific papers have analyzed and presented this information (24, 31, 33). As is true of any reporting system, however, it provides no information on people not in contact with authorities and relies on the abilities and commitment of those who are doing the recording. In addition, it has a number of other limitations which have been discussed elsewhere (46).

Thus, recording and reporting systems have been widely used in Canada in the study of illicit drug use.

Special Studies

In the context of this chapter, special studies are those which are not covered by the five approaches already discussed but which are designed to answer significant questions about the epidemiology of illicit drugs. The chief advantage of a special study is its flexibility; it can be designed to answer any empirical question thought to be important at the time. Its main limitations are that it is often limited in scope and may be expensive to carry out.

A number of special studies conducted in Canada have added to our knowledge of the epidemiology of illicit drug use. One of the earliest was a study carried out by Stevenson and his colleagues among prisoners in British Columbia (44). This research compared heroin-using prisoners with non-using prisoners on a wide range of variables including their childhood and family life, their sexual history and behaviour, and their cultural attitudes and beliefs. A variety of means including records and questionnaires was used to obtain this information. No differences between the heroin-using and non-using prisoners were identified, but a substudy found that the only variable distinguishing addicts from their non-dependent siblings was a friendly, continuous, and close relationship with opiate-using delinquents (44). Thus, this research helped to identify one of the potentially important factors in determining dependent use of illicit drugs.

Another more recent example of a special study is a longitudinal study carried out by Schlegel and his colleagues at the University of Waterloo (36). Although this research used standard survey methodology, it differed from the population surveys mentioned earlier in that an attempt was made to study the same people at different points in time—an approach that has not often been used in the study of illicit drugs. It began in 1974 with a survey of a random sample of almost 1,800 Ontario students. They completed a questionnaire measuring a wide range of social-psychological variables relevant to marijuana and non-medical drug use. Testing was repeated in 1975, 1976, 1978, and 1980, and is scheduled to be repeated again. This study provides an extraordinarily valuable data base for studying changes in the use of marijuana and other drugs by the same individuals over time. Although a great deal more analysis remains to be done, analyses to date have suggested among other things that "cross-sectional data are inadequate predictors of use in times of changing social milieu" (36, p. 92). Thus again, it appears as if one method needs to be supplemented by another if we are to obtain a complete picture.

A third example of a special study which used an innovative methodology for studying illicit drug use was a one-day census of drug problems in Kingston, Ontario in 1975 (35). Specifically, the city's hospitals, social agencies, courts, and police departments were canvassed on September 17 of that year to determine how many people with drug-related problems were in contact with these agencies on that day and what some of their characteristics were. The investigators used reports from staff and records to obtain the required information. This method proved to be a relatively cost-effective way of assessing the magnitude and nature of drug problems in a small city, although there were certainly deficiencies in some of the information obtained because of a lack of knowledge on the part of staff or inadequacy of records. Among the conclusions reached was the observation that the three major clusters of agencies offering services to people with drug-related problems (i.e., medical, legal, and social) appeared to act independently, rarely providing a multi-faceted approach to drug problems. In spite of the potential of this method, it has not to the knowledge of this author been used subsequently in Canada.

A fourth special study that deserves some mention because of its unique methodology was a special geographic study of methadone users in Toronto (48). In this case, a sample of 103 of the 354 who had entered the Addiction Research Foundation methadone program between 1964 and 1974 and had survived were interviewed in depth. In addition, the study mapped the addresses of the 590 entrants during that period, to examine their geographic concentration at the time of treatment. The residences of those who were interviewed were mapped at the inception of heroin use, at the beginning of treatment, and at the time of interview. Among other things, it allowed the investigator to conclude that over time the heroin users and subsequently methadone users dispersed away from earlier concentration zones. He suggested that this indicated a reorientation into other social groups and a movement away from the drug subculture both as a spatial and social phenomenon—a suggestion which has considerable significance for our understanding of the epidemiology of illicit drug use. Again, however, this author is not aware of any subsequent Canadian studies using this socio-geographic approach.

A final example of a special study was an attempt to project future patterns of cannabis use under different conditions. Specifically, two methods were used in 1978 to predict what cannabis use rates would be in 1984 (3). The first was a modified Delphi Exercise and the second involved projecting for age cohorts using the results of earlier surveys. The two methods appeared to produce similar results and in fact when subsequently checked against 1984 data proved reasonably accurate. Again, the author is not aware of subsequent attempts to use these methods to project future illicit drug use.

There are Canadian examples of other special studies to examine aspects of illicit drug use. It is not necessary to cite all of them to make the point that such studies can be extremely useful in enhancing our knowledge of the epidemiology of illicit drug use. In addition, the examples given here demonstrate that the methods they use need not be constrained by traditional approaches to epidemiology.

DISCUSSION AND CONCLUSION

This chapter has discussed the strengths and limitations of six different approaches to the epidemiologic study of illicit drugs, and has given Canadian examples of the use of each of these approaches. One theme that runs throughout is that each approach can make a unique contribution to our understanding of illicit drug use but that none is sufficient alone. What seems to be needed is rather the use of multiple approaches, to obtain what might be called "triangulation." The use of multiple approaches in the same context, however, appears to be the exception rather than the rule. How then can we encourage such a strategy?

One possibility is to establish what have been called "epidemiologic field units," described in detail elsewhere (25). Briefly, each unit gathers a team of people who focus on the epidemiology of drug use (or on some other topic) within a limited geographic area such as a city. The team uses all of the approaches described in this chapter in complementary ways. An attempt to establish such a unit in Canada was made in the late seventies (10). For a variety of reasons the research was discontinued before the completion of its pilot phase, even though it had produced some useful results. Drawing on this experience, it would be possible to develop successful units elsewhere if there were the will to do so, and the resources.

If neither is available, however, it is still possible to encourage the use of multiple co-ordinated approaches to the study of illicit drug use by reorienting research currently being done by Health and Welfare Canada and by Canadian alcohol and drug commissions and foundations. In particular, more emphasis needs to be placed on the use of approaches such as observational and key informant studies. These methodologies are not often used now but are relatively inexpensive and, as demonstrated in this chapter, helpful as well.

An alternative is to encourage research funding bodies such as the National Health Research Development Programme (NHRDP) to support investigations using multiple approaches. Perhaps through these means and simply making researchers aware of the need for "triangulation," it will be possible to improve the quality and comprehensiveness of research on the epidemiology of illicit drug use in Canada.

This is not to say that research in this field in Canada has not been of high quality. In fact, using some of the examples cited in this chapter, it might be argued that Canadians have been in the forefront of research on the epidemiology of illicit drug use internationally. It is simply to say that we probably could do even better than we have.

In addition to encouraging the use of multiple approaches, there are a number of other steps we could take. These include continued monitoring of trends in illicit drug use; studies of the health consequences of illicit drug use; longitudinal studies; development of innovative methods; and development of standardized methods.

With regard to monitoring, as mentioned earlier, a Federal-Provincial Working Group has recommended a number of steps to ensure that monitoring of illicit drug use and its consequences will continue and indeed improve (50). It is to be hoped that these recommendations will be implemented.

As for studies of health consequences of illicit drug use, we in fact know very little about the nature and magnitude of such consequences on an ongoing basis. In particular, we need systematic research on drug-related casualties coming to the attention of health and social facilities in Canada. Health and Welfare Canada and the Addiction Research Foundation are currently collaborating on the development of such a study.

Very few longitudinal studies of illicit drug use have been conducted in Canada, one exception being the study of Schlegel and his colleagues mentioned earlier (36). There is clearly a need to continue this kind of work if we are going to understand the processes which bring people in and out of illicit drug use. Thus, granting agencies and research institutions should encourage such studies even though they require considerable commitment of time and resources.

As described in this chapter, a number of attempts have been made to develop innovative methods for the study of illicit drug use in Canada (e.g., a one-day census). Such experimentation needs to continue if we are to improve the quality of our knowledge. Investigators should be encouraged to do so.

As for standardized methods, there has been a recent attempt to develop them for student surveys; in the past, these surveys have often been designed without much attention to the standardization necessary to permit comparability. Researchers should be made aware of the existence of guidelines and encouraged to use them (41). In addition, similar guidelines may be needed for other types of studies (e.g., household surveys).

Although this chapter has focused on methods for epidemiologic research on illicit drug use, it has not discussed the technical details of such methods to any great degree. If it had, the chapter might have taken over the book. Fortunately, there are a number of convenient publications which discuss such matters constructively. In particular, the World Health Organization has published a series of reports on the epidemiology of drug and alcohol problems which are available through the Canadian Public Health Association

(14, 15, 29, 30, 38, 40). The publication on alcohol problems (30) might be especially useful as a starting point, since it contains annexes on most of the approaches discussed in this chapter.

In any case, the author hopes that this chapter has provided a helpful introduction to the methods used in the epidemiology of illicit drugs, and that it will encourage researchers to enter this challenging field.

REFERENCES

1. Addiction Research Foundation. *Statistical Supplement to the Annual Report 1977–78*. Toronto: Addiction Research Foundation, 1979.
2. Addiction Research Foundation. *Statistics on Drug Use*. Toronto: Addiction Research Foundation, 1985.
3. Buckner, T. H. *Cannabis Use and Its Consequences: Projections for Canada in 1984*. ERD79–172. Ottawa: Non-Medical Use of Drugs Directorate, 1979.
4. Canada. Commission of Inquiry into the Non-Medical Use of Drugs. *Final Report*. Ottawa: Information Canada, 1973.
5. Clark, S. C., Rootman, I., and Lander, A. Contacts with a Canadian "street level" drug and crisis centre, 1972–76. *Bulletin on Narcotics, 30*(4): 23–42 (1978).
6. Clark, S. C., Rootman, I., and MacLean, B. Contacts with a Canadian drug information and crisis centre, 1971–74. *Bulletin on Narcotics, 29*(1): 1–11 (1977).
7. Delgaty, R. Heroin use in Niagara Falls, Ontario. *Addictive Diseases, 2–3*:403–19 (1976).
8. Desranleau, C. *Use of Drugs among Young People in Secondary Schools in Montreal*. Montreal: Commission des Écoles Catholiques de Montréal, 1985.
9. Garceau, S. *A Summary Report on Tobacco, Alcohol and Marijuana Use and Norms among Young People in Canada, Year 4*. Ottawa: Health Promotion Directorate, 1986.
10. Gerson, L. W. *Alcohol and Other Drug-related Problems in Hamilton-Wentworth*. Ottawa: Health and Welfare Canada, 1977.
11. Health and Welfare Canada. Health Promotion Directorate. *Canadian Drug Indicators: A Compilation of Current Statistics on Alcohol, Tobacco and Other Drugs*. Ottawa, 1977.
12. Hollander, M. J. *Client/Agency Monitoring System*. Vancouver: Alcohol and Drug Commission of British Columbia, 1977.
13. Hollander, M. J., and Davis, B. L. *Trends in Adolescent Alcohol and Drug Use in Vancouver*. Vancouver: Province of British Columbia, Ministry of Health, Alcohol and Drug Programs, 1983.

14. Hughes, P.; Venulet, J.; U Khant; Mora, M.; Navoratnam, V.; Poshyachinda, V.; Rootman, I.; Salan, R.; and Wadud, K. S. *Core Data for Epidemiological Studies of Non-medical Drug Use*. World Health Organization, Offset publication no. 56. Geneva: WHO, 1980.
15. Johnston, L. *Review of General Population Surveys of Drug Abuse*. World Health Organization, Offset publication no. 52. Geneva: WHO, 1980.
16. Killorn, J. *Chemical Use among P.E.I. Students*. Charlottetown: Alcohol and Drug Problems Institute, 1982.
17. King, A. J. C., Robertson, A. S., and Warren, W. K. *Canada Health Attitudes and Behaviours Survey: 9, 12, and 15 year olds, 1984–85*. Kingston: Queen's University, 1985.
18. Lamarche, P., and Rootman, I. Drug use by Canadians. In: *Technical Report on 1985 Canada Health Promotion Survey*. Ottawa: Health and Welfare Canada, 1987.
19. Lanphier, C. M., Peskun, P., and Somogyi, A. *Patterns of Use of Alcohol and of Non-Medical Use of Drugs among Members of the Canadian Forces: Extent, Context and Effect*. Ottawa: Dept. of National Defence, 1983.
20. Liban, C. B., and Smart, R. G. *The Value of the Key Informant Method for Studying Drinking Habits*. Toronto: Addiction Research Foundation, 1980.
21. Mitic, W., and Newmann, B. *Drug Use among Halifax Adolescents, 1983*. Halifax: Nova Scotia Commission on Drug Dependency, 1983.
22. Murphy, H. B. M. Explaining a new type of alcoholism survey. *International Journal of Epidemiology, 8*:119–26 (1979).
23. Orenstein, M. *Pilot Study Report: National Health Promotion Survey*. Ottawa: Health Promotion Directorate, 1984.
24. Richman, A., and Humphrey, B. Epidemiology of criminal narcotic addiction in Canada. *Bulletin on Narcotics, 21*:31–40 (1969).
25. Richman, A., and Rootman, I. Epidemiologic field units on narcotic-related problems. *Bulletin on Narcotics, 34*:17–28 (1982).
26. Rootman, I. *Final Report: Federal-Provincial Task Force on Heroin Epidemiology*. Ottawa: Health and Welfare Canada, 1977.
27. Rootman, I. Recent trends in cannabis use in Canada. *Drug and Alcohol Dependence, 4*:425–35 (1979).
28. Rootman, I., and Clark, S. C. Street level drug crisis intervention. *Drug Forum, 3*(3): (Spring 1974).
29. Rootman, I., and Hughes, P. H. *Drug Abuse Reporting Systems*. World Health Organization, Offset publication no. 55. Geneva: WHO, 1980.
30. Rootman, I., and Moser, J. *Guidelines for Investigating Alcohol Problems and Developing Appropriate Responses*. World Health Organization, Offset publication no. 81. Geneva: WHO, 1984.
31. Rootman, I., and Richman, A. Trends in reported narcotic use in Canada 1956–73. *Bulletin on Narcotics, 27*(4): 27–40 (October-December 1975).
32. Rootman, I., and Smart, R. G. A comparison of alcohol, tobacco and drug

use as determined from household and school surveys. *Drug and Alcohol Dependence, 16*:89–94 (1985).

33. Rootman, I., and Yard, G. Trends in reported illegal narcotic use in Canada:1956–75. *Bulletin on Narcotics, 30*(3): 13–22 (1978).
34. Rootman, I., Read, J., and Larsen, D. Community health services for drug-related problems. *Canada's Mental Health, 22*(3): 10–13 (September 1974).
35. Rosenbaum, P. *A One Day Census of Drug Problems in Kingston, Ontario.* Toronto: Addiction Research Foundation, 1975.
36. Schlegel, R., d'Avernas, J. R., and Manske, S. R. Longitudinal patterns of beer, liquor and marijuana consumption: An examination of issues arising from these patterns. In: Rush, B., and Layne, N. (eds.). *Alcohol, Drugs and Canadian Youth.* Toronto: Addiction Research Foundation, 1985.
37. Single, E., and Storm, T. *Public Drinking and Public Policy.* Toronto: Addiction Research Foundation, 1985.
38. Smart, R. G. *A Methodology for Student Drug Use Surveys.* World Health Organization, Offset publication no. 50. Geneva: WHO, 1980.
39. Smart, R. G. A trial of a new method for studying drinking and drinking problems in three countries of the Americas. *Bulletin of the Pan American Health Organization, 14*(4): 319–26 (1980).
40. Smart, R. G. *Drug Use Among Non-student Youth.* World Health Organization, Offset publication no. 60. Geneva: WHO, 1981.
41. Smart, R. G. *Guidelines for the Development of Surveys on the Consumption of Alcohol and Drugs among Students in Canada.* Ottawa: Health and Welfare Canada, 1985.
42. Smart, R. G., and Adlaf, E. M. *Alcohol and Drug Use among Ontario Adults in 1984 and Changes since 1982.* Toronto: Addiction Research Foundation, 1984.
43. Smart, R. G., Adlaf, E. M., and Goodstadt, M. S. Alcohol and drug use among Ontario students: An update. *Canadian Journal of Public Health, 77*:57–58 (January/February 1986).
44. Stevenson, G. H., Lingley, L. R. A., Trasov, G. E., and Stanfield, H. *Drug addiction in British Columbia.* Unpublished manuscript, University of British Columbia, Vancouver, 1956.
45. Stoddart, K. *Observations of Non-medical Drug Use in Vancouver.* Ottawa: Health and Welfare Canada, 1974.
46. Thomas, E. The epidemiology of narcotic-related problems in Canada: Use of the BDD narcotic users file. In: Rootman, I., and Billard, C. (eds.). *Epidemiology of Drug-related Problems in Canada 1975.* Ottawa: Health and Welfare Canada, 1975.
47. Thomas, E. Canadian heroin indicators: The effect of delay between arrest and conviction on official statistics. *U.N. Bulletin on Narcotics, 29*(3): 33–39 (1977).
48. Walker, G. *Methadone Users in Toronto: A Social-geographic Profile.* ERD77–110. Ottawa: Non-medical Use of Drugs Directorate, 1977.

49. White, J., Pickett, E., and Fallis, A. *A Study to Determine the Consistency among Student, Teacher and Administrator Estimates of the Prevalence and Effects of Alcohol Use by Students.* Ottawa: Health and Welfare Canada, September 1976.

50. Working Group on Drug Monitoring. *Interim Report to the Federal-Provincial Sub-committee on Alcohol and Other Drug Problems.* Ottawa: Health Promotion Directorate, April 15, 1986.

14

An Overview of Canadian Illicit Drug Use Epidemiology

JUDITH BLACKWELL

THE DEVELOPMENT OF CANADA'S FIRST DRUG PROBLEM

In the absence of drug laws, there could be no illicit drug use in the early years of Canada's exploration and settlement. This is not to say, however, that people did not use drugs without the authorization of a physician, or that all of the drugs outlawed today were unavailable to the pioneers. We know, for example, that in 1606 marijuana was being cultivated in Nova Scotia by Louis Hébert, the apothecary of Samuel de Champlain (2a). There is also every reason to assume that the early settlers brought opium with them, as this was the all-purpose painkiller used widely in a time when, with no specific remedies to treat diseases, symptomatic relief was the only alternative. In a colonial society where medical professionals were few and medical education and certification haphazard, early Canadians were more or less on their own with regard to medication.

Young (28) tells us that colonial Americans "dosed themselves with galenicals and chymicals, and swallowed complicated concoctions containing disgusting ingredients, in their efforts to drive away the ills that attacked them" (p. 8). The view that God would provide remedies wherever diseases flourished prompted a search for curative botanicals in the New World and interest in the healing arts of its native citizens. In Britain, patent medicines were being sold by the middle of the seventeenth century, and they appeared in British America at least by the early 1700s.

Concerns about self-medication, however, did not come to the fore until the late nineteenth century. Glenn Murray has described the debates attending the regulation of the patent medicine industry in Chapter 6 of this book. It is interesting that, although these nostrums may well have been causing health and safety problems in Canadian society, this issue was not directly addressed. Rather, the patent medicine industry was brought under regulation as a result of lobbying efforts on the part of pharmacists and doctors who were acting to protect their professional interests.

The morbidity and mortality attributable to nineteenth-century home remedies and patent medicines containing alcohol, cocaine, or opiates would be an interesting area for historical research. Apparently some degree of dependence developed from taking opium medications, but the associated abstinence syndrome was typically mild and often not recognized as a product of drug use (2b). We know little of other adverse effects of the opiates or of self-medication with other drugs in that era. Nevertheless, that it did not seem to be a major moral or legal issue suggests either that the problem was not severe or that adverse consequences went unrecognized.

As a general rule, to create a substantial drug "problem," one that captures the public imagination and stirs legislators to action, drug use needs to be associated with other social problems of concern. Thus, nineteenth-century temperance movements gained impetus by attributing a wide spectrum of social ills to drinking (16). Alcohol explained away all the problems of life in a rapidly expanding industrialized and urbanized society, including poverty, crime, slums, abandoned spouses and children, business failure, and personal ruin. In the same vein, Oriental opium dens were to supply Canada with its first "drug menace," and concern was to focus on the opium smokers' moral character, or lack of it, rather than on the dangers of the drug to those who indulged in it.

The first Chinese immigrants arrived in British Columbia in 1858, coming north from the United States where they had been employed as railroad workers (27). They were followed in the 1880s by several thousands of their compatriots, who had been imported by the Canadian Pacific Railway to complete its line. The Chinese saw themselves as sojourners, not as immigrants. They came as single men, not in families as did other immigrant groups, and they tended to save their wages and return to their homeland. They worked hard and turned to their opium pipes for rest and recreation.

In British Columbia in the 1880s, there were more than 10,000 Chinese, 30,000 native people, and 20,000 whites (27). Among the latter were many respectable and hardy pioneers, but there were also adventurers attracted by gold and the other natural resources of the West Coast. The socially unstable element included shiftless and dishonest transients, "given to alcoholism, gambling and sharp practices" (27, p. 446). A contrast between the white and Chinese citizens at the time was made in the Port Moody *Gazette*, reporting on the occasion when the rail line was completed and the workers paid off:

> The scene at Yale on Saturday last beggars description. A thousand white men lately employed on the railroad rushed out of cars and into the saloons. In two hours the streets were full of lunatics; they roared and raved and attempted to force their way into private homes. Twelve hundred Chinese arrived by the same train and went into the woods and cooked their rice. It is amusing to see the difference between pagans and Christians. (27, pp. 446–7)

The Chinese communities on the West Coast were isolated, both physically and psychologically, and they were viewed with some hostility by respectable white society. Denizens of the underworld, however, were willing to mix with Orientals and avail themselves of the pleasures of the opium dens. According to Kane (13), the first white American to smoke opium, in 1868, was a "sporting character"; thence, the practice spread rapidly and quietly among gamblers, prostitutes, and other less than respectable elements. We do not know exactly when white people began smoking opium in Canada, but they were definitely involved by 1884 when the Royal Commission on Chinese Immigration held its hearings (27). At the time of the Commission, British Columbia had been importing over 36,000 pounds of opium each year, averaged over three years; this represents about one-half pound per B.C. resident. Some of it, however, may have been intended for the U.S. market.

According to Courtwright (4), the American opium den became a kind of vagabonds' inn, a friendly and safe refuge for itinerant salesmen and actors, as well as for underworld characters. By the 1870s, "the opium den had become the matrix of a deviant subculture, a tightly knit group of outsiders whose primary relations were restricted to themselves" (4, p. 74). They did not attract attention and outrage, however, until the public began to perceive the Oriental population as an economic threat, and when putatively respectable white men and women of the better classes began to frequent the dens.

The shady and disreputable character of the first white opium smokers helps to explain the seemingly illogical attribution of vice and immorality to smoking in an age when opium taking was widespread and socially accepted as a form of self-medication. The dens were safe havens for the criminal classes, a place to relax, socialize, and exchange information in the company of friends and strangers who shared the same code of honour. "In virtually all particulars—peer reinforcement, exclusive membership, common argot, and shared rules of appropriate behavior—opium smoking anticipated the pattern of the various twentieth-century drug subcultures" (4, p. 74). Thus, the link between drug use and deviance was forged, not only in the public mind but among drug users themselves. As a nineteenth-century observer noted, making opium smoking illegal did little to dampen the enthusiasm of the smokers but rather "seemed to add zest to their enjoyment" (13, p. 2).

THE FIRST HALF OF THE TWENTIETH CENTURY

By all indications, at the turn of the century the population of opiate users who took the drug for medical or quasi-medical reasons was in decline. New analgesics were becoming available, vaccination and public health measures had reduced the incidence of illnesses, and a new generation of medical educators cautioned against liberal prescribing of opiates (4). Thus, the subculturally deviant users of opium, morphine, and later heroin constituted an increasingly large part of the addict population. In 1908, when Canada's first legislation to outlaw opium smoking was coming into force, the drug trade in British Columbia was being taken over from the Chinese by whites.

Meanwhile, United States opium smokers and their underworld compatriots had discovered cocaine as a recreational drug during the 1885–1900 period (4). According to the popular press, House of Commons debates, and health profession journals, cocaine use became an issue in Canada between 1906 and 1910 (7). Until 1908, cocaine was legal, was available not only in patent medicines but also in its pure form, and could be purchased without a prescription. As long as the drug was being used for self-medication, its use remained morally neutral, but when the criminal classes began to indulge in cocaine for pleasure, it became a "monstrous vice" (7). Legislation to control opium smoking had encouraged the use of morphine in its place, and this drug was associated with the "dope fiends" who were the object of the cocaine crisis in 1910.

Opium is a bulky commodity compared to morphine, and morphine is less powerful and compact than heroin. Once drug legislation was in place, the price of illicit opiates rose and smoking opium was gradually replaced by morphine and then heroin. This was a logical choice, since they were so much easier to smuggle, deal in, and conceal. For economic reasons, users began injecting the powdered opiates, a more efficient mode of administration than either sniffing or smoking.

Because opiates were still available on prescription, addicts turned to doctors as a source of supply. There is every reason to believe that respectable people who had become habituated to opiates through medical practice or self-medication were quietly maintained on prescribed drugs if they could not be cured. Certainly, that was the case in the United States (18). Concern at the time focused on subculturally deviant or criminal users and their attempts to divert medical supplies to their own uses. Records of the investigation and prosecution of physicians in the 1920s are available in the Public Archives in Ottawa. These documents suggest that there were a number of medical men at the time who prescribed to addicts for a fee and were eventually entrapped by informers posing as patients. In his memoirs, a Canadian country doctor recalls that during the 1920s he would receive transient morphine addicts in his practice: "Each was in great misery from sweating and shaking as he pleaded for a small hypo of morphine. Largely out of sympathy, I always granted the request though I was convinced that it was illegal to do so" (11, p. 96). Single administrations of this kind were unlikely to draw the attention of the authorities, who were more concerned with physicians who regularly prescribed for a number of users.

Levels of illicit opiate consumption in British Columbia apparently remained fairly stable in the first decades of the century. Conviction statistics suggest that there was more activity in Montreal in the early 1930s than elsewhere in the country, and in Toronto in the 1939–1941 period.

In the United States in the 1920s and 1930s, drug use began to be associated with musicians and entertainers, and some of the popular songs of that era refer to the use of cannabis and cocaine (18). Heroin, too, had a following in this group, and throughout the era observers noted an increasing involvement in drug use by black Americans (4). Little reliable information exists about the Canadian situation at the time. Apparently cannabis use was observed to be a problem in the 1930s, in Ottawa, Toronto, Windsor, Montreal, and British Columbia (10). Judging by conviction statistics, however, the numbers of users were probably low; there were only 25 cannabis-related convictions nationally between 1930 and 1946.

The opiate-using community declined dramatically during the Second World War, as international smuggling routes were cut off and susceptible young men were siphoned off into the armed services. Some users survived the war years, nevertheless, as can be seen in a study of "criminal addicts" in British Columbia, conducted by an RCMP constable in 1945 (21). Based on 52 case histories, a picture of the "average addict" was presented: white, male, in his mid-thirties, arrested before he began using drugs, and convicted repeatedly thereafter. The effects of the war on the black market are evident here, as these 10-year veterans of the drug scene had cut their morphine consumption considerably, from over 4 grains daily before the war to under 1 grain afterwards. This study is interesting, too, in that it indicates that heroin had not yet supplanted morphine in 1945; less than 20 percent of the addicts used heroin, and about the same proportion were still using opium.

Amphetamines were introduced in medicine in the 1930s, and their stimulating properties were widely exploited by both Allied and Axis soldiers during the war (2b). Night-shift workers, long-distance vehicle drivers, and students cramming for exams also discovered the ability of these drugs to counteract fatigue. Athletes used amphetamines in hopes of enhancing their performance and others used them for stimulation alone, for pleasure or for fun.

Although information on the non-medical use of barbiturates or other sleeping preparations is scanty, after their introduction in the 1930s it was evident that lawful manufacture and import of such drugs exceeded the requirements of legitimate medical use or exportation (2b). Illicit drugs were scarce in the 1940s and prescribing standards less rigorous than today. It is thus reasonable to assume that some medical mood modifiers found their way into the hands of recreational users.

Overall, the war years are unique in the twentieth century for their low rates of non-medical drug use. Before we leave the 1940s, however, note that this decade witnessed the appearance of a new and quite extraordinary chemical, LSD. On April 16, 1943, its inventor unwittingly ingested the drug and was launched on the first recorded LSD "trip" in history. Little did he know that 25 years later this chemical invention would become one of the major symbols in a youth movement that set off a most remarkable drug epidemic in Canada and throughout the Western world.

THE POST-WAR ERA

In the United States, cannabis continued to be seen as a social problem throughout the war years and into the 1950s. Meanwhile, in Canada it had all but disappeared from sight (5, 24). In British Columbia, even heroin users had little experience with it, and in the course of two years in the early 1950s there was only one marijuana conviction in the province (27). (This case involved an American importing cannabis for his fellow countrymen, who belonged to a travelling circus and carnival.) Cocaine was also not perceived as a problem, with only one user known to the Bureau of Dangerous Drugs in 1956 (23).

By the late 1950s, marijuana was in vogue in Vancouver artistic circles (19), and research conducted on Toronto users in the mid-sixties uncovered some who had been smoking it for a decade or more (3). Thus, it would seem that cannabis was used in Canada in the early to mid-1950s, but the numbers of users were so small and their activities sufficiently clandestine that they went virtually unrecognized by the authorities.

In addition, it is reasonable to assume that cannabis use was localized in cities large enough to contain established deviant subcultures. Certainly, the mid-sixties Toronto users belonged to groups that one would not have expected to encounter in small towns or rural areas; they were identified as "beats" (bohemians under age twenty-five); "swingers" (entertainers, criminals, or those on the fringes of these subcultures) and "squares" (the "yuppies" of that era, well-educated professionals between thirty-five and fifty years of age). There is evidence, too, of some Canadian interest in LSD during the 1950s, but it was apparently restricted to a few professional, academic, and artistic experimenters, many of whom would have been aware of medical and psychotherapeutic research with the drug (2b).

The most significant illicit drug problem of the 1950s involved heroin. Much of the furor over this drug was inspired by the situation in the United States, where evidence of use among blacks and Puerto Ricans in poor urban neighbourhoods began to emerge late in 1950 (18). There is good reason to believe that the ensuing heroin epidemic represented an old problem that re-emerged once the disruptive effects of the war had subsided. However, it was perceived as a new and threatening menace in the 1950s, and received a good deal of media attention. Reverberations in Canada led to the formation of a Senate Committee to look into the matter (24) and, most fortunately, to funding for one of the most comprehensive and insightful studies of heroin users ever conducted in North America, *Drug Addiction in British Columbia* (27).

How serious was Canada's problem at the time? Clearly, Vancouver's opiate users had re-established themselves as a lively subculture after the war, but informed estimates of the day suggested that there were fewer addicts in the country as a whole than at any time since 1920 (27). Vancouver was the only city where heroin was in relatively constant supply; British Columbia, with just 8.5 percent of Canada's population, was estimated to have over half of its heroin users. A high estimate of the numbers of "criminal addicts" in the province at the time suggested there were about 900. We have no information on the numbers of hidden users, those who used occasionally or were wealthy enough to keep their habits secret. It is probably safe to estimate that there were about 2,000 regular heroin users in the country as a whole, and epidemiologically they represented the lion's share of our illicit drug problem in the 1950s.

Most of our information about heroin users in that era comes from the research of Stevenson and his colleagues in British Columbia (27). Not only was the Canadian heroin scene on a smaller scale than in the United States, but its composition was different. Whereas heroin was a minority group and urban ghetto problem in the U.S. and there was much talk of how smoking marijuana had caused this generation to go on to the "hard stuff," in B.C. most heroin users were white, they had grown up in economically marginal but not impoverished circumstances, and very few of them had even seen cannabis.

The B.C. study exhaustively reviewed the social and psychological characteristics of "criminal addicts," comparing them to prisoners who did not use heroin. The research team found few differences between these groups. On the basis of this investigation, as well as a comparison of addicted and non-addicted siblings, the authors concluded that the most important factor leading to heroin use and dependence was close and friendly association with other users, and that B.C. addicts were "basically ordinary people." With regard to the "psychopathology" commonly attributed to addicts at that time, the report notes: "Certainly it is far easier to see neurotic features in oneself and one's associates than in the addict group" (27, p. 305).

THE PSYCHEDELIC SIXTIES TO TODAY

Illicit drugs maintained a relatively low profile in the early 1960s, although clearly the use of cannabis was slowly moving out of its subcultural confines into the colleges and universities, and into the younger age groups. By the mid-1960s, however, cannabis use began to spread rapidly. It followed patterns already observed in the United States and was a product of the same social forces (10). Throughout the decade, the Canadian cannabis market remained relatively informal and loosely structured; smuggling endeavours were intermittent and largely conducted by entrepreneurially-inspired users. Domestic dealing networks mirrored friendship networks.

Personal psychological experiments with LSD and other hallucinogens also continued into the 1960s (2b). As governments began to place restrictions on these drugs, however, they were capturing the public imagination and becoming increasingly available to non-therapeutic users. In their wake came an alphabet soup of synthesized drugs with hallucinogenic properties: MDA, STP, PCP, DMT, and others. In addition, amateur botanists were searching out cacti and mushrooms, and bringing mescaline and psilocybin to curious friends and customers.

As elsewhere in the Western world, Canada's "drug problem" in the late 1960s was intimately related to the youth movements of the time. Young people deserted the suburbs and congregated in costumed array in central city neighbourhoods. In the summertime, they roamed across the country as hitch-hiking transients. The media were fascinated by these "hippies" or "flower children," and sensationalized their drug use. Political attitudes, social ideology, and a psychedelic ethos were intertwined into a modern youth ideology which was propagated through informal social networks and the movement's own "underground" media. As in generations before, there was a widespread belief that the nation's youth was "going to pot," literally as well as idiomatically.

In retrospect, cannabis use rates in the late sixties seem modest, although by all indications use was rapidly growing. The national surveys sponsored by the Le Dain Commission (2a) suggest that between 1966 and 1969 the proportion of post-secondary students who had used the drug grew from around 4 percent to 17 percent. By 1970, the proportion was 29 percent, and for high-school students the estimate was 11 percent. A household survey of Canadians not in school suggested that use rose from around 1 percent to 3.6 percent between 1966 and 1970. For methodological reasons, these surveys missed uncounted thousands of "street people" or "transient youth," a large proportion of whom were expected to have smoked hashish or marijuana. Overall, the Commission estimated that about 850,000 Canadians had tried cannabis by 1970.

In 1973, the Commission estimated that 3 percent of Canadians aged 12 and over had at some time taken LSD or similar hallucinogens.

The sixties also witnessed the appearance of a new phenomenon, young multiple-drug users who injected massive doses of amphetamine drugs. The non-medical use of amphetamines, largely taken orally, had continued through the 1950s and early 1960s, but as the decade progressed "speed freaks" aroused new concerns about this class of drug. Although to this day users continue to inject amphetamines, the epidemic of high-dose intravenous use in North America was blessedly short-lived. Indeed, this is a good example of how informal sanctions and social controls generated from within the drug-using community can have powerful positive effects. "Speeders" were perceived to be violent, paranoid, unhealthy, and generally undesirable as associates. Youth-oriented media, popular musicians, and other influential figures spoke out against speed use. Potential new recruits were deterred by such messages or by the attitudes of their peers, and the population of users declined as the self-limiting nature of such an unhealthy practice took its toll on current users. The Le Dain Commission (2b) estimated that the numbers of regular, high-dose, intravenous amphetamine users peaked at approximately 2,000–3,000 in the summer of 1970.

Cocaine, meanwhile, had largely disappeared from the scene. Only a handful of users were known to the Bureau of Dangerous Drugs in the late 1960s, but by the time of its 1973 report, the Le Dain Commission was declaring that "cocaine is back." Although it was no longer considered rare in Canada, its use was restricted by high prices and limited availability. During 1973, almost 300 cocaine users were known to the Bureau of Dangerous Drugs, up from around 50 two years earlier (23).

The Le Dain Commission also observed that the numbers of "habitual narcotics users" known to the Bureau of Dangerous Drugs had remained fairly stable through the 1960s, but were increasing in the 1970–1972 period. Methodological problems made difficult the interpretation of these statistics; the upsurge observed may have reflected changes in law enforcement practices or may have occurred because newer users were more visible or were appearing for treatment earlier than their older counterparts had. Nevertheless, reports from the regions and the available indicators suggested a recent rise in use. The Commission estimated that there were some 15,000 regular heroin users and perhaps 50,000 people who used the drug occasionally in Canada. In that case, there were probably 6,000–7,000 dependent users; no one will ever know the exact figure, but this is a reasonable guess based on the estimates of the using population as a whole.

It is interesting to note that the Le Dain report speculated, on the basis of the San Francisco experience, that the apparent increases in heroin use would reach a plateau by 1974. The peak year for heroin convictions was 1973, when almost 1,300 were recorded. From 1970 to 1979, inclusive, Canada averaged fewer than 700 convictions a year for heroin offences. In British Columbia, the number of new users reported annually also reached a peak in 1973 and declined consistently thereafter (6). Nationally, the annual numbers of heroin convictions went steadily down in the late 1970s and remained around 300 a year in the first half of the 1980s.

When heroin is scarce on the street, users turn to other opioid drugs diverted from the legitimate market. Looking only at opiate convictions under the *Narcotic Control Act* between 1976 and 1984, we note there were on average just over 800 a year, never more than 900 and about 750 in the lowest year. In the 1985 statistics, convictions jumped to almost 1,500, but most of the excess can be accounted for by convictions for multiple doctoring, that is, obtaining prescriptions for codeine or other opiates from more than one doctor. The figure coincides with an increased interest by the authorities in this particular problem. Excluding multiple doctoring convictions, we see a gradual rise from 495 to 581 convictions for all opioid drugs between 1981 and 1985.

Indirect indicators suggest that heroin use reached its peak around the time of the Le Dain *Final Report* (2b), declined during the rest of the 1970s, and then stabilized. The early 1980s plateau probably represents a level of approximately 3,000 addicted users. This estimate can only be an informed guess, because there are insufficient data to draw firm conclusions.

While heroin use was apparently on a downward curve in the 1970s, the use of cannabis was steadily growing. Importing and domestic dealing enterprises became better organized, and the potency of the product improved.

Through the seventies, a number of regional studies were conducted in various populations and all indicated that cannabis use was spreading rapidly (22, 25). Most of this research involved student populations, and by the mid-seventies the rate of current use among students was fast approaching 25 percent. In Toronto, where student surveys have been conducted every two years since the late 1960s, it appears that 1979 was a peak year. In that survey, over 30 percent in grades 7, 9, 11, and 13 reported use in the previous 12 months (26). In addition, half of the 16- to 17-year-olds identified themselves as current users. Since then, reported use rates in Toronto students have been steadily declining.

Since 1978, regular Gallup poll household surveys have inquired into cannabis use across the nation. The first year, persons aged 18 and older were polled, and 17 percent reported use of marijuana or hashish, 10 percent within the previous year (22). In the 18- to 29-year-old age bracket, 40 percent had used cannabis at least once; their current use rate rose to over 25 percent in 1981, but was down to 21 percent in 1983 (12).

Four subsequent polls have sampled 12- to 29-year-olds between 1983 and 1986 (8, 9, 15). These surveys indicate that use stabilized in this age group, with about 20 percent using in any given year. Meanwhile, the regular Gallup polls of 18- to 29-year-olds had shown evidence of decreasing use as early as 1980 (12). Thus, although youthful cannabis use could be viewed as an epidemic in the seventies, in the early eighties it had apparently become an endemic situation, with the first indications that it was in decline.

In June 1985, a national survey of Canadians aged 15 years and older found that 5.6 percent had used marijuana or hashish in the previous 12 months (14). In men, the rate was 6.9 percent; in women, 4.3 percent. The age category with highest use included 20- to 24-year-olds (14.2%); use was also relatively high in the 25–34 age group (8.9%). Cannabis use was more frequently reported by single (never married) respondents, students, people looking for work, and, in the working population, blue-collar workers. From a regional perspective, rates were highest in the Northwest Territories (19.9 percent) and in the Yukon (15.2%). Among the provinces, British Columbia and Alberta ranked relatively high, approaching 9 percent.

If indeed the number of Canadian cannabis users reached a plateau in the early 1980s and then began to abate slowly, a review of the conviction statistics in this era provides an object lesson in the risks of using such indirect indicators to estimate changes in the size of drug-using populations. Since 1981, cannabis convictions have plunged dramatically, from a high of over

44,000 to fewer than 25,000. (The most recent statistics record fewer than 23,000 cannabis convictions for 1985, but late reports will eventually raise this figure by about 2,000–3,000.)

Meanwhile, the numbers of cocaine convictions have increased steadily each year, from an average of 500 annually in the late 1970s to over 1,600 a year in the early eighties. In 1984 and 1985, they exceeded 2,200. Recently, a great deal of media attention has been devoted to the cocaine "epidemic," with much of the excitement spilling across the border from our southern neighbours. Data to evaluate the extent of use in Canada are scanty, but use would seem to be on a considerably smaller scale than in the U.S. (7). Up to 3 percent of Canadians have probably tried it, with perhaps 1 percent using in any given year. The 1985 national survey (14) indicated that cocaine was most popular among single men, students, and the residents of British Columbia, who constituted 30 percent of Canadian users. Information to monitor trends in cocaine use is not available at the time of writing.

Although conviction statistics are a very crude gauge of use rates, they suggest that hallucinogen use may have been declining in popularity in the 1980s. Convictions for LSD, MDA, PCP, and psilocybin combined have steadily dropped from over 3,000 in 1981 to less than 2,000 in 1985. This occurred despite an enormous increase in psilocybin convictions, an artifact of a Supreme Court decision that the *Food and Drugs Act* applied to mushrooms in their natural state, as well as to dried or processed mushrooms; thus, psilocybin convictions did not necessarily reflect trends in use. High-school surveys in the 1980s suggest that hallucinogen use has been stable to declining, with minor regional and subgroup increases (12, 25).

Information on other illicit drug use is even more inadequate, but the overall trend in the 1980s appears to be stabilization or reduction, with the probable exception of cocaine. Furthermore, there is some indication that an increasing proportion of young people claim to use no drugs at all, licit or illicit (26). There remains a possibility, as Pollin suggests (20), that the reliability of survey data has declined in these conservative times, and respondents have become less willing to report drug use candidly when polled. Nevertheless, the 1980s has been a quiet period in Canada with regard to non-medical drug use, a social problem area in which "no news is good news." As a rule, the media are quick to seize on new drug fads or to report on drug problems in their infancy, and treatment and other helping agencies do not tend to remain silent when presented with unexpected demands for their services. In the relatively quiescent eighties, therefore, it is not unreasonable to assume that the epidemic of the late 1960s and 1970s is over.

Further monitoring of illicit drug use is no less crucial if this is the case. In the first place, the phenomenon is still very much with us; if we take into account that survey data under-represent the extent of use, an estimated one-half of Canadians have at least experimented with cannabis by the time they reach age 30, and thereby will have violated the *Narcotic Control Act*. Further, new waves of drug use are not easy to anticipate, except insofar as Canadians can sometimes see new fads or fashions as they develop in the United States. Thus, when we hear from the south of designer or "microchip" drugs (17) or of "crack," the cheaper and smokable version of cocaine, we are understandably concerned that these problems will move north. We can take some comfort from the observation that our use rates for all illicit drugs have been modest in comparison to those of the U.S., even at the peak of epidemic phases. Yet that does not excuse us from continuing to assess the Canadian situation.

Historically, as new drugs or new styles of drug use have been introduced, we have seen slow dissemination initially, followed by steady increases during the epidemic phase. It is then that the media become interested, the authorities alerted, and the public alarmed. Such reaction increases exponentially in an era like the late 1960s and early 1970s, when successive and overlapping epidemics occurred in a short period of time. However, just as infectious diseases move rapidly at first through the most vulnerable populations yet eventually begin to encounter resistance, drug use, too, finally reaches a plateau.

Nevertheless, there are important differences between drug and disease epidemics. By all indications, waves of drug use begin to level off, not only because they start to exhaust the vulnerable pool of potential users, but because people change and thereby become less vulnerable. The rise and fall of the "speed freak" phenomenon described above is a case in point. As illicit drug epidemics spread through neighbourhoods and friendship networks, potential new users have the opportunity to observe the adverse consequences that befall the pioneers of the outbreak. As a result, attitudes change and initiation is discouraged. Of equal importance, those who do begin use in the later stages of an epidemic develop strategies for minimizing the risks they are taking. Thus, there always seems to be a saturation point at which a drug epidemic levels off, but it is a malleable one, and this provides hope for programs aimed at ameliorating drug problems in Canada.

For most users, illicit drugs are a youthful adventure and certainly nothing like a chronic disease. Even cannabis, the most commonly used illegal substance and the one most amenable to social and recreational consumption in a manner similar to alcohol, tends to be abandoned after the age of 30 (14). Higher rates of use are found among students, the young, the unemployed, and among people who have never been married. Despite the popular belief that heroin inevitably lures users into a life of dependence, it too is taken up and then abandoned by many users (1). Illicit drug use requires an investment of money and of time, both of which need to be rationed once people adopt adult roles and make investments in their jobs, their marriages and children, and their mortgages.

Although epidemiologic methods have grown more sophisticated and numerous in recent decades, and have thus increased our ability to obtain more precise data on which to base estimates, there is much more work to be done. We badly need longitudinal research so we can learn about drug-using careers. We should know more about multiple-drug use and the factors that predict it, and research in this line should also address the problems that arise with the use of licit and illicit drugs in combination. Considering that non-medical drug use in one form or another has always been with us, it is unrealistic to assume that it will be eradicated in the near future. It is of utmost importance, therefore, to focus on the development of the patterns of drug use that lead to adverse consequences, including dependence, and the factors that inhibit these processes.

The historical record suggests that Canada will continue to experience drug epidemics, but it is important to remember that each new one will be self-limiting and that the illicit drug-using careers of many users are short-lived. Furthermore, the lessons of the past suggest that the more devastating the adverse consequences of any given drug use pattern, the more self-limiting will be the epidemic. With these observations, this review of the epidemiology of illicit drug use in this country can end on a note of cautious optimism.

REFERENCES

1. Blackwell, J. Drifting, controlling, and overcoming: Opiate users who avoid becoming chronically dependent. *Journal of Drug Issues, 13*:219–35 (1983).
2. Canada. Commission of Inquiry into the Non-Medical Use of Drugs.
   a. *Cannabis*. Ottawa: Information Canada, 1972.
   b. *Final Report*. Ottawa: Information Canada, 1973.
3. Coleclough, A., and Hanley, L. G. Marijuana users in Toronto. In: Mann, W.E. (ed.). *Deviant Behaviour in Canada*. Toronto: Social Science Publishers, 1968.
4. Courtwright, D. T. *Dark Paradise: Opiate Addiction in America before 1940*. Cambridge, Mass.: Harvard University Press, 1982.
5. Curran, R. E. Some aspects of Canada's narcotic drug problem. *Food Drug Cosmetic Law Journal, 10*:850–60 (1955).
6. Davis, B. L. *Trends in Heroin Use*. Technical Report Series A–81–1. Vancouver, B.C.: Ministry of Health, 1981.
7. Erickson, P., Adlaf, E. M., Murray, G. F., and Smart, R. G. *The Steel Drug: Cocaine in Perspective*. Lexington, Mass.: Lexington Books, 1987.
8. Garceau, S. *A Summary Report on Tobacco, Alcohol and Marijuana Use and Norms among Young People in Canada—Year 3*. Ottawa: Health Promotion Directorate, 1985.
9. Garceau, S. *A Summary Report on Tobacco, Alcohol and Marijuana Use*

and Norms among Young People in Canada—Year 4. Ottawa: Health Promotion Directorate, 1986.

10. Green, M., and Miller, R. In: Rubin, V. (ed.). *Cannabis Use in Canada*. The Hague: Mouton, 1975.
11. Johnston, W. V. *Before the Age of Miracles*. Toronto: PaperJacks, 1972.
12. Jossa, D., and Rootman, I. Recent trends in drug use among Canadian young people. *Chronic Diseases in Canada*, 5(2): 31–33 (1984).
13. Kane, H. H. *Opium-smoking in America and China*. 1882. Reprint. New York: Arno Press, 1976.
14. Lamarche, P., and Rootman, I. *Health Promotion Surveys: Drug Use by Canadians*. Ottawa: Health Promotion Directorate, 1987.
15. Layne, N. *Alcohol, Tobacco and Marijuana Use and Norms Among Young People in Canada: Year 2*. Ottawa: Health Promotion Directorate, 1984.
16. Levine, H. G. The alcohol problem in America: From temperance to alcoholism. *British Journal of Addiction*, 79:109–19 (1984).
17. MacLennan, A. Future shock drugs will defy current concepts. *The Journal*, 15 (January, 1986).
18. Morgan, H. W. *Drugs in America: A Social History, 1800–1980*. Syracuse, N.Y.: Syracuse University Press, 1981.
19. Paulus, J., and Williams, H. R. Marihuana and young adults. *British Columbia Medical Journal*, 8:240–44 (1966).
20. Pollin, W. Drug abuse, U.S.A.: How serious? How soluble? *Issues in Science and Technology*, Winter: 20–27 (1987).
21. Price, H. F. The criminal addict. *R.C.M.P. Quarterly*, 12:149–58 (1946).
22. Rootman, I. Recent trends in cannabis use in Canada. *Drug and Alcohol Dependence*, 4:425–34 (1979).
23. Rootman, I., and Richman, A. Trends in reported illegal narcotic use in Canada: 1956–1973. *Bulletin on Narcotics*, 27(4):27–40 (1975).
24. Senate of Canada. *Proceedings of the Special Committee on the Traffic in Narcotic Drugs in Canada*, 1955.
25. Smart, R. G. *Forbidden Highs: The Nature, Treatment, and Prevention of Illicit Drug Abuse*. Toronto: Addiction Research Foundation, 1983.
26. Smart, R. G., Adlaf, E. M., and Goodstadt, M. S. Alcohol and other drug use among Ontario students in 1985, and trends since 1977. Unpublished report, Addiction Research Foundation, Toronto, 1985.
27. Stevenson, G. H., Lingley, L. P. A., Trasov, G. E., and Stanfield, H. *Drug Addiction in British Columbia*. Vancouver: University of British Columbia, 1956.
28. Young, J. H. *The Toadstool Millionaires: A Social History of Patent Medicines in America before Federal Regulation*. Princeton, N.J.: Princeton University Press, 1961.

15

The Enforcement of Narcotics Violations in a Canadian City: Heroin Users' Perspectives on the Production of Official Statistics*

KENNETH STODDART

INTRODUCTION

Attempts to answer fundamental questions relating to the extent and distribution of non-medical drug use have often used some version of an officially-produced case register as a major data source, such as the one provided by Canada's Bureau of Dangerous Drugs. Traditionally the examination and analysis of official statistical records has been regarded as amongst the most valuable ways of uncovering features of the activity's volume and morphology.

During the past fifteen years, however, a considerable amount of social scientific research focussing on arrest situations and decision making by police—major contributors to official statistics—has called into question the utility of such records in general. Basically, the discovery that police activity introduces systematic distortions rather than random, self-cancelling ones, has suggested that official statistics may be more an artifact of enforcement procedures and routines than a reliable index of community lawbreaking. That this is likely the case for statistical portrayals of non-medical drug use has been claimed for a variety of jurisdictions; analyses of the Canadian situation, however, are conspicuous in their absence.

In the hope of partially filling this gap the present report offers a set of materials descriptive of some of the police activities that contribute to official portrayals of the volume and morphology of heroin use in a large city in the Canadian West. Drawing on data produced from unstructured interviews with heroin users residing in Western City, this report examines the potential significance for official heroin use statistics of two police-related matters: (a)

*Financial support for the research reported herein was provided by the Social and Epidemiological Research Division of the Non-Medical Use of Drugs Directorate (Irving Rootman, Chief). The author is solely responsible for the interpretations presented.

the responsiveness of crucial decision making to certain features of narcotics violators and (b) the organization of policework.

VIOLATOR FEATURES

As has been documented in numerous investigations, the law is unevenly enforced by personnel charged with the task. Rather than as a programme to be applied uniformly over all situations, enforcement personnel confront the law as a scheme of interpretation that they can invoke or not invoke for a variety of reasons. Indeed, an increasing volume of research, which describes how persons are assembled by police for induction into the criminal justice process, suggests that however that assembly occurs, it is inadequately depicted as proceeding via the "matching" of observed conduct with prospectively-defined illegal conduct. Study after study has shown that a meeting of legal specifications for arrest is merely one of the criteria informing the decision to arrest, not exhaustive of them. Unsurprisingly, police assembly is revealed as responsive in unknown measure to a host of other considerations. As Bittner (1) has suggested, policemen "often make decisions based on reasons that the law probably does not recognize as valid" (1, p. 709). Some of these "reasons" relate to the policeman's perception of the violator. For example —independent of technical possibility—arrests may or may not be made because of the violator's social status in the community (3) or appearance and demeanour (4).

This section of the chapter explores the influence of such "violator features" on two police decisions which are routine to the narcotics enforcement process: the decision to arrest and the decision to pursue a heroin user as a candidate for arrest.

There's No Way You Can Talk Them Out of It: The Restricted Relevance of Extralegal Considerations

In line with other research findings regarding decision making in the criminal justice system and in the hope of uncovering the potential influence of violator features on official portrayals of community heroin use, informants were queried about their own encounters with enforcement personnel. Perhaps not surprisingly, their accounts revealed that—unlike other kinds of violations—narcotics violations were enforced, in their words, "to the letter of the law." Indeed, some informants found incredible the suggestion that police suspended the relevance of legal considerations and did not arrest a violator when it was technically possible. On occasion, variations of the question: "Have there ever been any times when they got the dope but didn't pinch you for it?" were greeted with ridicule. For example:

> INTERVIEWER: Have there been any times when they got the dope but didn't pinch you for it?
>
> RESPONDENT: You mean just let you go or something?
>
> INTERVIEWER: Yeah, something like that.
>
> RESPONDENT: Fuck, you gotta be kidding. Once they got it outa you you're pinched and that's it. No two ways about it, you're fuckin' pinched. You gotta be crazy to think they'd let you off just like that, fuck no, that's not the way it happens.

As suggested in the following excerpts from interviews, such a thing was beyond the realm of possibility. The reason typically given was either police contempt of heroin users or the difficulty the police experienced in apprehending them.

> Once they've got ya, it's a good catch for them, they got some brownie points, y'know. They just don't say "well that's a bad habit you've got, sonny" and forget it 'cause for one thing it's a lot of work for them, y'know. We put them through their paces, believe me.

> The bulls hate us junkies. The more of us they pinch the happier they are.

Whatever the underlying reason, however, informants suggested that, after police have obtained evidence sufficient to warrant an arrest, legal considerations are afforded priority over all others. According to this portrayal, the police systematically employ the law to decide a course of action independent of anything that one might do, say, or be. Unlike the situation with other violations, any and all features of the violator—save one, as will be indicated below—seem irrelevant vis-à-vis the decision to make an arrest for a narcotics offence. In the following excerpt from an interview, a woman recently arrested for the first time relates her "surprise" that this is the case. As she discovered, "traditional" ways of altering the probability of arrest were thoroughly ineffective:

> The way the narco bulls operate is different from other kinds. They're harder . . . Like I was pinched for boosting, shoplifting a couple of times and you know I'd just start bawlin' about things. What's gonna happen to my baby if I go to jail, what's gonna happen . . . They'd say "okay, we'll give you a break" . . . Try that with the fuckin' narco bulls and they'll tell you to shut your fuckin' mouth. There's no way you can talk them out of it.

Should a violator be "let off," it was held that it would be because of an offer to perform as an informant:

> The only way they're gonna let you off once they've got you is if you offer to go rat for them.

In general, the likelihood of altering one's fate after evidence had been obtained was received as virtually non-existent; from informants' point of view, "there's no way you can talk them out of it." This alleged overriding priority attributed to legal considerations is a matter of some importance to those interested in the research utility of official rates of heroin use. For example, the observation that the successfully detected cohort appears to pass into official records in its intact version suggests that the underreporting due to the operation of other-than-legal considerations is minimal.

Some People Have a Better Chance on the Street: Social Categories and Enforcement

Though informants asserted that legally irrelevant considerations exerted no influence upon police decision making after a successful investigation, they claimed that such considerations played an important role in determining who would be selected as a candidate for investigation in the first place. They saw the likelihood of being pursued by police as dependent on somewhat more than the "mere fact" that one was known to be in possession of heroin. While being in possession made one liable for pursuit, it did not guarantee it:

> INTERVIEWER: So every time you score you're taking a chance of getting pinched or at least having them come after you.
>
> RESPONDENT: Oh yeah, the chance is there, but there's more to it than that, y'know.

Indeed, informants were of the opinion that not all heroin users in possession were equally likely to be selected as candidates for pursuit:

> INTERVIEWER: So does pretty well everybody have the same chance of getting followed after they score, or what?
>
> RESPONDENT: Oh no, no. Some people have got a better chance on the street.

In part these differential probabilities were structured by the responsiveness of enforcement personnel to a variety of legally-irrelevant factors.

One's membership in certain social categories was portrayed by community members as prominent amongst those factors. For example, a heroin user identified as a "rat," i.e., a provider of information to the police, is obviously unlikely to be selected for pursuit. As one informant put it:

> Well if somebody's rattin' to the bulls they're not gonna pinch him, are they?

It was suggested that women, too, enjoyed "a better chance on the street."

> INTERVIEWER: Do the police give the women as bad a time, as rough a time as they give the men?
>
> RESPONDENT: Well they're pretty rough all around, y'know. I don't think they go after the chicks as much as the guys, though. Not that they leave us alone or anything, but they don't come after us as much.

Informants were not united regarding *why* women were selected as candidates for investigation less frequently than men. Some suggested that the police perceived female heroin users as less threatening to society than their male counterparts:

> Well, the bulls leave the working girls pretty much alone, usually. I guess they figure "what the fuck, they're workin' for their money, providin' a service and so on." We're not stealin' or nothin', y'know.

> I guess they figure it's the guys that are the ones to get 'cause of what they do, steal and the like.

Others accounted for the difference by referring to the practical problems women pose for investigative work carried out primarily by males:

> A lot of girls carry dope internally, y'know, so it's a lot of trouble for the bulls. They gotta take you down to [the public safety building] and wait for a qualified doctor to come and give you an internal search. That could take hours.

What was paramount among the theories advanced to explain the lesser likelihood of pursuit of women, however, was the notion that enforcement personnel perceived female heroin users as having "female" and not "heroin user" status. Despite their use of heroin they were understood to be *women* first and foremost. This itself was portrayed as creating a practical problem for police. Indeed, a notable feature of their regard for female heroin users in this way, it was asserted, was a reduction in the amount of physical vigour applied to obtain arrest-producing evidence. Informants attributed to police sensibilities that did not permit them to be egalitarian in their treatment of the sexes. As one informant put it:

> They're not . . . they don't beat the shit outa chicks the way they do with the guys. Sure, they're rough alright, but the guys've got it worse.

Informants claimed, however, that the difference enjoyed by women in general was enjoyed to a greater extent by particular types of women. Other types, it was told, were treated " . . . just like the guys."

> Well some broads they treat just like the guys. I've seen lots with broken teeth from handcuffs going down their throats, scars. . . . They beat the shit outa them to get the dope, just like they'd do to a guy.

It was suggested that the women who had "a better chance on the street" were those with an appearance and demeanour approximating those of "ordinary," i.e. non–heroin using, women. For informants, a woman's "better chance" eroded precisely to the extent that her presentation *strayed* from the one just suggested, as:

> the bulls don't mind beatin' on an old douche-bag with rotten teeth and dirty hair. Some chicks let themselves get so scraggy, it's no wonder they take shit.

One informant formulated the effect of a conventional presentation as functionally equivalent to an adaptive strategy:

INTERVIEWER: So what do you spend all that money on. Besides junk.

RESPONDENT: Well there's clothes and groceries. Getting my hair done and stuff. Makeup. You gotta keep yourself up, y'know.

INTERVIEWER: Keep yourself up?

RESPONDENT: Yeah, it's not good if you let yourself go like some chicks do.

INTERVIEWER: It's not good to . . .

RESPONDENT: Let yourself go, get . . . be a slob about yourself. I don't like gettin' that way. I never have. It's a personal thing. But if you look like shit you're gonna get treated that way too, y'know.

INTERVIEWER: By who?

RESPONDENT: By everybody.

INTERVIEWER: By the cops?

RESPONDENT: Oh yeah. If you look like a decent person they're not gonna bother you as much as if you walk around lookin' like a fuckin' dirty junkie asshole. Broads who do that are just askin' for it.

INTERVIEWER: Okay, so what you're saying then is that if you look like a . . . if you look pretty good then you're not gonna get the hassle you would if you didn't. Is that right or am I missing something?

RESPONDENT: No, that's about it. If a chick looks good the bulls are definitely not gonna . . . they're probably not gonna give her the usual shit.

These observations appear massively relevant to research and policy decisions based on officially-located heroin users. Consider, for example, the issue of *who*—in the sense of social type—*gets assembled into official statistics*. Indeed, notation of the pre-investigation significance of such presentational considerations as demeanour and appearance underscores the fact that an official heroin user—as opposed to a person who "merely" uses heroin—is the product of a social judgment made by the police. To paraphrase Piliavin and Briar (4), he or she is a heroin user because someone in authority has defined him/her as one, often on the basis of the public face presented to officials rather than the kind of offence committed. Quite obviously, if similar "public faces" are being assembled, heroin users start to look alike, a fact of no little clinical relevance.

If They Want Ya, They're Gonna Get Ya: The Particularization of Enforcement

For informants, however, category membership did not exhaust the list of extralegal factors potentially influential upon the choice of *who* from a range of possibles might be pursued as a candidate for investigation. Indeed, they asserted the relevance of a number of other considerations. For example, they claimed that "for personal reasons," enforcement personnel singled out some heroin users for vigorous pursuit. When members of the community realized that this was the case in their situation, i.e. that they had been selected for special investigation attention, they characterized the police as "having a burn" for them:

RESPONDENT: . . . well if they've got a burn for you for some reason . . .

INTERVIEWER: How do you mean have a burn?

RESPONDENT: Well if they really want you bad, y'know. Really want to see you pinched.

They suggested that this state of affairs would eventually result in their arrest, as "if they want ya, they're gonna get ya."

Once they've got a burn for ya, y'might as well start sayin' goodbye to everybody 'cause you'll be in jail before ya know it. If they want ya, they're gonna get ya, no two ways about it.

Informants indicated that one could become attractive as an enforcement target for a variety of reasons. In general, their own and their colleagues' experience suggested that anything one might do to further alienate the police, i.e. "to make them hate you even more than they do," stood to heighten the probability of investigative pursuit and, eventually, arrest.

If you fuck them around, treat them . . . if you don't play it right they're gonna be after you. If you do anything that . . . anything to make them hate you even more than they do, then watch out 'cause that's it for you.

It was held that further alienation of enforcement personnel could be accomplished by irritating them in any number of ways. One could, for example, make their work more difficult by interfering with it:

RESPONDENT: Well I did what you might call a stupid thing, what I think's a stupid thing anyway.

INTERVIEWER: What? What kind of stupid thing did you do?

RESPONDENT: Well I got the narco bulls mad at me, but I couldn't help it, I couldn't just . . . I couldn't hold myself back.

INTERVIEWER: Well what was the stupid thing?

RESPONDENT: Well one of my buddies—she's in here now as a matter of fact. She was gettin' roughed up a little and I was pissed off. I started screamin' at 'em, callin' them dumb fuckers and so forth. Kickin'. They told me to fuck off and mind my own business but I just got more frantic, y'know. After I thought about it I thought "Fuck, these guys are gonna be after me now for makin' them so fuckin' mad and all." So then I got pinched.

INTERVIEWER: This last time?

RESPONDENT: Yeah, just before Christmas. Anyway when I got pinched one of them said "that'll teach you to keep your fuckin' nose outa other people's business." So there ya go. If I'd . . . if I'd just turned away I'd probably still be on the street, y'know.

Also, one could refuse to cooperate:

> INTERVIEWER: Have the police ever approached you, ever asked you to rat for them? Like be an informant or something?
>
> RESPONDENT: Not in any kind of a formal way or nothing! Like offering me money. One time they asked me, on the street just out of the blue . . . asked me to tell them who's doin' things. I said just forget it and they said "things have been known to happen to guys like you. You'd better watch out from now on."
>
> INTERVIEWER: What was that supposed to mean?
>
> RESPONDENT: Well they were tellin' me in so many words that they'd be watching me a little bit closer for the next while.
>
> INTERVIEWER: Did they?
>
> RESPONDENT: Fuckin' right they did. I got jumped three times the next week.

Informants claimed that one could irritate the police—and thus potentially cause them to "have a burn for you"—by persistently frustrating their attempts at successful, arrest-producing investigation. The following excerpt from an interview provides an example:

> RESPONDENT: I know they were after me 'cause they told me they were.
>
> INTERVIEWER: Oh yeah, they told you?
>
> RESPONDENT: Oh yeah, it was just a matter of time. I haven't taken a pinch for years, y'know and it's not 'cause they haven't tried. I just been smarter than them and they were pissed off . . . So every time I scored I figured "well it's gonna be this time, this time they're gonna get me" so I was pretty careful, y'know. And they tried but I kept outsmartin' the fuckers. "We're gonna get ya," they said, "we're gonna get ya." I was . . . hurtin' their pride I guess, always outsmartin' 'em like that.

Irritating the police by verbally abusing them or by suggesting the superiority of a deviant lifestyle were portrayed as making them "hate you even more than they do" and thereby increasing the likelihood of being selected as a candidate for pursuit. For example:

> These young kids you see on the street, they think they're smart callin' the bulls names, dirty pig and all that. All they're doin' by that is makin' it worse for themselves 'cause they'll be harder on 'em and bug 'em.

> RESPONDENT: You can be on the street for a long time with no trouble then all of a sudden something happens and bingo, you're pinched.
>
> INTERVIEWER: Like what can happen, for example.
>
> RESPONDENT: Well you do somethin' stupid. Like I started makin' fun of a bull, one bull in particular. I told him one day that I was savin' up for a downpayment on a house and he said "Oh yeah, how long'll that take ya?" I said "Oh, about

a month or so." And he said "Fuck, it'll take you five years." So every time I saw him I said "Well are ya still savin'?" Fuck he got pissed off.

INTERVIEWER: He couldn't take a joke...

RESPONDENT: I guess not 'cause he was sure after me for a while. I couldn't go on the street without gettin' some hassle. I was a real heatbag.

Informants indicated that the likelihood of being singled out for special investigation was increased by one's ignoring recent court orders:

The judge told me that I had 48 hours to get out of the Province of British Columbia and the bulls knew it, things get around. So when I scored they just naturally came right after me. Figured I'd really get the book thrown at me, what with gettin' it for possession when I shoulda been out of town.

THE ORGANIZATION OF POLICEWORK

In addition to violator features there are, of course, numerous other considerations which influence narcotic enforcement and—ultimately—official portrayals of community drug use. This section of the chapter discusses the potential impact of changes in size of the enforcement unit and quality and style of enforcement on official rates.

They're Better and There's More of Them: Asserted Changes in the Size and Quality of the Enforcement Unit

Notations of change in the rate of a given deviant behaviour presume— among other things—that the number and quality of personnel assigned to deal with the behaviour have remained static. Black (2) explains how crime rates and size of enforcement units influence each other:

Crime rates that are produced in proactive police operations, such as arrests for... narcotics violation, directly correlate with police manpower allocation. Until a point of total detection is reached and holding all else constant, these vice rates increase as the number of policemen assigned to vice control is increased.

The influence of enhanced *quality* of enforcement is more difficult to establish. It is the case, however, that since the early 1970s recruits to all municipal police departments in the province have been receiving narcotics investigation training through the Western Province Police College. The putative "spread" of heroin use from metropolis to hinterland thus becomes potentially more related to the diffusion of knowledge than narcotics. Some informants added documentation to this notion via their complaints about the declining number of places thought to be "safe" for engaging in drug-relevant activities. Consider the following excerpts from an interview with a drug trafficker who used to conduct business in such places "before it got too hot."

> INTERVIEWER: So what happened after that?
>
> RESPONDENT: Well after that I started to stay out of town pretty much. I'd take a half-a-dozen bundles or so and go up through the Interior and places like that. There was always people lookin' for dope up here and there wasn't the heat.
>
> INTERVIEWER: This was when.
>
> RESPONDENT: Oh, shit, 10–12 years ago or so.
>
> INTERVIEWER: So you'd stay out of town.
>
> RESPONDENT: Yeah, I'd head up to the Interior. That was before it got too hot. The bulls are all wise now, not like before.
>
> INTERVIEWER: They used to be . . .
>
> RESPONDENT: They didn't know what dope was, not at all. Then you could even go out to the Russell Hotel in (a municipality adjacent to Western City). Cops didn't know what was goin' on.
>
> INTERVIEWER: Now they do?
>
> RESPONDENT: Oh yeah, they're wise all over now. Nowhere's safe anymore, like it used to be.

Undercover operations, too, were portrayed as increasingly more sophisticated. One informant insisted that "the bulls are getting smarter" and documented this assertion with observations of the changed appearance and manner of personnel attempting to infiltrate the heroin community:

> RESPONDENT: Oh yeah, the bulls are gettin' smarter, there's no doubt about it . . . Look at the guys they send down now, the undercover bulls. They used to be big healthy lookin' assholes with size 12 shoes, hangin' around bein' a bit too pushy. Now they get these guys who look so much like dope fiends y'could never tell. Y'wonder how they ever got to be cops . . . They're cooler, too. Take their time gettin' in.

They Don't Do Things the Way They Did Before: Asserted Changes in the Style of Narcotics Enforcement

As potentially influential upon drug use statistics as the number and quality of enforcement personnel, is the *style* of enforcement. Informants were virtually unanimous in asserting that enforcement procedures and priorities had undergone dramatic stylistic revisions, that they appeared different from the way they did at an earlier period in the history of the local community. One informant expressed recognition of such changes in the following way:

> The bulls don't do things the way they did before. Older people like me—not

necessarily old but who've been around, y'know . . . I can remember when the bulls did things very differently from the way your average one is now.

She continues, specifying the character of the stylistic changes:

> Well for one thing you knew where you stood, they played by the rules. And they weren't as chickenshit about things.

Informants frequently spoke of current enforcement practices as "chickenshit" or "petty." For them, this implied an emphasis on the letter of the law, on offences of small magnitude, on "things that you wouldn't get busted for before." For example, informants suggested that unlike an earlier period in the history of the local community, police would now attempt to arrest a person for being in possession of any heroin-using paraphernalia that might bear a minute trace of the substance—in their words, "anything that might analyze."

> RESPONDENT: The bulls are chickenshit now. They're out to pinch you for anything that might analyze—a spoon, a fit, an empty cap. That's what I got in on, a fuckin' cap for fuck sake, a fuckin' cap with hardly anythin' in it.
>
> INTERVIEWER: Just a cap?
>
> RESPONDENT: Yeah, fuck, there was . . . I'd used better than three-quarters of it, more than that and they got it outa my purse.

Also, consider the following excerpt from an interview wherein an informant describes the activity that resulted in her imprisonment for trafficking in narcotics:

> INTERVIEWER: So what was the offence that landed you in here this time?
>
> RESPONDENT: Trafficking, they say I put out to an undercover bull.
>
> INTERVIEWER: But you didn't?
>
> RESPONDENT: No. It's a bum rap. I just passed it to him. I wasn't puttin' out at the time. I was just with somebody when it happened.
>
> INTERVIEWER: Tell me what happened.
>
> RESPONDENT: Well I was just in my car with this person I know and he was going to . . . He was putting out some stuff. This Rick guy—you've heard about him—he was gonna score from my friend. He was talkin' to me. My friend's next to me in the passenger seat. So he takes the joint out and Rick goes around to the driver's side where I am—right out in the road—and my friend passes the joint to me and I give it to Rick. He just did that so he could get two busts at once.

Though informants characterized their adversaries as going to great lengths to enforce narcotics laws, i.e., "the bulls'll do anything to make a pinch," they reasonably expected enforcement to be constrained by proprieties they sometimes called the "rules of the game":

> RESPONDENT: It's just a game, cops and junkies.

INTERVIEWER: Games have got rules.

RESPONDENT: So's this one, believe me. If you don't go by the rules of the game you're fucked. Even the bulls go by the rules.

In short, informants had a sense of activities that the police *would* and *would not* engage in "to make a pinch." This notion was informed in part by an understanding of them not only as policemen but as citizens, members of society, persons possessing sensibilities uncongenial to doing literally anything to enforce narcotics laws. Recently however, informants claim that the latitude of personally-congenial behaviours has widened considerably. Some related this widening to the presence in enforcement units of more committed personnel. In the words of an informant:

They've got bulls now who don't give a shit about nothin' except making pinches. Nothin' . . .

For informants, the following excerpt from an interview would exemplify this new, *liberated* enforcement style. In the late 1970s the events it relates were being spread—rumour-like—throughout the heroin-using community.

INTERVIEWER: What about this guy Fred, the narc who was just under.

RESPONDENT: Oh that asshole.

INTERVIEWER: Did you ever run into him?

RESPONDENT: Oh, for sure. Everybody knew him. He was always around. Fuckin' carrying on, just one, y'know. Big nigger hairdo. Fuckin' weird he looked. Leather jacket. Everybody knew the prick. People figured he was solid. He even had me fooled, which is why I'm fuckin' here.

INTERVIEWER: So everybody knew him.

RESPONDENT: Oh yeah. He was really into it. Only went home once in the eight fuckin' months he was on the street. That's dedication. I knew girls . . . Well he was with a couple of girls. They were supportin' him, turnin' tricks for fuck sake. He was their old man. They were keepin' him fixed.

INTERVIEWER: Keeping him fixed?

RESPONDENT: Fuck yes. He was wired up. He had to spend a whole week in the hospital afterwards. He was fuckin' wired up.

Another stylistic change cited by some informants was a refusal on the part of enforcement personnel to make "deals" with violators, particularly on occasions where a detected offence involved more than one party. Solomon (5) provides an observation of the sort of deal in question:

[Name] boots in the bathroom door, knocking the girl inside into the bathtub. [Name] fishes into the sink for the needle in the midst of the scramble. They find the needle and take them both into the station. The guy had just shot up and was just about to fix his chick. He says he'll cop the rap if they let her go. The police agree to this deal.

An informant related an instance of the contemporary suspension of this practice:

> INTERVIEWER: So where's your husband now?
>
> RESPONDENT: Oh he's over there (in the men's unit of the provincial prison), we got pinched together.
>
> INTERVIEWER: Two for the price of one.
>
> RESPONDENT: Oh yeah, shit. He woulda taken the rap 'cause I was pregnant at the time, but the bulls wouldn't let him. He tried, though.

From informants' point of view, narcotics enforcement patterns in Western City have undergone dramatic revisions in terms of quality and style. Time and time again in interviews and casual conversation heroin users characterized current police strategies as "better" and stylistically "different" than they were at an earlier period.

That a number of changes appear to have occurred in enforcement activities is a matter of more than passing interest to those concerned with the quality of official statistical portrayals of the volume, and volume trends, of narcotics use. Indeed, the changes tend to erode one's faith in a reasonable correspondence between the portrayals and their referents. For example, the enforcement revisions appear to be patterned, suggesting not only the presence of systematic—rather than random and self-cancelling—error influences in the statistics, but the possibility as well that recent assertions of increases in the number of heroin users may be more an artifact of the revisions than a reflection of what is happening in the community. Taken together the changes in style and quality of enforcement provide for the appearance of an enlarged population independent of any *actual* enlargement.

The influence of enhanced quality of enforcement upon official portrayals of narcotic use is virtually self-announcing. Quite obviously, better enforcement increases the probability of arrest and thereby "builds in" an apparent increase in the number of drug users. Furthermore—as suggested earlier—it provides for the "spread" of drug-related activity to previously untainted communities.

Stylistic changes, too, suggest a potentially artificial swelling of community size. For example, the alleged refusal on the part of police to charge only one person in a multiple violator situation stands to inflate the number of arrests in unknown but potentially significant ways. Similarly, informants' characterization of enforcement personnel as newly "chickenshit" suggests not only that previously unnoticed offences are now being recorded but also that the official records include arrests for violations that are technically but not socially valid.

CONCLUDING REMARKS

A continuing debate in the sociology of deviant behaviour concerns the degree to which official statistics accurately depict the actual volume and morphology of community deviance. At issue is not *whether* official portrayals depart from perfect correspondence with their referents: indeed, that they are somehow biased, somehow incomplete is widely acknowledged. Instead, debate centres on another question, specifically: can official statistics be taken as standing in some determinable relationship to the actual volume and morphology of a given activity or are the departures such that official statistics are essentially useless?

Commonly, sociologists have endeavoured to make the relationship determinable by attempting to identify the source of acknowledged bias, incompleteness, etc. Potentially more important than knowing the sources of such errors, however, is knowing their character. Indeed, the usefulness of official rates of deviant behaviour for research and policy design persists only when it can be demonstrated that factors which might erode the correspondence between such rates and their referents display a random character, thereby cancelling each other out.

This report has examined some of the enforcement activities that produce official portrayals of the volume and morphology of heroin use in and around a large city in the Canadian West.

Using data obtained via a program of unstructured interviews with heroin users resident in Western City, this report has described some of the ways in which police activity potentially influences official portrayals of the volume and morphology of non-medical drug use. In general, the data suggest *pattern* and an unevenness of enforcement over time.

That the enforcement component of the narcotics environment cannot be presumed to be static is hardly a revelation. It remains the case, however, that many who use official statistics for research, policy, and political purposes attribute an unchanging nature to police procedures.

Recognition that a situation of uneven enforcement exists has numerous implications for users of official statistics. Some of these have been indicated here, though many more await explication. In general, however, the data presented suggest the rationality of a decreased reliance on official statistics as indicators of the extent and distribution of community heroin use.

REFERENCES

1. Bittner, E. The police on skid-row: A study of peace keeping. *American Sociological Review, 32*:699–715 (1967).
2. Black, D. J. Production of crime rates. *American Sociological Review, 35*:733–48 (1970).

3. Cicourel, A. V. *The Social Organization of Juvenile Justice.* New York: Wiley, 1968.
4. Piliavin, I., and Briar, S. Police encounters with juveniles. *American Journal of Sociology*, 70:206–14 (1964).
5. Solomon, R. Fieldnotes prepared for the Commission of Inquiry into the Non-Medical Use of Drugs. Unpublished manuscript, 1970.

THE CRIMINAL JUSTICE SYSTEM: ARRESTS AND PROSECUTIONS

Previous sections have sketched the features of Canadian drug law and the extent of illicit drug use in this country. Now we turn to the social collision between the criminal justice system and the drug user. Contributors in this section draw on interview studies, official statistics, and case law to show how the legal abstractions of the drug legislation are put into practice. This process begins with a decision to investigate a possible offence and carries through arrest, court appearance, sentencing outcome, and the possibility of appeals that may reach as high as the Supreme Court of Canada.

Illegal drug use and distribution are consensual activities usually conducted in private or in inconspicuous surroundings, and as such present a particular challenge to enforcement efforts. In predatory crimes with victims, the police can normally rely on a complainant to report the offence. How then are police to detect drug crime, and on what powers do they rely to make arrests? When offenders are successfully prosecuted, the law provides a wide range of sentencing options. How do judges determine what sentence to impose for the various drug offences and what are the patterns in sentencing? The *Canadian Charter of Rights and Freedoms* has the potential to alter traditional enforcement and sentencing practices. How are the *Charter*'s precepts being applied in the actual conduct of drug cases? The selections that follow attempt to answer these questions, as they focus on the functioning of the criminal justice system.

Chapter 16, an original contribution by Robert Solomon, describes the extraordinary powers of search and seizure given to the police in the investigation of drug cases. Since the 1920s, many of the *Criminal Code* requirements for lawful search and arrest have been considered inadequate to meet the threat to society posed by the drug addict and drug pusher. The writ of assistance, which from 1929 on enabled police to make warrantless searches of dwellings, was finally abolished in 1985. Many of the other special powers remain.

Professor Solomon also presents a number of decisions based on the *Canadian Charter of Rights and Freedoms* and highlights their impact on the processing of drug cases. It has taken some time since the passage of the *Charter* for this case law to build up. Since it will continue to accumulate, no interpretation can be deemed conclusive unless it is delivered by the ultimate arbiter, the Supreme Court of Canada. Nevertheless, Professor Solomon shows how some previous abuses of individual rights and freedoms in drug cases may be ameliorated. At the same time, the traditional claim that the public has special needs for protection from illicit drugs and drug users may remain unaltered by the *Charter*. It is perhaps unrealistic to expect the *Charter* to resolve all the many inconsistencies and conflicts inherent in the drug lesiglation. The precarious balance between the individual drug user's rights and the necessity of enforcement will no doubt continue for some time yet.

Patricia Erickson's interviews with cannabis possession offenders show how police powers, initially deployed against a deviant minority, have been activated against a modern generation of mainly middle-class youth. Contrary to the conventional wisdom that most cannabis arrests result from accidental discovery, the offenders' experiences suggest a fairly high level of drug-directed activity by police. What this research cannot reveal, of course, is the extent to which the police exercise their discretion *not* to enforce the law by ignoring an infraction or letting the user off with a warning. Moreover, some of Erickson's subjects reported that the police offered to drop or reduce the charges if the person would act as an informant, and those potential arrestees who complied would also not be found in a study of actual offenders.

Neil Boyd discusses how the judiciary, in the face of mounting numbers of cases and in the absence of legislative activity, has assumed the execution of drug policy by default. Through case reports, he extracts some of the guiding principles that judges have utilized in determining sentences. Since most of the pronouncements come to light through appeals, much more case law is available on the distribution offences than on simple possession. One notable exception was the trial of guitarist Keith Richards, a member of the Rolling Stones, for heroin possession. Professor Boyd juxtaposes the official sentencing statistics with available law and discerns a trend toward leniency, particularly leniency to the cannabis possession offender, and to the cannabis trafficker in comparison with the heroin trafficker. The interested reader may wish to refer to Appendix A for the most recent available official statistics, and also for a wealth of information on the legal response to illicit drugs in Canada.

Since these national conviction statistics reflect important aspects of the criminal justice system's response, we digress here to a discussion of some trends that can be discerned in Appendix A. While cannabis remains by far the leading drug in number of convictions, annual totals have been declining for cannabis and increasing for cocaine (Table A.1). Although a similar trend is found in each province, Quebec has a relatively low number of cannabis convictions but a high number for cocaine compared to Ontario, the other most populous province (Table A.2). Numbers alone, however, are deceptive.

When we turn to conviction rates (Table A.3), the variations by province and by drug are revealed more clearly. In 1985, Quebec displays the highest conviction rate of any province for cocaine, at 21.5 per 100,000 population aged 16 and over, followed by British Columbia at 10.6. In the same year, however, Alberta has the highest rate for cannabis, 216.7, while Quebec shows the lowest, 63.1. British Columbia and the three prairie provinces, topped by Alberta at 11.8, have the highest conviction rates in 1985 for the hallucinogens (i.e., the restricted drugs under the *Food and Drugs Act*, Part IV). Convictions for the only hallucinogen under the *Narcotic Control Act*, phencyclidine or PCP, are highest in Quebec (5.0 in 1985). The leader in heroin convictions is British Columbia, showing a decline from 18.2 in 1975 to 4.0 in 1985. Rates in the Maritime provinces for all drugs are generally lower than in the rest of the country, and Ontario, despite its pre-eminence in population, lies for the most part in the middle range of conviction rates. Special mention should be made of the Yukon and the Northwest Territories where, despite a very small population, the conviction rates for cannabis, cocaine, and FDA hallucinogens are very high, exceeding those in all provinces. Judith Blackwell's review of drug use patterns in Canada (Chapter 14) notes also that survey data suggest very high levels of cannabis consumption in the Yukon and the Territories.

Tables A.4 and A.5 compare sentences awarded in 1980 and 1985 for the possession and trafficking offences. For cannabis possession, the earlier trend (noted by Boyd) towards greater leniency appears to have reversed recently in that the proportion of offenders receiving discharges has declined while the proportion jailed has doubled. A fine remains the most common outcome, however, as it does for possession of cocaine or the hallucinogens. Only for heroin possession is incarceration the most likely disposal. When the distribution offences of trafficking and possession for the purpose of trafficking are examined, the distinct trend is for imprisonment in a majority of cases, regardless of drug. The proportion imprisoned remained quite stable for cannabis and hallucinogens, declined for cocaine, and increased for heroin. The majority of convicted heroin traffickers are incarcerated for more than one year, while more than half of cannabis and hallucinogen dealers receive less than one year's imprisonment. The data in Appendix A illustrate the lack of a uniform, monolithic legal response to illicit drugs, and suggest instead considerable variability over time, by province, and by drug.

Chapter 19 describes the second wave of empirical research on Canadian cannabis possession offenders conducted by Patricia Erickson, this time with the assistance of Glenn Murray. Seven years later, the second sample had personal and legal characteristics that were similar to the first; the impact of criminalization on their lives was also similar. What had changed was the efficiency with which the cases were processed in 1981, compared to 1974. At the time the Le Dain Commission was formed, overloading of the system with cannabis possession offences was considered a problem, but 12 years later the system had been streamlined to accommodate levels three or four times greater. The production of tens of thousands of cannabis criminals annually had become a routine part of the justice system's workload, and thus one pressure for the reform of the cannabis law had been removed.

Drug users who run afoul of the criminal justice system face potentially serious consequences. As these chapters amply demonstrate, drug users may find themselves unexpectedly searched, arrested, fingerprinted, publicly tried, and threatened with loss of freedom. They are then faced with a lifelong criminal record that may have unforeseen adverse consequences for their future livelihood. The individual so singled out may feel a sense of injustice, but can be certain that the criminal justice system does not take infractions of the drug laws lightly. The criminal sanction is the most serious response society has to offer.

16

The Noble Pursuit of Evil:
Arrest, Search, and Seizure
in Canadian Drug Law

ROBERT R. SOLOMON

INTRODUCTION

Since the first federal drug law was enacted in 1908 (130b), the police have attributed the growth of the illicit trade to the drug users' cunning, the shortage of police resources, the leniency of the courts, and deficiencies in the law, particularly the need for greater police powers. During the last 80 years, the government and police officials responsible for drug enforcement have successfully lobbied Parliament for special enforcement powers (129; see also Chapter 7 of this book). As a result, police have far broader enforcement powers in even a minor drug case than they have in a murder, arson, rape, or other serious criminal investigation.

Most of Canada's special legislative powers were enacted during the 1920s, following a successful crusade to depict addicts as fiendish criminals obsessed with a need to addict others. The target population was relatively small and predominantly Chinese; the public had little contact with drug users or objective information about drugs. The government allayed concerns about the extraordinary breadth of the new legislation by indicating that it would be used against only the Chinese and the white criminal class—not against ordinary citizens (129, pp. 319–25). For the most part, Canadian courts shared Parliament's sympathy for narcotics enforcement officials and broadly interpreted these special powers (3, 17, 40, 59, 70, 78, 80, 81, 116, 123).

Until the mid-1960s, the federal drug law was enforced almost exclusively by the Royal Canadian Mounted Police drug squads. The annual number of convictions rarely exceeded 500, and all but a small percentage of the charges involved opiates (61, p. 719). The dramatic rise in the use of cannabis and other non-opiates in the last 20 years has prompted a parallel increase in enforcement activities. Scores of municipal, provincial, and RCMP officers now invoke the special drug enforcement powers daily, and the targets of these powers are drawn largely from Canada's population of four million cannabis users (42). For example, 93 percent of the more than 322,900 federal drug convictions under the *Narcotic Control Act* between 1977 and 1985 were for cannabis offences, whereas approximately 1.5 percent involved opiates (13,

Table 5; 14, Table 5). Of the cannabis offences, 84.5 percent were for simple possession (13, Table 5; 14, Table 5). The available data suggest that the vast majority of these offenders are young (13, Table 13; 14, Table 13) and the quantity of cannabis involved is small (12).

As the number of people subjected to these provisions increased, so too did the controversies surrounding their use. Few aspects of Canadian drug policy have generated such heated debate. Viewed by critics as wholly unwarranted intrusions on civil liberties, these same powers have been steadfastly defended as an essential tool in the fight against the illicit trade.

For our purposes, the basic policy issue is whether the current drug legislation strikes an appropriate balance between the demands of effective enforcement and the preservation of individual freedom. Ultimately, we must decide whether the risks posed by illicit drug use, relative to those inherent in other criminal activities, justify foregoing some of our traditional rights and freedoms. Even if we conclude that the current patterns of illicit use present a sufficiently grave threat to warrant giving the police special enforcement powers, a reasonable relationship must exist between the measure of liberty we give up and the actual enforcement benefits we receive.

Until the 1982 proclamation of the *Canadian Charter of Rights and Freedoms* (130d), Parliament and the courts willingly sacrificed the rights of drug suspects, presumably on the assumption that they were not entitled to, or deserving of, the rights of ordinary citizens. The *Charter* has intensified debate about the legitimacy of Canada's drug enforcement powers and is forcing both Parliament and the courts to address the underlying issues that they had avoided.

This chapter focuses on the nature of the special drug enforcement powers and how they differ from general enforcement powers. The first part examines the general powers of arrest and the courts' relaxed application of these principles in drug cases. The second part begins with an outline of the Canadian *Criminal Code*'s (130e) general search warrant provisions. This is followed by a detailed analysis of the special search and seizure powers of the *Narcotic Control Act* (NCA) (130m) and the *Food and Drugs Act* (FDA) (130j).

POLICE POWERS OF ARREST

Sources of Police Powers to Arrest in Drug Cases

The NCA and FDA both contain special powers of search and seizure, but make no reference to arrest procedures. However, by virtue of the *Interpretation Act* (130l, s. 27(2); 103) the *Criminal Code*'s procedural provisions, including those governing arrest, apply to offences created by other federal legislation, unless this legislation provides otherwise. Consequently, police authority to search and seize in drug cases is derived from the NCA and FDA (106), but their power to arrest is dictated by the *Code*'s general arrest sections.

Peace officers have the authority to enforce both federal and provincial law, regardless of the police force that employs them or their assigned duties. In appropriate circumstances, police may invoke their enforcement powers under the *Code*, other federal statutes, and provincial legislation (see, for example, 131a, s. 190(2); 131b, ss. 48(2) and 54; 131c, ss. 9 and 10). These independent sources of authority can be used to further a drug investigation. For example, a detective on the RCMP drug squad may stop a suspected drug offender for violation of the provincial highway traffic Act. If, in the course of this investigation, evidence of a drug offence is found, a drug charge may also be laid. Thus, the general arrest provisions of the *Code* represent only one of many discrete sources of police power in drug investigations.

Arrest without Warrant

English common law protected individual freedom by strictly limiting police authority to arrest without a warrant. This power was not granted for misdemeanours, and could only be invoked for felonies and treason in a limited number of situations.[1] In all other circumstances, an officer had to bring information before a judge who would determine if there was sufficient evidence to justify issuing an arrest warrant. Officers who acted without authority or who exceeded their authority were shown little sympathy (32, pp. 93–96; 41, pp. 566–67; 132, pp. 193–94).

The English common law of crimes was largely supplanted in Canada with the enactment of the first *Criminal Code* in 1892 (130f). While maintaining many features of the common law, the *Code* greatly expanded police powers of arrest without a warrant and police immunity from criminal and civil liability. Various sections of the *Code* authorize arrest for specific offences (130e, ss. 31(1) and 181), but it is the general arrest powers in section 450 which are most relevant in drug cases.

Section 450(1)(a)

This provision authorizes the police to arrest without warrant in three situations involving indictable offences. The term "indictable offence" includes those offences in which the prosecutor has the option of proceeding either by indictment or by summary conviction, generally referred to as "hybrid" or "dual procedure" offences (97; 130l, s. 27(1)(*a*)). Since all the common drug offences are either indictable or hybrid offences, they fall within this subsection.

First, the police may arrest without a warrant a person who has committed an indictable offence. To rely on this provision, the officer must establish that the suspect actually committed an indictable offence (120, p. 47). Second, the police may arrest without a warrant a person who, on reasonable and probable grounds (16, 18, 27, 43, 52), they believe has committed an indictable offence. The arresting officer need not prove that the suspect committed an indictable offence, only that there were reasonable and probable grounds for so believing. Third, officers may arrest without a warrant a person who they believe, on reasonable and probable grounds, is about to commit an indictable offence. Although the purpose of this measure is to prevent the commission of indictable offences, its use necessarily entails the arrest, search, and detention of individuals who have not yet committed any criminal act (4, pp. 140–41; 62, pp. 56–57; 75).

Section 450(1)(b)

This subsection authorizes the police to arrest without warrant a person whom they find committing a criminal offence, which includes indictable, hybrid, and summary conviction offences. Rejecting earlier authorities (6, 86), the Supreme Court of Canada held in a 1975 case that the term "finds committing" means "apparently finds committing" (8; 23, pp. 556–59; 77). This controversial interpretation significantly increased the scope of police arrest powers.

Section 450(1)(c)

This subsection authorizes the police to arrest without a warrant a person who they have reasonable and probable grounds to believe is named in an arrest warrant in force within the jurisdiction. Provided the police act reasonably and in good faith, the arrest is lawful even if they have arrested the wrong person (33, 36).

Reasonable and Probable Grounds

The legality of an arrest frequently depends on whether the police had reasonable and probable grounds to suspect the accused. The courts apply an objective test in making this determination, asking whether the facts were sufficient to cause a reasonably careful and prudent person to have a strong and honest belief in the guilt of the accused. Therefore, mere suspicion is not enough. For example, knowledge of a suspect's prior criminal record does not constitute reasonable and probable grounds. The officer must approach the issue objectively and make a careful assessment of the facts, including the statements given by the witnesses and the suspect. The case against the suspect need not be conclusive, and the officer may rely on evidence that would not be admissible in court. Having completed the initial investigation, the officer must make a decision based on the facts, formulate a charge, and then arrest the suspect on that charge (16, 17, 18, 25, 27, 33, 43, 50, 52).

Arrest with Warrant

When acting pursuant to an arrest warrant, the police are considered to be agents of the court. Sections 455 and 456 of the *Code* set out the procedures for obtaining an arrest warrant, the contents of the warrant, and the manner in which it is to be executed. Section 28 of the *Code* protects officers from criminal liability for arresting the wrong person under a warrant, provided they act in good faith and on reasonable and probable grounds. At common law the police were held liable in this situation, thereby protecting an innocent suspect's rights, regardless of how reasonable the officers' mistake had been (32, p. 93; 33; 36).

Rights and Obligations in the Arrest Process

Although the arresting officer is under an obligation to make a thorough investigation, the law does not impose a general duty on the suspect to assist the officer. With few exceptions, individuals may refuse to identify themselves, account for their presence, answer questions, remain on the scene, accompany the officer, or submit to a search.[2] The law recognizes the citizens' right to go their own ways unless they have been lawfully arrested. An individual's assertion of his or her right to be left alone does not constitute the criminal offence of obstructing a police officer, nor does it provide reasonable and probable grounds for arrest. An officer cannot arrest individuals in order to question them, gain their assistance, or punish them for being unco-operative (11, 23, 24, 44, 45, 49, 52, 69, 79, 114, 134).

Private citizens are entitled to resist an unlawful arrest, using whatever amount of force is reasonably necessary for that purpose (4, 24, 45, 52, 121, 134). Nevertheless, suspects must submit to a lawful arrest, even if they are innocent of any wrongdoing. If, instead, a suspect physically resists or attempts to flee, he or she may be convicted of several criminal offences, such as obstruction, assaulting an officer, resisting arrest, or escaping lawful custody. Consequently, the parties' rights and obligations are dictated by the exact point at which a lawful arrest occurs.

In criminal law, an arrest occurs when an officer informs the suspect of the arrest and takes him or her into custody. If a suspect submits to a verbal command, nothing more is needed. Should a suspect refuse to submit, an officer must physically assert control. The courts have held that an officer merely has to touch a suspect to satisfy this requirement[3] (37, 39, 83, 101, 119, 122). The *Code* provides that an officer shall not take a suspect into custody for certain offences, unless it is necessary to do so in the public interest or to ensure the suspect's attendance in court. If an arrest is made the *Code* provides that the suspect must be released once his or her continued custody is no longer necessary (130e, ss. 450(2) and 451). These complex provisions help to ensure that minor offenders are released expeditiously, without being held in custody or formally processed.

The law defines not only the criteria for lawful arrest, but also how the arrest is to be made and how the suspect is to be treated. Whether or not the police had legal authority to make the arrest, they may incur criminal and civil liability if they act unlawfully during the remainder of the arrest process.

Reasons for Arrest

The common law principles of civil liability require the police to inform a suspect of the reasons for the arrest at the time of the arrest, unless the reasons are obvious or the suspect is fleeing, resisting, or incapable of appreciating the explanation. Even in these latter cases, the suspect must be told at the first reasonable opportunity. The courts have held that suspects need not submit to an arrest until they have been properly informed of the reasons, and that an officer who fails to meet this obligation is acting unlawfully (18, 50, 52, 94). The true reasons for the arrest must be given. An officer cannot arrest on a charge for which there are no reasonable and probable grounds, in order to look for evidence of a second undisclosed offence. However, if there are reasonable and probable grounds to arrest the suspect for more than one offence, the officer may inform the suspect of one charge without disclosing the others. The charge does not have to be specified in formal language; it is sufficient to indicate the factual circumstances that give rise to the arrest (18, 50, 52, 94).

Section 29(2) of the *Code* imposes a corresponding criminal law duty on the police to disclose the reasons for the arrest.[4] However, section 29(3) explicitly protects an officer from criminal liability for breach of this provision. The granting of criminal immunity does not alter the fact that the arrest is unlawful. Therefore, a suspect can physically resist arrest without incurring criminal liability until informed of the reasons for arrest (52, 94, 121). Nevertheless, it must be emphasized that a suspect runs a risk when resisting what he or she believes to be an unlawful arrest. The court may reject the suspect's interpretation of the facts, disbelieve the suspect's testimony, or conclude that the officer's conduct constituted an exception to the general legal principles. In such situations, otherwise innocent suspects who have erred in asserting what they honestly believed to be their rights may be convicted of obstructing or assaulting a peace officer.

Search pursuant to a Lawful Arrest

The common law vigorously protected private citizens from arbitrary and unauthorized searches (29, 66, 124). In the absence of specific statutory authority, the police have no general right to search a suspect until after he or she has been lawfully arrested. Following an arrest, an officer may search the suspect, the suspect's personal effects, and the area within the suspect's immediate physical control for evidence of the offence and for weapons (26; 38; 53, pp. 261–335 and 498–508; 55, pp. 19–22; 58; 63; 108). If evidence of other offences is found, it may also be seized and additional charges may be laid.

The Use of Force

The police may use as much force as is reasonably necessary to perform their duties (130e, ss. 25–27, 30, 32). Nevertheless, as a general rule, suspects must be given an opportunity to submit peacefully. The right to resort to deadly force is restricted to situations in which it is necessary to protect an officer or a third person from serious harm, or to prevent the escape of a fleeing suspect who cannot be stopped in a less violent manner (1; 74; 95; 115; 130e, s. 25(3) and (4); 144). An officer may incur criminal and civil liability for using excessive or unnecessary force, or for using any force when acting unlawfully (31; 58; 65; 130e, s. 26; 144).

Release of Suspects

Once the police make a lawful arrest, they may take reasonable steps to investigate the incident prior to releasing the suspect or bringing the suspect before a justice of the peace. If the suspect is held in custody, he or she must be brought before a justice without unreasonable delay and, in any event, within 24 hours if a justice is available (87; 130e, s. 454).

The Court's Redefinition of Police Powers in Drug Enforcement

Canadian courts have held that police officers engaged in drug enforcement need not fulfil the duties normally imposed upon arresting officers. In their attempt to facilitate drug enforcement, our courts have suspended several fundamental safeguards of citizens' rights and freedoms.

Perhaps this antipathy to drug suspects is best illustrated by the 1949 Ontario Court of Appeal decision in *R.* v. *Brezack* (78). In this case two officers, without warning, grabbed Brezack from behind by the throat and arms. When one of the officers forcibly attempted to search his mouth for drugs, Brezack struck the officer and bit his finger. Brezack was convicted of assaulting a peace officer in the execution of his duty, even though the police had accosted him without identifying themselves, making a formal arrest, notifying him of the reasons, or allowing him to submit peacefully. The court held that there were reasonable and probable grounds to believe that Brezack had drugs in his mouth and that he would swallow them unless he was taken by surprise. While recognizing that these tactics fell far short of the traditional requirements of a valid arrest, the Court concluded that such measures were justified when dealing with drug users:

> It is well known that, in making arrests in these narcotic cases, it would often be impossible to find evidence of the offence upon the person arrested if he had the slightest suspicion that he might be searched. Constables have a task of great difficulty in their efforts to check the illegal traffic in opium and other prohibited drugs. Those who carry on the traffic are cunning, crafty and unscrupulous almost beyond belief. While, therefore, it is important that constables should be instructed that there are limits upon their right of search, including search of the person, they are not to be encumbered by technicalities in handling the situations with which they often have to deal in narcotic cases, which permit them little time for deliberation and require the stern exercise of such rights of search as they possess. (78, p. 270)

The Court noted that Brezack had a previous drug conviction, and emphasized the fact that heroin was subsequently found in his car. Had drugs not been found, the Court might have been forced to consider Brezack's right to use reasonable force in self-defence.

Until the enactment of the *Charter*, the use of throat-holds was such an accepted method of dealing with suspected heroin users that its legality was rarely challenged.[5] More importantly, by characterizing drug users as crafty and manipulative criminals, the Court in *Brezack* suggested that their rights might be justifiably dismissed or ignored in the pursuit of effective enforcement. This view has come to dominate much of the case law and explains why a broad range of violent, intrusive, and otherwise unsavoury enforcement practices have been condoned by Canadian courts in drug cases (3, 17, 59, 70, 116, 123).

The Realities of the Law of Arrest

Charting the exact legal bounds of police powers may have been of greater theoretical than practical concern. Even if the arrest and hence the search of the suspect was unlawful, any illegally obtained evidence was generally admissible in court. Prior to the *Charter*, the test for admissibility was the relevance of the evidence, and not the manner in which it was obtained (102, 116). Section 24(2) of the *Charter* now provides that evidence obtained in violation of the suspect's *Charter* rights may be excluded, if the suspect can establish that the admission of the evidence would bring the administration of justice into disrepute. So far, the hundreds of cases involving section 24(2) have done little to clarify this exclusionary rule. Although it is still too early to define the specific police behaviour necessary to bring the administration of justice into disrepute, it is clear that section 24(2) permits the continued admissibility of illegally obtained evidence in many cases.[6]

In addition, relatively few civil suits are brought against the police, and officers are rarely subject to internal disciplinary proceedings or criminal prosecution for overstepping their legal authority (4, 22, 46, 143). Consequently, fear of legal censure has provided little incentive for the police to adhere strictly to the bounds of their authority. This is especially true in drug cases, where the majority of suspects are young and legally naive, the law is complex and generally misunderstood, and arrests might otherwise be difficult to make (7, 30, 128, 133).

While the law of arrest does little to deter police misconduct, it may have profound effects on the suspect's reputation and community standing. The *Identification of Criminals Act* (130k) allows the police to fingerprint and photograph any suspect charged with an indictable or hybrid offence— which includes all of the common drug offences. These records become part of the local police department's permanent criminal records. A copy of the suspect's fingerprints and photograph are routinely forwarded to the RCMP's central record-keeping division in Ottawa. Once entered into the RCMP's information systems, these data are available to all Canadian police forces, many other domestic criminal justice agencies, and some foreign enforcement officials. Even if the charge is dropped or the accused is acquitted, he or she cannot require the local or federal police to seal or destroy these records (7). Moreover, citizens have no general right to inspect police records (130a, s. 16; 130n, ss. 22–23). This is troubling given that a British Columbia study has revealed inconsistencies in the collection, dissemination, and retention of criminal records; factual errors in police records; and the unauthorized release of confidential data (2). In addition, once a suspect appears in adult court, the charge becomes a matter of public record and may be reported by the media. However, it should be noted that suspects tried under the *Young Offenders Act* are protected from some of these adverse consequences of arrest and conviction (130a, ss. 40–46).

POLICE POWERS TO SEARCH PREMISES

The NCA and FDA contain specific provisions governing the searching of premises and their occupants (130m, s. 10; 130j, s. 37). These special powers are in addition to the right to search a suspect pursuant to a lawful arrest, the search provisions of the *Code*, and the powers of search provided by other federal and provincial legislation. The cumulative effect of these powers is to endow officers in drug investigations with virtually unequalled authority to search suspects and premises. Nevertheless, the enactment of the *Charter* and subsequent amendments to the NCA and FDA have narrowed the gap between drug and general enforcement powers.

Search and Seizure under the *Criminal Code*

One of the basic tenets of English common law was that a man's home was his castle, where no one could enter without permission or explicit legal authority. Even an officer of the Crown who entered private premises without consent or a duly-issued search warrant was liable for damages in trespass and could be forcibly ejected. No amount of suspicion or urgency could excuse the absence of legal authority to trespass. In executing a search warrant for a dwelling-house, an officer was required to identify himself, state his legal authority and purpose, and request entry before using force (24, 28, 29, 67, 84, 90, 124).

Although the Canadian law of search is now almost exclusively dictated by statute, the courts have indicated that the common law's concern for privacy and the sanctity of private property "is good ground for construing with some strictness statutory provisions which authorize searches . . . on private premises" (84, pp. 174–75).

Except as a lawful incident of arrest or in cases involving special common law or statutory powers, an officer must possess a valid search warrant to enter and search private property. The general search warrant provisions are contained in sections 443 and 444 of the *Code*. These sections govern search warrants for *Criminal Code* offences and, by virtue of the *Interpretation Act*, also apply to offences created by other federal legislation, unless this legislation provides otherwise. Since the NCA and FDA both contain special search and seizure provisions, *Criminal Code* search warrants are not generally available in drug cases (106).

Criminal Code *Search Warrants*

Section 443 of the *Code* empowers a justice to issue a search warrant if he or she is satisfied, by information given under oath, that there are reasonable grounds to believe that the premises contain anything relating to a *Code* offence; anything that will provide evidence of a *Code* offence; or anything that is intended to be used in an offence against the person for which the offender may be arrested without a warrant. An application for a search warrant must clearly set out the basis of the officer's belief, the articles to be seized, the place or object to be searched, and the offence to which the evidence relates (34, pp. 1–60; 68). The courts have held that these provisions must be strictly adhered to before a search warrant is issued. In essence, the justice must critically assess the police information and decide if he or she is satisfied that the objects sought are on the suspected premises (84, 105, 107, 110).

Section 444 requires that the warrant be executed during the day unless the justice specifically provides otherwise. The police must have the search warrant with them, show it to the occupant, and request entry before resorting to force. While executing a search warrant, an officer apparently has legal authority to prevent occupants from wandering about, leaving the premises, answering the phone, or interfering with the search in any way (59). Note that section 443 search warrants do not empower the officer to search the occupants of the premises (84). Articles seized must be brought before a justice and are usually detained until the investigation and criminal proceedings are over (34, pp. 120–56; 61, pp. 426–90; 130e, ss. 445–47).

The Supreme Court of Canada has recognized an exception to the general rule that police must have a search warrant to enter private premises. It has held that the police have a common law right to enter a dwelling-house of a third party in order to search for a wanted individual. The police must have reasonable and probable grounds for believing that the wanted person is on the premises, give notice of their purpose and authority, and request entry. The Court also stated that in urgent circumstances, such as cases involving protection of life or preservation of evidence, an officer may break in without giving notice (28, 88).

The Supreme Court of Canada first laid down these principles in a case involving a drug suspect. Subsequently, both the U.S. Supreme Court and the English House of Lords rejected such a sweeping interpretation of the common law powers of entry (67, 73). The Supreme Court of Canada may have to re-examine its position in light of section 8 of the *Charter*, which guarantees everyone protection from unreasonable search or seizure.

The Criminal Code*'s Telewarrants Provisions*

The *Criminal Code* amendments proclaimed in force on December 4, 1985 (130g, s. 70) created a new type of search warrant, called a "telewarrant." Section 443.1 provides that the police may apply for a telewarrant if they believe that an indictable or hybrid offence has been committed and that it is impractical to appear personally before a justice to apply for a search warrant. The officer must submit information under oath by telephone or other means of telecommunication to a designated justice. The information must include (1) a statement of the circumstances that make it impractical for the officer to appear personally; (2) a statement of the alleged offence; (3) the premises to be searched; (4) the evidence sought; (5) a statement of the grounds for believing that the evidence will be found on the premises; and (6) a statement about any prior application for any search warrant regarding the same matter.

If the justice is satisfied that there are reasonable grounds for the search, the officer will be authorized to conduct it. Both the officer and the justice must complete special telewarrant forms, and the officer is required to file a separate written report after the search is completed. The legislation was designed to ensure that telewarrants are used as a last resort, permitting judicially-screened searches in urgent circumstances (56, pp. 202–6; 61, pp. 453–55). Since there is evidence to suggest that search warrant issuing practices may fall far short of the *Code* requirements even when the officer applies in person, it is questionable whether justices will require strict compliance with the telewarrant application criteria.[7]

The telewarrants and the amendment repealing the NCA and FDA writs of assistance (which are discussed later in this chapter) were introduced in the same legislative package. Although clearly intended to replace the drug writs in urgent circumstances, the telewarrants may not be available in drug investigations. If the courts view the search warrant provisions of the drug *Acts* as a complete and exhaustive package, then by virtue of the *Interpretation Act*, the *Criminal Code* telewarrants will not be applicable in drug cases. However, if the telewarrants are held to be a new type of search warrant which is distinct from the drug *Acts'* search powers, then telewarrants will be available in drug cases. The latter approach will prevail if the courts focus on the legislative intent of the telewarrant provisions. Traditionally, however, Canadian courts have refused to speculate about the legislative intent of statutes. It may be some time before this issue is resolved (61, pp. 453–55).

The Drug *Acts'* Special Search Provisions

The NCA and FDA extend police search powers in drug cases well beyond the bounds of the common law and the *Criminal Code*. Nevertheless, it should be noted that the NCA's and FDA's search provisions are narrower in some minor technical ways than the *Code's* provisions. Unlike the *Code*, these *Acts* specifically distinguish between dwelling-houses and other private premises.

Drug Searches in Premises other than Dwelling-Houses

Both *Acts* authorize police to search without a warrant, day or night, any place other than a dwelling-house in which they reasonably believe an illicit drug is present (130j, s. 37(1); 130m, s. 10(1)). The bases of the officers' beliefs are not subject to judicial scrutiny, either before or after the search is made. Their decision to search may be based on hearsay and similar kinds of information that would not be admissible as evidence in court. Unless the police are sued, they will not be required to explain the facts upon which they relied or to otherwise justify their decision. Even if sued, the police may raise the police-informant privilege to prevent disclosing the grounds for the search.[8] For example, in *Levitz* v. *Ryan* (59), the Ontario Court of Appeal held that an officer's testimony that he had acted on confidential information was sufficient to meet the officer's obligation to establish reasonable grounds for the search. A court's acceptance of this uninformative explanation practically eliminates the occupants' chances of ever discovering why their premises were searched, and creates an obvious potential for police abuse.

Unlike the *Criminal Code* search warrant provisions, sections 10(1)(*b*) of the NCA and 37(1)(*b*) of the FDA authorize the police to search any persons found on the premises. There need not be any evidence or suspicion that such persons are violating the drug law or, for that matter, any law. An individual's mere presence is sufficient. One must submit to the search even though one has not been arrested and there are no possible grounds for arrest (123). Regardless of their innocence, occupants who refuse to submit to a police search may be charged with willfully obstructing or resisting an officer in the execution of his duty.

The police have used these search powers to raid taverns and conduct strip searches. One such incident at the Landmark Hotel in Fort Erie prompted the Ontario government to establish a royal commission to investigate the police conduct (118). While acknowledging that the searches were legal, the Commission seriously questioned the police officers' judgment in raiding the tavern and searching its patrons. The Commission seemed most concerned about the strip search of all of the female occupants, stating on page 69 of its *Report*:

> On the whole of the evidence, in respect to the search of the female patrons by causing them to disrobe and subject themselves to a cursory glance of their buttocks and genital areas, I am satisfied that there was not a shred of evidence to support a suspicion that any female patrons had concealed heroin or any like substance on their persons prior to the search. In this sense, the wholesale search was foolish and unnecessary, as not one female was even seen with a known heroin or other drug trafficker.

The Commission recommended that the federal government amend the legislation to narrow this exceptional search power and that doctors and nurses be employed to conduct intimate physical searches of suspects.

Despite the Commission's report, the law has not been changed and these tactics continue to be used. During a 1978 raid on a tavern in Hull, the female patrons reported that they were forced to submit to vaginal examinations performed in unsanitary conditions by a female civilian employee of the police force who had no medical training[9] (60).

Prior to the *Charter*, Canadian courts accepted that techniques such as random occupant searches, throat-holds, and intimate physical searches were lawful provided that the amount of force used was reasonable (17, 59, 78, 113, 123). Such an extremely broad interpretation of the drug *Acts'* search powers is inconsistent with our traditional concerns with the dignity, privacy, and autonomy of the individual. It remains to be seen whether section 8 of the *Charter*, which guarantees everyone protection from unreasonable search or seizure, will change these judicial attitudes.[10]

In carrying out a drug search, the police are authorized to break down doors, ceilings, floors, containers, and similar objects (130j, s. 37(4); 130m, s. 10(4)). They may seize illicit drugs and anything they suspect was used in, or provides evidence of, the offence. This may include scales, address books, drug paraphernalia, and money. Both *Acts* contain complex provisions that permit suspects to apply to have their property released, once it is no longer needed as evidence. The money and drugs used by a convicted drug offender in the illicit transaction are subject to forfeiture (34, pp. 265–90; 61, pp. 458–90; 130j, s. 37(1)(*c*), (5)–(8); 130m, s. 10(1)(*c*), (5)–(8)). Except in possession and cultivation cases, the NCA also authorizes the seizure and forfeiture of the offender's vehicle or other conveyance if drugs were concealed or carried in it (130m, s. 10(1)(*a*), (*c*), (9)).

In addition to the broad seizure and forfeiture provisions of the NCA and FDA, the police can also invoke the *Criminal Code* and perhaps even the common law to seize an offender's drug-related assets and profits. Section 312 of the *Criminal Code* makes it an offence to knowingly possess any property or proceeds, directly or indirectly obtained, in whole or in part, from the commission of an indictable or hybrid offence. A suspect may be convicted of this offence even though he or she has not committed a drug offence or any other offence. Aside from a conviction under section 312, the suspect's tainted assets and profits can be seized and forfeited under the *Criminal Code*'s search warrant provisions (54; 99; 109; 130e, s. 446.2; 136). As well, at least one court has invoked the common law concept of *bona vacantia* (ownerless property) to order that the assets of a drug offender be forfeited to the Crown. The judge justified this extension of the common law on the basis that offenders should not be allowed to benefit in any way from their illegal conduct (137).

Despite these extensive powers, the RCMP have been lobbying Parliament for even broader seizure and forfeiture powers in drug cases. They have called for a new drug offence, which would prohibit the intentional acquisition, possession, or use of the profits or proceeds of drug trafficking. Moreover, they have sought special seizure provisions for tracing, seizing, freezing, and forfeiting drug-related profits and proceeds (117, pp. 74–79). The scope of such legislation is exceedingly broad, encompassing bankers, car dealers, real estate agents, stockbrokers, and even the accused's dependents. In such cases, records relating to transactions with the suspect, or assets derived in part from any financial dealings with the suspect, may be seized. Presumably, a criminal lawyer defending a drug suspect would be in the same position.

In a manner consistent with the early history of our drug enforcement legislation, these proposed amendments are being justified as necessary to combat the particular evils of drug trafficking. They appear to be inspired by the United States *Racketeer Influenced and Corrupt Organization Act* (RICO–140a) and *Continuing Criminal Enterprise Act* (CCE–140b). While the RCMP have repeatedly stated that the provisions are essential to their fight against the drug trade, they have not publicized the costs, delays, and constitutional problems that have plagued RICO and CCE prosecutions (71, 135). Although the American legislation has not significantly affected the illicit trade in the United States, the RCMP continue to argue for parallel Canadian legislation in the name of effective enforcement.

If the police do not have sufficient grounds to invoke the drug *Acts*' search provisions, they may rely on other federal or provincial legislation to further their investigation. For example, the Ontario *Highway Traffic Act* provides that an officer "may require the driver of any motor vehicle . . . to submit such motor vehicle . . . to such examinations and tests as the . . . officer may consider expedient" (131a, s. 65(1)). Although this provision does not authorize the search of drivers or passengers, suspicious circumstances gleaned from a safety inspection may provide the officer with a reasonable belief that the vehicle contains illicit drugs. In this case, the officer can invoke section 10(1) of the NCA or section 37(1) of the FDA to search the vehicle and its occupants for drugs. Provincial legislation concerning such matters as trespass, parks, fishing, hunting, and liquor may be used in a similar fashion.

Drug Searches in Dwelling-Houses

Prior to December 4, 1985, the drug *Act*s contained two separate provisions for searching dwelling-houses; namely, special search warrants and writs of assistance. With the abolition of the writs of assistance, the search of the dwelling-houses is now governed exclusively by the special search warrant provisions.

Sections 10(2) of the NCA and 37(2) of the FDA authorize a justice to issue a search warrant if he or she is satisfied, by information given under oath, that there are reasonable and probable grounds to believe that a dwelling-house contains illicit drugs. Unlike search warrants available pursuant to the *Code*, these special warrants can be executed day or night, and authorize the search of a dwelling's occupants.

The writs of assistance were a major source of controversy, particularly in the late 1960s and 1970s,[11] as illicit drug use and drug enforcement increased (51, 56, 64, 72, 125). Although the NCA and FDA authorized Federal Court judges to issue writs of assistance, the judges had no authority over the granting or use of the writs (130j, s. 37(3); 130m, s. 10(3)). Once the federal attorney general applied on behalf of an officer, the judge had to issue a writ to that officer. In practice, drug writs were sought only for RCMP drug officers. The writ was not limited with regard to time or place and was valid for the officer's entire career. The judge who issued a writ had no control whatsoever over when, where, how often, or in what circumstances it was invoked.

The writ of assistance was a continuing blanket search power that authorized its holder to enter and search without a warrant any dwelling-house, day or night, if he or she reasonably believed that it contained illicit drugs. The writ also authorized the officer to search all of the occupants of the dwelling-house. The holder of a writ was empowered to enlist the assistance of additional officers to aid in the entry and search. In *Levitz* v. *Ryan* (59), the Ontario Court of Appeal held that the officers' failure to show the occupant the writ at the outset of the search did not render the search unlawful. It further held that during the search, the officers were entitled to prevent the occupants from moving about or answering the phone. In order to prevent the possible destruction of evidence, officers holding writs have been allowed to break into dwelling-houses without making any prior announcement.[12]

The enactment of the *Charter* doomed the writs of assistance, although their death knell had been sounding for many years. The 1985 amendments abolishing the writs (130g, s. 200(2)) prevented the Supreme Court of Canada from resolving the question of their constitutionality—a decision which would have almost certainly found them unconstitutional.[13] What was most surprising about the writs was their longevity, given that they represented such a grave departure from traditional principles of search and seizure.

CONCLUSION

Despite police complaints that their efforts were thwarted in drug cases by the expansion of civil liberties, exactly the opposite appears to have been true, at least until the enactment of the *Charter*. Parliament created sweeping drug law enforcement powers in the NCA and FDA, and the Canadian courts broadly interpreted them. Violent and unsavoury methods of drug law enforcement were either ignored by Canada's judges or justified as a necessary ingredient of effective policing.

As a result, drug suspects had relatively few legal rights. Those rights which they did have, the courts were reluctant to protect. Drug suspects were required to submit to arrest and search in circumstances in which suspects in other cases could lawfully resist. Furthermore, if the police did exceed their authority, the illegally obtained evidence they seized was still admissible against the accused in court. Even if the suspect realized that the police were acting unlawfully, there was relatively little he or she could do about it. Common sense alone may dictate submitting to police action which one has a legal right to resist. After the initial police confrontation, private citizens— regardless of their innocence—faced major obstacles in redressing any police violation of their rights.

The *Charter* has given the courts a means of rigorously protecting individual rights and freedoms. However, those who expected the *Charter* to suddenly transform Canadian drug law enforcement may be disappointed. Nevertheless, some of the statutory search powers and tactics used in enforcing drug laws will be limited or struck down by the *Charter*. Perhaps more importantly, the *Charter* provides, for the first time, a public forum in which the nature of these police powers and practices can be discussed. Regardless of the outcome, a *Charter* challenge focuses attention in open court on whether an individual's constitutionally guaranteed rights and freedoms have been violated. The changes that police and prosecutors make in their practices in order to avoid such constitutional challenges may have a more profound effect in safeguarding rights than the successful court challenges themselves. Moreover, as illustrated by the abolition of the writs of assistance, the *Charter* may induce Parliament and the provincial legislatures to amend existing legislation and to carefully consider the question of individual rights when drafting statutes.

Finally, it seems appropriate to return to the basic policy issue that was raised at the outset. Do the current drug enforcement powers and practices strike an appropriate balance between the competing demands of effective enforcement and preservation of individual rights and freedoms? In my view, both Parliament and the courts have largely ignored the rights of drug suspects in an attempt to facilitate enforcement. While there have been very significant and verifiable encroachments on the rights of drug suspects, there has been no proof of corresponding enforcement gains. Regardless of whatever other effects it might have, the *Charter* should encourage us to fundamentally re-examine Canadian drug law enforcement policy.

NOTES

1. The terms "misdemeanour" and "felony" are not used in the Canadian *Criminal Code*. Instead, offences are divided into those punishable on summary conviction, those prosecuted by indictment, and those in which the prosecutor is given the option of proceeding either by way of summary conviction or by indictment. The distinction between summary conviction and indictable offences formally relates to the procedures used in prosecuting the two categories of offences, not their relative gravity. Nevertheless, as a general rule, summary conviction offences are less serious than indictable offences and are subject to less onerous sanctions.

2. This issue has become increasingly complex. At common law, individuals found themselves in one of two legal positions. If arrested, an individual was subject to a clearly defined set of rights and liabilities. However, an individual who had not been arrested was free to go his or her own way, even if this meant being unco-operative with the police. Arrest marked the boundary between freedom and detention.

   Both the federal and provincial governments have enacted legislation that empowers the police to stop and question individuals, to carry out investigations and tests, and to search suspects, without having to first make a lawful arrest. For example, section 238(2) of the *Code* authorizes an officer to demand a breath sample for analysis on an ALERT machine from any driver the officer reasonably suspects has alcohol in his or her body. The driver is not free to leave without risking a charge of failure to provide a breath sample under section 238(5) of the *Code* or a charge of obstructing an officer in the execution of his or her duty pursuant to section 118(*a*).

   Nevertheless, in *Chromiak* v. *The Queen* (19), the Supreme Court of Canada held that such drivers were neither arrested nor detained. Consequently, they were not entitled to the legal protections that the *Canadian Bill of Rights* (130c) affords arrested or detained suspects. This controversial decision subjected individuals who were being investigated to almost all of the liabilities of arrest, without the benefit of any of the corresponding rights.

However, in *R.* v. *Therens* (100), a *Charter* decision, the Supreme Court of Canada implicitly, if not explicitly, reversed its earlier decision in *Chromiak*. In *Therens*, the Court broadly defined the concept of detention to include any situation in which an individual is subject to a police demand or direction that the individual feels compelled to obey. The police had demanded that Therens accompany them to the police station to take a breathalyzer test, but did not inform him of his right to legal counsel. The Supreme Court concluded that Therens, although not arrested, was detained. Consequently, section 10(*b*) of the *Charter* required that Therens be informed of his right to counsel.

The broad police powers created by federal and provincial legislation will continue to complicate the Canadian law of arrest. *Therens* does not alter this fact, but rather ensures that individuals subjected to these procedures are entitled to at least some protection under the *Charter*.

3. It should be noted that for the purposes of civil liability in tort law, the concept of arrest is more broadly defined. Thus, in a false imprisonment action, plaintiffs need not prove that they were taken into physical custody, but rather only that their freedom of movement was totally restrained (10, 142, 143). Such restraint may be imposed by an implicit or explicit threat of force, an assertion of legal authority, or the seizure of the plaintiff's property (5, 57). Consequently, an officer may be held civilly liable for false imprisonment, even if he or she has not made a criminal arrest. Once the plaintiff proves that he or she has been restrained, the burden of proof shifts to the officer to establish a valid defence (35, 121).

4. The Supreme Court of Canada has held that the section 29 disclosure requirements are not as stringent as those imposed by the civil cases. The majority in *Gamracy* v. *The Queen* (36) indicated that the officer fully discharged his section 29 obligations by telling Gamracy that he was being arrested pursuant to an outstanding warrant. Although the officer could have obtained the warrant or ascertained its contents, the Court stated that he was not required to do so. Since the officer was acting lawfully in this situation, it was held that Gamracy had no right to resist arrest and was properly convicted of assaulting a peace officer in the execution of his duty.

It should be noted that section 10 of the *Charter of Rights and Freedoms* now guarantees everyone who is arrested or detained the legal rights

(a) to be informed promptly of the reasons therefor;
(b) to retain and instruct counsel without delay and to be informed of that right; and

(c) to have the validity of the detention determined by way of *habeas corpus* and to be released if the detention is not lawful.

5. During the author's periods of observation with the Vancouver drug squads in 1970, this tactic was routinely used in dealing with suspected heroin users (128). In *Scott* v. *The Queen* (123), apparently the only other pre-*Charter* appeal case in which the issue was raised, the Court assumed that the possible loss of evidence justified the officer's use of a throat-hold. No authority was cited to support this assumption, and the Court failed to consider seriously the violent nature of this enforcement technique.

Several post-*Charter* cases have involved the use of throat-holds in drug cases. Of particular concern are the British Columbia Court of Appeal cases of *R.* v. *Collins* and *R.* v. *Cohen* (80, 81). In both cases female suspects, who were in fact concealing nothing in their mouths, were subjected to a throat-hold. In *Collins*, heroin found in the accused's hand was admitted into evidence at trial. Similarly in *Cohen*, evidence found in the accused's purse was admitted, even though the Crown conceded that the use of the throat-hold was unreasonable in the circumstances. In both cases, the Court of Appeal upheld the convictions, reasoning that if the police had grounds to believe that a suspect had drugs somewhere on his or her person, the use of a throat-hold did not violate the *Charter*'s section 8 prohibition against unreasonable search or seizure. *Collins* was appealed to the Supreme Court of Canada. The Supreme Court held that due to an error made by the trial judge, a new trial had to be convened. The Court did not address the propriety of using throat-holds.

6. There have been two Supreme Court of Canada decisions involving the exclusion of evidence under section 24(2) of the *Charter*. In *R.* v. *Therens* (100), the Court excluded the accused's breathalyzer results from evidence, because he had been denied his right to counsel pursuant to s. 10(*b*). The second case, *Clarkson* v. *The Queen* (20), also involved an infringement of the accused's right to counsel. In *Clarkson*, the accused, who had been arrested on a charge of murder, made an incriminating statement while intoxicated and without the benefit of counsel. The Court found that the police had deliberately exploited the accused's condition by continuing to question her without counsel. As a result, the evidence was excluded under section 24(2).

These two decisions do not provide a sufficient basis for determining the limits of the *Charter*'s exclusionary rule. However, it is clear that the courts consider a number of factors, including the seriousness of the offence; the gravity of the *Charter* violation; whether the police conduct was deliberate; and whether there was any urgency which might have justified the violation (80, 82, 85, 92, 95, 98).

7. The Law Reform Commission of Canada undertook an empirical study of search warrant issuing practices in seven Canadian cities. The exam-

ining panel of superior and appellate court judges, assembled by the Commission to assess the search warrant applications, concluded that 60 percent of the warrants in the sample were invalidly issued. Although there were many purely technical errors, the judicial panel found that 32 percent of those warrant applications capable of conclusive assessment did not provide sufficient grounds to justify their issuance as required by statute (9).

8. The police privilege not to reveal their sources of information in criminal and civil proceedings is very well established (47, 76, 104, 127). As stated in *Humphrey* v. *Archibald* (47, p. 270):

> The only exception to that rule which I can find, is that if upon the trial of the prisoner the Judge should be of opinion that the disclosure of the name of the informant is necessary in order to show the prisoner's innocence, then one public policy is in conflict with another public policy, and that which says that an innocent man is not to be condemned when his innocence can be proved is the policy which must prevail. But except in that case this rule of public policy is not a matter of discretion.

9. In both the Landmark Hotel and Hull raids, the major issue was the intimate, rather than violent, nature of the searches. The Commissioner investigating the Landmark Hotel raid was critical of the intimate searches, but indicated that they were lawful. Similarly, in the cases of *Reynen* v. *Antonenko* and *Soenen* v. *Director of Edmonton Remand Centre*, the courts appeared to assume that there were no limits on an officer's power to perform intimate searches, provided that the amount of force used was reasonable (113, 126). This broad interpretation of statutory and common law search powers is not supported by the relevant case law.

The *Reynen* case also raises the issue of whether the power to search carries with it the right to subject drug suspects to surgical or other medical procedures for the purpose of obtaining evidence. In *Reynen*, the police took the suspect to a hospital where a doctor examined his rectum using a "sigmoidoscope." The doctor then used a metal instrument to remove from the suspect's rectum two rubber condoms containing heroin capsules. Although the suspect did not physically resist during the procedure, it appears that the judge would have approved of this practice even if the suspect had physically objected. However, the weight of legal authority suggests that there is no right to perform searches by surgical means (108). In the words of the Canadian Committee on Corrections, "the right to search the person and clothing of a person under arrest to obtain evidence of the offence does not authorize the withdrawal of blood, the use of stomach pumps or other quasi-surgical measures to obtain evidence" (15, p. 62).

10. Several cases suggest that some courts remain willing to countenance intrusive search procedures (80, 81, 91, 96, 126).

11. The drug writs have always been a subject of controversy in Canada. They were introduced in 1929 in response to enforcement difficulties encountered by RCMP drug officers. To gain the necessary committee support for the writs, the government drug administrator promised that few writs would be issued and then only to officers he personally trusted. The administrator envisaged that there would be a maximum of 10 writs. However, when a moratorium on writ applications was imposed in 1977, the RCMP held over 240 writs under the NCA and a similar number under the FDA. The RCMP also held a large number of writs of assistance under the *Customs* and *Excise Acts* (130h, s. 145; 130i, s. 78). The writs had generated even greater controversy in England and the American colonies. As the Law Reform Commission of Canada noted:

> This kind of sweeping discretion has been the focus of bitter conflicts in common law jurisdictions. Confrontations occurred in eighteenth-century England, for example, in connection with the broad warrants used in efforts to muzzle the press. The general reaction of the English courts was to brand such warrants as "oppressive", "nameless", and "worse than the Spanish Inquisition", and invalidate them in the absence of express statutory authority. The great historical conflict over so-called "general" warrants, however, occurred in pre-revolutionary America, culminating in *Paxton's Case*, in which the Superior Court of Massachusetts, ignoring the example of certain sister courts, agreed to issue the unpopular "Writ of Assistants", thus triggering a series of protests that were to lead to the struggle that became the American Revolution. (55, pp. 36–37)

12. During the author's periods of observation with the Vancouver drug squads in 1970, the general practice was to enter forcibly without giving notice (128). It is difficult to find any direct authority empowering the police to make an unannounced entry pursuant to a writ of assistance. In *Eccles* v. *Bourque* (28), the Supreme Court of Canada indicated that police might forcibly enter without notice in urgent circumstances, but failed to cite authority for this proposition. In any event, *Eccles* deals with the common law power to search for a wanted man, not writs of assistance. While the drug *Acts* give the police broad powers to break open doors, fixtures, and other things, the legislation does not confer a power to enter without notice. The issue in *Levitz* v. *Ryan* (59) was whether the officer had to show the writ to the occupant at the outset of the search, not whether the officer could enter without giving notice. If, indeed, the writ did confer authority to make unannounced forced entries into dwelling-houses, this power would stand in sharp contrast to the general principles governing the execution of search warrants. In the leading Canadian case, *Wah Kie* v. *Cuddy (No. 2)*, Beck J. stated:

> The court [in *Launock* v. *Brown* (1819), 106 E.R. 482] ... held that a search warrant under the statute was unlawfully executed inasmuch as no demand

of admittance had been made before breaking open the outer door of the . . . plaintiff's house.

I think this rule is applicable to all search warrants or orders for search unless it is clear from the statute authorizing the search warrant that a demand to open is not necessary. The second preliminary . . . to the execution of a search warrant, is . . . a demand to open (141, p. 355).

13. In *Hunter et al.* v. *Southam Inc.* (48), the Supreme Court of Canada established several general principles governing section 8 of the *Charter*. The Court held that the purpose of section 8 is to protect citizens from unjustified state intrusions. Section 8 must be used as a means of preventing unjustified searches or seizures before they occur, and not simply as a vehicle for determining their legality after the fact. Consequently, the Supreme Court held that where it is feasible to obtain prior authorization, such authorization is a precondition for a valid search or seizure. The presumption is that a warrantless search is per se unreasonable, and therefore a violation of section 8. The authorization procedure, to be meaningful, requires that the person authorizing the intrusion be capable of assessing the conflicting interests of the state and the individual in an entirely neutral and impartial manner. In addition, the person seeking authorization must establish, by information provided under oath, that there are reasonable and probable grounds to believe that an offence has been committed and that the place to be searched contains evidence of that offence.

The *Hunter* decision leaves no doubt that the courts will view warrantless searches or seizures with extreme suspicion, even if they are specifically authorized by statute. In the absence of clearly established urgent circumstances which make it impossible to apply for a warrant, warrantless searches or seizures would appear to violate section 8. The broad warrantless search and seizure powers created by the writs of assistance would almost certainly have been struck down under the principles established in the *Hunter* case.

REFERENCES

1. Abraham, J., Field, J., Harding, R., and Skurka, S. Police use of lethal force: A Toronto perspective. *Osgoode Hall Law Journal, 19*:199–236 (1982).
2. Albright and Dent. Confidentiality of juvenile records. Unpublished study. The Law Foundation of British Columbia, 1978.
3. *Amato* v. *The Queen* (1982), 140 D.L.R. (3d) 406 (S.C.C.).
4. Archibald, B. The law of arrest. In: Del Buono, V. (ed.). *Criminal Procedure in Canada*. Toronto: Butterworths, 1982.

5. *Ashlands Dry Goods* v. *Wages* (1946), 195 S.W. (2d) 312 (Ky. C.A.).

6. *Attorney-General* v. *Pritchard* (1961), 130 C.C.C. 61 (Sask. C.A.).

7. Bailey, P., and Solomon, R. Police processing of cannabis cases. Unpublished. Health Protection Branch, Department of Health and Welfare, Ottawa, 1979.

8. Ball, D. Case comments: *R. v. Biron. Saskatchewan Law Review*, 41:143–58 (1976–77).

9. Becker, C., et al. Search warrant practices in seven Canadian cities. Unpublished. Law Reform Commission of Canada, Ottawa. N.d.

10. *Bird* v. *Jones* (1845), 115 E.R. 668 (Q.B.).

11. *Blundell* v. *A.G.*, [1968] N.Z.L.R. 341 (C.A.).

12. Bryan, M., Jarvis, K., and Brooks, B. The quantity of marijuana, hashish and hash oil involved in convictions for cannabis offences in Canada during 1975. Unpublished. Department of Health and Welfare, Health Protection Branch, Ottawa, 1979.

13. Canada. Bureau of Dangerous Drugs. Health Protection Branch, Department of Health and Welfare. *Drug Users and Conviction Statistics 1981*. Ottawa, 1982.

14. Canada. Bureau of Dangerous Drugs. Health Protection Branch, Department of Health and Welfare. *Narcotic, Controlled and Restricted Drug Statistics 1985*. Ottawa.

15. Canada. *Report of the Canadian Committee on Corrections*. Ottawa: Queen's Printer, 1969.

16. *Chartier* v. *Attorney-General of Quebec* (1979), 48 C.C.C. (2d) 34 (S.C.C.).

17. *Cheese* v. *Hardy* (1974), 56 D.L.R. (3d) 113 (B.C. S.C.).

18. *Christie* v. *Leachinsky*, [1947] A.C. 573 (H.L.).

19. *Chromiak* v. *The Queen*, [1980] 1 S.C.R. 471.

20. *Clarkson* v. *The Queen*, [1986] 1 S.C.R. 383.

21. *Cluett* v. *The Queen* (1985), 21 D.L.R. (4th) 306 (S.C.C.).

22. Cohen, S. *Due Process of Law*. Toronto: Carswell, 1977.

23. Cohen, S. The investigation of offences and police powers. *Ottawa Law Review*, 13:549–70 (1981).

24. *Collet* v. *The Queen*, [1981] 1 S.C.R. 2.

25. *Crowe* v. *Noon*, [1971] 1 O.R. 530 (H.C.).

26. *Dillon* v. *O'Brien* (1887), 16 Cox C.C. 245.

27. *Dumbell* v. *Roberts*, [1944] 1 All E.R. 326 (C.A.).

28. *Eccles* v. *Bourque* (1975), 50 D.L.R. (3d) 753 (S.C.C.).

29. *Entick* v. *Carrington* (1765), 95 E.R. 807 (K.B.).

30. Erickson, P. G. *Cannabis Criminals: The Social Effects of Punishment on Drug Users*. Toronto: ARF Books, 1980.

31. *Ex parte Kane* (1915), 27 D.L.R. 494 (N.B. S.C.).

32. Fleming, J. *The Law of Torts*. 6th ed. Agincourt, Ont: The Law Book Company, 1983.

33. *Fletcher* v. *Collins* (1968), 70 D.L.R. (2d) 183 (Ont. H.C.).

34. Fontana, J. *The Law of Search and Seizure in Canada*. 2d ed. Toronto: Butterworths, 1984.

35. *Frey* v. *Fedoruk*, [1950] S.C.R. 517.

36. *Gamracy* v. *The Queen*, [1974] S.C.R. 640.

37. *Genner* v. *Sparks* (1704), 87 E.R. 928.

38. *Gottschalk* v. *Hutton* (1921), 36 C.C.C. 298 (Alta. C.A.).

39. *Grainger* v. *Hill* (1838), 132 E.R. 769.

40. Green, M. A history of Canadian narcotic control: The formative years. *University of Toronto Faculty of Law Review*, 37:42–79 (1979).

41. Hall, J. Legal and social aspects of arrest without warrant. *Harvard Law Review*, 49:566–92 (1936).

42. Health and Welfare Canada. Health Promotion Directorate. *Canadian Health Facts: Cannabis—Extent and Patterns of Use in Canada, 1980*. Ottawa, 1981.

43. *Holgate-Mohammed* v. *Duke*, [1984] 1 All E.R. 1054 (H.L.).

44. Holland, D. Police powers and the citizen. *Current Legal Problems*, 20:104–19 (1967).

45. Honsberger, J. The power of arrest, and duties and rights of citizens and police. In: *Special Lectures of the Law Society of Upper Canada 1963*. Toronto: Richard De Boo, 1963.

46. Humphrey, D. Abuse of their powers by the police. In: *Special Lectures of the Law Society of Upper Canada 1979*. Toronto: Richard De Boo, 1979.

47. *Humphrey* v. *Archibald* (1893), 20 O.A.R. 267 (Ont. C.A.)

48. *Hunter et al.* v. *Southam Inc.* (1984), 14 C.C.C. (3d) 97 (S.C.C.).

49. *Kenlin* v. *Gardiner*, [1967] 2 Q.B. 510.

50. *Kennedy* v. *Tomlinson* (1959), 20 D.L.R. (2d) 273 (Ont. C.A.).

51. Ketchum, P. Writs of assistance. *Chitty's Law Journal*, 19:90–92 (1971).

52. *Koechlin* v. *Waugh* (1957), 11 D.L.R. (2d) 447 (Ont. C.A.).

53. La Fave, W. *Search and Seizure*, Vol. 2. St. Paul, Minn.: West Publishing, 1978.

54. *Largie* v. *R.* (1982), 25 C.R. (3d) 289 (Ont. C.A.).

55. Law Reform Commission of Canada. *Police Powers—Search and Seizure in Criminal Law Enforcement*. Ottawa: Minister of Supply and Services Canada, 1983.

56. Law Reform Commission of Canada. *Writs of Assistance and Telewarrants*. Ottawa: Minister of Supply and Services Canada, 1983.

57. *Lebrun* v. *High-Low Foods Ltd.* (1968), 69 D.L.R. (2d) 433 (B.C. S.C.).

58. *Leigh* v. *Cole* (1853), 6 Cox C.C. 329 (Q.B.).

59. *Levitz* v. *Ryan* (1972), 29 D.L.R. (3d) 519 (Ont. C.A.).

60. Macdonald, N. Intimate search in police raid angers women. *The Ottawa Citizen*. May 8, 1978, 1.

61. MacFarlane, B. *Drug Offences in Canada*. 2d ed. Toronto: Canada Law Book, 1986.

62. Martin, G. Police detention and arrest privileges in Canada. *Criminal Law Quarterly*, 4:54–62 (1961–62).
63. *Mayer v. Vaughan (No. 2)* (1902), 6 C.C.C. 68 (Que. Q.B.).
64. McConnell, W. Unreasonable searches and seizures: A "Fourth Amendment" for Canada. *Revue de Droit Université Sherbrooke*, 11:157–96 (1980).
65. McDonald, B. Use of force by police to effect lawful arrest. *Criminal Law Quarterly*, 9:435–66 (1966–67).
66. *Money v. Leach* (1765), 19 How. St. Tr. 1002.
67. *Morris v. Beardsmore*, [1980] 3 W.L.R. 283 (H.L.).
68. Paikin, L. *The Issuance of Search Warrants*. Ottawa: Minister of Supply and Services, 1982.
69. Paikin, S. The right of a citizen . . . . *Chitty's Law Journal*, 14:300–303 (1966).
70. *Palmer v. The Queen*, [1980] 1 S.C.R. 759.
71. Parcels, S. An analysis of federal drug-related civil forfeiture. *Maine Law Review*, 34:437–58 (1982).
72. Parker, G. The extraordinary power to search and seize and the writ of assistance. *University of British Columbia Law Review*, 1:688–728 (1963).
73. *Payton v. New York; Riddick v. New York* (1980), 100 S. Ct. 1371 (U.S. S.C.).
74. *Priestman v. Colangelo*, [1959] S.C.R. 615.
75. *R. v. Beaudette* (1957), 118 C.C.C. 295 (Ont. C.A.).
76. *R. v. Blain* (1960), 127 C.C.C. 267 (Sask. C.A.).
77. *R. v. Biron*, [1976] 2 S.C.R. 56.
78. *R. v. Brezack*, [1950] 2 D.L.R. 265 (Ont. C.A.).
79. *R. v. Carroll* (1959), 23 D.L.R. (2d) 271 (Ont. C.A.).
80. *R. v. Cohen* (1983), 5 C.C.C. (3d) 156 (B.C. C.A.).
81. *R. v Collins* (1983), 5 C.C.C. (3d) 141 (B.C. C.A.); appeal granted and new trial ordered, [1987] 1 S.C.R. 265.
82. *R. v. Duguay, Murphy and Sevigny* (1985), 18 C.C.C. (3d) 289 (Ont. C.A.).
83. *R. v. Erickson*, [1977] 4 W.W.R. 374 (Alta. S.C.).
84. *R. v. Ella Paint* (1917), 28 C.C.C. 171 (N.S. C.A.).
85. *R. v. Hamill* (1984), 14 C.C.C. (3d) 338 (B.C. C.A.).
86. *R. v. Hurlen* (1959), 17 D.L.R. (2d) 603 (Ont. C.A.).
87. *R. v. Koszulap* (1974), 20 C.C.C. (2d) 193 (Ont. C.A.).
88. *R. v. Landry* (1985), 26 D.L.R. (4th) 368 (S.C.C.).
89. *R. v. Leveillee* (1984), 15 C.C.C. (3d) 258 (B.C. C.A.).
90. *R. v. Lyons* (1892), 2 C.C.C. 218 (Ont. Co. Ct.).
91. *R. v. Meikle* (1983), Charter of Rights Annotated (Ont. Co. Ct.).
92. *R. v. Perras; R. v. Robertson; R. v. Lastuka* (1985), 22 C.C.C. (3d) 1 (Alta. C.A.).
93. *R. v. Poharetsky; R. v. Ramage; R. v. L. A. R.* (1985), 18 C.C.C. (3d) 104 (Man. C.A.).
94. *R. v. Quinlan* (1978), 22 Chitty's L. J. 186 (Ont. C.A.).

95. *R. v. Roberge* (1983), 46 N.R. 573 (S.C.C.).

96. *R. v. Rousseau*, [1985] 1 & 2 R.L. 108 (C.S.P.).

97. *R. v. Seward*, [1966] 4 C.C.C. 166 (Y.T. Mag. Ct.).

98. *R. v. Simmons* (1984), 11 C.C.C. (3d) 193 (Ont. C.A.); on appeal to S.C.C.

99. *R. v. Smolka*, B.C. Prov. Ct., Lemiski Prov. Ct. J., Jan. 16, 1985, unreported.

100. *R. v. Therens*, [1985] 1 S.C.R. 613.

101. *R. v. Whitfield*, [1970] S.C.R. 46.

102. *R. v. Wray*, [1971] 2 S.C.R. 272.

103. *Re Attorney-General of Canada and Doer* (1979), 49 C.C.C. (2d) 533 (Ont. H.C.).

104. *Re Bisaillon and Keable* (1980), 127 D.L.R. (3d) 368 (Que. C.A.).

105. *Re Borden and Elliott and The Queen* (1975), 70 D.L.R. (3d) 579 (Ont. C.A.).

106. *Re Goodbaum and The Queen* (1977), 38 C.C.C. (2d) 473 (Ont. C.A.).

107. *Re Kobernick* (1922), 39 C.C.C. 48 (Ont. H.C.).

108. *Re Laporte and The Queen* (1972), 29 D.L.R. (3d) 651 (Que. Q.B.).

109. *Re Regina and Edwards* (1983), 8 C.C.C. (3d) 510 (Ont. Co. Ct.).

110. *Re United Distillers Ltd.*, [1947] 3 D.L.R. 900 (B.C. S.C.).

111. *Re Writs of Assistance*, [1965] 2 Ex. C.R. 645 (Ex. T.D.).

112. *Re Writs of Assistance* (1975), 74 D.L.R. (3d) 725 (Fed. T.D.).

113. *Reynen v. Antonenko* (1975), 54 D.L.R. (3d) 124 (Alta. S.C.).

114. *Rice v. Connolly,* [1966] 2 Q.B. 414.

115. *Robertson v. Joyce*, [1948] 4 D.L.R. 436 (Ont. C.A.).

116. *Rothman v. The Queen* (1981), 121 D.L.R. (3d) 578 (S.C.C.).

117. Royal Canadian Mounted Police. *R.C.M.P. National Drug Intelligence Estimate 1984/85*. Ottawa: Minister of Supply and Services Canada, 1985.

118. Royal Commission on the Conduct of Police Forces at Fort Erie on the 11th of May, 1974. Ontario. John A. Pringle, Commissioner. *Report*. Toronto, 1975.

119. *Russen v. Lucas* (1824), 171 E.R. 930.

120. Salhany, R. *Canadian Criminal Procedure*. 4th ed. Toronto: Canada Law Book, 1984.

121. *Sandison v. Rybik* (1973), 39 D.L.R. (3d) 366 (Ont. H.C.).

122. *Sandon v. Jervis* (1859), 120 E.R. 760.

123. *Scott v. The Queen* (1975), 61 D.L.R. (3d) 130 (Fed. C.A.).

124. *Semayne's Case* (1604), 77 E.R. 194 (K.B.).

125. Skinner, J. Writs of assistance. *University of Toronto Faculty of Law Review, 19*:26–44 (1963).

126. *Soenen v. Director of Edmonton Remand Centre* (1983), 35 C.R. (3d) 206 (Alta. Q.B.).

127. *Solicitor General of Canada v. Royal Commission of Inquiry into Confidentiality of Health Records in Ontario* (1981), 23 C.R. (3d) 338 (S.C.C.).

128. Solomon, R. The enforcement of drug laws in Vancouver. Unpublished

research study, Commission of Inquiry into the Non-Medical Use of Drugs, Ottawa, 1970.

129. Solomon, R., and Green, M. The first century: A review of nonmedical opiate use and control policies in Canada, 1870–1970. *University of Western Ontario Law Review*, 20:307–36 (1982).

130. *Statutes of Canada.*
    a. *Access to Information Act*, S.C. 1980–81–82, c. 111.
    b. *An Act to prohibit the importation, manufacture and sale of Opium for other than medicinal purposes*, S.C. 1908, c. 50.
    c. *Canadian Bill of Rights*, R.S.C. 1970, Appendix III.
    d. *Canadian Charter of Rights and Freedoms*, being Part I of the *Constitution Act, 1982*, being Schedule B to the *Canada Act, 1982* (U.K.), c. 11.
    e. *Criminal Code*, R.S.C. 1970, c. C-34.
    f. *Criminal Code*, S.C. 1892, c. 29.
    g. *Criminal Law Amendment Act 1985*, S.C. 1985, c. 19.
    h. *Customs Act*, R.S.C. 1970, c. C-40.
    i. *Excise Act*, R.S.C. 1970, c. E-12.
    j. *Food and Drugs Act*, R.S.C. 1970, c. F-27.
    k. *Identification of Criminals Act*, R.S.C. 1970, c. I-1.
    l. *Interpretation Act*, R.S.C. 1970, c. I-23.
    m. *Narcotic Control Act*, R.S.C. 1970, c. N-1.
    n. *Privacy Act*, S.C. 1980–81–82, c. 111.
    o. *Young Offenders Act*, S.C. 1980–81–82, c. 110.

131. *Statutes of Ontario.*
    a. *Highway Traffic Act*, R.S.O. 1980, c. 198.
    b. *Liquor Licence Act*, R.S.O. 1980, c. 244.
    c. *Trespass to Property Act*, R.S.O. 1980, c. 511.

132. Stephen, J. *A History of the Criminal Law of England*, Vol. 1. London: Macmillan, 1883.

133. Stoddart, K. The enforcement of narcotics violations in a Canadian city: Heroin users' perspectives on the production of official statistics. Chapter 15 of this book.

134. *Swales* v. *Cox*, [1981] 1 All E.R. 1115 (Q.B.).

135. Taylor III, W. Forfeiture under 18 U.S.C. §1963—RICO's most powerful weapon. *American Criminal Law Review*, 17:379–98 (1979–80).

136. *The Queen* v. *Lanagan*, 1985, unreported (Ont. Div. Ct.).

137. *R.* v. *Smith and Smith*, Alta. Q.B., Edmonton 8403-3162-C2, St. Clair J., June 10, 1985, unreported.

138. *Toronto Star*. End writs of assistance. November 2, 1981.

139. Trueman, M. Ottawa plans new limits, controls on use of open search warrants. *The Globe and Mail*, April 17, 1978, 1.

140. United States. *Statutes.*
    a. 18 U.S.C. §1962 (1982).
    b. 21 U.S.C. §848(a) (1976).
141. *Wah Kie* v. *Cuddy (No. 2)* (1914), 20 D.L.R. 351 (Alta. S.C.).
142. *Warner* v. *Riddiford* (1858), 140 E.R. 1052 (C.A.).
143. Weiler, P. The control of police practices: Reflections of a tort lawyer. In: Linden, A. (ed.). *Studies in Canadian Tort Law.* Toronto: Butterworths, 1968.
144. *Woodward* v. *Begbie* (1961), 31 D.L.R. (2d) 22 (Ont. H.C.).

17

Becoming a Cannabis Criminal*

PATRICIA G. ERICKSON

In 1974, as part of a study of the social effects of punishment on drug users, a sample of 95 first time cannabis possession offenders was interviewed shortly after being sentenced in the Metropolitan Toronto court. One area pursued during the interview was the arrest process, in particular how the cannabis was detected and how the police treated the offender. Besides closed-ended questions about time and place, the respondents' anecdotes about their experiences with the police were described in lengthy field notes taken at the time of the interview.

The process of "becoming a cannabis criminal" is considered, here, from the viewpoint of the offender: How does one get caught? How do the police behave? How do offenders react? The object of this chapter is to impart the flavour of being on the "receiving end" of police powers. The offenders' subjective experiences provide one perspective of the effect of the activation of the drug law against users of cannabis. The shared experience of being arrested and processed for cannabis use followed different channels and involved a variety of circumstances in these 95 cases.

CIRCUMSTANCES OF ARREST:
HOW DO PEOPLE GET CAUGHT?

The drug must be detected and a charge laid before a person joins the faceless multitude of "official statistics." While most users do not receive police attention, an atypical minority do (4, 14). Prior research on cannabis arrest patterns has been based principally on official police versions of the event which characterize it as a coincidental by-product of routine police investigation (13, 19). The Le Dain Commission also concluded:

> Many, if not most, of the cases of simple possession are uncovered by accident in the course of some other aspect of law enforcement. . . . If people are careful not to be in possession in public places . . . they are relatively immune from detection. . . . The use of cannabis in private is, generally speaking, beyond the effective reach of law enforcement. (4, pp. 289–90)

The offender's account provides an equally important but neglected

---

*Reprinted from P. G. Erickson, *Cannabis Criminals: The Social Effects of Punishment on Drug Users,* 53–66. (Toronto: ARF Books, 1980.) By permission.

source of knowledge about drug arrest practices. The nature of the arrest incident will first be examined.

Routine auto or street checks by police were not uncommon for this group of cannabis users (with 62% reporting at least one such experience) but only two subjects acknowledged that cannabis had ever been found and confiscated without a charge. Thus, first detection resulted in arrest for the majority of the respondents. Nearly half of the incidents (48%) occurred in the 4 p.m. to midnight shift. The site of apprehension was most frequently a public place (41%),[1] followed by a residence (36%), or an automobile being driven on a public thoroughfare (23%). Although the typical arrest was handled by two officers, in one-fifth of cases four or more police were involved. Police were more likely to be in plainclothes than in uniform (52% compared to 38%) and, in the balance, both types of officer were present. In half the arrests, the drug was on the person of the accused, and in another 5 per cent, was found nearby. In the remainder, a search of a car or residence produced the necessary evidence, for 35 per cent when the accused was present and for 8 per cent in his or her absence.[2] One subject, a declared non-user, said the drug was planted on him.[3]

It has been established that in victimless crimes (i.e., those characterized by voluntary though illegal activity conducted in private), the police take the initiative in enforcing laws because of the absence of a complainant (1, 20, 21). Perhaps the classic example of pro-active enforcement is the "raid" resulting from undercover investigation. It is not known, however, to what extent the actions of the accused may play a part in attracting police suspicion in more public settings. There is also the possibility that a chance element may contribute when a non-drug-related matter is being investigated. Furthermore, the possibility that the police may engage in "stop and search" activity in a deliberate effort to uncover illicit drugs must be considered.

The 95 cannabis offender subjects were asked to describe the situation and their actions just prior to the police intervention. These accounts made possible a classification of four basic types of arrest circumstances. They were termed, in order of frequency, "deliberate drug-seeking," "general suspicion," "coincidental," and "self-victimization."

The most common type of arrest, termed "deliberate drug-seeking," was manifested by the search of a residence with the express purpose of locating drugs (22 cases) and by the stake-out investigation of public settings where drugs seemed likely to be found (11 cases). Some examples are:

> The police knocked at the door and showed a warrant. They found the ounce right away and didn't bother searching anymore. One cop said that someone who had been busted supplied our address.

> Two plainclothesmen with a search warrant showed up at my apartment. Apparently a girl who lived there previously had been a big dealer, but the police

didn't seem too clear on just who was supposed to be at the address. So they searched anyway and as luck would have it, I had some in the place.

We had just come out of a bar and got into my car. I took a few moments to put a tape on, and the police car pulled up behind so we couldn't get out and then they searched the car and me. The cops told me at the station that that tavern was a popular place for kids to smoke and they'd go back there that night.

It is possible that in such instances the police were hoping to discover other types of drugs, or quantities large enough to warrant trafficking charges, but the activity was nonetheless drug-seeking and the product was a cannabis possession discharge or conviction. It was not possible to ascertain whether a warrant was shown in residence cases since subjects often reported they had been too upset to notice or ask for one. Two respondents did report requesting to see a warrant but the police did not produce one.

The second most frequent arrest occurrence was typified as "general suspicion" because no motive was apparent beyond the routine exercise of police discretion in patrol situations. The "stop and search" approach was directed towards persons in public locations, either in a vehicle (15 cases) or on foot (13 cases). Some illustrations are:

I was in a car with two of my friends. The cop pulled us over and could smell it in the car, though we had finished [smoking] some time before. The cop said you can hand it over or go to the station and it'll be hard on you, so I handed it over.

I was waiting for a bus and started thumbing. Two cops going the other way made a U-turn and came back. They checked my pockets and found it.

I was going home on my bicycle about 3:00 a.m. Two cops pulled me over. . . . I had even stopped at the last light. First they asked me if the bike was stolen, then if I had any dope. I said no—they found it in my pocket.

The police in these circumstances were not necessarily attempting to find drug offenses, but neither can it be construed that a definite infraction or the visibility of the drug had prompted the intervention. The precipitating factors in this category of arrest therefore must remain uncertain.

In contrast, the third grouping of responses, the "coincidental," was characterized by the explicit investigation of some matter unrelated to drugs. Eighteen such cases were found in the sample, including these examples:

I was driving in my car and was about to roll a joint when the cops pulled me over. They said my trunk was opened. As they came up, they saw me try to put the bag under me.

[Subject was with several people having a picnic in a ravine. One person had a pellet gun, which two other people walking by could have seen and reported to the police. Several police cars arrived.] In the excitement, I forgot what I had in my pocket, then remembered suddenly and must have made some motion to the pocket it was in, because one of the cops came straight over and reached right into the pocket with the leaves.

While the contact with the police was not prompted by an interest in drugs, the possession charge which resulted showed that the police did not overlook the opportunity to lay a charge when it arose.

Almost as frequent as the coincidental circumstances of arrest were those of "self-victimization," accounting for 16 cases among the respondents. In this category were placed accounts of those "caught in the act" through their injudicious choice of a setting for using the drug. In three cases a citizen complaint (typically a neighbour or passerby) brought the police, and in 13 arrests the officers happened to be in the vicinity. Chagrin was often displayed by these "conspicuous consumers," such as:

I was walking home from a pub, smoking a joint. These two cops suddenly stopped me—they must have smelled it as I walked by.

We sat down on a bench in the Mall and a stranger offered me a joint and we passed it around. These guys nearby in army jackets turned out to be cops and searched us.

Although in these cases the police action was directed towards drugs, the users' indiscreet behaviour was a crucial factor in detection.

This description of the circumstances of cannabis arrests from the offender's perspective disputes the conventional wisdom about the accidental nature of most such arrests (4, 10, 12, 13, 14, 19). Only one-fifth of the cases in this study could be placed, without reservation, in the "coincidental" category involving an explicitly non-drug investigation. In another 30 per cent of arrests, no overt reason was apparent for the intervention—drugs or otherwise. In about half of all arrests, then, the police clearly took action for the purpose of drug law enforcement. In some of these instances, the offenders' indiscretions precipitated the intervention, but twice as often the investigation of residences on the basis of tips received, and surveillance tactics in areas frequented by young people, were used to actively seek out users. The conclusion that use "in private is, generally speaking, beyond the effective reach of law enforcement" (4, pp. 289–90) may be true with respect to the vast majority of undetected use incidents. But, considering that 36 per cent of the 95 sample cases resulted from detection of the drug in private residences, this statement does not accurately reflect the reality of the application of the law.[4]

The explanation for the unexpectedly high level of police pro-activity against drug users may be found in several interrelated factors. It has been argued that a basic feature of Canada's legal institution is the relative preference given to state agents over the public in matters pertaining to individual rights and civil liberties (11). This is illustrated by the admissibility of "illegally" obtained evidence in Canadian courts (15) as contrasted to the exclusionary rule in the U.S. This fundamental "crime control" orientation is combined with special powers of search and seizure accorded police in drug cases (see 22). The importance attached to law enforcement activity as a criterion for advancement in police careers may give rise to incentive to make drug arrests (9, 16). The rise in cannabis use has spawned a fertile area of arrest potential. Quotas for drug arrests are not unknown (7, 18).

One check on such activity may be the community's opposition to extensive sanctions against young, and particularly middle class, drug users (4, 5, 8). However, it has been observed that the police prefer to focus publicity on their large scale drug arrests, which the community generally supports, and avoid drawing attention to the routine incidents (16, 17). The combination of the principle of admissibility of illegally obtained evidence, special police powers of search, availability of potential arrestees, rewards to police for making arrests, and public ignorance of the true extent of minor drug arrests may have produced an enforcement pattern of deliberate cannabis-seeking activity which contributes to a significant proportion of all possession arrests in Canada. Additional research based on other sources of data, such as police accounts and observation studies, is needed to further test the accuracy of this interpretation. The offenders' accounts do suggest, however, that the predominantly "coincidental" explanation of cannabis arrests should not be accepted without closer scrutiny.

POLICE BEHAVIOUR:
THE CONDUCT OF THE ARREST

At the scene of the crime, what happened after the cannabis was detected? The police could have decided to issue a summons, set a date for court appearance, and release the accused; this was done in 29 per cent of the cases. The balance of those charged were taken to the police station where they were held for an average of 2½ hours. The basis for this detention decision was not investigated, but the summons appeared to be a fairly new option, utilized by police to save time when the amount of cannabis was small and no charge other than possession was contemplated.

Until July 1974, the procedure in Metro Toronto when a possession charge was laid was either to take the accused from the police station directly to police headquarters for fingerprints and photographs or to issue a notice to attend later. According to police sources, an administrative decision was made in mid-1974 to eliminate this procedure for simple possession of cannabis charges. (This was possible because of the hybrid nature of the offense, allowing summary or indictable proceedings.) As this policy change occurred during our data collection period, not all respondents experienced the same form of processing. In total, 13 per cent were taken to police headquarters at once, as part of the arrest incident, and 49 per cent were fingerprinted and photographed some days later. The 38 per cent who did not undergo this procedure included some who reported to headquarters as ordered but on arrival were told it was no longer necessary.

For most who were fingerprinted and photographed, the procedure was described as fairly routine. Some reported that the police who dealt with them at headquarters were "nice and friendly," others that the police made insulting remarks to them: "Are those your teeth?"; and, to an admitted homosexual: "Don't get excited just 'cause I'm holding your hand." A few subjects seemed affected very strongly by this aspect of the processing, such as this woman: "I feel dirty about this, like a prostitute." The diversity of responses may have been related in part to the particular police on duty and their attitude towards offenders, and also to the varying degrees of equanimity of subjects in the face of officialdom.

The conduct of the arrest, in terms of interactions between police and offender, varied greatly. Two types of police actions seemed to be described in especially negative terms by those arrested. The first category involved threats or use of violence by police, either in an attempt to extract leads to dealers (discussed later) or for the apparent purpose of establishing their authority in the situation. Some examples are:

> After they found the hash, one of them hit me in the mouth for lying [i.e., saying that he didn't have any]. I was shaking, I thought I was going to be a punching bag for them.

> Four of us were sitting in the car in the parking lot. Two cops came up and yanked the door open and told us to get out. I said "what the fuck for . . . what are you after?" They pulled me out and flung me hard in the back of the squad car. [a female subject]

> I was lipping off to the cop [at the station]. He took me into a room and pulled down the blind. He said, "I could hit you." I said, "Why don't you?" He said, "Because you're stupid, smoking this shit."

In the second category of police actions which generated adverse reactions from offenders, the police conveyed that they "were really out to make a bust," or "out to get promoted," regardless of the amount of cannabis. Some illustrations of this perception of the police are:

> I didn't think the police were so bad before, but you've got to be a real prick to bust for one joint.

> They had no right to come to my car and question me and search me. It's private property. I've had the attitude since then that they're out to get someone.

> I'm resentful that I was busted for only six joints. I've heard of police taking it away and not charging.

> After the cop busted us, he let us go to the concert. He seemed elated. He said, "You wouldn't believe the number of people I've arrested tonight."

In contrast, the role of police as agents of the law, when they were viewed as only doing their job and not unfairly singling people out, seemed to be acceptable to some of those arrested. In these cases, police appeared to operate in a more disinterested, jocular, or even sympathetic manner:

> The cop said it was a chickenshit offense, but the law was there and he had to take me in.

> Afterwards [i.e., the search and charging] they drove us back downtown and dropped us off, joking that, "Anyone who sees you in the back of our car will think you're narcs." I asked why they busted us and one said, "Politicians pay us to bust you."

> They found the ounce right away . . . and then we sat around drinking beer. They seemed a bit apologetic for having to bust us.

The different stances adopted by police when confronting cannabis users, though doubtless affected to some extent by the individual characteristics and manner of the arrestee, suggest that police officers have differing concerns and perhaps skills in defusing a potentially hostile reaction by those arrested.

Another notable feature of the manner in which the police conducted the arrest was the attempt to obtain information from users about sources of cannabis or other illicit drugs. This was reported to be an element of the arrest by one-fifth of those interviewed. Eleven persons said the police offered to drop or reduce charges, and eight others that the police threatened or performed violence for the purpose of obtaining leads to suppliers. Some examples of police efforts to negotiate the charge are:

> They asked me who I bought it from and offered to drive me home and only tell my parents, but no charges, if I'd tell.

> The police said if I brought in someone bigger, they'd let me go.

> They kept me in the cells for about 6½ hours and questioned me a lot. They said if I named a supplier they'd charge me only with possession [not trafficking].

Some illustrations of actual or threatened use of force are:

> At the station, one cop said, "Tell me where you got it or I'll ram my fist down your throat."

> When I wouldn't go along with this [telling him about the supply] the big one grabbed me by the neck and called me a dirty bastard. I thought they were going to beat me up.

> Four cops came to our apartment. . . . One took me and my friend into a bedroom and closed the door. He shoved us around, pushed us up against the wall, had us strip, and searched us . . . and then when we were standing facing the wall he placed his hand under my crotch and said, "You want to lose your jewels?"

In only this last instance and one other did the respondent acknowledge that the name of a "pusher" had been provided to the police in response to these tactics. (In the one case involving several vials of hash oil, and in the other 14 grams of hash, the charges laid were simple possession only.) It has been reported in studies based on the police version of arrests that the accused, not the police, take the initiative in the transaction with police (19, footnote 61, p. 1526). This was not supported by the offenders' accounts. However, since these cases represent those brought to court, and successful negotiations may mean the case proceeds no further than initial police contact, the true nature of these interactions may lie somewhere in between the offender and the police version.

The routine application of such tactics as paid informants, bargaining, planting evidence, threats, violence, entrapment, and illegal search in drug law enforcement has been documented in a number of studies in other jurisdictions (2, 6, 18, 21). Given the extraordinary powers of search granted to Canadian police by the *Narcotic Control Act*, and the supportive role of the courts towards aggressive drug-seeking practices (22), it would not be surprising that such incidents occur in a significant minority of cannabis arrests. It should also be noted that the examples of attempted bargaining, threats, and violence by police from the offenders' accounts were associated almost exclusively with plainclothes officers. It seems likely that these were drug squad members, who have a greater stake in generating further drug enforcement activity than have uniformed police constables.

These descriptions of police behaviour during the arrest situation underline the diversity of experience en route to becoming a "criminal." At one extreme, offenders were treated in a civil manner with the minimum of interference: detected, summonsed, no fingerprinting, no violence or threats. The more common form of processing involved some inconvenience, some anxiety: being held at the station for a relatively short time, an appearance later at headquarters for fingerprinting, tension in confronting the police. At the other extreme were those instances of force, of prolonged detention, of derogatory treatment, in which the state's right to assume control of the individual on the evidence of cannabis possession was brought home very sharply. Such is the heritage of narcotics laws that the police were exercising their legitimate discretion to enforce the prohibition against cannabis. Even within legally allowable limits, the options available to police for performing this role would seem to assure differential processing of offenders long before they reach court.

NOTES

1. The 41% of occurrences in public places could be further divided into those which would normally be covered by routine police patrols, such

as streets, parks, or fairgrounds (24%), and those in which police presence was likely the result of a summons or a surveillance effort, such as bars, concert halls, restaurants, and adjacent parking lots (17%). Instances of persons apprehended while sitting in a parked car were placed in the latter category, while the moving vehicle category was restricted to those incidents occurring in vehicles being driven on public thoroughfares.

2. When a car or home was searched *in absentia*, the police sometimes were waiting for the person to return, or even left a handwritten note saying, "telephone the RCMP detachment at _____ ."

3. According to this subject's account, he had had the misfortune to sit down at a lunch counter next to a stranger who was the subject of surveillance by the drug squad. When he was searched at the station, he said, the officer dropped a cube of hash among his clothes, then pressed for details of the other person's supplier in exchange for not pressing the possession charge against him.

4. In 1977, Prime Minister Trudeau made the following remark in a session with students: "Certainly the spirit of government policy—and it hasn't been passed in law yet—is that if you have a joint and you're smoking it to your private pleasure—you shouldn't be hassled." (Quoted in 3, p. 181)

REFERENCES

1. Black, D. and Reiss, A. J., Jr. Police control of juveniles. *American Sociological Review*, 35:63–77 (1970).
2. Blum, R. The narcotics law in action. In: Blum, R. (ed.). *Drug Dealers—Taking Action*. San Francisco: Jossey-Bass, 1973.
3. Bryan, C. M. Cannabis in Canada—A decade of indecision. *Contemporary Drug Problems*, 8:169–92 (1979).
4. Canada. Commission of Inquiry into the Non-Medical Use of Drugs. *Cannabis*. Ottawa: Information Canada, 1972.
5. Cook, S. Canadian narcotics legislation, 1908–1923: A conflict model interpretation. *Canadian Review of Sociology and Anthropology*, 6:36–46 (1969).
6. de Fleur, L. B. Biasing influences on drug arrest records: Implications for deviance research. *American Sociological Review*, 40:88–103 (1975).
7. Ford, R. E. and Wachtel, D. Deterrence, drugs and New York State's 1973 Controlled Substance Act. Paper presented at the American Society of Criminology annual meeting, Tucson, Arizona, 1976.
8. Glaser, D. Criminology and public policy. *American Sociologist*, 6:30–37 (1971).
9. Glaser, D. The counterproductivity of conservative thinking about crime. *Criminology*, 16:209–24 (1978).
10. Goode, E. *The Marijuana Smokers*. New York: Basic Books, 1970.

11. Hagan, J., and Leon, J. S. Philosophy and sociology of crime control: Canadian-American comparisons. In: Johnson, H. M. (ed.). *Social System and Legal Process*. San Francisco: Jossey-Bass, 1978.
12. Johnson, B. D. *Marijuana Users and Drug Subcultures*. New York: Wiley, 1973.
13. Johnson, W. T., and Bogomolny, R. The crime of cannabis: From detection to disposition. In: *Marijuana: A Signal of Misunderstanding. Technical Papers of the First Report of the National Commission on Marijuana and Drug Abuse*, Appendix 2. Washington, D.C.: U.S. Government Printing Office, 1972.
14. Johnson, W. T., Peterson, R. E., and Wells, L. E. Arrest probabilities for marijuana users as indicators of selective law enforcement. *American Journal of Sociology, 83*:681–99 (1977).
15. Leon, J. S. Rights, fairness and effectiveness in Canada and the United States: Counsel and client in the criminal process. *Criminal Law Quarterly, 20*:29–67 (1977).
16. Manning, P. K. *Police Work: The Social Organization of Policing*. Cambridge, Mass.: M.I.T. Press, 1977.
17. Manning, P. K. *The Narcs' Game*. Cambridge, Mass.: M.I.T. Press, 1980.
18. Manning, P. K., and Redlinger, L. J. Working bases for corruption: Organizational ambiguities and narcotics law enforcement. In: Trebach, A. S. (ed.). *Drugs, Crime and Politics*. New York: Praeger, 1978.
19. Morton, A. S., Ohlgren, J., Pearson, R. W., and Weisel, S. Marijuana laws: An empirical study of enforcement and administration in Los Angeles County. *U.C.L.A. Law Review, 15*:1499–1585 (1968).
20. Schur, E. *Crimes Without Victims*. Englewood Cliffs, N.J.: Prentice-Hall, 1965.
21. Skolnick, J. H. *Justice Without Trial*. New York: Wiley, 1966.
22. Solomon, R. The noble pursuit of evil: Arrest, search and seizure in Canadian drug law. Chapter 16 of this book.

18

Canadian Punishment of Illegal Drug Use: Theory and Practice*

NEIL BOYD

The criminalization of certain psychoactive substances has been state policy in Canada since 1908. For the past 79 years successive federal governments have contributed millions of taxpayer dollars to "fight the good fight"—the elimination of certain forms of drug use. In the past fifteen years, however, the wisdom of criminalization has been subjected to increasingly critical inquiry. In 1972 the Liberal government appointed a Commission to inquire into the meaning of "non-medical" drug use. The past fifteen years have also seen widespread use of marijuana by Canadian youth—a reality that has acted as a catalyst for a re-examination of the social utility of substance criminalization (4, 8).

THE LEGACY OF ARBITRARINESS: A CONTEMPORARY HISTORY OF CANADIAN "DRUG" PENALTIES

The history of substance criminalization has been the subject of a significant body of socio-legal research, some of which is reproduced elsewhere in this volume. My focus in this paper will be on the present and on our recent past, the most immediate fallout from the initial 1908 legislation.

The intervening 79 years have seen significant changes in both Canadian theory and practice with respect to the social control of certain kinds of drugs. Though penalties for both distribution and use are now far more Draconian than was the case in 1908, the 1973 publication of the Le Dain Commission's *Final Report* (6) signalled that some doubt as to the wisdom of a severe state response had arrived in the Canadian state.

Indeed it was not until the 1970s that the social perception of drug use and distribution as more properly a medical problem began to rival the hypothesis that "drug" use and distribution is immoral and deserving of punitive response. With the publication of the Le Dain report and with books like *Licit and Illicit*

---

*Reprinted from the *Journal of Drug Issues, 13*, no. 4 (1983): 445–59, with revisions by the author.

Drugs, Ceremonial Chemistry, and *The Natural Mind* (2, 12, 20) filtering into public consciousness, some segments of Canadian society are now seriously questioning the wisdom of a criminalization strategy for the social problems created by certain forms of self-destructive drug use.

What is most disappointing, however, is that Canadian government policy remains at a most infantile stage. Punitive repression is still the primary medium of state response. In 1961 the government enacted the *Narcotic Control Act,* a document which remains largely unchanged today. The maximum sentence for trafficking was raised at that time to life imprisonment. An amendment that would have provided a possible death sentence for "narcotic" distributors failed (7). The member for Vancouver East echoed sentiments heard some 50 years past when he said, "I think about the lowest depths that any man or woman can sink to is to be a trafficker in narcotics. A murderer kills and that is it. But one who traffics in drugs, who brings a person to addiction, to that insatiable craziness, makes an absolute hourly and daily hell for life for the the addict. I, therefore, have no sympathy for him, and I agree that for the trafficker there should be a penalty of up to life" (7, p. 5610).

At the present time Canadian criminalization of certain psychoactive substances resides in two federal statutes, the *Narcotic Control Act* of 1961 and the *Food and Drugs Act* of 1962. The latter legislative initiative followed on the heels of the thalidomide tragedy (10). The statute deals with, among other concerns, the "restricted" drugs, LSD, DMT, MDA, and psilocybin. Penalties of imprisonment are provided for both possession and trafficking. The *Narcotic Control Act* provides a generally more severe range of sentencing options for possession, trafficking, importing, and cultivation of "narcotic" substances, principally marijuana, cocaine, and heroin. Canada still endorses the legislative principle of a minimum term of seven years' imprisonment for the importation of any amount of any "narcotic."

What is most disturbing about sentencing in Canadian drug cases is that there is a substantial gulf between legislative theory and judicial practice. Though the 1961 passage of the *Narcotic Control Act* provided for life imprisonment for individuals convicted of either trafficking or importing, a survey of sentencing statistics reveals that this option is rarely if ever used today. Through both 1976 and 1977, 407 Canadians were convicted of trafficking in heroin (10, p. 568); over 78 per cent of these individuals received between one month and eight years' imprisonment. By 1979 this figure had risen to 84 per cent.[1] More significantly, however, the most recent sentencing statistics for trafficking in heroin reveal that Canadians are rarely sentenced to 20 years in prison or more. In 1979, for example, only 4 of 202 heroin traffickers received sentences of 10 years' imprisonment or greater.

The Canadian government has made only one significant amendment to the *Narcotic Control Act* since 1961. In 1969 an amendment gave to federal prosecutors the option of proceeding summarily against individuals charged with possession of a "narcotic" (11). The harsh necessity of procedure by indictment was eliminated, permitting federal prosecutors to treat possession as a less serious "summary" offence. Be that as it may, the statistical picture conveyed by Canadian drug enforcement reveals a lack of legislative will. The federal government has handed the business of prescribing "drug" penalties to the judiciary. The judiciary has effectively reduced the onerous maximum penalties prescribed in 1960 for both trafficking and importing. Canadian drug enforcement policy is properly understood as falling under the judicial arm of the Canadian government, albeit with some significant shaping by Canadian police officers.

A HUMAN PROCESS, IF NOT HUMANE: THE LESSONS OF JUDICIAL LAW MAKING

While Canadian sentencing statistics reveal a judicial tempering of legislative severity, the common law pronouncements of Canadian judges offer no clear explanation of the process. The highest courts have persistently decided that only in the most exceptional and persuasive circumstances are trafficking convictions to be met with non-custodial sentences. The major Canadian legal treatise, *Drug Offences in Canada,*[2] notes, "the courts have consistently ruled that deterrence and protection of the public are the paramount considerations and that, in the absence of exceptional circumstances, a period of incarceration should generally be imposed" (10, p. 548). Recent statistics reveal that over 1,000 of 4,000 convictions for marijuana trafficking were punished with non-custodial sanctions in 1979; similar kinds of patterns appear from 1980 to 1985. The "exceptional circumstances" that the judiciary has spoken of are now beginning to strain the credibility of our most persuasive case law. The judiciary has yet to elaborate seriously the principles upon which non-custodial sentences for trafficking are to be based.

Our courts have generally reserved their greatest displays of displeasure for those who might extract vast amounts of capital from the business of distributing certain illegal drugs. In the 1971 case of *The Queen* v. *Robert, Shacher, Young, and Smith* (19), Justice Aylesworth of the Ontario Court of Appeal quoted with approval the following principle, "What must be taken into consideration is that the profits available from this kind of traffic are so substantial that the courts will not be doing their duty if they fail to impose such sentences as will make it clear to these young men and to others who might think of following their example that this kind of crime will not be allowed to pay."

Not surprisingly, the statement fails to justify the imposition of a lengthy term of incarceration. The court merely asserts that this kind of business endeavour by the accused shall not be allowed to survive. What is not analyzed is the appropriateness of the means used to achieve the desired end.

Canadian courts have no illusions about the distribution of illegal drugs.

As Justice Clement noted in *The Queen* v. *Lecapoy* (16), "Trafficking comprises a chain of activities, stretching from the importer or manufacturer to the ultimate purchaser. Each link is important and essential to the success and profit of the operation. . . . It is the magnitude of the individual's participation in the operation that may, with some justification, be taken into account for the purposes of sentencing" (pp. 499–500). The Court fails to explain the meaning to be given to the word "magnitude." Justice Clement argues that "the final sale [is] not less [important] than the intermediary steps, for it is then that the drug reaches its destination and the ultimate profit [is] made" (pp. 499–500). It is unclear, then, whether a drug distributor is to be punished in relation to his or her role in the hierarchy of distribution. While the variable of the profit motive is clearly taken into consideration, Canadian courts also seem to want a mechanism to express some form of equal condemnation for all those who distribute illegal drugs. The issue remains somewhat unclear, though it does seem fair to say that the most significant penalties will be reserved for those deriving the greatest revenue from such activities.

Canadian courts have also tended to treat especially harshly any drug distributors who might use force or the threat of force in the conduct of their business. Chief Justice Gale of the Ontario Court of Appeal noted in *The Queen* v. *Bosley and Duarte* (14) in 1970, "There is also the feature of the guns. We are not sentencing these two men because of the possession of guns, but we give some consideration to the fact that their scheme was carried out with guns. This was not the prank of two collegiate boys just trying to sell some marijuana to their friends. It was a deliberate and planned operation" (p. 331).

This statement purports to make two rather questionable points. First it tends to dismiss middle-class distribution of marijuana as a "prank" of "collegiate boys." The Chief Justice appears to believe that marijuana distribution can be equated with the likes of college initiation "hi-jinks." Second, however, and more important, the statement creates the imagery of offences that are not before the court. While the use of handguns as business insurance and worse is clearly deplorable, the accused should face separate charges relating to weaponry, if warranted. The Canadian *Criminal Code* provides the possibility of lengthy imprisonment for both carrying a concealed weapon and possession of certain prohibited weapons.

More recently, Justice Thomas Berger of British Columbia's Supreme Court noted the possibility of violence in passing sentence upon those involved in the distribution of cocaine. In *The Queen* v. *Bengert et al.* (13), Justice Berger conducted a thorough review of the literature relating to the harmfulness of cocaine, and heard testimony from medical experts. Justice Berger concluded that cocaine did not appear to present a significant social or health problem to Canadians, and yet he imposed lengthy terms of imprisonment upon the accused. He appeared to be most concerned about the very real possibility that the accused might have used violence in the regulation of their business.³ Justice Berger was placed in a most unenviable position. The social harm generated by the use of cocaine appeared minimal; the social harm generated by the prohibition of the cocaine industry could not be ignored.

Canadian case law has also embraced the theory that marijuana is to be treated differently from heroin, although both are classified as "narcotics." In *The Queen* v. *Johnston and Tremayne* (15), Chief Justice Gale of the Ontario Court of Appeal noted, "The maximum sentence prescribed by the Narcotic Control Act . . . is life imprisonment. Thus, the framers of the Act regarded, and presumably still do regard, both offences as very grave, although I must confess at once that the Court takes a different view of the use or importation of marijuana as compared with the more serious drugs embraced by the Act such as heroin" (p. 66). Similarly, Mr. Justice Aylesworth noted in *The Queen* v. *Robert, Shacher, Young, and Smith* (19) that, "Having regard to the potentialities of trafficking in the 'hard' drugs, one who engages in that exercise ought to be and is now alerted to the probability that he will be treated in a different manner than one trafficking in marijuana" (p. 150). Canadian courts have tended to put this theory into practice. While 88 per cent of all heroin traffickers received jail terms in 1979, only 70 per cent of all marijuana traffickers were so sentenced. More important, of those marijuana distributors incarcerated, over 80 per cent went to jail for less than six months in 1979; only 26 per cent of all incarcerated heroin distributors were granted such leniency. The most frequent sentence for Canadian heroin traffickers falls between two and four years' imprisonment; the most frequent sentence for Canadian marijuana traffickers falls between one and six months (5).

Bruce MacFarlane has noted of Canadian drug offences, "At the very heart of [our sentencing] philosophy is the desire to protect that portion of the population which is presently uncommitted to the use of illicit drugs" (10, p. 557). Canadian courts have consistently ruled that the young are to be shielded from harsh punishments and that those who distribute illegal drugs to the young are to be punished severely. MacFarlane quotes approvingly from the English Court of Appeal judgement in *The Queen* v. *Macauley*, "Holy Writ has in dread terms declared what is the fitting fate of those who place a stumbling block in the path of the young. And Parliament has rightly had regard to the growing menace of drug addiction. Anybody supplying to a mere child, a boy of fifteen, a hard drug is doing a most terrible deed which calls for grave punishment" (17, p. 232). Unfortunately the thorny issue of informed consent has not been raised here. Though the age of majority might simply be said to represent the point at which an uninformed child becomes a fully informed adult, our social reality reveals a rather blurry line. Though selling illegal drugs to some young people can truly transform a drug distributor into a drug pusher, the distinction here actually resides in the individual case; the judiciary has not yet explored the dynamics that lead a young person to a given illegal psychoactive substance. It is probably most fair to say that young people sell illegal drugs to their peers—willing consumers, for the most part, of the substance in question.

The courts have simultaneously adopted a policy of treating youthful drug offenders less harshly. Although none of those convicted and under the age of 20 went to jail for possession of heroin, 33 per cent of convicted heroin users between the ages of 20 and 29 were jailed. While only 3.3 per cent of those under 20 and convicted of marijuana possession were jailed in 1979, the figure for those in the 20 to 29 age group was 4.9 per cent. More significantly, the Canadian judiciary has absolutely or conditionally discharged almost 34 per cent of convicted marijuana offenders under the age of 20; the most lenient option of the discharge has only been used for 24 per cent of offenders in the 20 to 29 age category (5). In the context of nearly 30,000 Canadian convictions for possession of marijuana, this is an important distinction. The theory of judicial pronouncements has, in this instance, significant correlation with judicial practice.

Perhaps the most "celebrated" of all Canadian drug sentencing decisions is that of the Ontario Court of Appeal in *The Queen* v. *Richards* (18). The case concerns the appropriate disposition for Keith Richards of the Rolling Stones, convicted of possession of heroin in Toronto, in October of 1978. Not surprisingly perhaps, counsel for Mr. Richards noted statistics from Canada's Bureau of Dangerous Drugs. As the Court put it, "Mr. Maloney argued with great force that the non-custodial sentence imposed upon the respondent was in line with the sentences imposed upon approximately half of the persons convicted of simple possession of heroin during the last five years" (18, p. 523). The prosecutor had to establish that this celebrity case called for a term of imprisonment. He argued that Keith Richards' public stature, his encouragement of the use of drugs through his music, and a prior drug conviction made deterrence here "the paramount and overriding factor" (18, p. 524).

In systematic fashion the Court dismissed these arguments. Of Mr. Richards' public stature, the Court said, "The principle is well established that [our] appellate Court should not lightly interfere with the sentence imposed by the trial Judge and should not do so merely because some or even all members might have imposed a different one" (18, p. 525). The Court went on to note that Mr. Richards was not allowed to escape the sanction of Canadian criminal law: "A person released on suspended sentence and probation does not go scot-free. In this case, the respondent was required to continue his treatment for addiction and perform the community service directed in the probation order" (18, p. 525). Mr. Richards' sentence essentially involved a requirement that he continue treatment for heroin "addiction"[4] in New York and that he perform two benefit concerts for the Canadian National Institute for the Blind.

Of the claim that the Rolling Stones' music encouraged the use of drugs, the Appeal Court noted, "The trial Judge deplored the fact, if it was a fact, that the music of the Rolling Stones glorified and sanctioned the use of drugs, but considered that the respondent's efforts to remove himself from the drug subculture could only have a salutary effect on those who might be open to his influence" (18, p. 525). Of Mr. Richards' previous drug offence the Court said, "In considering the weight to be given to the prior conviction it is right to observe that the respondent both before and after the conviction endeavoured, albeit unsuccessfully, through treatment to rid himself of his addiction" (18, p. 525).

What is most noteworthy here is that thousands of dollars were spent in the litigation of the appropriate sentence for a simple charge of possession of heroin. The accused's material circumstances were such that he was able to make a significant community contribution in the repayment of his "debt" to society. But the appropriateness of the criminal label was not debated, in media reports or elsewhere. The judiciary was preoccupied, for its part, with the business of defending its "non-punitive" response. Some words from one of the minority reports of Canada's Le Dain Commission seem particularly instructive here: "It seems . . . illogical, ineffective and inhumane to use the criminal law against opiate dependents . . . on the one hand we define heroin and other opiate addicts as vulnerable and dependent individuals with a compulsive physiological or psychological drug need (or perhaps both), and on the other, we react to their dependence with police searches, apprehension, detention in police cells, criminal trials, fines and incarceration" (6, p. 244). While the words "vulnerable" and "dependent" do not entirely fit the material circumstances of Keith Richards, the comments here regarding criminalization are nonetheless appropriate.

MARIJUANA: THE PITH AND SUBSTANCE OF CANADA'S WAR ON ILLEGAL DRUGS

In 1979 Canada recorded approximately 35,000 convictions under both the *Narcotic Control Act* and the *Food and Drugs Act*. Almost 28,000 of these 35,000 convictions were for possession of marijuana; more significantly, marijuana offences of all types accounted for almost 32,000 of total drug convictions—an overwhelming 90 per cent of Canada's war on illegal drugs. There were only 973 convictions relating to LSD, 294 convictions relating to heroin, and 433 convictions relating to cocaine (5).

Not surprisingly, the 28,000 individuals convicted of marijuana possession represent only the tip of the iceberg with respect to use. The government's Department of National Health and Welfare has conservatively estimated that at least four million Canadians had tried marijuana by January of 1979 —approximately 20 per cent of the country's population (8). While a lack of consumer interest might best account for the small number of convictions relating to heroin and LSD, the same cannot be said for marijuana.

The federal government has passed two legislative initiatives that have served to soften penalties for marijuana use. I have noted that in 1969 the right to proceed summarily was given to federal prosecutors. As Michael Bryan has said, "This amendment had the immediate effect of reducing the proportion of convictions for cannabis possession resulting in prison sentences. In 1968, 44 per cent of possession convictions resulted in imprisonment, compared with 10 per cent in 1970" (4, p. 172).

In 1972 the government responded to the recommendations of its own Le Dain Commission. The Commission proposed that the criminal offence of possession of marijuana be abolished. Then Health Minister John Munro told the Canadian Parliament, "The Criminal Law Amendments Act that came into force on July 15 of this year makes it possible for judges, instead of convicting an accused person, to direct that he be discharged absolutely or under probation conditions. If a person receives this kind of discharge he is not considered to have been convicted of the offence" (4, p. 181). The Liberal government was attempting to satisfy diverse interest groups by moving towards a muddled middle ground. The indignity of appearance in a criminal court would be retained, but a certain number of "deserving" cannabis users would now be spared some of the most onerous consequences of a criminal record. The government set out no principles that would guide the appropriate imposition of these new discharge provisions; this was apparently a task to be left to the judiciary. In the years that the discharge provisions have been in place, we have seen a Canadian judiciary that is occasionally anxious to "discharge" offenders for possession of marijuana. While the discharge was awarded in only 16 per cent of all possession cases in 1973, the 1979 statistics reveal that almost 30 per cent of all possession convictions were punished by this means.

As Michael Bryan has so aptly put it, cannabis policy in Canada during the 1970s represents a "decade of indecision." In 1974 the federal government introduced Bill S-19, a legislative initiative that would have eliminated incarceration as a sentencing option in marijuana possession cases. Though this Bill would still have allowed a jail term in default of payment of a fine, and though the Bill clearly retained the criminal nature of the offence of possession of marijuana, it was not a compromise that the government was inclined to push. The Bill simply died on the Order Paper of the Canadian Parliament in 1976 (4).

Perhaps the many criticisms of Bill S-19 did not fall on deaf ears. As Michael Bryan has noted, recent Canadian experience with prison admissions in default of payment of a fine "suggests that, in time, more people would be imprisoned as a result of simple possession each year than is currently the case" (4, p. 178). Further, "the police were to have retained their authority to fingerprint and photograph persons (including juveniles) charged with simple possession under Bill S-19. Like the discharge provisions enacted in 1972, the 'automatic pardon' provision of Bill S-19 was a legal fiction that would not have altered the fundamental criminal character of the offence or of records of the offence" (4, p. 180).

At the present time the criminal nature of marijuana use remains intact. While a majority of both the country's lawyers and doctors have, in the past, favoured the decriminalization of marijuana,[5] the Canadian Association of Chiefs of Police and the Royal Canadian Mounted Police stand opposed to any change in the law. This conflict has apparently rendered impotent the legislative will of both Liberal and Conservative governments over the past decades. The words of former Prime Minister Trudeau have a hollow ring. In 1977 he told a collection of aspiring young Liberals, "Certainly the spirit of government policy . . . is that if you have a joint and you're smoking it to your private pleasure . . . you shouldn't be hassled" (4, p. 181). In 1987, young Canadians convicted of smoking marijuana sit in jails across the country. Theory such as that espoused by Pierre Trudeau is not always in accord with the reality of governmental practice.

A CLAMOUR FOR CHANGE: THE SKEPTICISM OF THE ACADEMIC COMMUNITY

While government policy respecting the social control of certain psychoactive substances has been resistant to change, this resistance does not appear to be shared by the Canadian academic community. The writings of many academic commentators have touched upon both substantive law and developments within judicially made law. There have been repeated criticisms of both legislative and judicial methods for the control of illegal drugs.

Perhaps the strongest attack against Canadian "drug" law was that launched by British Columbia philosophy professor Donald Brown in a 1972 article in the *University of British Columbia Law Review* (3). Brown notes, "The belief that trafficking is peculiarly evil rests in part on something other than the basic analysis I have been attempting of the nature of using and supplying, and of the types of harm to be prevented. It rests rather on a pragmatic determination to do whatever is necessary, after the decision has been taken to apply a particular administrative and quasi-military solution to the problem. The trafficker is evil because he is the enemy, and he is the enemy because war has been declared" (3, pp. 7–8). Brown insists that we have a faulty diagnosis of the social problem of drug abuse. He concludes that "doctors should climb down from their purism and paternalism about the user's welfare, and allow patients the choice of heroin maintenance over uncontrolled illegal use. . . . The enforcement agencies should trust the medical profession and get out of its way, so that the elements of the doctor-patient relation could be re-established for addicts and for others with occasional drug problems" (3, pp. 15–16).

Brown's article appeared shortly after the Le Dain Commission published a number of sections from its *Final Report* on "non-medical" drug use in

Canada. In 1972 the appropriate question for discussion within legal discourse concerned the wisdom of substance criminalization as a state strategy.

Since that time academic attention has focused on narrower concerns —on the specifics of Canadian "drug" law procedure. Both the absolute and conditional discharge provisions and the procedural anomalies that drug enforcement necessitates have been subjected to critical analysis. It is not surprising that the discharge provisions have been subjected to academic attack; they represent a highly compromised enactment. Health Minister John Munro had told the Canadian House of Commons, "If a person receives this kind of discharge he is not considered to have been convicted of the offence" (4, p. 173). Munro was essentially telling Canadians that the discharge would enable the government to label a drug user as criminal for some purposes and non-criminal for other purposes. A "discharged" individual need not admit to a criminal record for the purposes of employment and mobility, yet the indignity of appearance in criminal court was still required. Further, the Royal Canadian Mounted Police could continue to retain a record of the given offence for future use.

Toronto lawyer Jeffrey Leon has been sharply critical of the lack of legislative criteria set out to guide the judicial imposition of discharges. Leon concludes, "the desire for appropriate use of new sentencing alternatives implies a further need to make relevant sentencing criteria explicit. So far the Canadian Parliament appears to have left this task to various Courts of Appeal. With respect, it may be that the sources of information and resources necessary for this task are more accessible to Parliament than to the courts" (9, p. 68). Leon stops short, however, of criticizing the sense of the discharge itself. He appears to embrace the symbolism of leniency that this provision represents. He notes, "it is likely that frequent use will be made of the discharge provisions. . . . It must be emphasized that such an effect does not render the use of the criminal process for such offences futile. The effect of the process itself on the drug offender, combined with the imposition of a discharge, may equal the desired effects of the more drastic dispositions" (p. 68).

Frederick Bobiasz similarly attacks the use of the discharge provisions in a 1974 article in the *Ottawa Law Review*. Bobiasz, like Leon, assumes the validity of the change in sentencing law, but asks for some "rather clear cut guidelines as to the relevant considerations [in passing of such a sentence]" (1, p. 619). Bobiasz does note, however, that, "The most serious criticism is that a discharge, even an absolute one, does not in fact free the offender from a criminal record" (p. 618). It may seem inconsistent, nonetheless, that Bobiasz and Leon can support the discharge as a sentencing option, its symbolic leniency notwithstanding. A term of probation is typically attached to a conditional discharge. This compromised "leniency" is a rather convoluted state response to the phenomenon of widespread marijuana use by Canada's young.

Canadian case law concerning illegal drugs has similarly been the subject of much academic criticism. Particularly useful is Joseph Weiler's critique of *The Queen* v. *Kundeus* in a 1976 volume of the *Osgoode Hall Law Journal* (21). Richard Kundeus was convicted of trafficking in LSD, even though he believed that the substance he was selling was, in fact, mescaline. As Canada imposes more lenient penalties for distributing mescaline than for distributing LSD, this honest mistake of fact represented a contentious legal issue. There was no "mens rea," no evil intent to traffic in LSD, but our Supreme Court ultimately convicted Kundeus of this specific offence, nonetheless. As Weiler rather harshly notes, "The Kundeus case is a significant benchmark in the development of the criminal law in Canada since it illustrates disturbing characteristics of our Supreme Court ... the legal craftsmanship exhibited by the majority is totally inappropriate for our highest tribunal. The obfuscation of the issues in Kundeus has created a situation where lower courts need resort to a form of psychoanalysis in order to determine the real basis for the Supreme Court's decision. ... Finally, the ... case is disturbing because it illustrates that the Supreme Court is not acting in a collegial fashion. ... The opinion of the majority and dissent bear no relation to each other and if we didn't know better, would suggest that the authors heard different appeals on different days" (21, pp. 479–80).

Perhaps Weiler could have been even more sardonic here; the anomaly of which he speaks is one that is perhaps produced by the criminalization of certain proscribed substances, in itself. The offence of which Kundeus is actually guilty—the distribution of a psychoactive substance—is not to be found in either our *Narcotic Control Act* or our *Food and Drugs Act*. To suggest that this distribution of mescaline was deserving of penalty is to suggest that a pharmaceutical representative who inadvertently sells a restricted or controlled substance could quite properly be imprisoned for his actions. While this was probably not the desired thrust of the Court's decision in *Kundeus*, it does seem a fair inference. The Court's desire to control certain psychoactive substances and to correspondingly ignore others has overridden its adherence to the conditions required for criminal conviction.

In 1987 the legislative and judicial dances continue. While governments have promised legislation to soften penalties for marijuana use, there has been no substantial retreat from the hypocrisy that the criminalization of certain psychoactive substances represents. The reality of four million marijuana users is a social fact that successive Canadian governments have been slow to face. Perhaps most lamentably though, no government has been able to implement alternative policies to the repressive modality of criminalization. This reality does not set Canada apart from other nation states; it only suggests that we have perhaps unwisely followed the bad examples of others. As Andrew Weil has so perceptively noted, "drugs are perfect examples of the ambivalence of external things. They are potential keys to better ways of using the mind; they are also potential traps that can keep us from using our minds in better ways.... Like the fantasy that drugs can be made to go away, the idea that people who want drugs can be discouraged from using them is an impossible dream that gets us nowhere except in worse trouble.... drugs are merely means to achieve states of nonordinary awareness and must not be confused with the experiences themselves. They have the capacity to trigger highs; they do not contain highs. Moreover, the experiences they trigger are essentially no different from experiences triggered by more natural means.... The *real* risk of using drugs as the primary method of altering consciousness is in their tendency to reinforce an illusory view of cause and effect that makes it ultimately harder to learn how to maintain highs without dependence on the material world" (20, pp. 192, 194, 196).

NOTES

1. This figure can be arrived at by using Charts A-15 and A-16 in *Drug Users and Conviction Statistics* (5).
2. MacFarlane's text (10) is used by most prosecutors and defense counsel involved in "drug" litigation.
3. Justice Berger noted, "There is evidence that the organization was prepared to kill those who crossed it or cheated it. They had their own system of private justice" (13, p. 111).
4. The word "addiction" and, in other contexts, the word "drug" must be placed within quotation marks, in recognition of their problematic status. See the National Institute on Drug Abuse's *Theories on Drug Abuse*, Rockville, Md., 1980.
5. In 1969 the Canadian Medical Association argued that the marijuana laws result in effects on the users that are far more deleterious than the use of the drug; the Canadian Bar Association followed suit in 1978.

REFERENCES

1. Bobiasz, F. Absolute and conditional discharge. *University of Ottawa Law Review,* 6:608–19 (1974).
2. Brecher, E. M., and the Editors of Consumer Reports. *Licit and Illicit Drugs.* Boston: Little, Brown, 1972.
3. Brown, D. G. Drugs and the problems of law abuse. *University of British Columbia Law Review,* 7:1–16 (1972).
4. Bryan, M. Cannabis in Canada—A decade of indecision. *Contemporary Drug Problems,* 8:169–92 (1979).
5. Canada. Bureau of Dangerous Drugs. Health Protection Branch, Depart-

ment of National Health and Welfare. *Drug Users and Conviction Statistics*. Ottawa: 1979.

6. Canada. Commission of Inquiry into the Non-Medical Use of Drugs. *Final Report*. Ottawa: Information Canada, 1973.
7. Canada. House of Commons. *Debates*. 1960.
8. Erickson, P. G. *Cannabis Criminals: The Social Effects of Punishment on Drug Users*. Toronto: ARF Books, 1980.
9. Leon, J. Drug offences and discharges in Canada: The need for reform. *University of Toronto Faculty of Law Review, 35*:36–68 (1977).
10. MacFarlane, B. A. *Drug Offences in Canada*. Toronto: Canada Law Book, 1979.
11. *Statutes of Canada. An Act to amend the Narcotic Control Act*, S.C. 1968–69, c. 41.
12. Szasz, T. *Ceremonial Chemistry: The Ritual Persecution of Drug Addicts and Pushers*. Garden City, N.Y.: Anchor Press/Doubleday, 1974.
13. *The Queen* v. *Bengert et al.* (1979), 15 C.R. (3d) 97 (B.C. S.C.).
14. *The Queen* v. *Bosley and Duarte* (1970), 1 C.C.C. (2d) 328 (Ont. C.A.).
15. *The Queen* v. *Johnston and Tremayne* (1970), 4 C.C.C. 64 (Ont. C.A.).
16. *The Queen* v. *Lecapoy* (1974), 18 C.C.C. (2d) 496 (Alta. C.A.).
17. *The Queen* v. *Macauley* (1967), 52 Cr. App. R. 230.
18. *The Queen* v. *Richards* (1978), 49 C.C.C. (2d) 517 (Ont. C.A.).
19. *The Queen* v. *Robert, Shacher, Young and Smith* (1971), 3 C.C.C. (2d) 149 (Ont. C.A.).
20. Weil, A. *The Natural Mind*. Boston: Houghton-Mifflin, 1972.
21. Weiler, J. *The Queen* v. *Kundeus*: The saga of two ships passing in the night. *Osgoode Hall Law Journal, 14*:457–80 (1976).

19

Cannabis Criminals Revisited*

PATRICIA G. ERICKSON AND GLENN F. MURRAY

INTRODUCTION

> Criminal law, like other law, exacts a threefold price [the costs to individual
> lawbreakers, the restriction on personal liberty, and the economic cost to society
> of legal control]. Only the cost is higher. Other law imposes inconvenience.
> Criminal law means that people get hurt. (10, p. 36)

The imposition of criminal sanctions on cannabis users has been at the heart
of much of the debate over cannabis policy from the mid-1960s to the present.
In Canada, as elsewhere, the impact of criminal conviction on young lives
was identified as one of the most serious costs generated by the current
prohibition. These adverse individual consequences of criminalization have
been documented (4). More recently, health concerns have regained ascen-
dancy, and thwarted much of the impetus for legal reform (5). It is timely,
then, to re-examine the nature of the costs to individual cannabis users arising
from their criminalization and also to consider the reciprocal pressure that
the criminalization policy exerts on the processing of offenders.

This study utilizes interview data, collected from similar groups of cannabis possession offenders in 1974 and 1981 in Toronto, to address three
questions. These are the following: (i) Who gets caught; have offender characteristics changed? (ii) What is the impact; have offenders' responses to the
experience of criminalization altered? (iii) How has the system responded;
have the police and courts changed their procedures and practices regarding
cannabis offenders? That such questions retain significance is indicated by
the national criminalization data for Canada shown in Table 19.1. Since 1974,
at least 25,000 persons annually have been designated criminals for the offence
of cannabis possession.

METHOD

Full descriptions of the methodology of the original study and the replication
are available elsewhere (4, 9). Briefly, both samples consisted of first offenders,
defined as those without a pre-existing conviction for any adult criminal
offence. Respondents, numbering 95 in 1974 and 48 in 1981, were interviewed
right after final disposition of their cases had occurred. Six months after

---

*Reprinted from the British Journal of Addiction, 81, no. 1 (1986): 81–85. By permission.

Table 19.1
Convictions Involving Cannabis under the Narcotic Control Act,
Canada, 1968–1982*

Year	Total Convicted	Simple Possession	Trafficking	Possession for the Purpose of Trafficking	Importing	Cultivating
1968	1,429	1,078	211	131	2	7
1969	2,964	2,313	454	179	6	12
1970	6,292	5,419	448	356	26	43
1971	9,478	8,389	476	533	22	58
1972	11,713	10,695	290	620	33	75
1973	19,929	18,603	299	914	27	86
1974	20,067	27,202	429	1,281	24	131
1975	27,367	25,056	649	1,523	34	105
1976	33,281	30,523	886	1,709	29	134
1977	37,812	33,961	1,296	2,376	34	145
1978	31,718	27,609	1,714	2,215	24	156
1979	31,738	27,400	2,008	2,172	33	125
1980	37,244	32,475	2,052	2,542	28	147
1981	40,436	34,535	2,564	3,180	8	149
1982	31,884	26,020	2,664	3,063	6	131

*Source: Bureau of Dangerous Drugs, Health Protection Branch, Health and Welfare Canada

sentencing, a follow-up telephone interview was conducted with 72 per cent of the first group and 54 per cent of the second. In the initial study, a one-year personal follow-up was also carried out, but this was not repeated in 1981. Since it was found that the situation of most individuals in the first study altered little in the interval between six months and one year post-court, the lack of a longer follow-up for the later study does not place a serious limitation on comparability of results.

RESULTS

Offender Characteristics

To be considered here are personal, legal, and drug use characteristics of those interviewed in 1974 and 1981 (see Table 19.2). The background and drug use characteristics of the respondents were quite similar in the two time periods. Young, single males who were regular users of cannabis (twice a week or more) predominated. In 1981, respondents were less likely to be employed, and more likely to be living at home with parents, than in 1974. The change in both of these characteristics was likely related to the general worsening of economic prospects for young people in that period.

The legal case profile of each sample did not vary greatly either. All, or

Table 19.2
Sample Characteristics of Cannabis Offenders

Characteristics	1974 (N=95) %	1981 (N=48) %
Personal		
Male	90	88
Age 21 or less	65	65
Position:		
In school	17	29
Employed	72	50
Unemployed/other	12	21
Live with parents	43	58
Drug Use		
Use of cannabis twice per week or more	73	77
Legal		
Charge of possession of one form of cannabis only	84	94
Plea of guilty	98	100
Amount of cannabis ≤14 g	74	75
Legal Representation:		
None	41	65
Own lawyer	32	21
Duty counsel	27	15

nearly all, pleaded guilty and the amount of cannabis was quite small (14 g or less in about three-quarters of cases) in both groups. Charges were somewhat more likely to involve only one count of cannabis possession in 1981 compared to 1974 (94% versus 84%). The chief difference was in the type of legal representation—in the later year, offenders were not represented by counsel in 65 per cent of cases, compared to 41 per cent in 1974. This finding is likely related to the more routine and less punitive treatment of cases by 1981; these observations will be elaborated below in the section on police and court administrative practices.

Impact of Criminalization on Offenders

The costs to individuals encompass pre-court deprivations which occur as a result of the arrest, as well as post-conviction effects on personal identity, economic standing, and respect for the law. Here we are not so much concerned with the automatic disqualifications or handicaps imposed on holders of a criminal record (3, 8), but rather with the socially transmitted consequences of punishment. These will, in part, be determined by the attitudes and beliefs about cannabis, held by users and non-users alike, in the offenders' milieu (1). Thus any changes over time in the impact of criminalization on individuals may be indicative of shifts in the social meaning of cannabis use and the perceived appropriateness of criminal sanctions for this behaviour.

The stigmatization of personal identity was examined in relation to criminal self-perception, and the perception as criminal by others. In both studies, very few respondents had a self-perception as criminal at the time of sentencing (only 6% in 1974 and 4% in 1981). Only 5 per cent of respondents in the first study, and none in the second, thought their friends might consider them criminals. About the same proportion of mothers and fathers in both studies (between 25% and 30%) would think of their children as criminals according to the respondents. There was also considerable similarity in both groups of offenders as to their perception of the group most likely to view them as criminals, namely, the police (56% in 1974 and 61% in 1981). A sense of stigmatization as a result of their cannabis conviction, especially in relation to self-perception and from those closest to them, was not pronounced in either time period. The personal and social stigma of a criminal record would appear to have been even more diluted with the passage of time.

The economic impact of criminalization is felt most directly in relations with current employers and the potential of job loss, and secondarily, in the jeopardization of future job prospects. The necessity of attending court required some sort of strategy for slightly more than half the respondents in both studies. A contrast in the two time frames was that 1974 offenders were five times as likely to tell bosses the specific reason for needing time off for the cannabis possession charge as the 1981 offenders (21% versus 4%). The later group was more likely to mention court without stating the real reasons (55% versus 31% in 1974). The balance of each group was similar in offering either no explanation or a non-court one (e.g., sick, appointment). No respondents at follow-up, in either group, reported losing their jobs because employers had become aware of the cannabis offence.

In terms of job prospects, such a relatively short follow-up can provide only a preliminary taste of any repercussions from a criminal history. Both groups had been quite active in seeking jobs in the interval after their court appearances. The positions being sought were mainly of a semi-skilled or unskilled nature. While 42 per cent of the 1974 group were asked a question on job applications about a criminal record, 27 per cent of the 1981 group were. It would appear that the record was not a major handicap in the short run. Respondents seemed to be more generally disadvantaged by their youth and lack of experience.

Respect for the law was gauged in terms of both respondents' perceptions of how they were treated personally by the court and their attitudes to the law as a basic social institution (6). Based on other research, a contradiction between specific and general assessments of the role of courts would not be surprising (7). Such was the case in the present study. Perception of fairness of their treatment by the court was strongly related to sentence received. Those who were awarded fines or probation (rather than an absolute discharge) were much more likely to view these outcomes as more severe than usual, and also to continue to see them as unfair at the time of follow-up. These reactions were especially characteristic of those fined (65% of the 1974 group and 75% of the 1981 group). Nevertheless, when asked to express agreement or disagreement with three statements about the legitimacy of the law in general, over 90 per cent of both samples expressed favourable attitudes. This was in marked contrast to the lack of acceptance of the law prohibiting cannabis use, also manifested in both samples (also by more than 90%). Thus, findings in the cost area of disrespect for the law were consistent at both points in time.

Administrative Practices

Now we turn to the area where some striking differences emerged between 1974 and 1981, namely, the response of the criminal justice machinery to cannabis possession offenders. The police processing of offenders had speeded up considerably. While most still were taken to the police station (71% at both times), 92 per cent of 1981 arrestees were charged and given a date to appear in court without being subjected to fingerprinting and photographing, compared to 38 per cent of those arrested in 1974. Court processing had also accelerated. In the later study, 81 per cent of respondents went to court only once, 15 per cent went twice and the remaining 4 per cent went three times. In contrast, 48 per cent of the earlier group went once, 32 per cent twice, and 20 per cent three or more times. The time between arrest and final disposition in court was halved: the average of 2.6 months in 1974 was reduced to 1.3 months in 1981. "Not guilty" pleas were extremely rare in both periods, as were cases which took longer than 2 or 3 minutes between the plea of "guilty" and the pronouncement of sentence. Clearly, what was already a fairly rapid procedure in 1974 had become even more streamlined by 1981.

What about the actual sentencing of cannabis offenders? Here the trend was towards greater leniency, and a continuation of the judges' preference for absolute discharge. In 1981, a greater proportion of the respondents (58%) received this outcome than in 1974 (42%), while the proportion being convicted and fined was reduced from 24 per cent to 8 per cent. The awarding of conditional discharges, which imposes a probationary period, remained constant as the outcome for one third of both samples.

The sentencing of cannabis possession offenders in Toronto may be compared to the national pattern shown in Table 19.3. Evidently, either form of discharge is awarded much less frequently in the nation's courtrooms overall: only about one quarter of those sentenced in both 1974 and 1981 received this option; fines predominated in about two thirds of all cases. Still, it would be misleading to conclude that sentencing practices in Ontario generally are as lenient as those in Toronto. Another study (9) found considerable variation

Table 19.3

Sentences Awarded (%) for Simple Possession of Cannabis, Canada, 1967–1982*

Year*	Imprisonment	Fine Only	Suspended Sentence	Discharge	Total *N*
1967	46.0		53.0		431
1968	46.3		52.7		1,078
1969	33.9	17.6	48.5		2,313
1970	10.1	68.2	21.6		5,419
1971	6.8	77.3	15.9		8,389
1972	5.3	70.4	11.5	12.8	10,695
1973	4.7	70.8	8.5	16.0	18,603
1974	3.7	68.6	7.6	20.1	27,202
1975	4.4	66.1	6.9	22.6	25,056
1976	4.1	66.4	7.1	22.4	30,523
1977	3.9	65.7	5.9	24.5	33,961
1978	4.3	62.7	6.3	26.7	27,609
1979	4.1	61.9	4.5	29.5	27,400
1980	4.1	63.7	3.9	28.3	32,108†
1981	5.3	65.5	3.5	25.7	34,157†
1982	6.9	66.5	4.5	22.1	25,759†

*Sources: 1967–1971, Commission of Inquiry into the Non-Medical Use of Drugs, *Cannabis* (Ottawa: Information Canada, 1972), pp. 249, 290, 324–25.

1972–1982, Bureau of Dangerous Drugs, Health Protection Branch, Health and Welfare Canada.

†The category of "other" sentence was excluded from the total.

between 18 Ontario locales in the percentage of simple possession cases ending in discharge (range 9%–75%).

DISCUSSION

In two similar studies conducted 7 years apart, the personal and legal case characteristics of cannabis possession offenders were found to be largely unchanged. The costs to offenders, while not pronounced in 1974, seemed much the same in 1981. It seems possible that recent offenders may gain some reassurance from a generally accessible "pool" of knowledge to the effect that most bosses and future employers do not actively seek out criminal record histories. What had altered was the efficiency with which cases were processed by both police and courts. The decline in legal representation may also reflect the tendency to minimize the court's time; moreover, the relative leniency of dispositions in such cases may have further motivated offenders to avoid the delay and expense of seeking legal counsel. While the actual volume of cases had remained high, severity of sentence had lessened.

What these results point to is the inescapable conclusion that the system has learned to accommodate the large number of cannabis offenders processed through it each year. This particular pressure for reform—the over-extension of police and court resources—would appear to have been defused. Other pressures, such as the youth of offenders and the costs they incur from criminalization have not dramatically altered, but are now tolerated. It might be argued that the greater leniency of sentences and the social dilution of stigma as a "cannabis criminal" has tended to minimize the impact on offenders' identity and lives. Nevertheless, most respondents were quite similar at both times in wishing to maintain secrecy about their criminal record as far as family and employers were concerned. The unanswered question is how successful they will be in the long run, and what the lifelong repercussions will be.

During the time span from the first study to the present, no new legislative proposals have been introduced in Canada and none is anticipated. Many writers on the cannabis controversy have captured this impasse, but none better than the following:

> Generally speaking, criminal prohibitions are easier to enact than to repeal. They may be inscribed in the criminal code effortlessly, even thoughtlessly; but any effort to erase them must hurdle a presumption of wisdom and righteousness. This burden is difficult to sustain even if the original legislative decision was demonstrably misconceived. The marijuana laws provide a case in point. (2, p. 1)

REFERENCES

1. Auld, J. *Marijuana Use and Social Control*. London: Academic Press, 1981.
2. Bonnie, R. J. *Marijuana Use and Criminal Sanctions*. Charlottesville, Va.: Michie, 1980.
3. Damaska, M. R. Legal consequences of conviction and their removal: A comparative study. *Journal of Criminal Law and Criminology, 59*:347–60 and 542–68 (1968).
4. Erickson, P. G. *Cannabis Criminals: The Social Effects of Punishment on Drug Users*. Toronto: ARF Books, 1980.
5. Erickson, P. G. La réforme des lois sur le cannabis: un mouvement inachevé. *Psychotropes, 2*:96–98 (1985).
6. Erickson, P. G. Drug sentencing and perceptions of law. In: Rush, B. and Layne, N. (eds.). *Alcohol, Drugs and Canadian Youth*. Ottawa: Health and Welfare Canada, 1985.
7. Flanagan, T. J., McGarrell, E. F., and Brown, E. J. Public perceptions of the criminal courts: The role of demographic and related attitudinal variables. *Journal of Research in Crime and Delinquency, 22*:66–82 (1985).
8. Leon, J. S. Post-sentencing problems: Some consequences of a finding of guilt in criminal cases. *Criminal Law Quarterly, 21*:318–60 (1979).

9. Murray, G. F., and Erickson, P. G. Regional variation in criminal justice system practices: Cannabis possession in Ontario. *Criminal Law Quarterly, 26*:74–96 (1983).
10. Senate of Canada. *Proceedings of the Standing Senate Committee on Legal and Constitutional Affairs*. Issue no. 19, 1975. Ottawa: Information Canada, 1975.

POLICY ANALYSIS: LESSONS FROM THE PAST AND PROPOSALS FOR CHANGE

This book has led us across the vast, unresolved territory of Canadian drug policy, from the past, through the present, and now into futures that might be. Our journey has been tortuous because of the many routes, crossroads, and contradictory road signs along the way. A yellow brick road leading to a clearly defined destination would have been preferable. Lack of clarity with regard to the destination—the objective of Canada's drug policy—underlies much of the seeming illogic of the efforts made to date, and hence the detours and dead ends encountered.

What should be the objective of drug policy? "To discourage drug use," perhaps, but this is not a particularly useful statement of social policy. It is merely a general aim, and does not imply any specific goals or the preferred strategies to achieve them. A more precise objective would be "to minimize the adverse health and safety consequences of drug use at an acceptable level of social cost." Once the key terms such as "adverse consequences," "drug use," and "acceptable cost" are defined, we have not only clear goals, but flexibility in policy implementation, and the potential to empirically evaluate its success or failure. In contrast, a policy objective such as "the achievement of a drug-free society" seems much closer to a total declaration of a war in which the chances of victory are remote.

Definitions are crucial in determining tactics, and the contributors to this section share an appreciation of this fundamental principle: the need to clarify our social policy objectives regarding non-medical drug use. With the lessons we have learned from the past, we now have the background to examine recent efforts at drug law reform and to consider future prospects for change.

It is fitting that this section begins with an overview of the global drug distribution system. Since the Opium Wars of 1839–42, when Britain forced China to continue receiving imports of opium, it has been apparent that no nation can function totally autonomously in determining the drug consumption behaviour of its citizenry. Economic interests underpinned this particular British foreign policy initiative, and to this day the power of the international drug trade is based on the immense profits it generates. In an original contribution written for this book, Judith Blackwell discusses how the global drug market is moulded by, and gains its strength from, geopolitical and economic factors over which Canada has little or no control. It is of utmost importance that this country develop a unique policy response to our particular drug problems, but it would be unwise to do so without considering the wider picture beyond our borders.

The section continues with a review of the origins, functioning, and recommendations of the Le Dain Commission. Patricia Erickson and Reginald Smart have abstracted this material from *Cannabis* and the Commission's *Final Report.* The division among the Commissioners on specific legal recommendations—resulting in a majority and two minority reports—has obscured their consensual preference for the overall direction of policy: a gradual shift away from reliance on the criminal law to control the user. This thinking represents a fundamental redefinition of appropriate strategies to prevent or reduce illicit drug use, ones which blur the boundary between legal and illegal. This is a topic that is taken up again in Chapter 25. The Commission's proposals met with considerable resistance. This is perhaps not surprising, since by questioning the wisdom of criminalizing the drug user, they challenged a policy to which Canada has been devoted for the better part of this century.

James Giffen and Sylvia Lambert pick up the post–Le Dain threads and ask what has become of these recommendations in the intervening years. The process of law reform, or rather *non*-reform, is a fascinating chronicle of competing interest groups, political backtracking, scientific claims and counterclaims, and ultimately, inaction. They argue that the inherent inertia of social control systems creates a strong resistance to any fundamental alteration. Hence, the various challenges to the traditional institutions of illicit drug management were absorbed or transformed into minor alterations, a response particularly evident in the processing of cannabis possession cases. The criminal justice system has remained the dominant force in Canada's drug policy.

Robert Solomon, Eric Single, and Patricia Erickson conduct a critique of the recent regime of cannabis control policy, concluding that the costs of criminalizing users far exceed the deterrent benefits. They then dissect three other policy alternatives to total prohibition: mitigation, partial repeal, and legal availability. For each, they ask how individual and social costs can be minimized with the least risk of increasing harmful levels of use. Drawing on data generated since the completion of the Commission's reports, these authors reach the same preferred option as that favoured by the Le Dain majority, namely, the partial repeal of the offence of simple possession. They suggest several forms such an option could take, and forecast only slight increases in use under such a policy. It is of interest to note that since their paper was published (1983), cannabis use levels have tapered off (Chapter 14) in the absence of legislative change. We will never know whether the same phenomenon would have occurred if the laws had been modified.

Neil Boyd, Christopher Millard, and Christopher Webster describe the problems of British Columbia's compulsory drug treatment legislation for opiate dependents. Despite apparently declining numbers of addicts, the government introduced a scheme for compulsory treatment that met with a wave of opposition from civil libertarians, drug treatment specialists, and the medical and legal professions. In the constitutional challenges that followed, the plan was dropped after only two years and without ever having been fully implemented. Ironically, in legal arguments discussed by the authors, the Supreme Court of Canada later unanimously upheld the legality of British Columbia's initiative. This was a pre-*Charter* decision, and thus any future attempts to reintroduce compulsory treatment would be likely to face challenges under the *Charter*. Echoing many of the concerns raised in Chapter 10, the authors discuss the thorny issues of punishment versus treatment and freedom versus coercion.

In the final chapter, Chester Mitchell begins with the premise that all psychoactive drugs, licit and illicit, share enough common features to justify a consistent societal response. After reviewing current legal and scientific classifications of drugs, and analyzing the principles of justice as they apply to drug control, he presents five policy options. He then selects tax-licensing controls as the most rational and justifiable possibility at this time. Mitchell implements the guiding principle of the Le Dain Commission: rational policy analysis. Then he takes it several steps further by developing an imaginative framework for the uniform regulation of all psychoactive drugs. In so doing, he adopts the "pure" approach that the theoretician would take in facing all drug problems for the first time, simultaneously. Although historical and political considerations have produced a social climate in which serious consideration of such a comprehensive scheme is highly unlikely, Professor Mitchell provides an important model for a critical, unbiased approach to our drug problems.

20

Canada in a Global Setting: Notes on the International Drug Market

JUDITH BLACKWELL

A thorough analysis of the international illicit drug trade and Canada's place in it would take up at least a volume of its own. Here there is only space for a brief review of its salient features and the problems faced by the law enforcement agencies whose mandate is to control it. In the media we hear of international treaties, diplomatic negotiations, new schemes for co-operation and information sharing among police agencies, and crop substitution or eradication projects in the countries where drugs originate. Reports such as these tend to be optimistic in their promise of major initiatives against international trafficking. The notes presented here have been written to generate a healthy and realistic pessimism, to explain how ineffable is the task of controlling this traffic or protecting our country from its inroads.

The development of Canada's drug policies must be guided by an awareness of our situation as a geographically large country with a relatively small population. As such, we have few defences against an innovative multinational business devoted to the production and distribution of illicit drugs. This vulnerability is shared to a greater or lesser degree with other countries around the globe, large and small, and it continues to increase for all nations as trafficking organizations grow wealthier and more technologically sophisticated.

The sources of data that inform this chapter are of a different order than those on which the rest of the book is based. By its nature, the drug market is resistant to intrusion and investigation. Most of the information about it comes from journalists, law enforcement agents, or police informants. Few scholars care to run the risk of infiltrating the trade to do field work. Thus, there are many concerns about accuracy, not only regarding the reliability of the data, but also about potential reporting biases. A number of academics have evaluated and synthesized what we do know, or think we know, about the illicit drug market. This chapter, too, is a synthesis based on scholarly sources as well as journalistic and enforcement accounts.

Recent technological developments have increased the reliability of intelligence-gathering. For example, satellite surveillance can now be used to detect and estimate the size of drug crops. Despite such improvements, knowledge of the drug trade is largely based on informed guesswork, sifting fact from folklore. Nevertheless, the broad features of the trade can be outlined without complete data accurate in every detail. As an illustration of this point, there is disagreement about whether marijuana is the largest cash crop in the United States, or the second, or the third (16); no one knows its exact proportions, but its potential economic significance is evident in these conflicting estimates. By necessity shrouded in secrecy, the international illicit drug trade eludes precise description, but its importance to policy analysis is such that an outline of its features cannot await better data.

THE MERCURIAL MARKET

With a few notable exceptions, such as northern California (16), the crops that produce cannabis, cocaine, and the opiates are cultivated in Third World countries. They are grown where these drugs have traditionally been used for self-medication or recreational purposes by indigenous populations, or where demand from the developed nations has encouraged cultivation. Clandestine cultivation normally takes place in remote, inaccessible areas, where access by law enforcement agents is difficult. Climatic conditions partly explain the south-to-north flow of drugs, but we will see in this chapter that political and economic factors are also very important.

Take the opium poppy, for example. The traditional methods of its cultivation are so labour-intensive that it would be economically unattractive to North American or European farmers. It has been estimated that up to 250 person-hours may be required to produce one kilogram of opium. The ideal political economy of a source country, then, is one featuring underutilization of labour and low per capita income, and where the government lacks political and administrative resources to suppress drug farming (21).

Western countries have frequently blamed their drug problems on the source countries (9), but the south-north flow of illicit drugs should not be characterized as the revenge of the poor nations on the rich. It is no more so than the north-south trade in pharmaceutical psychoactive drugs (13). History, economics, and politics explain the nature of the traffic much more satisfactorily than do international conspiracy theories.

One of the most important facts to keep in mind about the illicit international drug trade is this: the only time it has been seriously disrupted was during the Second World War (11). This should come as no surprise, since all international trade was thrown into disarray at the time. Except for the war years, North America has seen only short-term periods of scarcity, when one or another of the illicit drugs has been off the market or more difficult to obtain than usual.

Resourcefulness and flexibility are characteristics the drug trade shares with legitimate business enterprises. They are illustrated by the way the trade quickly adapts to and recuperates from each new measure taken against it.

Another feature the trade has in common with legal enterprises is the motive force of profit:

> In recent years the belief has grown both in law enforcement and in professional crime that drugs can generate profits as great as any other form of illegal enterprise. The extent of such profits are sometimes exaggerated but they are impressive by any standards. (9, p. 9)

At each level of the trade, from growers to processors, to smugglers, to wholesale and retail dealers, there is sufficient profit to ensure its continuation.

Furthermore, creativity and innovation flourish on every level of the trade. A "kingpin" heroin or cocaine distributor can be captured, but an aspiring replacement will be ready to step out of the wings and take over the role. An international trade route is cut, but is almost immediately re-established using other ports of call. When one method of concealment is identified by the authorities, another is invented to take its place. Drug enforcement agencies increase their intelligence-gathering capabilities, while the trade responds with counter-intelligence based on equally sophisticated technology. When a source country is persuaded to ban cultivation or eradicate its crops, growing areas elsewhere increase production and take up the slack (9).

Naturally, measures taken against this resourceful industry are costly. To recoup some of this expense, the United States, Canada, and Australia have legal provisions whereby they can appropriate the proceeds of crime from convicted drug traffickers (5). Between 1983 and 1985, the RCMP Anti-Drug Profiteering Program acquired over twenty million dollars in money and assets (17c). In some U.S. jurisdictions, forfeitures and fines have not only paid for law enforcement expenses, but have turned a profit. Wisotsky (25) characterizes this as a "perpetual motion machine," a state of symbiosis where "black market profits can finance both the police and the policed in mutual prosperity forever after" (p. 175).

INTERNATIONAL CONTROL POLICIES: MAKING MATTERS WORSE

The profit generated by the drug trade underlies its adaptability. This is well illustrated by the failure of a 1971 policy initiative in Turkey, a source country for both licit and illicit opiates at the time (14). Turkish farmers were required to sell their entire opium crop to the government at the equivalent of less than ten U.S. dollars a kilogram. The drug would then be used for legitimate pharmaceutical purposes. However, black market buyers offered a higher price, and the amounts available to the government thus represented only what remained after illicit diversion was completed. In an effort to reduce this diversion, United States government officials persuaded Turkey to pay the farmers up to $15 a kilogram; the illicit traders promptly offered $25 a kilogram. By the time the opium had been converted to heroin, smuggled to North America and diluted, the extra cost at the source represented only one-quarter of a cent on a $5 unit sold to heroin users on the streets of New York City (2). Profit rendered impotent this well-intentioned policy.

The Turkish policy initiative made little difference, but other policies have succeeded only in making matters worse. As a general rule, increased law enforcement against the supply of illicit drugs, if successful, reduces their availability. For a drug like heroin, this in turn can lead to price increases at the retail level, which can also increase drug-related crime and raise individual and social costs (2). Furthermore, when potential profits increase, participation in the trade becomes more attractive to potential entrepreneurs, and the trade continues (7).

The economic effects of supply-oriented law enforcement vary somewhat, depending on the drug and the level of the trade at which the effort is aimed (18). Nevertheless, unintended adverse effects of such policies can be spectacular. A case in point is the way in which U.S. policies directed against the cannabis trade unwittingly set the stage for a cocaine epidemic in that country.[1]

In the mid-1960s, the cocaine industry was one of modest proportions with worldwide production estimated to have been about half a tonne, or, as Ricks puts it, "about one of today's plane loads" (19). In the mid-1980s, an estimated eighty tonnes a year were entering the United States alone (20). The events that were to radically increase the supply of and demand for cocaine were mediated by changes in the international cannabis market.

In the early 1960s, about 90 percent of the marijuana entering the United States came from Mexico (22). In 1969, Operation Intercept began—an initiative designed to stop the flow of cannabis across the border (2). When that proved unworkable, the U.S. began supplying Mexico with helicopters, airplanes, communications systems, and chemical herbicides to be used for search and destroy missions against the opium and cannabis crops.

Mexican marijuana eradication had the twin effects of reducing both the supply and the U.S. demand for the product. Demand declined because consumers were concerned about the potential hazards of using plants that might have been sprayed with harmful chemicals. The next logical source country was Colombia which, although further afield, had a reputation for producing high-quality marijuana, superior to that of Mexico.

By 1979, a regular Colombia-U.S. marijuana traffic was well established. Indeed, it was estimated that Colombia had acquired a 70 percent share of the market. Furthermore, importers began ordering South American cocaine to be included in cannabis shipments (19). Cannabis overproduction in this era, however, meant that the quality of the Colombian product was declining. Meanwhile, North American growers were learning how to produce a high-grade domestic product (16).

Throughout the late 1970s, the United States stepped up its enforcement efforts against the boats that were bringing the marijuana north. Thus, while the demand for Colombian cannabis was slipping, the risk of transporting it was increasing. Chances of success for cannabis smuggling vessels are said to have declined from an estimated 90 percent to 50 percent. As a result, importers began switching from boats to airplanes, and from marijuana to the less bulky cocaine. With increased availability of cocaine on the U.S. market, the price began to fall.

By the early 1980s, the South American cocaine industry was controlled by a number of vertically integrated corporations. These were large criminal syndicates that controlled the trade from raw material to product delivery abroad (15). In Florida, murderous internecine warfare among cocaine distributors had ended; the trade became better organized and had fewer police informants. At the same time, production of the drug at the source became more streamlined and efficient. Rather than the 100-kg lots that had previously been transported, cocaine was now being sent in larger aircraft, in shipments of 300–500 kg. With rising availability, the price of the drug in the U.S. dropped once again, by more than one-half between 1982 and 1985. "As supplies increased, prices plummeted and the once exotic drug became the people's choice" (19).

Thus, a well-intended effort to curb imports of Mexican and then Colombian marijuana accomplished its goal. It did not have the full desired effect on the availability of cannabis in the United States, because domestic production began to replace foreign imports. Of more concern, however, is the unanticipated side effect of this enforcement initiative: encouraging the importation of cocaine, a potentially more dangerous drug.

GEOPOLITICS AND THE DRUG TRADE

The profits of the drug trade have been used not only for the personal enrichment of the entrepreneurs involved, but also for supporting armed struggles and political movements around the world. When those exploiting drug trafficking are also defending themselves against or actively resisting communist regimes, they present an obvious conflict of interest for Western foreign policy. As we shall see below, drugs have no politics, but drug profit promises political as well as economic power.

The historical evolution of the international drug trade has been shaped by political events. For example, pre-revolutionary Cuba was a major cocaine transshipment point (3), and a meeting place for the American Mafia and the French-Corsican syndicates, a haven for the world's leading heroin traffickers (22). After Castro seized power in 1959, the expatriates who fled to the United States included drug traffickers who then established themselves in the cocaine and heroin distribution systems in Miami and New York. Solomon (22) reports that eight percent of the Cuban exiles involved in the Bay of Pigs invasion were subsequently investigated or arrested on drug charges. Expatriate Cubans were also involved in the early years of the Colombian-U.S. cannabis and cocaine trade (19).

Taiwanese, Soviet, and American governments have repeatedly blamed the People's Republic of China for contributing to the international heroin supply (10). In fact, after assuming power the Chinese Communist government quickly eliminated domestic production and, by the mid-1950s, had reduced its estimated ten-million-strong addict population to insignificant proportions (3). However, refugees from Chinese communism have played an important role in the opium trade. For decades after 1949, remnants of the Kuomintang military controlled opium collection and transportation in Burma and in northern Thailand (12). In Hong Kong, those involved in heroin processing and international distribution included expatriate Chinese who had previously been attached to drug syndicates in Shanghai (22).

Alfred McCoy (12) has claimed that American cold war foreign policy was the root cause of its own domestic heroin problems in the early 1970s. This is a debatable point, and one could argue that the heroin market is such an attractively profitable enterprise that it would continue without the intervention of the U.S. abroad. It is clear, however, that the activities of the Central Intelligence Agency (CIA) in the Golden Triangle (contiguous areas of Burma, Thailand, and Laos) enhanced the opiate trade and did nothing to encumber it (12). According to RCMP estimates, roughly two-thirds of the heroin on the Canadian market originates there (17c).

The other third comes from another part of the world where strategic interests collide with the interests of drug law enforcement. This is in the Golden Crescent, the opium-growing region that overlaps the borders of Iran, Afghanistan, and Pakistan. It has been estimated that upwards of six tonnes of heroin are produced annually in illicit refineries in the latter two countries (17b), and the number of refineries continues to grow (17c). The Northwest Frontier of Pakistan is a tribal area that traditionally has resisted central government interference or control. Afghan opium, virtually indistinguishable from the Pakistan product, has been cultivated for years by similarly autonomous tribal groups. In their case, however, this fierce independence has been turned against the Soviet occupation (9). It has been claimed that the drug trade finances and arms the resistance movement against the Kabul regime (14, 23). Clearly any sustained enforcement campaign against the opium trade would destabilize this important border region.

"On the whole, drug trafficking has adapted to the complex political situation that presently exists in Lebanon" (17b, p. 65). Of course, the RCMP are referring here to the civil war that has been raging in that country for over a decade. It has been reported that there is only one place in Lebanon where "Druze, Sunni, Christian, Palestinian and Shia live together without constant bloodshed": the Bekaa valley (4). This is the traditional cannabis-growing area, and drug enforcement officials estimate that roughly two-thirds of the hashish consumed in Canada originates there (17a, b, c). In recent years, Bekaa farmers have increased their productivity and diversified in a significant way. They have discovered double-cropping: they harvest opium poppies in the spring and then use the same land for a cannabis harvest in the autumn.

Favret (4) cites a U.S. Drug Enforcement Administration estimate that drug profits account for about a 50 percent share of the Lebanese economy. Satellite surveillance suggests that cannabis production amounts to 4,000 tonnes a year. A Beirut diplomat estimated that without the drug trade the Lebanese Christian forces would not last much longer than a fortnight, and a U.S. drug enforcement officer concluded: "You can't have any power in Lebanon, whether military or political, if you don't profit from drugs" (4).

The link between guns and drugs is money, not politics (14). Both right-wing and left-wing groups have obtained the resources to support and arm themselves by participation in the drug trade. Members of the Sri Lankan independence movement are said to act as drug couriers, and the Burmese Communist Army has taken over opium-growing areas in that country (17c). The Colombian Revolutionary Forces (FARC) control coca-growing areas, although it is claimed that they permit continuing cultivation only because the farmers cannot subsist with ordinary crops (20). FARC and another Colombian guerrilla faction, Movimiento 19, as well as Peruvian guerrillas, are said to have accepted cocaine money and arms in return for protecting the cocaine industry (15, 25).

Before the revolution in Nicaragua, the Somoza regime is said to have abetted the drug traffic from South to North America. The United States has accused the present regime of complicity in the trade (25), but there are counter-allegations that jungle airstrips built for the right-wing anti-Sandinista forces are used as refuelling stops for smugglers' aircraft (6). This may be yet another example of contradiction between U.S. foreign policy and drug law enforcement interests. Whatever the truth of the allegations on either side, they reflect the reasonable assumption that drug profits can be irresistible in political power struggles.

In his analysis of the international "hot money" economy, Naylor (14) observes that the financial power of the drug trade overwhelms the economies of small nations and undermines the fiscal integrity of larger ones. The scale of this financial power can be judged by the situation in Colombia, where the top cocaine barons have reputedly offered to repatriate their assets and pay off the national debt (some $13 billion U.S.) in return for immunity from prosecution or extradition to the United States (20). This offer was not accepted. In Bolivia, cocaine traffickers needed no such negotiation, as their interests were secured by direct government takeover: the military government that came to power there in the 1980 "cocaine coup" formed a mutually profitable syndicate with the cocaine producers (25).

Where there is drug money, there is the potential for the kind of corruption that not only compromises individual police or customs agents, but also can reach into the highest levels of government (25). Notwithstanding the geopolitical forces that have shaped the international drug trade and at times loaned it support, what drives it is enormous untaxed and unregulated profit.

MAKING CANADA "DRUG FREE"

This chapter began by noting the sheer geographic size of this country for its relatively small population. No nation can seal its borders against the global drug trade, but the prospect of doing so is even more remote where there are many miles of uninhabited coastline facing two oceans. We also have a long, undefended border with a neighbouring country where drug problems have always been on a larger scale than ours. Not only do drugs come north across the border, but traffickers have also used Canada as a transshipment point for drugs destined for the U.S. market.

At ports of entry into Canada, customs officials are faced with tonnes of imports among which drugs may be concealed. In 1985, Canadian residents made almost 40 million trips outside the country, and almost 36 million foreign residents visited us. Including diplomats, military personnel, and others, there were over 80 million border crossings into Canada that year (24).

Even if it were possible to stop drugs coming from foreign sources, or to raise the chances of apprehension enough to make the risks of smuggling unacceptable, the supply of illicit drugs would not necessarily cease. Cannabis grows wild here, and in recent years outdoor farming and indoor production facilities have expanded. Factory farming can yield three crops a year; timed artificial lighting, climate control, chemical fertilizers, and hydroponic growing techniques allow cultivation to be conducted away from public view in any part of the country. Canadian underground chemists have been manufacturing methaqualone, methamphetamine, LSD, and other hallucinogens for decades. With simple laboratory techniques, a few hundred dollars' worth of ingredients, and a week of work, it is possible to make a product that is virtually indistinguishable from high-quality heroin, but up to 200 times stronger (8). This is "China White," a derivative of the synthetic drug fentanyl. Some "new" drugs, like "Ecstacy" (XTC), have actually been around for some time, but have been rediscovered. Others, the so-called designer drugs, are created by tinkering with molecules, using information readily available in scientific journals.

So, what can be said about controlling the illicit drug supply?

> Unless you want to defoliate the entire planet and pave it over and outlaw the science of chemistry and cooking, you'll probably never stop the use of synthetic drugs or natural drugs. (Siegel, quoted in 8, p. 96)

On one hand, we are defending ourselves against a sophisticated and highly profitable international drug trade, elusive and resistant to law enforcement. On the other, we have a virtually unlimited domestic production capacity, one that will only improve as scientific knowledge advances.

Not long ago, it was generally believed that if only enough resources could be found for law enforcement, for customs and for border patrols, the supply of illicit drugs could be minimized. Awareness of the gargantuan proportions of such an effort has now impelled reanalysis of the problem. Any new solution will have to encompass both sides of the economic equation: supply and demand.

NOTES

1. The sequence of events described here follows an article by Thomas Ricks from the *Wall Street Journal*, reprinted in the "Report on Business" section of the Toronto *Globe and Mail* on July 16, 1986. The illicit cocaine trade is analyzed as would be any other "maturing industry" that has grown up from its cottage industry roots to become stable and dominated by a few well-entrenched giants.

REFERENCES

1. Brecher, E. M. Drug laws and drug law enforcement: A review and evaluation based on 111 years' experiences. *Drugs and Society*, *1*:1–27 (1986).
2. Brecher, E. M., and the Editors of Consumer Reports. *Licit and Illicit Drugs*. Boston: Little, Brown, 1972.
3. Canada. Commission of Inquiry into the Non-Medical Use of Drugs. *Interim Report*. Ottawa: Queen's Printer, 1970.
4. Favret, R. Deadly Harvest. *The Globe and Mail*, November 22, 1986, p. D5.
5. Freemantle, B. *The Fix*. New York: Tom Doherty Associates, 1985.
6. Greenhaw, W. *Flying High: Inside Big-Time Drug Smuggling*. New York: Dodd, Mead, 1984.
7. Kaplan, J. *The Hardest Drug: Heroin and Public Policy*. Chicago: The University of Chicago Press, 1983.
8. Kirsch, M. M. *Designer Drugs*. Minneapolis, Minn.: CompCare Publications, 1986.
9. Lewis, R. Serious business: The global heroin economy. In: Henman, A., Lewis, R., and Malyon, T. (eds.). *Big Deal: The Politics of the Illicit Drugs Business*. London: Pluto Press, 1985.
10. MacLennan, A. China drug tales are "nonsense." *The Journal*: April 1979, 1.

11. McCoy, A. W. Flowers of evil: The CIA and the heroin trade. *Harper's*, July 1972, 47–53.
12. McCoy, A. W. *The Politics of Heroin in Southeast Asia*. New York: Harper & Row, 1973.
13. McNicoll, A. *Drug Trafficking: A North-South Perspective*. Ottawa: The North-South Institute, 1983.
14. Naylor, T. *Hot Money and the Politics of Debt*. Toronto: McClelland and Stewart, 1987.
15. Nicholl, C. *The Fruit Palace*. London: Pan Books, 1985.
16. Raphael, R. *Cash Crops*. Mendocino, Calif.: The Ridge Times Press, 1985.
17. RCMP. Drug Enforcement Branch, Public Relations Branch, Royal Canadian Mounted Police.
    a. *RCMP National Drug Intelligence Estimate 1983*. Ottawa: Quorum Graphics, 1984.
    b. *RCMP National Drug Intelligence Estimate 1984/85*. Ottawa: Quorum Graphics, 1985.
    c. *RCMP National Drug Intelligence Estimate 1985/86*.Ottawa: Quorum Graphics, 1986.
18. Reuter, P., and Kleiman, M. Risks and prices: An economic analysis of drug enforcement. In: Tonry, M., and Morris, N. (eds.). *Crime and Justice: An Annual Review of Research*, vol. 7. Chicago: The University of Chicago Press, 1986.
19. Ricks, T. E. Cocaine: A study in pure capitalism. *The Globe and Mail*, July 16, 1986, Report on Business.
20. Riding, A. Cocaine billionaires: The men who hold Colombia hostage. *New York Times Magazine*, March 8, 1987, 27.
21. Simmons, L. R. S., and Said, A. A. The politics of addiction. In: Simmons, L. R. S. and Said, A. A. (eds.). *Drugs, Politics and Diplomacy*. Beverly Hills, Calif.: Sage Publications, 1974.
22. Solomon, R. The development and politics of the Latin American heroin market. *Journal of Drug Issues, 9*: 349–69 (1979).
23. *South: The Third World Magazine*. Poppies in battlefields. February, 1984, 113–14.
24. Statistics Canada. *Travel between Canada and Other Countries*. Ottawa: Minister of Supply and Services, 1986.
25. Wisotsky, S. *Breaking the Impasse in the War on Drugs*. New York: Greenwood Press, 1986.

21

The Le Dain Commission
Recommendations*

PATRICIA G. ERICKSON AND REGINALD SMART

The Le Dain Commission is formally entitled the Commission of Inquiry into the Non-Medical Use of Drugs. During its more than four years of existence, commencing in mid-1969, the commission produced four reports. These were the *Interim Report, Treatment, Cannabis*, and the *Final Report* (1a, b, c, d). This chapter will not deal with the material and issues covered at length in these four volumes. Rather it will concentrate on the genesis and modus operandi of the commission, its recommendations regarding the legal status of certain drugs, and official reactions to these proposals.

ORIGIN AND FUNCTIONING
OF THE COMMISSION

The buildup of conflicting pressures on the federal government with regard to its drug control policies in the late 1960s, which is extensively documented in Cook (2), culminated in the formation of the Le Dain Commission. The concerns that gave rise to the commission, as set out by the Minister of Health and Welfare, were described in these terms:

> The Committee of the Privy Council have had before them a report from the Minister of National Health and Welfare, representing:
>
> That there is growing concern in Canada about the non-medical use of certain drugs and substances, particularly, those having sedative, stimulant, tranquillizing or hallucinogenic properties, and the effect of such use on the individual and the social implications thereof;
>
> That within recent years, there has developed also the practice of inhaling the fumes of certain solvents having an hallucinogenic effect, and resulting in serious physical damage and a number of deaths, such solvents being found in certain household substances. Despite warnings and considerable publicity, this practice had developed among young people and can be said to be related to the use of drugs for other than medical purposes;
>
> That certain of these drugs and substances, including lysergic acid diethylamide,

LSD, methamphetamines, commonly referred to as "Speed," and certain others, have been made the subject of controlling or prohibiting legislation under the *Food and Drugs Act*, and cannabis, marijuana, has been a substance, the possession of or trafficking in which has been prohibited under the *Narcotic Control Act*;

That notwithstanding these measures and the competent enforcement thereof by the R.C.M. Police and other enforcement bodies, the incidence of possession and use of these substances for non-medical purposes, has increased and the need for an investigation as to the cause of such increasing use has become imperative (3).

The appointment of the commission on May 29, 1969, was authorized by the Order in Council which set the following terms of reference:

That inquiry be made into and concerning the factors underlying or relating to the non-medical use of the drugs and substances above described and that for this purpose a Commission of Inquiry be established, constituted and with authority as hereinafter provided,

a) to marshal from available sources, both in Canada and abroad, data and information comprising the present fund of knowledge concerning the non-medical use of sedative, stimulant, tranquillizing, hallucinogenic and other psychotropic drugs or substances;

b) to report on the current state of medical knowledge respecting the effect of the drugs and substances referred to in a);

c) to inquire into and report on the motivation underlying the non-medical use referred to in a);

d) to inquire into and report on the social, economic, educational and philosophical factors relating to the use for non-medical purposes of the drugs and substances referred to in a) and in particular, on the extent of the phenomenon, the social factors that have led to it, the age groups involved, and problems of communication; and

e) to inquire into and recommend with respect to the ways or means by which the Federal Government can act, alone or in its relations with Government at other levels, in the reduction of the dimensions of the problems involved in such use.

The five commissioners, all university educated, occupied academic or professional positions at the time of appointment. They were drawn from the fields of law, criminology, political science, psychiatry, and social work.[1] The lack of direct representation from the law enforcement field is itself noteworthy, in view of the strong enforcement bias in traditional Canadian drug control policy. The first task of the commissioners was to interpret their terms of reference. They did so first by defining non-medical drug use very broadly to cover a wide range of psychotropic substances, including tobacco and alcohol, and secondly by attempting to draw a line between medical and non-medical drug use. This definition was presented in the *Interim Report* and was applied throughout the inquiry:

> Medical use of drugs is taken by the Commission to be use which is indicated
> for generally accepted medical reasons, whether under medical supervision or
> not; all drug use which is not indicated on generally accepted medical grounds
> is considered to be non-medical use. (1a, p. 3)

The commission functioned in a variety of ways. It conducted two sets
of public hearings, spanning 27 cities, many educational institutions, 46 days,
and 50,000 miles traveled in all. These hearings provided an opportunity for
members of the public to express their views anonymously in diverse settings
that varied in informality. Although tape recordings and stenographic records
were kept, no audiovisual record or photographs by the press were allowed.
In addition, the commission gave assurance that the hearings would not be
exploited for law enforcement purposes (1a). Written and oral submissions
to the commission, from individuals and organizations, numbered 639. The
commission's research program encompassed 120 projects and a reference
collection of 14,600 pieces of literature. The cost of the commission, by the
time the last report was issued, was $3.5 million.

LEGAL RECOMMENDATIONS

Although the commissioners were in general accord regarding recommendations in the areas of treatment and rehabilitation, and the noncoercive
influences of research and education, there was considerably less agreement
displayed in their recommendations on the role of legal restraints. Both
Cannabis and the *Final Report* contained a majority report and two minority
reports on the subject of appropriate legal controls. These three contrasting
positions have been labelled variously by media commentators as "conservative, liberal and radical," and "hard-line, middle-of-the-road, and soft-line."
Whatever the label applied, it does seem that the differing points of view of
the Le Dain Commissioners reflect unresolved conflicts in Canadian society
at large as to the proper control of non-medical, and particularly illicit, drug
use.[2]

The recommendations on legal controls may be grouped according to
type of offense and type of drug. First, with regard to the offense of simple
possession, the commission recommended against any further extension of
the criminal sanction, stating: "We believe that we should gradually withdraw
from the use of the criminal law against the non-medical user of drugs rather
than extend its application" (1d, p. 129). Thus, they were not in favor of
creating an offense of simple possession for amphetamines (i.e., "controlled
drugs" under the *Food and Drugs Act* [FDA]). However, the majority were
opposed to removing the offense at this time for opiate narcotics and cocaine
(in the *Narcotic Control Act*) and the strong hallucinogens (i.e., those classified as "restricted drugs" under the FDA). One minority report favored the
elimination of the criminal offense of simple possession for all these latter

substances. In contrast, the majority supported the abolition of the offense for cannabis only, but the other minority report favored its retention.

Regarding penalties for simple possession, when this offense would be retained the general recommendations were toward greater leniency. The commissioners would abolish imprisonment for possession of the restricted drugs and reduce it to a maximum of two years for the simple possession of opiate narcotics and cocaine. The maximum penalties suggested for possession of cannabis were $25 for a first offense and $100 for a subsequent one.

The recommendation in the *Final Report* that has generated a great deal of controversy was the majority view favoring short-term compulsory confinement for opiate dependent persons.[3] This approach would be distinguished from creating a crime of use (favored in one minority report, to be detected by analysis of bodily fluids) in that it would represent a form of diversion from the criminal process to a treatment facility. The time suggested was for not less than one month and not more than three months. One minority report was opposed to compulsory confinement for opiate addicts.

Regarding the offenses related to availability and distribution—trafficking, possession for the purpose of trafficking, importation, and manufacture—the commissioners were in general agreement that present Canadian laws and penalties concerning the opiates, cocaine, and controlled and restricted drugs were adequate and need not be changed.[4] They would shift the burden of proof for the possession for purpose of trafficking offense from the accused to the prosecutor, for all illicit drugs. The recommendation that minor exchange of cannabis between users be excluded from the definition of trafficking was not extended to the other drugs listed above. One commissioner was in favor of the controlled, legalized sale of opiates to drug-dependent persons, but the majority opposed this view, and favored instead the treatment approach of methadone maintenance over heroin maintenance in most cases.

With regard to cannabis, the majority recommended that the offense of importation be included in the definition of trafficking, with no mandatory minimum penalty. The majority also favored awarding the courts greater flexibility in dealing with the two types of trafficking offenses (by providing the option of summary or indictable proceedings) and reducing maximum penalties. It was proposed that cultivation of cannabis for the purpose of trafficking, but not for one's own use, remain an offense subject to the same penalties as trafficking. A minority report supported the removal of all cannabis offenses from the *Narcotic Control Act*, and favored the legal sale and regulation of cannabis under government control. The commission's recommendations for legal control are summarized in Table 21.1.

Table 21.1

The Le Dain Commission Recommendations for Legal Controls, by Type of Offense and Drug

Type of Offense	Recommended Legal Control								
	Cannabis			Opiates and Cocaine			Strong Hallucinogens (Restricted Drugs)		
	Le Dain Majority	Bertrand Minority	Campbell Minority	Le Dain Majority	Bertrand Minority	Campbell Minority	Le Dain Majority	Bertrand Minority	Campbell Minority
Simple possession	No offense.	No offense.	First offense: A fine of $25. Subsequent offense: a fine of $100.	Maximum penalty: 2 years.	No offense. Confiscation if unjustified possession.	Offense of use for opiates. Move cocaine to FDA.	No imprisonment.	No offense. Confiscation if unjustified possession.	Same as majority.
Trafficking	Summary: Maximum penalty 18 months. Fine in lieu of imprisonment. Indictment: Maximum penalty 5 years. Fine in lieu of imprisonment. Exclude exchange of small amount between users.	All stages of production and marketing should be conducted by the federal and/or provincial governments. Penalties for illicit production and distribution not specified.	Same as majority.	No change.	Controlled, legalized sale of opiates to drug-dependent persons.	Same as majority.	No change.	No change.	No change.
Possession for the purpose of trafficking	Same as trafficking, but it should be sufficient for accused to raise a reasonable doubt as to his intention to traffic.		Same as majority.	No change.	Same as trafficking.	Same as majority.	No change, except shift of burden of proof.	No change.	No change.

Table 21.1 (continued)

The Le Dain Commission Recommendations for Legal Controls, by Type of Offense and Drug

Type of Offense	Cannabis			Opiates and Cocaine			Strong Hallucinogens (Restricted Drugs)		
	Le Dain Majority	Bertrand Minority	Campbell Minority	Le Dain Majority	Bertrand Minority	Campbell Minority	Le Dain Majority	Bertrand Minority	Campbell Minority
Importing or exporting	Importing and exporting should be included in definition of trafficking but subject to higher maximum penalties. No mandatory minimum penalty.	All stages of production and marketing should be conducted by the federal and/or provincial governments. Penalties for illicit production and distribution not specified.	Same as majority.	No change.	Retention and reorganization of criminal penalties.	Same as majority.	No change.	Same as for opiates.	No change.
Cultivation	Not a punishable offense unless it is cultivation for the purpose of trafficking. If for the purpose of trafficking, same punishment as for trafficking.		If not for trafficking, same as simple possession. If for trafficking, same punishment as for trafficking.	No change.		Same as majority.			

Source: P. G. Erickson and R. G. Smart, "Canada." Ch. 4 in *The Community's Response to Drug Use*, ed. S. Einstein, pp. 105–106. New York: Pergamon Press, 1980.

REACTIONS TO THE COMMISSION'S
RECOMMENDATIONS

One area of reaction to the commission might have been creation of new drug laws. Although *Cannabis* was tabled in May 1972 and the *Final Report* in December 1973, no legislative proposals to alter drug laws were put forward by the government until late 1974, and then only regarding cannabis. However, in May 1972, the Minister of Health announced that the government would not remove the criminal penalty against simple possession of cannabis (as the Le Dain majority had recommended in *Cannabis*), but would introduce legislation to move cannabis to the *Food and Drugs Act* (5). This government proposal resembled that contained in the *Interim Report*, tabled in April 1970. At that time, the commissioners were not willing to recommend the repeal of the prohibition against simple possession, but did favor classifying cannabis with the restricted drugs in the *Food and Drugs Act* (1a). Other interim measures favored by the commission were the abolition of imprisonment for the simple possession of any psychotropic drugs and the provision of a maximum fine of $100.

The government finally did introduce its cannabis bill (S-19) in November 1974 (4). The proposed amendments, particularly regarding simple possession, were more similar to those contained in the minister's statement of 1972 and in the *Interim Report* (1a) than they were to those found in *Cannabis* (1b). This 1974 bill would move cannabis to its own special section of the FDA, reduce the maximum penalty for a first possession offense to $500 with jail only in default of payment, and provide greater flexibility and lower maximum penalties for the distribution offenses. Thus, it is evident that in terms of specific legislative proposals, the commission's final recommendations on cannabis have not been adopted for possession, but have to some extent for the distribution offenses.

In a second area, that of bringing relevant information before the lawmakers as a basis for their decision, the commission's impact again appears limited. When Bill S-19 was introduced into the Senate in November 1974, its committee on legal and constitutional affairs initiated a set of hearings on the amendment. The hearings, which began in February 1975, involved submissions from organizations and individuals, a number of whom had contributed to the Le Dain deliberations. The Senate passed Bill S-19 after incorporating a provision for automatic pardon after discharge. The Bill's fate was to die on the order paper of Parliament in 1976.

In a third area related to the formation of public policy, the commission's impact is difficult to assess. This is the area of knowledge, beliefs, and attitudes to non-medical drug use held by the general public, and by significant subgroups such as members of the judiciary and drug users themselves. The commission's work, particularly the public hearings, may have performed a significant educational role. One commissioner has suggested that the commission contributed to increasing the information level on drugs and debunking the stereotypes of drug users (6). It has been suggested that the commission may have seen itself as functioning to decrease the alienation of Canadian youth, especially over the illegality of marijuana (2), but such an outcome is difficult to gauge.

In summary, the formal reaction to the commission's legal recommendations, in terms of legislation and policy making, appears negligible; however, the informal impact, in terms of more elusive changes in social attitudes, is a result that is impossible to calculate. It should be remembered that the constitutional framework of Canada disallows any change in current criminal drug laws at other than the federal level. Thus a small-scale experimental change in the law, such as the one in Oregon making simple possession of one ounce or less of marijuana a civil offense,[5] is not permitted under Canadian law. This constitutional situation would seem to reinforce the traditional enforcement approach to drug control, and contribute to very slow changes in the direction of liberalization of drug laws.

NOTES

1. The names of the Canadian commissioners and their affiliations were as follows: Gerald Le Dain, dean of law; Marie-Andrée Bertrand, criminology professor; Ian L. Campbell, dean of arts; Heinz E. Lehman, psychiatrist; J. Peter Stein, community worker.
2. The emphasis in this chapter on legal responses should not lead the reader to suppose that the issues surrounding *licit*, medical and non-medical, use of drugs in Canada have been resolved, and no longer present problems. The Le Dain Commission represented alcohol as Canada's most serious drug problem, and also expressed concern over the use of tobacco, barbiturates and other sedative-like drugs, stimulants, and solvents. However, the origins of internal discussion, and external reactions to the Le Dain Commission, have been marked by controversy about legal control of illicit substances. The law is a major instrument of social policy. In Canada, the official response of the community at large to drug use has been primarily tolerance of "acceptable" (licit) drugs and enforcement against illicit ones. Hence the emphasis throughout.
3. This is the significant exception to the commission's unanimity on treatment matters. Since the primary enforcers of this recommendation are designated as the police, it is included in this section on legal recommendations. The boundaries between coercive treatment and criminal sanction approaches are not easily distinguished (see Chapter 24).
4. Under the *Narcotic Control Act* (covering opiates and cocaine as well as cannabis) the maximum penalty for the two trafficking offenses and impor-

tation is life imprisonment. The *Food and Drugs Act*, which applies to controlled and restricted drugs, includes importation within the definition of trafficking. The maximum penalty upon summary conviction is imprisonment for 18 months, and upon indictment for ten years.
5. This occurred in October 1973, only 18 months after the United States National Commission on Marijuana and Drug Abuse completed its own report on cannabis, including a recommendation favoring decriminalization of marijuana for personal use.

REFERENCES

1. Canada. Commission of Inquiry into the Non-Medical Use of Drugs.
   a. *Interim Report*. Ottawa: Queen's Printer, 1970.
   b. *Cannabis*. Ottawa: Information Canada, 1972.
   c. *Treatment*. Ottawa: Information Canada, 1972.
   d. *Final Report*. Ottawa: Information Canada, 1973.
2. Cook, S. Variations in response to illegal drug use. Unpublished research study, Addiction Research Foundation, Toronto, 1970.
3. Order in Council P.C. 1969–1112.
4. Senate of Canada. *Proceedings of the Standing Senate Committee on Legal and Constitutional Affairs*. Issue no. 19, 1975. Ottawa: Information Canada, 1975.
5. *The Journal* 1(4): September 1972.
6. *The Journal* 3(2): February 1974.

22

What Happened on the Way to Law Reform?

P. James Giffen and Sylvia Lambert

In this chapter we examine what has happened to Canada's two major anti-drug laws—the *Narcotic Control Act* and the *Food and Drugs Act*—since the Le Dain Commission's *Final Report* (16d). First, the changes in the laws since the *Report* are summarized, a tale not long in the telling. Then we go back in time for a brief examination of the forces responsible for the awesome development of anti-drug legislation in the period from 1911 to 1961. This provides a comparative basis for examining the reasons for the lack of reform in the post–Le Dain period. "Reform" is, of course, a term generally applied to changes that are in the direction desired by the beholder. We try to confine it here to the types of changes recommended by the Le Dain majority: broadly, those in the direction of decriminalization and due process, however cautious. (See Chapter 21.)

The main thing, then, to be explained is legislative inaction. Although the sociology of law is not usually concerned with non-events, the study of non-law, like the study of deterrence, makes sense if the supposedly aborted outcome is in the realm of what "might have been." The government's remarkable restraint from significant drug law reform appears to be a fruitful object of study because of the seemingly widespread support for liberalization at the time of the Le Dain Commission.

In retrospect, the Commission appears to have served the same function as many other government-sponsored inquiries: namely, to quell a demand for immediate action, thus allowing action to be postponed indefinitely. The courts, especially since the *Charter of Rights and Freedoms*, have been much more active in lawmaking, thereby reflecting both the remoteness of the judiciary from the ballot box and the fact that the law has a logic of its own.

VARIATIONS ON A THEME

No amendments have been enacted, since the *Final Report* was published in 1973, to diminish the scope of the *Narcotic Control Act*. The maximum penalties remain the same; convictions for illegal importing or exporting still require a minimum sentence of seven years in prison. Marijuana continues to be classed with the opiate narcotics and cocaine; and the cultivation of the marijuana plant, like the opium poppy, is still an indictable offence with a maximum seven-year sentence—despite the Le Dain Commission's sympathetic view of recreational gardening.

The only significant change in the offence structure has gone in the opposite direction from the withdrawal advocated by the Commission. A 1985 amendment to both anti-drug Acts created the offence of "double doctoring" or "prescription shopping" (as described in Chapter 8). By bringing this offence from the *Regulations* to the body of the *Acts,* the government was able to increase the penalty and ensure a criminal record for the offender. At the same time, the net for both controlled and restricted drugs was cast wider by adding to the definition of "sell" in the *Food and Drugs Act* the words "whether or not the distribution is made for consideration" (72j, s. 192), thus ensuring that altruism would not go unrewarded.

Another major change dealt with legal civil liberties rather than the punishability of behaviour, and resembled euthanasia more than therapy. The *Criminal Law Amendment Act* (72k) repealed sections of four statutes (including the *Narcotic Control Act*) that authorized writs of assistance. The demise of these blanket search warrants was inevitable. Criticism, previously sporadic, mounted in Parliament after a judge of the Federal Court was reported in 1977 to have taken strong exception to being forced by statute to authorize the "clothing of an unknown Government officer with such extensive unlimited powers" (15). The Liberal Minister of Justice, Ronald Basford, hesitated until he had time to sniff the wind. He then announced that no more writs would be sought for RCMP purposes until the situation had been reviewed. This de facto moratorium lasted from 1977 until the legislative axe descended in 1985.

Students of RCMP history will not be surprised to learn that the Force fought gallantly to the end (14). The Solicitor General, Robert Kaplan, revealed in 1981 that he had been lobbying his cabinet colleagues to lift the moratorium. The RCMP, he said, considered that the situation with hard drugs was getting worse, while the number of officers holding writs had dwindled from 332 to about 72 (69). Less than two years later, however, Kaplan admitted to reporters that even if the Supreme Court eventually ruled that the writs did not violate the *Charter*, they still "won't be rehabilitated in public opinion" and would have to be replaced (31h). By the time of the next election, the RCMP had been asked to turn in their writs "and none was being used, even the outstanding ones" (39i, p. 1393).

The replacement that made the loss of the writs something less than unbearable was the "telephonic warrant." The Law Reform Commission, in its report on search and seizure, coupled a recommendation for the abolition of writs of assistance with a proposal for warrants obtained by telecommunication in situations where a first-hand application to a judge or justice was impractical (43c). The recommendations were embodied in the *Criminal Law Reform Bill* introduced by the Liberal government in early 1984 and in the version brought down by their Conservative successors later that year.

Because the new "dial-a-writ" was added to the *Criminal Code*, the procedure became available to all peace officers, and for the investigation of all types of indictable offences. This breaks with the tradition of justifying extraordinary powers on the basis of the unique dangers of illicit drugs.

The Le Dain recommendation that the reverse onus on the accused in possession for the purpose of trafficking trials be limited to raising a reasonable doubt (see Chapter 21) landed in a pool of silence and has since been submerged in the larger issue of whether or not the reverse onus should exist at all. The onus has been criticized in the past as an abrogation of the traditional presumption of innocence (39c), but court challenges were few until the *Charter* provided a constitutional basis. The Supreme Court of Canada eventually ruled in February 1986 that the reverse onus in possession for the purpose of trafficking was an unconstitutional violation of the presumption of innocence (Mr. Justice Le Dain concurring) (60). The provisions for the two-part trial were rendered ineffective.

Otherwise the penalties and offences under both anti-drug *Acts* remain what they were at the time of the Le Dain Commission. The hair-raising maximum penalties (see Chapter 8) are, of course, a form of symbolic righteousness made endurable by an absence of minimum penalties and sentencing that is considerably less punitive than the statute.

But statutes and court decisions do not exhaust the law-creation process—just the reader. There remains that fertile, flexible instrument of low-visibility lawmaking, the enactment and amendment of regulations under various statutes by the Governor in Council, which is to say, by the government. Such new regulations are in the public domain and open to scrutiny in the sense that they are announced (in their thousands) in the *Canada Gazette* (a periodical whose regular readership has never been adequately assessed), and are, from time to time, brought together for the true connoisseur in published consolidations. A recent round-up of regulations under the *Narcotic Control Act* contains 72 sections with numerous subsections. The regulations for controlled and restricted drugs under the *Food and Drugs Act* comprise 118 sections and a wealth of subsections. The *Acts* and the *Regulations* are intended to perform complementary control functions; unintentionally, they join in making drug trafficking a highly profitable business. The *Acts* deal specifically with illicit use and trafficking by defining offences, punishments, and procedures—like other criminal law. The *Regulations*, in turn, are meant to govern the legal trade in drugs in such a way as to make available for medical use those "dangerous" drugs deemed therapeutic. Transactions at all stages are recorded, reported, and inspected; they are allowed to be carried out only by those who are licensed, permitted, or professionally beatified.

The penalty for breaches of the *Regulations* is picayune as a sanction compared to the power of the federal authorities to issue or withdraw licences and permits and to deny pharmacists, physicians, and other practitioners the right to sell, prescribe, or dispense certain dangerous drugs. This suzerainty over livelihoods and professional standing provides good reason for the faithful performance of tedious record keeping and reporting duties on the part of the subjects, and makes possible an imposed system of mutual policing within the legal drug trade. The *Regulations* create a duty for persons distributing, prescribing, and dispensing drugs to make sure that the other parties to the transactions have the proper authorization, and even to verify signatures which are unknown to them. The complex interlocking network of rules, too myriad to describe, contrasts with the more familiar system of control that deals with the illicit trade, where enforcement is almost entirely a matter of police initiative and surveillance, with little help from the governed. The discreet modes of dealing with errant businessmen and practitioners by regulation and backstage communication also contrast with the inherently alienating processes of criminal justice.

The power to add drugs to the Schedules of the *Acts* (or to delete them) by order-in-council is also, in effect, an extra-Parliamentary device for adding to (or reducing) the offences covered by the statute. A new proscribed drug automatically means an addition to each of the offences relevant to that class of drug: possession, trafficking, importing, etc. This opportunity has been generously embraced.[1] The prototype of Canadian anti-drug legislation, the *Opium and Drug Act* of 1911 (72a) had a modest Schedule consisting of opium, cocaine, and morphine (and their salts and derivatives, unspecified), plus eucaine, a little-known villain, later pardoned. By March 1986, the Schedule of the *Narcotic Control Act* had expanded to include the preparations, salts, and derivatives of 20 categories of drugs, a list totalling 100 substances. When the controlled drugs were elevated to dangerousness in 1961 (72h), only 3 substances were named: amphetamine, barbituric acid, and methamphetamine—a rogue's gallery that had grown to 14 by March 1986. The original list of 4 restricted drugs (known colloquially as LSD, DET, DMT, and STP) that were made objects of punishment in 1969 (72j) had expanded by 1986 to include 25 substances.

The significance of this fecundity is difficult for the lay person to assess. The research would require substantial pharmacological expertise,[2] extensive knowledge of the drug scene, and access to a plethora of touchy government documents, including correspondence with international bodies—the same qualifications that might be required for effective parliamentary overseeing of the process. Some additions are responses to apparent waves of abuse, as was the case with phencyclidine (PCP) in 1973; others appear to result from the growth of international regimes on the advice of the expert committees of the World Health Organization (WHO), the most suggestive of proscribers (7, 54). The listing of new drugs as a precautionary measure, rather than as a reaction to an existing problem, has become commonplace with the revolution in synthetics.[3] Given the momentum of the search, on both sides of the law, for better living through chemistry, it seems likely that the range of drugs diabolized, and thus the scope of potential punishment, will continue to expand.

To help isolate the factors that have run counter to significant changes in the anti-drug laws themselves, we briefly examine below the earlier, formative period when the statute law proliferated, almost always in the direction of an increasingly severe and intrusive criminal law approach.

BUREAUCRATIC HEGEMONY IN THE DEVELOPMENTAL PERIOD

The major role in shaping Canadian narcotic legislation was played by the officials responsible for enforcing it,[4] an example of bureaucratic lawmaking which Chambliss has uncharitably described as "akin to relying on General Motors as the prime source of automobile safety standards" (12, p. 89). The 1911 *Act* was left virtually unenforced until the Opium and Narcotic Drug Branch—subsequently the Division of Narcotic Control[5]—was created within the new Department of Health in 1920. The successive Chiefs of the Division filled this administrative vacuum with an extensive and powerful enforcement network centred on their office. Colonel C. H. L. Sharman, who reigned from 1927 to 1946, was particularly influential.

The Chief became de facto director of criminal investigation and prosecution, controller of legal trade and professional use, all-purpose expert on narcotics,[6] and, in Colonel Sharman's case, Canadian delegate to international control bodies. The RCMP served "as agents of this Department in the investigation of a large majority of cases dealing with illicit traffic"[7] (68, p. 539) as well as inspectors of pharmacy records (although the Division also employed its own "chemist-auditors" to inspect hospitals and wholesalers). Most prosecutions were handled by "standing counsel," prominent local lawyers retained for the purpose by the Division. The Chief was in communication with his U.S. counterpart (H. J. Anslinger, for most of the period) "practically daily" (68, p. 535). Thus the Chief came to be at the centre of a communication web that included police, prosecutors, officials of other departments, U.S. authorities, international bodies, and the various businesses and professionals in the legal trade. The powerful are often found in this type of strategic location (63, p. 145).

Two conditions helped to make acceptable the enforcement hegemony in lawmaking. First, legislators, and probably most voters, regarded severe measures as justified by the terrible effects and highly contagious nature of narcotic addiction. Second, enforcement efforts were directed at persons who were socially marginal, powerless, and, most of the time, out of view. Police efforts focused mainly on Chinese opium smokers and traffickers until the supply ran out in the 1930s.[8] The so-called "criminal" addicts[9] who succeeded them as eligibles were equally powerless but tougher to catch since they were users primarily of injectables. Except during transitory drug scares, narcotics issues had little importance for groups that could make trouble when their interests were affected. Not until the emergence of youthful drug use on a large scale in the 1960s was there reason for concern among legislators about the use of criminal sanctions against "respectable" people.

Most of the numerous amendments to the narcotic legislation from 1920 to 1954 were initiated within the enforcement network and represented responses to enforcement problems. Some new punitive measures were introduced by West Coast MPs during a drug scare of the 1920s: for example, deportation of convicted aliens (who were expected to be Chinese), and whipping as a penalty for selling to minors; for the enforcement interests these were, however, simply additional resources secured without toil. The enforcement problems of adapting to the changing wiles of users and traffickers, and of nullifying the effects of unfavourable court decisions, made for frequent amendments, usually in the direction of more offences, heavier penalties, and more encroachments on traditional legal safeguards.

In 1929, the punishment for trafficking, for example, was a fine of $500–$1,000 and/or one year in prison; by 1954 it was 14 years' imprisonment (no fine), plus whipping at the discretion of the judge. The pattern of legislating to offset the effect of court decisions was established with the creation of "constructive possession" in 1921. After two courts had dismissed possession cases against the occupiers of premises where drugs had been found, the new offence was enacted to shift the burden of proof by requiring the accused occupier to establish that the drug "was there without his authority, knowledge, or consent" (72b, s. 1(a)).

An example of responsiveness to enforcement discomfiture was the extension of trafficking, in 1929, to include "any substance represented or held out by such person to be a drug" (72e, s. 4(j)). This anomalous provision for punishing the seller of placebos resulted from a device used by wary traffickers to expose suspected undercover narcotic officers, namely, selling them an innocuous look-alike, later to be replaced by the real thing if the police failed to move in.

The third area of growth—the encroachment on traditional legal civil liberties—made narcotic legislation outstanding for the number of advantages it came to afford police and prosecutors. The right to search premises, other than a dwelling-house, without a warrant, and their occupants without arrest, was granted early. But MPs balked on several occasions at extending the hunting licence to dwelling-houses and their occupants. This privilege was eventually made available in 1929 through writs of assistance, after Colonel Sharman had assured a committee of the House that they would be issued only "on a small scale" (2a), the equivalent, it turned out, of being "slightly pregnant."

The 1911 *Act* stated that "the burden of proof thereof shall be upon the person so charged," thus establishing the pattern of attaching a reverse onus to new offences as they were created. In addition, offences involved strict liability until the Supreme Court decided otherwise in 1957 (5); mens rea had been effectively eliminated by not including, in the definition of offences, "knowingly" or other words indicating the need for criminal intent. This meant that individuals could be convicted of possession even if they were unaware that the thing possessed was a narcotic drug. The right of appeal was eliminated for summary convictions on possession or trafficking charges in 1923 on the grounds that it was being used too much and by the wrong people, and fingerprinting and photographing were allowed for summary conviction offences.[10]

The 1954 changes to the *Act* appear to mark the end of unchallenged enforcement hegemony in lawmaking. These amendments are mainly notable for creating the offence of possession for the purpose of trafficking (72f, s. 3), the capstone of the statutory war against traffickers. But by then, other voices were being heard in the land and the complaisance of the House in matters anti-narcotic could no longer be taken for granted.

CHALLENGES TO ENFORCEMENT HEGEMONY

The breakup of consensus, and thus of apathy, marked the end of the simple life for the lawmakers. The idea that addicts were sick rather than willfully evil made its belated appearance in the policy arena as the result of a drug scare in Vancouver in the early 1950s. Horrifying stories of rampant juvenile heroin use[11] led to the appointment by the Community Chest and Council of Greater Vancouver of a committee under Dr. Lawrence Ranta, to study the drug situation and make recommendations.

The Ranta committee's report argued that addiction was a medical problem (62). It called for a treatment approach made up of two new programs: an experimental treatment and rehabilitation centre for carefully screened volunteers, and the establishment of provincial "clinics where registered narcotics users could receive their minimum required dosages of drug" (62, p. 4), as occurred in Great Britain.

The clinic idea caught the imagination of the media and the public; it seemed the logical way to eliminate both the illegal traffic (which would dry up for want of customers), and predatory crime by addicts, since they would no longer have to raise large amounts of money to purchase drugs. The enforcement authorities reacted strongly—as they always have to suggestions of following the "British system." One consequence of the resulting furor was the appointment by the Senate of the Special Committee on Traffic in Narcotic Drugs in Canada, which held hearings across the country.

The transcript of proceedings shows that the law enforcement witnesses put on a more convincing show than the treatment advocates. The police and Department of Health representatives presented a united front—and successfully claimed credibility because of their first-hand experience. Many of the pro-treatment group, on the other hand, had had limited contact with addicts, and their opinions about treatment were discordant: voluntary outpatient treatment versus long-term commitment, maintenance doses or no maintenance doses, and optimism versus pessimism about the possibilities of cure.

Several enforcement arguments recurred: since addicts were primarily criminals and had been prior to using drugs, free drugs would do nothing to improve their behaviour. They would not limit their intake to the minimum doses provided by clinics; hence the black market would continue. Trafficking was too profitable to be eliminated by law enforcement methods; the answer was to dry up the demand by removing addicts from circulation, either for long periods or forever. Since users were recruited through contact with addicts, isolating addicts indefinitely in institutions would gradually eliminate the supply of eligibles. Compulsory commitment for treatment was acceptable if the patients were retained until cured—an outcome most considered unlikely.

The recommendations of the Committee were clearly influenced by the views of control officials and police officers. They firmly and unanimously rejected the clinics or "any proposals designed to provide legal supplies of drugs to criminal addicts" (67b, p. 693). While recognizing that "great numbers of drug addicts offer little or no promise for successful treatment" (67b, p. 696) and that addicts have "almost invariable criminal tendencies" (p. 695), the Committee recommended that the provinces provide treatment facilities, noting that many witnesses had recommended compulsory commitment for long periods, and that treatment within penitentiaries be considered. The most unequivocal recommendations were for "increased penalties for trafficking with a compulsory minimum" (67b, p. 700) and a special offence of importing "with a penalty of the utmost severity" (p. 699). The treatment movement could take little comfort from the report but, nevertheless, the subject had been broached.

For the purposes of this discussion, developments in treatment are relevant only insofar as they have affected the course of the law. The influence of the treatment movement on penological fashion manifested itself in 1956 in programs for inmates of provincial penal institutions in British Columbia (Oakala) and Ontario (Alex G. Brown) and, 10 years later, in the federal experiment at the Matsqui Institution near Vancouver. These, however, were simply appendages of the system. What had potentially greater consequences for lawmaking was the creation of somewhat independent centres of scientific and medical expertise—the advent of the Narcotic Addiction Foundation of British Columbia in 1955, and the extension in 1961 of the mandate of the Addiction Research Foundation in Ontario to include drugs other than alcohol.

Pressures to make concessions to treatment sentiment led the federal government to draft Part II of the 1961 *Narcotic Control Act*, providing for treatment, but of the type earlier conceded by enforcement interests. A person convicted of a possession or a trafficking offence and found after medical examination to be a narcotic addict, could be sentenced to "custody for treatment for an indeterminate period" (72g, s. 17(1)) within the penitentiary system. The time of release was to be determined by the Parole Board, which could have jurisdiction over first offenders for 10 years after release and over others indefinitely. To put non-addict traffickers out of circulation, a second conviction was made punishable by preventive detention for an indeterminate period.

The only opposition to custody for treatment came from Ontario's Addiction Research Foundation: MPS apparently were satisfied with the explanation that "a helping hand will be offered to those who will accept help" (39d, p. 5989). Twenty-six years later Part II remains unproclaimed. Whatever the nature of the earlier jurisdictional impasse with the provinces,[12] by now treatment as punishment seems to be an idea whose time has passed.

The 1961 housekeeping measure of moving all rules for the legal trade to the *Narcotic Control Regulations* did, however, have consequences for treatment. Amended regulations made possible "without undue publicity" (55, p. 655) the initiation of a methadone maintenance program by the B.C. Foundation in 1963 and the Ontario Foundation the next year, to be followed by many others. These programs were developed in "co-operation with the Division of Narcotic Control" (55, p. 655), signifying the extent to which participating physicians were to be gently enveloped by the control system. The *Regulations* came to require authorization from the Minister, detailed records open for inspection, upper limits on doses for self-administration, and other measures to police physicians' control of addicts. Clinics came to be preferred to isolated practitioners by the authorities because they offered superior control over both staff and patients, a parallel to the British development (16a).

The inroads of medicalization, such as they were, coincided with the piecemeal dispersion of the enforcement apparatus. Much of the influence of the enforcement network, as we have noted, rested on the de facto integration of control functions in the office of the Chief of the Division of Narcotic Control. This arrangement was increasingly at odds with the expanding role of trained professionals in the civil service, and with the processes of reorganization made necessary by the complexities of modern government (64). Inevitably, the appropriate government departments claimed control over police and prosecutors. The Chief's loss of direct contact with the RCMP drug squads became institutionalized when jurisdiction over the RCMP was vested in the Ministry of the Solicitor General in 1958.[13]

A year earlier, the Deputy Minister of Justice had directed that henceforth federally appointed standing counsel should report to the Department of Justice; this shift of control was consolidated, beginning in 1965, with the appointment of full-time "Federal Crowns" operating from permanent offices in major centres. Within the Department of Health and Welfare, the Legal Advisor, R. E. Curran, had begun by the mid-fifties to play a leading part in drafting drug legislation and in dealing with international bodies, a sign of the gradual assumption of key roles by specialists with backgrounds in law, science, and medicine. Decisions about legislation became a matter involving at least three federal departments, plus consultation with the provinces as they became feistier—an unwieldy process much less productive of change than the relatively direct conduit from enforcement to enactment.

Another source of opposition to enforcement preferences in legislation came from the burgeoning civil liberties movement. The accretion of exceptional powers in anti-drug laws made them particularly vulnerable to criticism as groups concerned with legal civil liberties became more influential. The institutionalization of these views in the *Canadian Bill of Rights* in 1960 and, more effectively, in the *Charter*, added force to criticisms as well as providing grounds for appeal. The *Bill of Rights* was taken into account in drafting the 1961 *Narcotic Control Act*, but not in a paralyzing way. The stated reasons for dropping the reverse onus in constructive possession (and thus the offence) were both the *Bill of Rights* and the RCMP view "that its retention could not be supported on grounds of its being essential to enforcement" (2c). On the other hand, the reverse onus in possession for the purpose of trafficking was retained, both on grounds of its importance to enforcement and the probability that the *Bill of Rights* would not be interpreted "too strictly in relation to a statute dealing with narcotics" (2b), a view that turned out to be prophetic. The *Bill of Rights*, however, did serve in that year as justification for the first strong parliamentary opposition to the reverse onus (39d). But not until the *Charter* did the changing temper of the times begin to have a significant effect.

The most serious threat to the authorized version of drug control came (as we all know) with the emergence of widespread youthful drug use in the 1960s. The new users differed markedly from the marginal, inconspicuous group of opiate addicts, small in number, around whom the law had been fashioned. These new drug seekers were young, increasingly numerous, largely from middle-class backgrounds, and, in varying degrees, adherents of a counterculture that celebrated the supramundane experiences to be derived from the newly popular drugs. They were not only an articulate lobby on their own behalf, but by their very numbers helped to mobilize an expanding audience that, in turn, fostered an unprecedented amount of writing and research on drugs and the youthful subculture.

Given their backgrounds, these new addicts tended to be seen as somebody's kids rather than as dope fiends or "real" criminals. The criminal records they risked were condemned as ruining lives and careers as well as creating a general contempt for the law. The credibility of orthodox beliefs about drug harms and the effectiveness of criminal sanctions were, of course, widely challenged. In Canada, as in the United States, "The sheer size and diversity of public discussion doomed the narcotic officials' monopoly over the issue" (38, p. 140). The protests, resolutions, petitions, debates, investigations, and reports of the period defy brief description. A recounting would only prove what is readily granted, namely, a plethora of new voices in the drug policy arena and a wide spectrum of viewpoints and misconceptions.

Following several calls in Parliament for an inquiry into the problems presented by marijuana, LSD, and other drugs of recent notoriety (39d, e), the Government in 1969 appointed a commission of inquiry headed by Professor Gerald Le Dain, which the Minister thought would be able to report in two years because "the terms of reference do not include hard drugs in the sense of such drugs as heroin" (39f, p. 3180). Little did he know.

The only change in the *Narcotic Control Act* in response to the new concern about criminalizing the young was a 1969 amendment to make possession a hybrid offence by adding the possibility of summary conviction with shorter imprisonment and the option of a fine. The stated purpose was to mitigate the punishment "of young persons who were not ordinarily of the criminal class" (58b, p. 958), as well as to cope with the problem that the courts "are simply chock-full of cases of possession" (58b, p. 961) by decreasing the not-guilty pleas and trials in higher courts that went with the indictable option.

The other legislative response was amendment of the *Food and Drugs Act* to criminalize the newly popular drugs. One reason for taking this route was expressed by a federal prosecutor: "Offences under the *Food and Drugs Act*, though serious, do not generate public 'hysteria' as do narcotics offences" (2e).

Barbiturates and amphetamines, the two basic controlled drugs, had aroused concern first in health authorities because of prescription scams and clinical evidence of dependence (23). Later, police and politicians became worried because of news about underworld traffic in these drugs (39c), concerns which led to the 1961 amendments to the FDA. In 1962 LSD and thalidomide were made unavailable on the basis of medical opinion (23, 72i), but no possession or trafficking offences and penalties were thought necessary since illicit use had not surfaced. Five years later, LSD had become a cult drug. The stereotypes that made strict legislation a political winner were reflected in the words of a senator who averred that LSD users "retreat to the periphery of society into a parasitic group of misfits, smouldering psychotics and unfulfilled messiahs" (67a, p. 1796). The bill to create the various offences and penalties for restricted drugs was enacted in 1969, having been delayed by federal elections and legislative overload. This appears to have been the last burst of consensus to inform the legislative process.

INDECISION AS A COPING MECHANISM

The proliferation of interest groups with conflicting views, by politicizing the process, has made legislative action risky for governments (41)—except during drug scares of sufficient scariness to legitimate strong measures. Social commentators have long pointed out that legislators are ordinarily cautious about liberalizing criminal penalties of any kind, even when they find considerable support among their constituents (29). Since public attitudes are hard to assess, politicians tend to "view the public relations hazard of maintaining a hard line on crime as being less dangerous to their positions than taking a more liberal stance" (33, p. 199). This is illustrated below by the ill-fated attempts to decriminalize (or less criminalize) marijuana.

The moral rootedness of dissent was manifest in the minority recommendations submitted by two members of the Le Dain Commission. Although the Commissioners were exposed to the same data and opinions, disagreement emerged left and right. On the left, Marie-Andrée Bertrand recommended elimination of the possession offence for both narcotics and strong hallucinogens; provision of the drug "necessary to him" to drug users through local clinics (10d, p. 253); and the legal distribution of cannabis on the same basis as alcohol. And on the right, Ian Campbell recommended a new offence of use for opiate narcotics, with provisions for monitoring convicted users, and with escalating penalties for falls from grace, as well as continuation of the cannabis offences of possession and trafficking, though with reduced penalties.

The government was faced with a dilemma, but perhaps not as grave a dilemma as unanimous recommendations would have presented. The lack of consensus provided an additional reason for consigning the matter to interdepartmental committees and other invisible hands. It is not surprising to find a cabinet minister reporting in 1978 that officials of the departments of Justice, National Health and Welfare, and the Solicitor General, were studying the whole area of dangerous drug legislation "on an urgent basis" (80).

The reform of marijuana law is the most anomalous victim of the hesitation waltz that continued until the orchestra died. In the period surrounding the Le Dain Commission, a majority of the views quoted in news reports and heard in the House favoured doing something about the criminalization of young users. The solutions proposed ranged from legalization through repealing simple possession as an offence, to decreasing the penalty, preferably in a form that would avoid imprisonment and a criminal record. By the time the Le Dain Commission awarded its seal of approval, the government appeared to have a strong mandate to do something perceptible by way of liberalization.

As soon as the Commission's cannabis report appeared, the Minister of Health responded by promising that marijuana would be moved to the *Food and Drugs Act*, the less radical remedy suggested in the Commission's *Interim Report* (10a). An immediate response took the form of amending the *Criminal Code* to allow an absolute or conditional discharge as a sentencing option.

Bill S-19, introduced two years later, would have created a new section of the *Food and Drugs Act* for cannabis. As amended by standing committee, the Bill made possession a summary offence only, reduced the penalties for all offences but cultivating, and provided automatic pardons for all first offenders given a discharge for possession. The effect of these measures on criminal records has been questioned (8; 71; Chapter 23 of this book) but the matter is academic because the Bill died on the order paper at the end of the session, never to be resurrected.

The saga of promise, hesitation, and retreat (47) can be traced through selected news items from 1976 to 1986. In the fall of 1976 the Hon. Mitchell Sharp said in an interview that the Bill would not be reintroduced in the short fall session, when there would be time for only high-priority legislation (11). Two years later, opposition leader Joe Clark told reporters that a Progressive Conservative government would decriminalize simple possession, but not for three or four years, since it was a matter of low priority (31b). At about the same time, a Gallup poll found that 46 percent of Canadians endorsed decriminalization in some form, and both the Canadian Bar Association and a Liberal party policy convention passed resolutions calling for decriminalization. Justice Minister Marc Lalonde said in December 1978 that the government hoped to introduce a bill before the next election (80), but two months later he accused the Social Credit Party of blocking the bill by refusing to agree to early introduction and speedy passage (81).

A new Conservative health minister, David Crombie, confirmed his government's intention of easing possession penalties soon, but signalled a change of mood by noting the danger of being "over-permissive" in view of recent studies showing health damage from marijuana (31c). Solicitor General Robert Kaplan reiterated in 1981 that possession penalties would be reduced, but promised that a public information campaign on health risks would be launched at the same time. Some provincial attorneys general did not find this trade-off satisfactory (31f).

Five years later the former Solicitor General reported in retrospect that the Cabinet had turned down the change: "A particular group of Ontario parents and teachers insisted upon a strong penalty for possession of marijuana" (82). A Cabinet study paper prepared by justice department officials had recommended making possession "a parking-ticket like offence" with a $50 fine (avoiding court appearances and criminal records) but this had been seen by critics as condoning marijuana use (82).

By the end of 1984 the tide had turned officially. The new Conservative Minister of Justice and the Solicitor General[14] both declared firmly that the law would not be altered (39i). Sufficient opposition had now emerged to make inaction the better part of valour. A formidable array of groups had become vocal about their objections: home and school associations, teachers' and principals' organizations, associations of chiefs of police, provincial attorneys general, the Council on Drug Abuse, the Canadian Addiction Foundation, and sundry others, including at least one provincial legislature.

Speeches in Parliament opposing decriminalization in any degree reached high tide in 1980–81 following the government's announcement in the throne speech of a move to the *Food and Drugs Act*. The anti-reform speeches, with one exception from the Conservative opposition, focused on health hazards and the worries of parents and teachers. The Liberal spokesman who rose in defence emphasized that the Government did not condone the use of marijuana and was not legalizing it but simply lightening the sentences for possession. The only strong pro-reform speech was given by an NDP member (39h).

Members of parliament may have been in contention at this time about penalties but they spoke with one voice on prevention through exhortation. From 1980 onward, education programs aimed at youth became a panacea favoured by conservatives of all political stripes. The focus was to be "hazards," "dangers," or even "untold damage." The Liberals' promise of an educational program did in fact result in publicity campaigns to influence the young. Starting in 1983 (53), these have helped to embalm the law by satisfying our collective proclivity for doing something.

A long and intense speech on the marijuana issue (39h), a year in preparation by an MP from Prince Edward Island, reflected the preoccupation with health concerns by 1981. The MP attributed his information on marijuana effects to *Marihuana Today* by Dr. George K. Russell (65), a book clearly intended for popular consumption. Dr. Russell was not given to understatement, and the MP was not given to caveats about the amount or duration of use, the reversibility of the symptoms, or the tenuousness of the evidence. The physical harms listed included organic damage to the brain, severe damage to lung tissue, damage to the entire cellular system, suppression of the immune system, and various other devastating outcomes. The psychic effects were also numerous and horrendous, including the familiar "amotivational syndrome, a massive chronic passivity" (39h, p. 13999). "Decriminalization," he concluded, "is too high a price for our young people to pay" (p. 14000). Dangers to health had clearly become the leading rationale for maintaining strong sanctions.

When marijuana was added to the *Act* in 1923, nothing was said for or against it in Parliament, though Judge Emily Murphy had written the year before that addicts under its influence "become raving maniacs and are liable to kill or indulge in any form of violence to other persons" (52, p. 333). With the development of the counterculture in the 1960s, the threat was interpreted as psychological and termed the "amotivational syndrome," a state of amiable fecklessness produced by the "drop-out" drug. These conceptions have now yielded, in both popular culture and official ideology, to beliefs about "new" scientific evidence of serious dangers to health. The "newness" has a function in helping to justify both recent conversions to doomsaying and previous neglect of medical evidence.

Obviously, most people's beliefs about scientific matters are not based on a direct examination of the technical literature. They depend on persons recognized as "experts," whose approach may range from skeptical to dramaturgical. For most citizens, these views are in turn filtered, simplified, and distorted through accounts in the media. Starting around 1980, alarming newspaper stories about the health effects of marijuana became quite frequent. The headlines reflected the tenor: "Physical, psychological effects of cannabis, a dangerous drug" said the *Halifax Chronicle-Herald* on May 18, 1981; and, "2,500 scientific studies indicate marijuana can be a health hazard—specialist" (31d).

It also seems possible that a change in the moral climate in recent years has made people more receptive to stories about the damaging health effects of marijuana, especially if these ideas have the cachet of science. In views about social policy, as in other matters, value beliefs and fact beliefs tend to be intertwined in such a way that they reinforce each other (26, 32, 38, 42). A moral shift in a socially conservative direction is more visible and probably more pronounced in the United States, where considerable publicity has been given to the mobilization of groups "aligned against the permissiveness of modern culture: anti-abortion groups, anti-homosexual groups, and various fundamentalist groups generally oriented toward traditional values" (42, p. 263).

But credulity as a factor in the influence of purportedly factual information obviously does not rule out causality in the other direction—from information to fact beliefs to moral stance on the strictness of marijuana laws. The bad news has probably changed some people's views about decriminalization.

INSTITUTIONAL INERTIA

The medical approach has never been a serious contender for sole possession of the drug problem since the criminal justice system took over. When the opiates virtually monopolized the field, pessimism about curing addicts led many liberal critics to embrace the "British system" (1, 44, 66) and later (some of them) methadone maintenance. The Le Dain Commission strongly supported a methadone policy, but with rigorous controls, arguing that it "holds out the greatest hope for management of opiate dependence" (10d, p. 149), and citing a U.S. estimate that 40 percent of the addict population could be "stabilized" on methadone (10d, p. 153). The decline in participation in methadone maintenance programs in both Canada and the United States since this honeymoon period, and the reasons for it, have been well documented elsewhere (6, 17, 18, 41, 56, 79). At present methadone maintenance seems to offer a relatively inexpensive way of keeping some addicts out of prison but under authority, though not in sufficient numbers to offer a real solution.

The credibility of therapeutic communities, accorded "a relatively limited role" by the Le Dain Commission (10d, p. 173), has been further attenuated by the failure of leading exemplars. And with the end of the B.C. experiment (see Chapter 24), compulsory commitment has had its brief day on stage and returns to the long wait in the wings. Most of the large number of users at the other end of the scale of imputed pathology—the middle-class consumers of soft drugs—have not been claimed as candidates for therapy.

The case for treatment has also been vitiated by a general change of heart among criminal justice officials, particularly those in the "corrections" business. Rehabilitative goals have lost ground to the "justice model." Extensive evaluations of treatment programs for delinquents and criminals led, in the mid-1970s, to wide acceptance of the conclusion that rehabilitative efforts have no appreciable effect on recidivism (21, 24, 45, 49). The studies provided a welcome rationale for stemming escalating expenditures on therapeutic institutions (13).

The Law Reform Commission contended about this time that there was no evidence of rehabilitation in prisons (43a), and asserted that "the criminal process should impose sanctions to show disapproval and exert control and only when this is done should rehabilitation be taken into account" (43c); even with aberrant sex offences, treatment should be a voluntary matter (43b).

In the wake of two committee investigations of the penitentiary system (46, 75), the Solicitor General announced in 1979 his intention to replace the "rehabilitation" model with an "opportunities-incentive" model. A review of criminal law published a few years later under the imprimatur of the Minister of Justice stated that the purpose of criminal sanctions was to be retribution, not rehabilitation or deterrence (15). The onus of proof had clearly shifted.

Increased resistance to change has been accompanied by a decline in active pressure for reform.[15] One factor is that police, prosecutors, and judges have exercised sufficient leniency to keep down the level of concern about criminalizing the young, and to protect the system from getting swamped. Increased forbearance in enforcement shows in the decline of charges for cannabis offences from 53,924 in 1981 to 27,328 in 1985 (9), although there is also evidence of a decline in actual use (see Chapter 14).

Department of Justice guidelines to its prosecutors help to account for the small proportion of prison sentences and the rarity of importing cases. Fines remain the most common disposition in simple possession cases[16]—68 percent in 1985 (9). Prosecutors have avoided the minimum sentence of seven years for importing by not using the charge unless the evidence indicates "a substantial commercial venture" (20, p. 20). The Department suggested twenty kilograms of marijuana as the threshold for eligibility in 1978; by 1981, approval was required at headquarters before laying a charge for any amount (20). Presumably the 44 persons convicted of importing in 1985 (9) were big-time operators whose fate was unlikely to become a public issue. Discretionary justice has served to protect the formal structure of punitive sanctions, leaving them intact to be called up at will.

The paucity of drug law reform is not simply a matter of declining faith in specific options or the failure of nerve of specific governments. It can also be seen as a particular case of the institutional or organizational inertia that tends to determine the shape of change in social control systems (30, 36, 57). According to this theory, social control organizations are subject to internal and external inertial forces that create a resistance to fundamental alteration. These include such conservative pressures as the vested interest of the staff in their jobs and professional careers, the investment in equipment and specialized training that cannot easily be allocated to other tasks, and the ideological support for the existing approach that has been engendered in various pressure groups.

Challenges to the system that cannot be fully resisted tend to be absorbed and transformed. Thus liberal reforms in methods of dealing with drug users have not altered the basic fact that control remains mainly within the criminal justice system. Most of the treatment efforts and other remedies that we have mentioned have served to protect the central role of the criminal justice system in the face of strong critical attacks. The most obvious examples are the treatment programs located within prison systems. Methadone maintenance programs may bear a more complex relationship to criminal justice control but they are still a method of co-opting the medical approach and its practitioners to the traditional control system. Research centres originally regarded with foreboding can be converted to the uses of the system as producers and distributors of anti-drug materials. While British and Canadian control systems have tended to converge in the face of similar pressures, the British system nevertheless retains significant structural residues of earlier medical dominance. We, for our part, are stuck with embellishments to the criminal justice system.

DRUG SCARES: UNPREDICTABLE CATALYSTS

Studies have found some lawmaking against deviance to be mainly "a response to panic, albeit a panic aggravated and focussed by the media" (35, p. 17). States of fear in the community, associated with media stories of a growing menace as well as with deeper structural factors (28, 37,74), create a demand that something be done. The cry most commonly has been for stricter laws. In responding, politicians have a chance to take the moral highroad at little or no cost.

This happened in Canada during the gestation of the 1911 *Act*. It started out as a bill to strengthen the law against opium and ended up as a full-fledged anti-narcotic statute because of concern among Montreal community leaders about a seeming epidemic of cocaine and morphine use by young people (39a). A Vancouver drug scare in the early twenties with strongly anti-Chinese overtones led to an escalation of the punitiveness of the law in the next few years (19). We have noted that another Vancouver scare in the 1950s brought treatment options to the fore but also helped to legitimate more severe legislation. The response to the crisis of youthful drug use in the 1960s was more complex, as we have seen, partly because of the social background of the users, unfamiliar drugs, and sheer numbers. One response was special legislation to deal with controlled and restricted drugs; another was the Le Dain Commission.

The enduring nature of the punitive response to crisis is to be seen in the U.S. drug scare that led to the enactment of the *Anti–Drug Abuse Act* in October 1986. An unanticipated wave of concern about drugs that exploded in the media and was given substance by public opinion polls (76) coincided with the approach of federal elections and a call by President Reagan for a national crusade. The resulting legislation was drafted and passed in a matter of weeks. It increased the penalties for federal drug offences, providing for life sentences for principals in major trafficking enterprises, and made some types of illegally obtained evidence admissible in drug trials. But it also reflected the contemporary diversity in approved responses,[17] from funds for local educational and treatment programs to provision for use of the military in a blitz to halt importing.

The Canadian drug scare is too amorphous at the time of writing to allow for prediction. The Prime Minister's clarion call for an epidemic (22) was echoed by a majority of respondents to a Gallup poll (77d), and a *Time* cover story (76) was followed by one in *Maclean's* (48). There is no indication, however, that these alarms and excursions have struck a responsive chord of national malaise as they have in the United States. Even if this happens, liberals can take comfort in the thought that there is little leeway for increasing the severity of statutory penalties. The high ground has been occupied.

NOTES

1. New offences can also be created by making special rules about certain drugs within the ambit of the statute. The amphetamines were declared "Designated Drugs" so that physicians could be forbidden to use them except for a short list of maladies—for example, narcolepsy and Parkinsonism—that did not include obesity.
2. Why, for example, was methylphenylisonipecotonitrile added in 1965?
3. The 1948 Protocol issued by the WHO provided for international control of synthetics; by 1963 these constituted two-thirds of the 90 drugs under international proscription (7).
4. Data for the period 1909–72 are derived from a forthcoming monograph by P. J. Giffen, S. Small and S. Lambert.
5. Now the Bureau of Dangerous Drugs.
6. Colonel Sharman wrote articles on narcotic drugs for medical journals and lectured to graduating classes of doctors and nurses, as well as being the leading authority in government circles.
7. The RCMP's role was protected by the Division's reluctance "to authorise retention of counsel to conduct prosecution at federal expense in other than [a] federally initiated narcotic case" (67b, p. 355).

8. The proportion of persons of Chinese birth convicted annually for narcotic offences in the 1927–1934 period fell from 82.1 percent to 46.6 percent, according to the official statistics.

9. The Division developed early a triple classification of "known addicts" for reporting purposes, which also represented differences in methods of control: (a) criminal addicts, who were treated as such; (b) professional addicts, members of the health professions, who were generally dealt with administratively; and (c) medical addicts, or persons under treatment for diseases other than addiction, who were left to the good offices of their physicians.

10. The 1922 provision for deportation of aliens convicted of possession or trafficking can also be regarded as a breach of civil liberties; it removed the exemption for aliens who had been domiciled in Canada for five years which was stipulated by the *Immigration Act*. It was thought that "this would help to some extent to solve the oriental question in this country" (39b, p. 2824).

11. Canadian perceptions were probably influenced by the publicity given teenage heroin use in the U.S. at this period; the "epidemic" in Vancouver was later found to have had no foundation in fact.

12. The Minister of Justice explained to the House in 1976 that Part II remained unproclaimed because of "a lack of facilities, a lack of agreement with the provinces as to treatment centres and a lack of agreement as to what the treatment should be" (39g, p. 1091).

13. In 1954, the Division of Narcotic Control was subsumed under the new Health Protection Branch of the Department of National Health and Welfare.

14. A role reversal occurred at a press conference in December 1984, when the RCMP Commissioner advocated easing marijuana penalties and the Solicitor General opposed any change (77b).

15. The fading of the issue among marijuana smokers is seen in the absence of the smoking rallies of earlier years and the disbanding of the National Organization for the Reform of Marijuana Laws (31a, 31d).

16. Despite early federal guidelines favouring discharges for first offences, this was the disposition in only 18 percent of possession convictions in 1985; the annual rate has never risen above 27 percent (9).

17. A flexible posture is also to be seen in urine-testing at the workplace.

REFERENCES

1. American Bar Association and American Medical Association Committee on Narcotic Drugs. Joint Committee. *Drug Addiction: Crime or Disease?* Bloomington, Ind.: University of Indiana Press, 1961.

2. Archives. Division of Narcotic Control, Department of Health. Canada.
   a. Memo from Chief, Division of Narcotic Control to RCMP Commissioner, May 25, 1929.
   b. Letter from RCMP Commissioner to Deputy Minister of National Health and Welfare, September 23, 1960.
   c. Letter from M. V. Dymond, Ontario Minister of Health, to J. W. Monteith, Minister of National Health and Welfare, March 27, 1961.
   d. Letter from J. W. Monteith, Minister of National Health and Welfare, to E. D. Fulton, Minister of Justice, September 18, 1961.
   e. Letter from federal prosecutor to Deputy Minister of National Health and Welfare, January 4, 1963.
3. Auld, J. *Marijuana Use and Social Control*. New York: Academic Press, 1981.
4. Bayer, R. Heroin addiction, criminal culpability and the penal sanction. In: Weissman, J. C., and Dupont, R. L. (eds.). *Criminal Justice and Drugs*. Port Washington, N.Y.: Rennikat Press, 1982.
5. *Beaver* v. *R.* (1957), 113 C.C.C. 129 (S.C.C.).
6. Bellis, D. J. *Heroin and Politicians: The Failure of Public Policy to Control Addiction in America*. Westport, Conn.: Greenwood Press, 1981.
7. Bruun, K., Pan, L., and Rexed, I. *The Gentlemen's Club: International Control of Drugs and Alcohol*. Chicago: University of Chicago Press, 1975.
8. Bryan, E. M. Cannabis in Canada—A decade of indecision. *Contemporary Drug Problems, 8*:169–92 (1979).
9. Canada. Bureau of Dangerous Drugs, Department of National Health and Welfare. *Narcotic, Controlled and Restricted Drugs*. Ottawa:1985.
10. Canada. Commission of Inquiry into the Non-Medical Use of Drugs.
    a. *Interim Report*. Ottawa: Queen's Printer, 1970.
    b. *Cannabis*. Ottawa: Information Canada, 1972.
    c. *Treatment*. Ottawa: Information Canada, 1972.
    d. *Final Report*. Ottawa: Information Canada, 1973.
11. Carruthers, B. Pot bill nears death by neglect. *The Journal, 5*:September 11, 1976.
12. Chambliss, W. J. The state and criminal law. In: Chambliss, W. J., and Mankoff, M. (eds.). *Whose Law? What Order?* New York: John Wiley and Sons, 1976.
13. Chan, J. B. L., and Ericson, R. V. *Decarceration and the Economy of Penal Reform*. Toronto: Centre of Criminology, 1981.
14. Cherry, Z. Discipline and caring are the keys to the Mounties' greatness. *The Globe and Mail*, October 24, 1969.
15. Chretien, J. *The Criminal Law in Canadian Society*. Report of the Criminal Law Review. Ottawa: Department of Justice, 1982.
16. Clausen, O. Writs of assistance: Canada's own "no knock" law. *The Globe and Mail*, December 15, 1977.
17. Committee of the Health Protection Branch, Department of National Health

and Welfare. Canada. Trends in methadone use in the treatment of opiate dependence in Canada. *Canadian Journal of Public Health, 68*:111–15 (1977).

18. Conrad, P. and Schneider, J. W. *Deviance and Medicalization: From Badness to Sickness.* St. Louis, Mo.: C. V. Mosby, 1980.
19. Cook, S. J. Canadian narcotics legislation, 1908–11: A conflict model interpretation. *Canadian Review of Sociology and Anthropology, 6*:36–46 (1969).
20. Copeland, Paul D. The dope sheet. *Criminal Lawyers Association Newsletter, 6*:20–22 (1985).
21. Cousineau, F. D., and Plecas, D. B. Justifying criminal justice policy with methodologically inadequate research. *Canadian Journal of Criminology, 24*:307–21 (1982).
22. Cruickshank, J. PM promises tax reforms, drug controls. *The Globe and Mail*, September 15, 1986.
23. Curran, R. E. Canada and narcotics. *Medical Services Journal, 17*:747–64 (1961).
24. Curran, R. E. Canada and controlled drugs. *Medical Services Journal, 18*:415–30 (1962).
25. Dampier, B., and Weller, L. Dope laws going to pot? Only a little bit. *Toronto Star*, April 19, 1980.
26. Davis, F. J. Toward a theory of law in society. *Sociological Focus, 11*:127–41 (1978).
27. Erickson, P. G. *Cannabis Criminals: The Social Effects of Punishment on Drug Users.* Toronto: ARF Books, 1980.
28. Galliher, J. F., and Tree, C. Edwin Sutherland's research on the origins of sexual psychopath laws: An early case study of the medicalization of deviance. *Social Problems, 33*:100–113 (1985).
29. Gibbons, D. L. Crime and punishment: A study in social attitudes. *Social Forces, 47*:391–97 (1969).
30. Giffen, P. J. The criminal courts and the control of addictions. In: Friedland, M. L. (ed.). *Courts and Trials.* Toronto: University of Toronto Press, 1975.
31. *Globe and Mail, The.*
    a. Marijuana master list. Editorial. August, 1973.
    b. You know where he stands. Editorial. September 26, 1978.
    c. Crombie promises fall bill to ease law on marijuana. September 3, 1979.
    d. June 5, 1981.
    e. 2,000 join rally to legalize pot. June 21, 1981.
    f. High price of pot starting to show. August 27, 1981.
    g. Ottawa stands firm on a softer pot law. December 10, 1981.
    h. RCMP writs to end, Kaplan says. July 12, 1983.

i.   PM promises tax reforms, drug controls. September 15, 1986.

32. Goode, E. Marijuana and the politics of reality. *Journal of Health and Social Behavior, 10*:83–94 (1969).

33. Green, P. A., and Allan, H. D. Severity of societal response to crime: A synthesis of models. *Law and Society Review, 16*:181–205 (1981–82).

34. Greenberg, D. F. *Corrections and Punishment.* Beverly Hills, Calif.: Sage, 1977.

35. Hagan, J. The legislation of crime and delinquency: A review of theory, method, and research. *Law and Society Review, 14*:603–28 (1980).

36. Hannan, M. T., and Freeman, J. The population ecology of organizations. *American Journal of Sociology, 82*:929–64 (1977).

37. Helmer, J. *Drugs and Minority Oppression.* New York: Seabury, 1975.

38. Himmelstein, J. L. *The Strange Career of Marihuana: Politics and Ideology of Drug Control in America.* Westport, Conn.: Greenwood Press, 1982.

39. House of Commons. Canada. *Debates.*
    a. 1910–11.
    b. 1922.
    c. 1958.
    d. 1961.
    e. 1967.
    f. 1969.
    g. 1976.
    h. 1981.
    i. 1984.

40. Joint Committee of the American Bar Association and American Medical Association. See American Bar Association and American Medical Association (1).

41. Kaplan, J. *The Hardest Drug: Heroin and Public Policy.* Chicago: University of Chicago Press, 1983.

42. Koski, P. R., and Eckberg, D. L. Bureaucratic legitimation: Marihuana and the drug enforcement administration. *Sociological Focus, 16*:255–73 (1983).

43. Law Reform Commission of Canada.
    a. *Imprisonment and Release.* Ottawa: Information Canada, 1975.
    b. *Sexual Offences.* Ottawa: Ministry of Supply and Services, 1978.
    c. *Police Powers—Search and Seizure in Criminal Law Enforcement.* Ottawa: Ministry of Supply and Services, 1983.

44. Lindesmith, A. R. *The Addict and the Law.* New York: Vintage Books, 1965.

45. Lipton, D., Martinson, R., and Wilks, J. *The Effectiveness of Correctional Treatment.* New York: Praeger, 1975.

46. MacGuigan, M. (Chairman). *Report to Parliament by the Subcommittee on the Penitentiary System in Canada.* Ottawa: Ministry of Supply and Services, 1977.

47. MacLennan, A. Canada will never approve pot. *The Journal, 10*: July 1, 1981.

48. *Maclean's*. A new drug crusade. September 29, 1986, 36–39.
49. Martinson, R. What works?—Questions and answers about prison reform. *The Public Interest, 35*:22–54 (1974).
50. McKenzie, P. The dope craze that's terrorizing Vancouver. *Maclean's*, February 1, 1955.
51. McNeill, G. Are new marijuana laws on the way? *Toronto Star*, July 10, 1983.
52. Murphy, E. F. *The Black Candle*. Toronto: Thomas Allen, 1922.
53. Paddy, V. A soft pitch against pot. *Maclean's*, March 14, 1983.
54. Pan, L. and Bruun, K. Recent developments in international drug control. *British Journal of Addiction, 74*:141–60 (1979).
55. Paulus, I., and Halliday, R. Rehabilitation and the narcotic: Results of a comparative methadone withdrawal program. *Canadian Medical Association Journal, 96*:655–58 (1967).
56. Peachey, J. E. *Report for the World Health Organization on Methadone Treatment in Canada*. Toronto: Addiction Research Foundation, 1984.
57. Peycot, M. Cycles of social problem development: The case of drug abuse. *Sociological Quarterly, 25*:83–96 (1984).
58. *Proceedings of the Standing Committee on Health, Welfare and Social Affairs*. Canada.
    a. November 7, 1968.
    b. April 28, 1969.
59. *R.* v. *Appleby* (1972), 16 C.R.N.S. 35 (S.C.C.).
60. *R.* v. *Oakes* (1986), 24 C.C.C. (3d) 321 (S.C.C.).
61. Report of a Committee of the Health Protection Branch, Department of National Health and Welfare. Trends in methadone use in the treatment of opiate dependence in Canada. *Canadian Journal of Public Health, 68*:111–15 (1977).
62. Report of the Special Committee on Narcotics. Community Chest and Council of Greater Vancouver. Mimeograph 1952. Reprinted as "Here's program to fight drug menace," Vancouver *Province*, July 30, 1952.
63. Rock, P. *Deviant Behavior*. London: Hutchinson, 1970.
64. Royal Commission on Government Organization. *Report*. Ottawa: Queen's Printer, 1962–63.
65. Russell, G. K. *Marihuana Today*. New York: The Myrin Institute for Adult Education, 1975.
66. Schur, E. M. *Narcotic Addiction in Britain and America: The Impact of Public Policy*. Bloomington, Ind.: University of Indiana Press, 1962.
67. Senate of Canada.
    a. *Debates*. 1967.
    b. *Proceedings of the Special Committee on the Traffic in Narcotic Drugs in Canada*. Ottawa: Queen's Printer, 1955.
68. Sharman, C. W. L. Narcotic control in Canada. *Police Journal, 3*:535–49 (1930).

69. Sheppard, R. Kaplan pushing to reinstate RCMP search-and-seizure power. *The Globe and Mail*, October 30, 1981.
70. Smart, A., Everson, A., Seghal, R., Finley, J., and Ballah, B. A four-year follow-up study of narcotic-dependent persons receiving methadone maintenance substitution therapy. *Canadian Journal of Public Health*, 68:55–58 (1977).
71. Solomon, R., Single, E., and Erickson, P. G. Legal considerations in Canadian cannabis policy. Chapter 23 of this book. Reprinted from *Canadian Public Policy*, 9:419–33 (1983).
72. *Statutes of Canada*.
    a. *The Opium and Drug Act*, S.C. 1911, c. 17.
    b. *An Act to amend the Opium and Narcotic Drug Act*, S.C. 1921, c. 42.
    c. *An Act to amend the Opium and Narcotic Drug Act*, S.C. 1922, c. 36.
    d. *An Act to amend the Opium and Narcotic Drug Act*, S.C. 1923, c. 22.
    e. *The Opium and Narcotic Drug Act, 1929*, S.C. 1929, c. 49.
    f. *An Act to amend the Opium and Narcotic Drug Act*, S.C. 1954, c. 38.
    g. *The Narcotic Control Act*, S.C. 1961, c. 35.
    h. *An Act to Amend the Food and Drugs Act*, S.C. 1961, c. 37.
    i. *An Act to Amend the Food and Drugs Act*, S.C. 1962, c. 15.
    j. *An Act to amend the Food and Drugs Act and the Narcotic Control Act and to make a consequential amendment to the Criminal Code*, S.C. 1969, c. 41.
    k. *The Criminal Law Amendment Act*, S.C. 1985, c. 19.
73. Stephens, R. Marijuana puzzle: How to cut penalties and not endorse use. *The Globe and Mail*, December 15, 1981.
74. Sutherland, E. H. The diffusion of sexual psychopath laws. *American Journal of Sociology,* 56:142–48 (1950).
75. Task Force on the Creation of an Integrated Canadian Correction Service. *The Role of Federal Corrections in Canada*. Ottawa: Supply and Services Canada, 1977.
76. *Time*. America's crusade. September 15, 1986, 58–69.
77. *Toronto Star*.
    a. Marijuana law change is planned. December 27, 1978.
    b. RCMP chief urges softer penalties for smoking pot. December 19, 1984.
    c. Ease our marijuana law. Editorial, December 20, 1984.
    d. 75% back view illicit drugs an "epidemic," Gallup says. November 3, 1986.
78. *Toronto Telegram*. Judge says tobacco worse than marijuana, November 2, 1968.
79. Trebach, A. S. *The Heroin Solution*. New Haven: Yale University Press, 1982.
80. Trueman, M. Ottawa reviving plan to ease marijuana penalties. *The Globe and Mail*, December 27, 1978.

81. Trueman, M. Socreds blocking bill on marijuana, Lalonde declares. *The Globe and Mail*, February 21, 1979.
82. Vienneau, D. $50 fine for marijuana studied in '81. *Toronto Star*, January 8, 1986.
83. Wilson, R. S. S. Drug clinic plan opposed in Canada. *Proceedings of the Special Committee on the Traffic in Narcotic Drugs in Canada*. Ottawa: Queen's Printer, 1955.

23

Legal Considerations in
Canadian Cannabis Policy*

ROBERT R. SOLOMON, ERIC SINGLE, AND PATRICIA G. ERICKSON

AUTHORS' NOTE

This paper presents an analysis of Canadian cannabis policy as it existed in 1982, at the original time of writing. The authors have not attempted to "update" the paper, because such an exercise would constitute a new analysis and a new paper. However, the reader should be aware of three important changes, and be directed to other parts of this volume for more recent material. First, there has been a decline in the number of cannabis convictions annually since 1981 (see Appendix A). Second, the *Charter of Rights and Freedoms*, since it was passed in 1982, has been used to challenge some aspects of drug law enforcement practices (see Chapter 16). Third, writs of assistance were abolished in 1985 (see Chapters 16 and 22).

INTRODUCTION

Since the late 1960s, cannabis and particularly the prohibition against possession have been perennial candidates for legislative reform in Canada. The law has not been changed, however, despite the recommendations of the Commission of Inquiry into the Non-Medical Use of Drugs (Le Dain Commission), the Canadian Medical and Bar Associations' calls for reform and the government's own policy reviews, cabinet discussion papers and ministerial pronouncements. *Bill S-19*, the government's only legislative initiative, was passed by the Senate in June 1975 only to die on the order paper in the House of Commons the following October (82a).

The cannabis issue is not likely to fade away, nor can it be easily ignored. The rates of cannabis use increased sharply throughout the late 1960s and the 1970s (3, pp. 23–27), and only recently have the rates begun to fall (17, 79). In January 1981, the Health Promotion Directorate of Health and Welfare Canada estimated that 4.1 million Canadians had tried cannabis (16). More recently, the Directorate put the number of Canadian teenagers who had used cannabis at 1.4 million (17). The illicit cannabis market has proven to be relatively impervious to the intensive international and domestic enforce-

*Reprinted verbatim from *Canadian Public Policy, 9*, no. 4 (1983): 419–33. By permission.

ment efforts to curtail it. In fact, cannabis appears to be more readily available and in more potent forms now than ever before. There has not been a major sustained shortage of cannabis in Canada and none is likely to develop in the foreseeable future (see generally, 3, pp. 20–23; 20, pp. 56–68).

The topic of cannabis policy still commands extensive media coverage. No doubt this issue is of special concern to many Canadians, given that approximately 500,000 charges have been laid for cannabis offences since 1969 (12, p. 14; 26, p. 21). In addition, the sheer volume of cannabis cases poses resource allocation problems in the Canadian criminal justice system.

In the first section of this paper, we examine the deterrent impact, social costs, and adverse individual consequences of the present law prohibiting cannabis possession. Our concerns about the efficacy of the current law lead us in Section 2 to evaluate three alternative legal approaches—mitigation of the consequences of a cannabis possession conviction, partial repeal of the possession offence, and government regulation of cannabis distribution. We have concentrated on the cannabis possession offence in order to limit the paper's scope. Furthermore, since the mid-1970s, it has accounted for nearly 90 per cent of all cannabis convictions, and over 80 per cent of all drug convictions (12, pp. 21–22; 26, pp. 20–21) under the *Narcotic Control Act* (NCA, 82j). Finally, most Canadian reform proposals have been limited to the possession issue.

I. THE CURRENT CANNABIS POSSESSION OFFENCE

The Development of the Law

Emily Murphy, a police magistrate and judge of the Juvenile Court in Edmonton, was apparently the first Canadian to have publicly voiced concern about cannabis. In Canada's first book on drug abuse, *The Black Candle* (53), published in 1922, Murphy included a chapter entitled, "Marahuana—a New Menace." Quoting the police chief of Los Angeles, she stated:

> Persons using this narcotic, smoke the dried leaves of the plant, which has the effect of driving them completely insane. The addict loses all sense of moral responsibility. Addicts to this drug, while under its influence, are immune to pain, and could be severely injured without having any realization of their condition. While in this condition they become raving maniacs and are liable to kill or indulge in any form of violence to other persons, using the most savage methods of cruelty without, as said before, any sense of moral responsibility.
>
> When coming from under the influence of this narcotic, these victims present the most horrible condition imaginable. They are dispossessed of their natural and normal will power, and their mentality is that of idiots. If this drug is indulged in to any great extent, it ends in the untimely death of its addict. (53, pp. 332–33)

It is not clear what effect, if any, this dire description had on the decision to prohibit cannabis possession and distribution in 1923 (82k). Only brief reference was made to cannabis in the Parliamentary debates and there was no discussion of the drug's health effects or the rationale for its inclusion (13, p. 230). In any event, Murphy's delineation of the scourge-like effects of cannabis soon came to characterize Canadian drug policy.

This assessment of cannabis went unchallenged for over forty years. The vast majority of the public had no contact with cannabis use or users, and there were no alternative sources of information. In fact, cannabis use was virtually unheard of in Canada until the early 1960s (13, pp. 187–88; 72, p. xii).

As long as cannabis use was perceived to be a moral evil which led to ruin, insanity, and violent crime, its elimination at any cost was an inherently desirable goal. The sudden and sustained increases in the rates of cannabis use which began in the mid-1960s rendered such an extreme view of the drug's effects untenable. In the course of a few years, large numbers of middle- and upper-class young people were subjected to consequences of arrest, conviction, and a criminal record. Canadian drug law and policy were for the first time the object of widespread criticism. Federal drug enforcement officials were no longer seen as having a monopoly on reliable drug infor- mation. Their views had to compete with, and were often directly challenged by, those of lawyers, doctors, social scientists, pharmacologists, researchers, and academics, as well as the growing number of users (23, pp. 133–80).

These developments made it increasingly difficult to justify the existing law on the basis that cannabis use was a moral evil. Subtle variations on this theme continued to arise in the late 1960s, primarily in discussions about whether cannabis use led to the commission of other crimes, dropping out of school, sexual promiscuity, and the use of "hard drugs" (23, pp. 133–80). In recent years, however, attention has shifted to discussions about the health and safety risks posed by cannabis. Controversies about the nature and extent of these risks have tended to preclude discussions of other factors that should be considered in formulating legal policy.

The primary justification now advanced for the cannabis prohibition is that it deters use, thereby limiting the drug's related health and safety risks. It is not the risks of cannabis use *per se* that are at issue, but rather the law's effectiveness in reducing the incidence of such risks. However, the preven- tative effects of law are difficult to measure, and deterrence is more frequently presumed than proven. Furthermore, relatively little attention has been given to the law's negative effects, which include the resources expended on enforcement, the adverse consequences borne by offenders, and the loss of traditional rights and freedoms inherent in the special drug enforcement powers. These are the issues which we will be focusing on in the remainder of the paper. In essence, our concern is to ensure that whatever deterrent benefits the law provides are not outweighed by the costs and adverse con- sequences of achieving them.

A Brief Outline of the Current Cannabis Law

The *Narcotic Control Act* does not distinguish in any material way between cannabis and the other drugs listed in its Schedule. For example, cannabis and heroin offenders are subject to identical police powers, processes of fingerprinting and photographing, criminal procedures concerning bail, trial and appeal, penalty provisions, and criminal record consequences.

The offences are defined broadly, and no statutory distinction is made between consumption-related behaviour and commercial trafficking. For example, an individual who gratuitously shares a joint with a friend and a distributor who sells marijuana in ten-kilogram units may both be charged with trafficking (82j, ss. 2, 6). Similarly, the offence of cultivation applies equally to an individual who grows cannabis by the hectare for resale and to an individual who keeps one cannabis plant in his basement to supply his own needs (82j, s. 6).

These broad criminal prohibitions are reinforced with severe sanctions, particularly for the distribution offences. If the prosecutor decides to proceed summarily in a possession case, the offender is liable to a maximum sentence of six months' imprisonment and/or a $1,000 fine for the first offence, and twelve months' imprisonment and/or a $2,000 fine for subsequent offences. If, however, the prosecutor elects to proceed by way of indictment, the maximum sentence for simple possession is seven years (82j, s. 3(2)). All of the other common offences can only be tried by way of indictment. Cultivation carries a maximum sentence of seven years, and both trafficking and possession for the purpose of trafficking carry a maximum of life imprisonment (82j, ss. 6(2), 4(3)). Those convicted of importing and exporting are subject to a mandatory minimum of seven years' imprisonment and a maximum of life (82j, s. 5(2)). Except for murder and high treason, no criminal offence carries as great a minimum sentence.

This brief review of the NCA creates an unduly harsh impression of the fate of cannabis offenders. As in many other areas of criminal justice, the law's potentially severe impact is cushioned by the exercise of police, prosecutorial, and judicial discretion. For example, federal drug prosecutors rarely lay cannabis importing charges except in cases involving large-scale commercial trafficking, thus protecting minor importers from the seven-year mandatory minimum sentence (8; 20, p. 56). Similarly, judges rarely impose the maximum sentences, or anything close to them, in cannabis cases (12, pp. 141–85). It would be erroneous to conclude, however, that those charged with cannabis possession never go to jail, or get criminal records. As we shall see, there is a broad range of adverse consequences that flow automatically from arrest and conviction.

The Deterrent Impact of the Law

The current prohibition appears to have had a relatively insignificant deterrent effect on the levels of cannabis use in Canada. Despite the special drug enforcement powers, unprecedented increases in drug enforcement man-power and expenditures, and the over 670-fold increase in cannabis convictions since 1965 (12, p. 54; 26, p. 20), the rates of cannabis use climbed sharply until the 1980s when they apparently began to level off (3, pp. 23–27; 17; 79, pp. 16–17).

Various studies indicate that perceived attitudes of one's family and friends, patterns of use among one's peers, and fear of health consequences are more important factors in shaping consumption decisions than the threat of legal sanction (1, 30, 50, 75). In a California study undertaken prior to the enactment of "decriminalization" measures, only 8 per cent of non-users reported that fear of legal prosecution was the primary reason for abstention (9, p. 11). Such findings are consistent with other research which indicates that the law has a limited deterrent impact if the actual and perceived risks of detection are very low, as is the case with cannabis use (84, 91). Epidemiological and conviction statistics suggest that about 1 per cent of cannabis users are convicted each year (14, p. 54; and see current user estimates and conviction statistics in 3, pp. 27, 51).

The experience of the eleven American states that have "decriminalized" cannabis possession provides further evidence of the law's limited deterrent effect. First, it should be pointed out that possession of even small amounts of cannabis is not lawful in the "decriminalized" states. Rather, it has been made a less serious offence that is subject to a maximum penalty of a fine for first offenders (for a review of the American provisions see 3, Appendix D). It is somewhat of a misnomer to describe such measures as "decriminalization" because possession remains a violation of the law, albeit subject to lesser penalties than had previously been the case. In any event, the available American data indicate that there were no increases in rates of cannabis use that could be attributed to the American "decriminalization" measures (38, 56, 70, 76, 83).

The law appears to have surprisingly little deterrent effect among even those convicted of cannabis possession. In the only Canadian study, Erickson found that 92 per cent of her sample reported using cannabis during the year following their trial, typically at their pre-trial levels of use. Although some of these offenders reported that they were using cannabis less often, this was attributed to changes in their lifestyle and greater maturity, not the threat of legal sanction. Those who stopped using tended to be the experimental or infrequent users. It is also noteworthy that the nature and severity of the sentences had no apparent bearing upon subsequent patterns of use (26, pp. 131–34).

The Social Costs and Adverse Individual Consequences of the Cannabis Possession Offence

(i) Financial Costs

Perhaps the most obvious cost of the current law is its financial expense, which was estimated in the late 1970s at roughly 60 to 100 million dollars a year (3, pp. 50–53). Moreover, this heavy concentration on the cannabis possession offence diverts criminal justice manpower and other fixed resources from more serious crimes. By the late 1970s, the cannabis possession offence accounted for almost 11 percent of all federal adult charges, excluding the drinking and driving offences (3, p. 45). The available data, albeit limited and dated, suggest that the quantity involved in the typical possession case is quite small, usually fifteen grams (one-half ounce) or less (8).

(ii) The Adverse Individual Consequences of Criminalization

The adverse consequences to the individual offender are a further cost of the criminal prohibition, and one that has only recently been documented. Erickson found that 32 per cent of the 95 subjects in her study reported having a more hostile attitude towards the police. Five offenders lost their jobs due to their arrest even before the final court disposition. Taking time off from work to attend court caused problems for many offenders, most of whom lied to their employers about the reason for their absence. The offender's financial losses included the amount of any fine, legal fees, and the loss of salary for missed work. One-third of the sample indicated that the "worst" parts of the entire experience were the arrest, the humiliating aspects of being fingerprinted and photographed, and the anxiety involved in facing a criminal charge. Many younger subjects also mentioned family conflicts, when their parents learned of the charge (26, pp. 69–86, 101–128).

The offender's sentence and the adverse consequences of having a criminal record are also important costs of the cannabis possession offence. Although it is not widely noted, the total number of individuals imprisoned for cannabis possession has risen sharply since the mid-1960s. While the percentage of custodial sentences awarded in possession cases has fallen from 46 per cent in 1967 to 5.2 per cent in 1981, this moderation in judicial attitudes has been more than offset by the tremendous increases in the number of convictions (12, pp. 147–49; 26, p. 22). Consequently, the number of cannabis possession offenders sentenced to imprisonment rose from less than 200 in 1967 to over 1,800 in 1981 (12, pp. 147–49; 26, p. 22). In addition to those sentenced to imprisonment, a large number of cannabis possession offenders are jailed for default in payment of their fines. Even this total does not include those held in custody prior to trial, and those jailed for failure to appear or breach of probation (7; 33).

The percentage of cannabis possession offenders who were granted discharges has increased since the mid-1970s, but the sizeable majority of offenders are still receiving fines (12, p. 147; 26, p. 22). For example, in 1981 only 25.3 per cent of the offenders were discharged, whereas 64.8 per cent were fined (12, pp. 147–49). Regardless of the sentence imposed, all cannabis offenders acquired a permanent federal criminal record, which in the long run may prove to be of far greater concern than the sentence itself.

(iii) Criminal Records and Their Impact

Although the term "criminal record" is not statutorily defined, it is generally used to refer to any official account of the finding or plea of guilty and the sentence imposed. This narrow definition ignores the massive trail of potentially harmful information that begins to accumulate from a suspect's first contact with the police. The arresting officer, the local police station, the RCMP police information system in Ottawa, the federal prosecutor, the drug analysts, and the local courts all generate extensive records of an arrest and charge. This information may also be recorded in the legal aid office, detention centre, and various criminal intelligence systems. Once the accused appears in adult court, the charge becomes a matter of public record, and may be reported by the newspapers and other media. Data from these official and unofficial sources are often widely disseminated prior to trial and, with few exceptions, are permanently maintained regardless of the outcome of the case. Generally, any Canadian police department, as well as customs, immigration, corrections, and similar agencies can gain access to these local, provincial, and federal police records. Moreover, there are reciprocal information-sharing arrangements between Canadian and foreign police agencies. Even if the charges are dropped or the suspect is acquitted, he has no legal right to review the police data, or to demand that these files be destroyed (3, pp. 38–42).

There are few empirical data in Canada regarding the impact of a criminal record, but the list of potential disabilities is extensive (13, pp. 292–98; 42). A cannabis offender is at a distinct disadvantage in any subsequent criminal proceeding. The fact that the suspect has a criminal record may: result in the police laying a charge, rather than giving a warning (2); be used to establish grounds for denying or increasing the accused's bail (82f, ss. 457, 458; 42); influence the prosecutor to proceed by way of indictment, rather than by summary conviction (48); and be raised in most cases to impeach the accused's credibility if he takes the witness stand (82b, s. 12; and see 25, 32). A suspect's criminal record may also have an adverse effect on the judge's exercise of his sentencing discretion (55, pp. 67–83; 68, pp. 83–105), the classification process in prison, and the granting of parole.

Entry into Canada (82i, s. 19(2), (3)) or other countries may be denied to persons convicted of cannabis possession. Once in Canada, a visitor, landed immigrant, and even a permanent resident in certain circumstances, may be deported if convicted of possession (82i, s. 27(1), (2)). Similarly, a conviction may prevent an offender from obtaining Canadian citizenship or a Canadian passport (42, 82e).

The cannabis offender's criminal record may severely limit his job opportunities in both the public and private sectors. Many jobs with the federal and provincial governments require a security clearance or are subject to broad employment criteria which could be used to deny jobs to those with criminal records. The provincial statutes governing the regulated professions and licensed occupations usually require applicants and members to be of "good moral character" and to refrain from "unprofessional," "dishonorable," or "improper" conduct. Given the generality of such terms and the discretionary powers of the admitting and disciplinary tribunals, a cannabis offender could be denied entry into, or forced out of these careers (3, pp. 55–57; 42). Furthermore, there are many other jobs in the private sector which require bonding or a security clearance which would pose difficulties for a cannabis offender (see generally 26, pp. 76–78; 27).

Various commentators have suggested that the collateral punitive consequences of a criminal record should be reduced, particularly in less serious cases (15, pp. 407–12; 42; 54, p. 244). The discharge provisions of the *Criminal Code*, s. 662.1 and pardons granted pursuant to the *Criminal Records Act* (82g) both address this concern. Contrary to what many believe, however, discharges and pardons provide only very limited relief.

Discharges were introduced in 1972 as a new sentencing option, primarily in response to the large number of young first offenders who were acquiring criminal records for cannabis possession. Following a guilty plea or a finding of guilt, a judge may discharge the accused absolutely or upon conditions in a probation order, if it is in the interest of the accused and not contrary to the public interest (82f, s. 662.1(1)). Since discharges can only be granted for offences that have no minimum sentence and a maximum of less than fourteen years, they are only available to those cannabis offenders charged with possession or cultivation. A discharged offender can honestly deny having been convicted of a criminal offence, because no conviction is in fact registered. By virtue of the *Canada Evidence Act* (82b), the criminal record of a discharged offender—unlike that of a convicted offender—cannot be raised to impeach his credibility if he takes the stand (63). It has also been held that an offender's prior discharge ought not to be taken into account in sentencing, except in cases where the offender is seeking another discharge (55, p. 71; 68, pp. 213–14).

However, a discharge has no impact on police and other records that accumulate prior to trial, nor does it limit the subsequent dissemination of this information. While a discharged offender can deny having been convicted, he must answer "yes" if asked whether he has ever been arrested for, pleaded guilty to, been found guilty of, or been sentenced for, a criminal offence. A discharged offender has a permanent federal criminal record which he cannot deny (41, 92). Erickson found that the likelihood of incurring adverse criminal record consequences did not vary according to whether the offender received a fine, probation, or discharge. The only discernible impact of the discharge appears to have been a heightened sense of unfairness among those who did not receive one (26, p. 143).

Much like a discharge, a pardon granted pursuant to the *Criminal Records Act* provides an offender with few tangible benefits. The granting of a pardon does not create the legal fiction that the crime never occurred. Consequently, a pardoned offender cannot truthfully deny having a criminal record (19, 54). The pardon merely vacates the conviction or discharge, which means that it removes any federal disqualifications that result from the commission of the offence. For example, a pardoned offender regains his right to hold public office.

(iv) The Special Drug Enforcement Powers and the Loss of Traditional Civil Liberties

An officer has far broader powers of search and seizure in even a minor drug case, such as simple possession of cannabis, than he has in a murder, rape, arson, or other serious criminal case. For example, section 10(1)(*a*) of the NCA basically authorizes any peace officer to enter and search, day or night, any place other than a dwelling house in which he reasonably believes there is a narcotic, and to search any occupant found therein. Contrary to the traditional principles governing the search of premises, the basis of the officer's belief is not subject to judicial scrutiny before entry or for that matter after entry. Unless the officer is sued, he would not be required to explain the facts upon which he relied. Even if sued, the officer's testimony that he was acting on "confidential and reliable police information" appears to be sufficient to satisfy the disclosure requirement (43).

An equally troubling aspect of section 10(1) is that it authorizes the officer to search any occupant found on the premises. There need not be any evidence, belief, or even suspicion that such persons are violating the drug law or any law—the occupant's mere presence is sufficient (71). In addition, regardless of his innocence, an occupant who refuses to submit to a police search of his person may be charged with wilfully obstructing or resisting an officer in the execution of his duty (82f, s. 118(a)). This represents a marked departure from the established principle that an individual is only required to submit to a search after he has been lawfully arrested, and the arrest to be lawful must be based on reasonable and probable grounds to believe that the individual has committed an offence.

The police have used these special drug enforcement powers to raid taverns and conduct strip searches. One such incident at the Landmark Hotel in Fort Erie prompted the Ontario government to establish a Royal Commission to investigate the police conduct. While acknowledging that the searches were legal, the Commission seriously questioned the police officers' judgment in raiding the tavern and searching its patrons (58). The Commission seemed most concerned about the strip searches of all the female occupants.

> On the whole of the evidence, in respect to the search of the female patrons by causing them to disrobe and subject themselves to a cursory glance of their buttocks and genital areas, I am satisfied that there was not a shred of evidence to support a suspicion that any female patrons had concealed heroin or any like substance on their persons prior to the search. In this sense, the wholesale search was foolish and unnecessary, as not one female was even seen with a known heroin or other drug trafficker. (58, pp. 67–70)

The Commission recommended that the federal government enact amendments to narrow this exceptional search power and that doctors and nurses be employed to conduct intimate physical searches of suspects (58, pp. 70–71).

Despite the Commission's report, the law has not been changed and these tactics are still being used. Following a 1978 raid on a tavern in Hull, the female patrons reported that they were forced to submit to vaginal examinations performed in toilet cubicles under the most unsanitary conditions by a female employee of the police force, who had no formal medical training (45).

Perhaps the most controversial feature of the special drug enforcement powers involves the search of dwellings pursuant to writs of assistance. Generally, the police can only enter a dwelling house if they have a valid search warrant duly issued by a judge. Judicial scrutiny of the police evidence and control over the issuance of the search warrant are designed to protect the sanctity of the home and the privacy of the individual (see generally, 60). However, the writ of assistance created by the drug Acts is a continuing blanket search power which authorizes its holder to enter and search any dwelling house without a warrant, day or night, if he reasonably believes that it contains illicit drugs (82h, s. 37(3), (4)); 82j, s. 10(1), (3), (4)). In order to prevent the possible destruction of evidence, the courts have permitted the police to break in without prior announcement, using whatever force is reasonably necessary (43).

Although the legislation empowers Federal Court judges to issue writs of assistance, they have no real authority over the granting or use of the writ. Once the federal Attorney-General applies for a writ on behalf of an officer, the judge must issue it to that person (82h, s. 37(3); 82j, s. 10(3)). The writ is not limited as to time or place, and it is valid for the officer's entire career. The judge who issues the writ has no control whatsoever over when, where, how often, or in what circumstances the writ is invoked (39; 47; 61; 77).

Judicial criticism prompted the government to impose a moratorium on requests for writs in 1977 (65, 66). The following year, the government announced that sweeping reforms would be introduced to give the judiciary greater control over the granting and actual use of the writs (21, 88). While such legislation has yet to be introduced,* Solicitor-General Kaplan lobbied strenuously for the lifting of the moratorium (11, 74, 89, 90).

It should be noted that RCMP policy requires writ holders to file a departmental report after each search (18, Part 1, p. 67). Even if this internal review were scrupulously performed, such procedures are a far cry from the traditional safeguard of having the judiciary specifically approve every police request to enter private premises.

The unsavoury enforcement methods associated with drug investigations also constitute a loss of established rights and freedoms. Although the use of wiretaps, paid informants, undercover agents, police dogs, arrest without warning, surprise raids, strip searches, and the granting of immunity to suspects in return for information have been held to be legal, such tactics are incompatible with the normal standards of conduct expected of police and prosecutors (see generally 81, for a discussion of the legal bases for such tactics in drug cases). These enforcement tactics have been widely criticized for impugning the integrity of the criminal justice system, particularly among the young (13, pp. 298–99; 26, pp. 78–79; 33, p. 32; 49).

In addition to the use of unsavoury enforcement methods, one must also consider the illegal police conduct that occurs in drug cases. While reports of corruption involving Canadian drug enforcement officials are increasing, they are still relatively uncommon compared to the United States (24, 31, 52, 86, 87, 93). There are, however, frequent complaints that Canadian drug officers have engaged in other illegal conduct, such as: opening private mail (73, 85); making surreptitious entries into private premises (10, 69, 80); seizing or destroying private property (24, 59, 69); and using unnecessary or excessive force (24, 40, 59, 94). Since interactions between police and drug users tend to be of low visibility, it is extremely difficult to assess the extent to which such practices exist in cannabis cases. Erickson reported that 12 per cent of her sample of cannabis offenders stated that the police had used or threatened to use unnecessary force. Based on the offenders' accounts, Erickson concluded that the extreme tactics which characterize other types of drug enforcement may also occur in cannabis cases (26, pp. 60–63).

Those who expect the recently-enacted *Canadian Charter of Rights and Freedoms* (82d) to dramatically curtail the intrusive and unsavoury aspects of drug enforcement may be sorely disappointed (see 81 for a detailed analysis of the *Charter's* impact on drug enforcement powers and practices; and also 36, 37). Granted, the *Charter* constitutes a significant advance over the *Canadian Bill of Rights* (82c). Unlike the *Bill*, the *Charter* is specifically made part of the supreme law of Canada, applies to both federal and provincial law, and takes precedence over all other regularly-enacted legislation, rendering inconsistent laws of no effect or force (34).

There are, however, a number of major limitations on the legal rights

---

*The writs of assistance were abolished in December 1985. See Chapter 16.

and freedoms guaranteed by the *Charter*. First, the *Charter* itself gives both Parliament and the provincial legislatures the power to enact legislation that takes effect notwithstanding these legal rights and freedoms (35). Second, section 1 provides that these legal rights and freedoms are subject "to such reasonable limits prescribed by law as can be demonstrably justified in a free and democratic society." Thus, even if an individual establishes that his rights have been infringed, he is not automatically entitled to redress. If the government can establish that this infringement is provided by law, is reasonable in the circumstances and is clearly justifiable in our society, then the individual's constitutional rights will not have been violated (see 22, 46). Third, many of the *Charter*'s key terms and concepts have been interpreted previously by the Supreme Court of Canada in a manner which facilitates law enforcement at the expense of the private citizen's traditional rights. Moreover, in few areas has this judicial attitude been more evident than in drug enforcement. There is no reason to believe that the court's interpretation of these terms and concepts will significantly change now that they have been included in the *Charter*.

While there are a number of lower court cases in which the *Charter* has been used to limit drug enforcement powers and practices, there appears to be an even larger number of decisions upholding these same powers and practices. (Contrast *R.* v. *Carrière* (62) and *R.* v. *Noble* (64).) Despite the publicity generated by this first round of lower court judgments, it must be remembered that the Supreme Court of Canada will ultimately determine the *Charter*'s impact on drug enforcement. Even if this court were to broadly interpret and apply the *Charter*—and there is little reason to believe this will be the case—many drug enforcement practices which infringe upon traditional civil liberties would be unaffected. These losses of established rights must be considered a very substantial social cost of the current law.

II. ALTERNATIVE APPROACHES TO CANNABIS POSSESSION

Introduction

Despite some confusion in terminology, cannabis reform measures generally fall within one of three broad categories. The most modest alternatives are those which retain the cannabis possession offence, but seek to mitigate its adverse individual consequences and social costs. The second type of approach involves the repeal of the possession offence in certain limited situations— usually those in which small amounts are possessed for personal use. The third group of alternatives is characterized by government control over the cannabis market through the provision of a legally-regulated source of supply. In this section, we will outline the major features of each alternative and briefly discuss their advantages and disadvantages.

Attempts to Mitigate the Adverse Consequences of the Cannabis Possession Offence: The "Fine Only" Option

The possible mitigation alternatives range from modest proposals that simply lower maximum penalties, to more elaborate schemes that encompass penalty reductions, simplified criminal procedures, and protection from some adverse criminal record consequences. A common feature of many of these mitigation alternatives is the elimination of incarceration as a direct sentencing option for first offenders. Since relatively few first offenders are sentenced to imprisonment for cannabis possession, the "fine only" option does not represent a major policy change. Indeed, the government itself has indicated on several occasions that it was about to adopt such measures (see, for example, 82a).

The mitigation alternatives are not designed to reduce the number of people criminalized, but rather attempt to lessen the negative effects of criminalization. In order to have a significant impact, these alternatives must address issues other than incarceration for first offenders. A comprehensive mitigation scheme might include: a ban against fingerprinting and photographing those charged with cannabis possession; the replacement of the present arrest, bail, and trial procedures with a less formal ticketing system; the redefinition of the possession and distribution offences to ensure that conduct which is functionally equivalent to possession, such as sharing a joint with a friend, is included in the possession rather than the trafficking offence; the amendment of the discharge provisions of the *Code* to ensure that they provide greater protection; the elimination of jail terms for those convicted of a subsequent cannabis possession offence and those who default in payment of fines; the development of special record-keeping systems to prevent the creation of a permanent federal criminal record; and the amendment of the *Criminal Records Act* to increase the benefits of a pardon.

The enactment of a broad mitigation package would significantly reduce some of the adverse consequences presently borne by cannabis possession offenders. Among other things, it would keep several thousand cannabis offenders out of jail each year. It would also lessen the offender's criminal record problems in employment and other areas. The American "decriminalization" experience indicates that adoption of a mitigation approach could also reduce cannabis enforcement costs and redirect criminal justice resources to more serious problems. For example, the costs of marijuana possession enforcement fell by roughly 75 per cent in California during comparable pre- and post-decriminalization periods; while marijuana arrests fell, heroin and other drug charges increased (9; see also 28). Moreover, the introduction of the American "decriminalization" measures did not produce any significant increase in the rates of use (9, 28, 38, 56, 70, 76, 83). This result is not surprising given the law's limited deterrent effects.

The mitigation alternatives have several major drawbacks. The large number of people subject to the special drug enforcement powers and the number of people criminalized for cannabis possession would not necessarily be affected by the enactment of mitigation legislation. Although the adverse consequences of a criminal record can be reduced, they cannot be eliminated. As long as cannabis possession remains a criminal offence, its enforcement will of necessity generate volumes of data, much of which the federal government cannot control. Finally, any serious attempt to limit the adverse consequences of the cannabis possession offence will involve drafting complex legislation, which would exacerbate the already widespread public misunderstanding of the drug law (see 3 and 4 for a discussion of the mitigation alternatives).

Partial Repeal of the Possession Offence

The basic characteristic of this approach is the reduction in the scope of the possession offence. An exemption from liability which included only possession of a small quantity for personal use in one's own home would have a very limited impact, because relatively few charges arise from such circumstances. On the other hand, a general exemption for possession of less than 30 grams (one ounce) would drastically reduce the number of people criminalized. A comprehensive model might exclude from liability at least some consumption-related behaviours now prohibited under the trafficking and cultivation offences. For example, home cultivation for personal use might be permitted to allow users to avoid involvement in the illicit market. A further benefit of such a policy is that domestically-grown cannabis tends to be less potent than foreign supplies (20, p. 67).

The partial repeal alternatives are predicated on the view that the deterrent benefits of the possession offence are outweighed in certain circumstances by its financial and social costs and adverse individual consequences. The adoption of a partial repeal alternative is compatible with a government policy of discouraging cannabis use. The criminal justice resources saved as a result of the partial repeal measures could be concentrated in curtailing large-scale cannabis trafficking, which would remain subject to heavy sanctions. The government could attempt to reduce the safety risks involved in cannabis use by creating special offences and enforcement programs to deal with consumption in high-risk situations, such as driving or operating machinery. The public use or even display of cannabis could be prohibited, and cannabis found in these circumstances could be made subject to seizure and forfeiture. These and similar legislative proposals could be coupled with public information programs related to the health and safety risks of cannabis use. The intent of such measures would be to limit use, particularly in situations of high risk, and to prevent the public from misinterpreting the partial repeal of the cannabis possession offence as a lessening of government disapproval of the drug (see 3, pp. 99–104; 13, pp. 299–303; and 44, pp. 19–32 for a discussion of various partial repeal options).

The major advantage of this option is that it would eliminate the social costs and adverse individual consequences of processing tens of thousands of cannabis users through the criminal justice system each year. Compared to the mitigation alternatives, the partial repeal option is straightforward and comprehensible. It could also result in a major redirection of criminal justice resources to more serious drug offences. The major disadvantage of partial repeal measures is their potential impact on consumption. Unfortunately, there are no data on cannabis consumption patterns in Alaska, the only North American jurisdiction in which partial repeal measures apply. If, as recent studies indicate, the current law has little deterrent impact, one would expect that partial repeal of the cannabis possession offence would not result in a significant increase in the rates of use.

Government Regulation of Distribution

The dominant feature of this option is the creation of a government-regulated legal source of supply. The regulatory schemes might range from general government licensing and taxing systems to highly restrictive regimes in which all aspects of production and distribution are directly controlled by the government. The latter type of scheme might rely upon consumer licences, rationed sales, limited retail hours, and proof-of-age requirements. Such a system would be more restrictive than, but otherwise similar to, the provincial alcohol distribution systems (see 3, pp. 104–106; 44, pp. 33–50; 51, 57).

Regardless of the specific model used, the government regulation alternatives have several unique advantages. They would not only minimize enforcement costs, but would likely generate very substantial government revenues (29). The government could also ensure the drug's purity and limit its potency. Such a system would free cannabis users from the necessity of associating with traffickers to obtain supplies. Finally, it would reduce the profits, violence, and corruption arising from large-scale trafficking. A contraband trade of some kind would probably survive to serve those markets not satisfied by the government distribution system, but this trade would be small relative to the present black market. In this sense, regulation may be seen as a more effective method of controlling cannabis consumption than the current prohibition (5, 6; 13, pp. 303–310; 51, 57, 78).

The regulation options, however, pose several serious problems. They would represent a fundamental change in government policy. At best, the government could argue that it was adopting a policy of neutrality towards cannabis use. Nevertheless, the public might interpret this policy change as indicating that the government is no longer concerned with the health and safety risks of cannabis. Given this possibility and the legal availability of the drug, there might be a significant risk of increased cannabis use.

Furthermore, in order to adopt this approach without violating its international treaty obligations, Canada would have to seek an amendment to or withdraw from at least some of the provisions of the 1961 *Single Convention on Narcotic Drugs*. The likelihood of obtaining such an amendment is remote and withdrawal might well trigger international criticism of Canada, traditionally one of the most forceful advocates of international co-operation in the drug field. (For discussion of the *Convention*'s implications for domestic policy see 3, Appendix A.) Finally, there would also be serious constitutional problems raised by this option. For example, it is doubtful whether the federal government has the authority to establish a retail cannabis distribution system within the provinces. Since considerable revenues would be at stake and public attitudes towards cannabis may vary from province to province, the constitutional issues would likely be contentious and politically volatile.

CONCLUSION

In our view, the current law can no longer be considered an acceptable option. It has generated substantial financial costs, consumed a sizeable proportion of limited enforcement resources, and burdened hundreds of thousands of young Canadians with permanent federal criminal records for conduct which is commonplace among their peers. In an effort to facilitate enforcement, we have sacrificed many of our traditional rights and freedoms, tolerated a broad range of unsavoury enforcement practices and created an environment that has fostered excessive force, unauthorized entry into private homes, unlawful seizure and destruction of private property, and other illegal police conduct. Yet, the law has not stemmed the flow of cannabis into Canada, nor apparently had a significant impact on consumption. In summary, the current control regime provides only marginal benefits at tremendous financial, social, and individual costs.

A strict prohibitionist policy generating limited deterrent benefits at extremely high costs might well be justified for grave conduct that threatened widespread death and injury. However, in our view, cannabis possession simply does not meet this test, even if we were to accept the more dire scientific assessments of the drug's effects.

The mitigation alternatives are clearly preferable to the present law since they would reduce at least some of the costs of criminalizing cannabis possession. Nevertheless, even the most comprehensive mitigation proposals would affect only the extent and not the fact of criminalization. Such schemes cannot undo all the adverse individual consequences of arrest and conviction, nor in and of themselves reduce the number of persons criminalized. Although the mitigation alternatives could substantially decrease the negative effects of criminalization, we believe that even this reduced level of costs cannot be justified, given the limited deterrent benefits of the general prohibition.

The government regulation alternatives could raise substantial revenues, control the potency and quality of licit supplies, and significantly curtail the illicit traffic. Yet, providing a legal source of supply might precipitate a substantial increase in use and related health and safety risks. Ultimately, the regulation options might prove to be the most appropriate vehicles for achieving our goals. However, at the present time, in light of the potential for substantially increased rates of use, we cannot advocate adopting a government regulation scheme.

The partial repeal alternatives provide the best prospect for minimizing the risks of cannabis use at the lowest social, financial, and individual costs. In adopting such an approach, the government prohibition could limit the possible offence to potentially high-risk situations and attempt to discourage use in other situations by resorting to less coercive means such as education. Although adopting this approach might lead to a limited increase in consumption, the evidence is inconclusive. Based on the available data, we favour a policy that acknowledges a possible slight increase in use levels, in return for eliminating the very substantial financial, social, and individual costs of maintaining the current cannabis prohibition.

REFERENCES

1. Anderson, L. S., Chiricos, T. G., and Waldo, G. P. Formal and informal sanctions: A comparison of deterrent effects. *Social Problems, 25*:103–14 (1977).
2. Bailey, P., and Solomon, R. Police processing of cannabis cases. Unpublished research study. Health Protection Branch, Department of Health and Welfare, Ottawa, 1979.
3. Blackwell, J., Green, M., and Solomon, R. Cannabis control policy: A discussion paper. Unpublished research study. Health Promotion Branch, Department of Health and Welfare, Ottawa, 1979.
4. Bonnie, R. J. Decriminalizing the marijuana user: A drafter's guide. *Journal of Law Reform, 11*:3–48 (1977).
5. Bonnie, R. J., and Whitebread II, C. H. *The Marihuana Conviction*. Charlottesville, Va.: University Press of Virginia, 1974.
6. Boyd, N. The question of marihuana control. *The Criminal Law Quarterly, 24*:212–32 (1982).
7. Bryan, E. M. Cannabis in Canada—A decade of indecision. *Contemporary Drug Problems, 8*:169–92 (1979).
8. Bryan, E. M., Jarvis, K., and Brooks, B. The quantities of marijuana, hash and hash oil involved in convictions for cannabis offences in Canada

1975. Unpublished research study. Health Protection Branch, Department of Health and Welfare, Ottawa, 1978.

9. Budman, K. B. *A First Report of the Impact of California's New Marijuana Law*. Sacramento, Calif.: State Office of Narcotics and Drug Abuse, 1977.

10. *Calgary Herald*. Police involved: Unauthorized entries in drug investigation. July 26, 1979, A-1.

11. *Calgary Herald*. Writ should be written. December 4, 1982, A-4.

12. Canada. Bureau of Dangerous Drugs, Department of National Health and Welfare. *Canadian Drug User and Conviction Statistics, 1981*. Ottawa, 1982.

13. Canada. Commission of Inquiry into the Non-Medical Use of Drugs. *Cannabis*. Ottawa: Information Canada, 1972.

14. Canada. Commission of Inquiry into the Non-Medical Use of Drugs. *Final Report*. Ottawa: Information Canada, 1973.

15. Canada. Committee on Corrections. *Report of the Canadian Committee on Corrections*. Ottawa: Queen's Printer, 1969.

16. Canada. Health and Welfare Canada, Health Promotion Directorate. *Canadian Health Facts: Cannabis—Extent and Patterns of Use in Canada, 1980*. January, 1981.

17. Canada. Health and Welfare Canada, Health Promotion Directorate. *Canadian Health Facts: Marijuana—Extent and Patterns of Use among Canadian Teenagers, 1982*. July, 1982.

18. Canada. Law Reform Commission. *Search and Seizure*. Draft working paper. Ottawa, 1982.

19. Canada. National Parole Board. *Pardon Under the Criminal Records Act*. Ottawa, 1982.

20. Canada. RCMP. *RCMP National Drug Intelligence Estimate 1981*. Ottawa: Minister of Supply and Services, 1982.

21. Carruthers, B. Search warrants under tighter control in Canada. *The Journal, 2*: May 1, 1978.

22. Christian, T. The limitation of liberty: A consideration of Section 1 of the Charter of Rights and Freedoms. *University of British Columbia Law Review* (Charter edition): 113–16 (1982).

23. Cook, S. Variations in response to illegal drug use. Unpublished research study. Addiction Research Foundation, Toronto, 1970.

24. CTV Television Network, W5. Drug squads in Vancouver. January 12, 1975.

25. Doob, A. N., and Kirshenbaum, H. M. Some empirical evidence on the effect of s. 12 of the Canada Evidence Act upon an accused. *Criminal Law Quarterly, 15*:88–96 (1973).

26. Erickson, P. G. *Cannabis Criminals: The Social Effects of Punishment on Drug Users*. Toronto: ARF Books, 1980.

27. Erickson, P. G., and Goodstadt, M. S. Legal stigma for marijuana possession. *Criminology, 17*:208–16 (1979).

28. Fulton, M. D., Clark, R. M., and Robinson, T. *The Decriminalization of*

Marijuana and the Maine Criminal System: A Time/Cost Analysis. Augusta, Maine: Maine Office of Alcoholism and Drug Abuse Prevention, 1979.

29. Garber, A. S. Potential tax revenues from a regulatory marketing scheme for marijuana. *Journal of Psychedelic Drugs, 10*(3):217–26 (1978).

30. Goodstadt, M. S., Sheppard, M. A., and Chan, G. C. *Non-Use and Cessation of Cannabis Use: Neglected Foci of Drug Education.* Substudy no. 1269. Toronto: Addiction Research Foundation, 1983.

31. Gray, M. Absolute discharge for ex-Mountie who took $11,000. *The Globe and Mail,* September 23, 1977, 1.

32. Hans, V., and Doob, A. Section 12 of the Canada Evidence Act and the deliberations of simulated juries. *Criminal Law Quarterly, 18*:235–53 (1975–76).

33. Hogarth, J., and Robertson, H. Policy alternatives for the regulation of cannabis. Unpublished research study: A background paper prepared for Provincial Attorneys-General Conference, 1978.

34. Hogg, P. A comparison of the Canadian Charter of Rights and Freedoms with the Canadian Bill of Rights. In: Tarnopolsky, W., and Beaudoin, G. (eds.). *Canadian Charter of Rights and Freedoms*, 1–23. Toronto: Carswell, 1982.

35. Hogg, P. *Canada Act Annotated.* Toronto: Carswell, 1982.

36. Hovius, B. The legacy of the Supreme Court of Canada's approach to the Canadian Bill of Rights: Prospects for the Charter. *McGill Law Journal, 28*:31–58 (1982).

37. Hovius, B., and Martin, R. The Canadian Charter of Rights and Freedoms in the Supreme Court of Canada. *Canadian Bar Review, 61*:354–76 (1983).

38. Johnston, L. D. *Marijuana Use and the Effects of Marijuana Decriminalization.* Testimony delivered to the U.S. Senate Judiciary Committee Subcommittee on Criminal Justice, January 16, 1980. Washington, D.C. 1980.

39. Ketchum, P. G. C. Writs of assistance. *Chitty's Law Journal, 19*(March): 90–92 (1971).

40. Lavigne, Y. Youth beaten in drug raid, commission inquiry hears. *The Globe and Mail,* July 13, 1978, 9.

41. Leon, J. S. Drug offences and discharges in Canada: The need for reform. *University of Toronto Faculty of Law Review, 35*:36–68 (1977).

42. Leon, J. S. Post-sentencing problems: Some consequences of a finding of guilt in criminal cases. *Criminal Law Quarterly, 21*:318–60 (1979).

43. *Levitz* v. *Ryan* (1972), 9 C.C.C. (2d) 182 at 188 (Ont. C.A.).

44. Logan, F. (ed.). *Cannabis: Options for Control.* Sunbury, U.K.: Quartermaine House, 1979.

45. Macdonald, N. Intimate search in police raid angers women. *The Ottawa Citizen,* May 8, 1978, 1.

46. Marx, H. Entrenchment, limitations and non-obstante. In: Tarnopolsky,

W., and Beaudoin, G. (eds.). *Canadian Charter of Rights and Freedoms*, 61–74. Toronto: Carswell, 1982.

47. McConnell, W. H. Unreasonable searches and seizures: A "Fourth Amendment" for Canada. *Revue de Droit Université Sherbrooke, 11*:157–96 (1980).
48. McKee, J. The prosecution of cannabis cases. Unpublished research study, Health Protection Branch, Department of Health and Welfare, Ottawa, 1978.
49. McLachlin, B. M., and Miller, A. *Rothman*: Policy trickery: Is the game worth the candle? *University of British Columbia Law Review, 16*:115–30 (1982).
50. Meier, R. F., and Johnson, W. T. Deterrence and social control: The legal and extra-legal production of conformity. *American Sociological Review, 42*(April): 292–304 (1977).
51. Mitchell, C. N. A comparative analysis of cannabis regulation. *Queen's Law Journal, 9*:110–42 (1983).
52. *Montreal Gazette*. Mountie who led drug busts accused of trafficking hashish. May 23, 1980.
53. Murphy, E. F. *The Black Candle*. 1922. Reprint. Toronto: Thomas Allen, 1973.
54. Nadin-Davis, R. P. Canada's Criminal Records Act: Notes on how not to expunge criminal convictions. *Saskatchewan Law Review, 45*:221–57 (1981).
55. Nadin-Davis, R. P. *Sentencing in Canada*. Toronto: Carswell, 1982.
56. National Research Council. Committee on Substance Abuse and Habitual Behavior. *An Analysis of Marijuana Policy*. Washington, D.C.: National Academy Press, 1982.
57. Oakes, R. T. Marijuana and economic due process: A transition from prohibition to regulation. *Contemporary Drug Problems, 9*:401–35 (1980).
58. Ontario. Royal Commission on the Conduct of Police Forces at Fort Erie on the 11th of May, 1974. John A. Pringle, Commissioner. *Report*. Toronto, 1975.
59. Ontario Police Commission. *Report of the Inquiry into Police Practices in the Waterloo Regional Police Force*. 1978.
60. Paikin, L. *The Issuance of Search Warrants*. Ottawa: Law Reform Commission of Canada, 1980.
61. Parker, G. E. The extraordinary power to search and seize and the writ of assistance. *University of British Columbia Law Review, 1*:688–728 (1963).
62. *R. v. Carrière*, Ont. Prov. Ct., Bélanger Prov. J., January 5, 1983.
63. *R. v. Danson* (1982), 35 O.R. (2d) 777 (C. A.).
64. *R. v. Noble*, Ont. Co. Ct., Doyle Co. Ct. J., June 2, 1983.
65. *Re Writs of Assistance*, [1965] 2 Ex. C.R. 645 (Ex. T.D.).
66. *Re Writs of Assistance* (1975), 34 C.C.C. (2d) 62 (Fed. T.D.).
67. Rosenthal, M. P. Partial prohibition of non-medical drug use: A proposal. *Journal of Drug Issues, 9*:437–89 (1979).

68. Ruby, C. *Sentencing.* 2d ed. Toronto: Butterworths, 1980.
69. Sallot, J. RCMP conduct 400 break-ins without warrants. *The Globe and Mail*, April 19, 1978, 1.
70. Saveland, W., and Bray, D. Trends in cannabis use among American States with different and changing legal regimes, 1972–77. Unpublished research study, Laboratory Centre for Disease Control, Health Protection Branch, Department of National Health and Welfare, Ottawa, 1980.
71. *Scott v. The Queen et al.* (1975), 61 D.L.R. (3d) 130 (Fed. C.A.).
72. Senate of Canada. *Proceedings of the Special Committee on the Traffic in Narcotic Drugs in Canada.* Ottawa: Queen's Printer, 1955.
73. Sheppard, R. Customs opening letters, documents show. *The Globe and Mail*, April 5, 1980, 1.
74. Sheppard, R. Kaplan pushing to reinstate RCMP search-and-seize power. *The Globe and Mail*, October 30, 1981.
75. Silberman, M. Toward a theory of criminal deterrence. *American Sociological Review, 41*(June): 442–61 (1976).
76. Single, E. The impact of marijuana decriminalization. In: Israel, Y., Glaser, F. B., Kalant, H., Popham, R. E., Schmidt, W., and Smart, R. G. (eds.). *Research Advances in Alcohol and Drug Problems*, Vol. 6. New York: Plenum, 1981.
77. Skinner, J. M. Writs of assistance. *University of Toronto Faculty of Law Review, 21*:26–44 (1963).
78. Skolnick, J., and Dombrink, J. The legalization of deviance. *Criminology, 16*:193–208 (1978).
79. Smart, R. G., Goodstadt, M. S., Adlaf, E. M., Sheppard, M., Chan, G., and Liban, C. B. *Preliminary Report of Alcohol and Other Drug Use among Ontario Students in 1981, and Changes Since 1977 and 1979.* Substudy no. 1203. Toronto: Addiction Research Foundation, 1981.
80. Solomon, R. The enforcement of drug laws in Vancouver. Unpublished research study, Le Dain Commission, 1970.
81. Solomon, R. Drug enforcement powers and the Canadian Charter of Rights and Freedoms. *University of Western Ontario Law Review, 21*:219–63 (1983).
82. *Statutes of Canada.*
    a. *An Act to amend the Food and Drugs Act, the Narcotic Control Act and the Criminal Code* (Bill S-19, 1974–75. Senate Third Reading June 18, 1975).
    b. *Canada Evidence Act*, R.S.C. 1970, c. E-10, s. 12.
    c. *Canadian Bill of Rights*, R.S.C. 1970, Appendix III.
    d. *Canadian Charter of Rights and Freedoms*, being Part I of the *Constitution Act, 1982*, being Schedule B to the *Canada Act*, 1982 (U.K.), c. 11.
    e. *Citizenship Act*, S.C. 1974–75–76, c. 108, s. 20(2).
    f. *Criminal Code*, R.S.C. 1970, c. C-34.

    g. *Criminal Records Act*, R.S.C. 1970 (lst Supp.), c. 12.

    h. *Food and Drugs Act*, R.S.C. 1970, c. F-27.

    i. *Immigration Act*, S.C. 1976, c. 52.

    j. *Narcotic Control Act*, R.S.C. 1970, c. N-1.

    k. *Opium and Narcotic Drug Act*, S.C. 1923, c. 22.

83. Suggs, D. L. A qualitative and quantitative analysis of the impact of Nebraska's decriminalization of marijuana. *Law and Human Behavior, 5*:45–71 (1981).

84. Teevan, J. Subjective perception of deterrence. *Journal of Research in Crime and Delinquency, 13*:155–64 (1976).

85. *Toronto Star*. 100 heroin letters Canada-bound, RCMP warns. November 25, 1977, A-1.

86. *Toronto Star*. Arrest of "honest" ex-cop in drug ring shocks friends. October 19, 1980, A-20.

87. *Toronto Star*. Policeman charged in weekend drug bust, March 28, 1982, A-3.

88. Trueman, M. Ottawa retreats from its intention to abolish long-running search writs. *The Globe and Mail*, March 14, 1978, 9.

89. Trueman, M. Ottawa plans new limits, controls and use of open search warrants. *The Globe and Mail*, April 7, 1978, 1.

90. Valpy, M. The important issue. *The Globe and Mail*, November 27, 1981.

91. Waldo, G. P., and Chiricos, T. G. Perceived penal sanction and self-reported criminality: A neglected approach to deterrence research. *Social Problems, 19*:522–40 (1972).

92. Wilkins, J. L. Absolute and conditional discharges. *Criminal Law Quarterly, 19*:454–70 (1976).

93. *Winnipeg Free Press*. Policeman Keating got $5000 to stay charge Dass hashish trial. November 18, 1977, 1.

94. *Winnipeg Free Press*. "Reprehensible" police behaviour, putting vice grip on genitals cut term for Henderson. February 25, 1977, 8.

24

Heroin "Treatment" in British Columbia, 1976–1984: Thesis, Antithesis, and Synthesis?*

NEIL BOYD, CHRISTOPHER J. MILLARD, AND CHRISTOPHER D. WEBSTER

Heroin use and heroin control constitute complex social problems. Though opium and its derivatives have been used by human beings for thousands of years (6, 21), the twentieth century has sounded a global alarm about the effects of both use and abuse. Opiate distributors are routinely shot, hanged, and imprisoned for life; opiate users can expect similar kinds of sanctions, if slightly less severe (9).

The opiates occupy a puzzling position in the realm of illicit drugs. Unlike alcohol and tobacco, they do not have the ability to break down human tissue (26, 31). The opium poppy gives the gift of killing pain, but with the price of a dependency often as compelling as that of tobacco (3).[1] And yet the poppy will not take years from life, in the way that tobacco and alcohol do. The opiates remain an enigma, the most dreaded of licit and illicit drugs, enjoying an image of doom that is difficult to comprehend.

Canada first criminalized the sale, manufacture, and importation of smoking opium in 1908 (23a). The Chinese opium industries resident on our country's West Coast were given six months to sell off remaining inventory; the typically Caucasian use of opiated tonics, elixirs, and analgesics retained a legal status for another decade (12). In time, opiate use, first viewed as a private indulgence, came to be seen as a public evil (12). Canada's *Narcotic Control Act* of 1961 settled on a maximum term of life imprisonment for opiate distributors, finally rejecting a proposed amendment that would have permitted imposition of the death penalty (11).

It was against this backdrop, then, that the province of British Columbia

*The authors would like to acknowledge the contributions of Bruce Alexander, Psychology, Simon Fraser University, and M. Douglas Anglin, Psychology, University of California, to the preparation of this article. The financial assistance of Simon Fraser University's Steel Fund is also appreciated. Early stages of this work were funded by the Department of Justice, Canada, through a contract with the Centre of Criminology, University of Toronto. The Department of Justice is not held responsible for the views expressed here.

Reprinted by permission from the *Canadian Journal of Criminology, 27*, no. 2 (1985): 195–208. Copyright 1985 by the Canadian Criminal Justice Association.

sent forward Bill 18 (5), a legislative initiative designed to permit the coerced confinement and treatment of opiate dependents.

THE RISE AND FALL OF COERCED TREATMENT:
THE POLITICAL ECONOMY OF BILL 18

In August of 1977, British Columbia's Social Credit government announced a compulsory treatment programme for the province's "addicts," noting that, "The scheme, which has full cabinet approval, will require new health legislation and will emphasize treatment of the addict as a sick person needing help rather than as a criminal" (6). The then Minister of Health, Robert McClelland, was suggesting that individuals in a state of "narcotic dependency" could be properly deprived of liberty for the purpose of treatment.

The Minister contended that there was an economic rationale for compulsory treatment. He noted, "The situation in the province of British Columbia has become intolerable when we consider availability and demand for illicit heroin, and the astronomical costs of the criminal justice system and to the business community. The purpose of this plan is to bring forward a treatment and community care program for the heroin user in B.C. which will have a major impact directly on demand, and subsequently on the supply and cost factors" (6).

The government's plan was indeed a bold innovation, but one fraught with difficulties from the outset. The programme was to cost approximately 13 million dollars a year to operate; no evidence could be led to suggest the potential of economic benefits that would offset the costs to be incurred. The Minister had argued that, "The law enforcement authorities, at current strengths and capabilities, are beginning to lose ground in their efforts to further reduce the importation and distribution of heroin." Again, the best empirical evidence available was not supportive. Data compiled by the Bureau of Dangerous Drugs indicate that British Columbia convictions relating to heroin declined in 1977 to 385 from a total of 445 in 1976 (9). By 1982, in the absence of compulsory treatment, the number of convictions in the province had dropped to 107. While these numbers are not entirely reliable reflections of the extent of heroin use over time, the British Columbia government had no evidence in 1977 to suggest increased difficulty in fighting the importation and distribution of heroin: the case for extraordinary resources could not really be made out.

Conviction statistics are, however, problematic in many respects. In the case of heroin possession and distribution, an observed decline, 1979–1982, is complemented by an observed increase in armed robberies of pharmacies in British Columbia, from a total of nine, in 1979, to 36 in 1982. While a decline in heroin convictions might be indicative of decreasing rates of heroin use, it presents us with a limited vision of the costs and benefits of criminal control, as now practised. A more effective programme of heroin control could be driving desperate opiate dependents towards opiate and opiate-like pharmaceuticals, resident in the province's pharmacies.

Further, the Department of National Health and Welfare reports that in British Columbia in 1982, there were 2,400 men and 968 women classified as "known users" of heroin (6). It would appear that criminal convictions represent a small fraction of total use.

It is difficult to document the intentions underlying the government's decision to establish compulsory treatment for opiate dependents. Japan's "hard-line" approach to heroin apparently impressed the Ministry; Britain's programmes of opiate maintenance apparently did not sway the Minister or the Cabinet (26). The press release of August 1977 noted, "the proposed scheme means British Columbia has decided that proposals to legalize heroin generally or as a treatment vehicle are 'completely unrealistic' " (6).

In April of 1977, the government had released the document on which the *Heroin Treatment Act* of 1978 would ultimately be based (7). *A Plan for the Treatment and Rehabilitation of Heroin Users in British Columbia* was a 75-page report prepared for the Minister of Health by the province's Alcohol and Drug Commission. The ideological impetus for the programme appeared to rest on a rather shaky foundation.

A scant two pages were devoted to setting out the philosophy underpinning the plan. There were many assertions put forward, but little argument was led in support of the assertions made. The document noted, "No solution to the problem of heroin will be found if our society accepts that an intolerable situation can be dealt with by legalizing the substance in question." The arguments against some form of legitimation of heroin use were not forthcoming; the arguments in favour were similarly not raised.

The government of British Columbia was perhaps very much unprepared for the antagonism that greeted the notion of coerced·treatment. The British Columbia Civil Liberties Association immediately expressed opposition to the project, ultimately supporting one individual's legal challenge to the constitutionality of the legislation. The federal government expressed doubts about jailing addicts (27), and was reluctant to commit itself to the scheme. The nation's leading newspaper, the Toronto *Globe and Mail*, termed the heroin plan "odious" (25). Members of the British Columbia bar expressed doubts about the plan's protection of civil rights.

It was amid some controversy, then, that the Bill was introduced in May of 1978. Section 3 of the proposed *Act* created professional evaluation panels that would determine whether a given individual would be best committed for treatment for up to six consecutive months (5). Individuals suspected by police of having "a dependency on a narcotic" would be compelled to attend at an "area co-ordinating centre" for the purpose of ascertaining the best course of treatment for their dependency. The definition of "narcotic" was essentially limited to opium, its derivatives, and synthetics. "Dependency" was defined as, "in relation to a narcotic, a state of psychic or physical dependence, or both, on a narcotic following its use on a periodic or continuous basis" (s. 1). The definition of narcotic dependency appeared to leave open the possibility that an occasional user of heroin could be committed for "treatment."

The public response to Bill 18 was immediate. Though the legislation had its supporters, its detractors appeared to be greater in number and more vociferous. The former chairman of the provincial Alcohol and Drug Commission argued at a public meeting in June, "There is an irony in the matter of Bill 18. Those who are backing the bill, and who view themselves as 'getting tough' on this problem, are in fact guilty of the worst form of patronizing, and (even worse than that) they are guilty of partially contributing to the continued irresponsibility of drug users. They are treating them as though they cannot be responsible for their own behaviour" (8, p. 16). The province's major newspapers, the *Sun* and the *Province*, ran headlines that were staunchly critical of the government's bill — "Heroin act unfit for free nation," "Addict's treatment plan made to look ludicrous," "Guilty until proven innocent" (27, 28). By year's end in 1978, the constitutionality of Bill 18 was being challenged in British Columbia's Supreme Court. A suburban housewife by the name of Brenda Schneider argued that her civil rights would be jeopardized by the passage of this legislative initiative. A woman dependent on an oral use of methadone provided by the province, she saw the legislation as having the potential to take her from her two children and her husband of 14 years; Brenda Schneider feared the possibility of a sudden commitment.

The following year, 1979, saw the beginning of the end of compulsory treatment of opiate dependents in British Columbia. A centre designed to treat "narcotic dependency" opened in February, but without the power of compulsory detention. Opiate dependents used the new facility as an alternative to incarceration; the programme was apparently not generally perceived by its clients as an offering of therapeutic value but rather as the lesser of two evils. In early October, the British Columbia Supreme Court declared the province's *Heroin Treatment Act* to be unconstitutional; a headline in the *Vancouver Province* noted, "Compulsory heroin treatment looks doomed." Finally, Health Minister Robert McClelland was transferred to another ministry in a Cabinet shuffle; the new Minister, a perceived "moderate" by the name of Rafe Mair, slowly laid the notion of compulsory treatment to rest. By July of 1980, the new Minister would label the heroin treatment plan a failure (29).

In retrospect, it appears that there was simply too much opposition to the notion of compulsory treatment. The medical profession, the bar, and the B.C. Civil Liberties Association attacked Bill 18; the federal government gave lukewarm responses to British Columbia's initiative, expressing grave doubts about the sense of coerced abstinence; the emergence of a court challenge to the constitutionality of Bill 18 weakened the government's hand. It was finally the government itself, through the medium of its new Health

Minister, that called an end to the scheme. The government had had to admit that there was much hypocrisy in the economy of this legislative initiative. The Alcohol and Drug Commission of the province had doubled its budget and quadrupled its size with its new scheme (17). The funding of existing drug abuse programmes was to take a back seat to funding the plan for heroin treatment. It could not seriously be argued that the problem of opiate dependence provided greater health and social costs for British Columbians than did the problem of tobacco and alcohol dependence. As the former director of the heroin treatment programme noted in late 1981, "We were the rich kids on the block ... There was a real feeling, at best of tolerance and at worst of resentment and subversion" (17).

The director, Jack Altman, went on to conclude about his experience with Bill 18, "I think it would be very difficult, if not impossible, to implement a compulsory treatment system within North American society, or any society with a long history of democratic traditions. . . . For things which are effective, for example, the compulsory treatment of people with the plague, you're going to find, despite the civil rights arguments, fairly good public support. But when you're advocating compulsory treatment for a problem — I hesitate to say disease — that can't be as clearly or as effectively handled as an epidemic, then I think public support is going to be far less" (17).

THE EFFICACY OF COMPULSORY TREATMENT: THE EMPIRICAL EVIDENCE

Any discussion of the efficacy of compulsory treatment for drug "addiction" must necessarily come to terms with the difficulties inherent in attempts to define "success." Although a specified period of abstinence from the drug in question might intuitively suggest itself as the best index of programme utility, abstinence is, in fact, a very deceptive measure. The opiate-dependent individual who ultimately ceases his or her involvement with opiates typically moves on to another form of drug dependence. Stevenson's 1956 research survey in British Columbia informs us that alcohol abuse is a common lifestyle for those opiate dependents who are "successful" in their efforts to cease involvement with illicit drugs (24). In Singapore, where very harsh treatment of heroin has apparently led to marked decreases in rates of use, observers of the regime note, "It would be unrealistic to expect that other drug usage will not at least partially replace the heroin problem. . . . Statistical data are not available, but many of the former Singapore heroin addicts are thought to be substituting cannabis, barbiturates, and tranquilizers to some extent (14, pp. 18–19).

From the perspective of public health, such results give great cause for concern. It appears that even if compulsory treatment programmes reveal themselves as widely "successful," they cannot be seen to diminish, in any appreciable sense, the problem of substance abuse that exists in the jurisdiction under scrutiny. Indeed, given the physical devastation that alcohol abuse imposes, it might be argued that opiate dependence could be appropriately cast as the lesser of the two "evils" (3, 21, 26, 31).

And yet this phenomenon of displacement is only the tip of the iceberg; the haunting spectre of compulsory treatment provides us with a litany of embarrassments in its role as a vehicle for public policy. Rigorous scientific evaluations of the merits of specific treatment programmes are immensely difficult, almost impossible, to conduct; studies which conform to the conventional standards of experimental design simply do not exist.[2] Individual Canadians cannot be randomly assigned to compulsory treatment and to control groups and then compared; ethical standards fortunately preclude such arbitrary impositions upon individual freedom. More important, the interpretation of results of any kind is always, and would always be, problematic. The size of the programme effect that is observed could be seen by some as indicating that the costs of such an approach outweigh the benefits, and by others as evidence that the benefits of such programmes outweigh the costs. So too, results that are obtained within one particular setting and with one particular mode of intervention may not be replicated elsewhere. The social context for which compulsory treatment is planned is of great importance; research findings, like some wines, do not travel well.

Even before the data that do exist are systematically analyzed, the notion of compulsory treatment can be seen to have taken quite a drubbing. The onus for state intervention ought always to be placed on those who wish to intervene; the state ought to be able to lead evidence of the social benefits that will accrue from the imposition of treatment. The investment of capital typically proceeds on the informed assumption that returns will be forthcoming. In the case of British Columbia, 13 million dollars were essentially thrown to the wind. No sound evidence of the benefits to be obtained could be put forward; the possibility that dependents might simply alter their drug preferences was not even discussed.

The empirical evidence that does concern itself with the efficacy of compulsory treatment programmes is, nonetheless, substantial, both with respect to its scope and its methodologies. While the criticisms set out above certainly apply to this general body of work, there remain, nonetheless, many insights to be culled from careful analysis of the data.

The literature from Anglo-American jurisdictions is, not surprisingly, the most voluminous. Of central interest in such discussion is the evolution of "treatment" policy within Great Britain, the only English-speaking country in the world that permits the dispensing of heroin to opiate dependents. It is a policy that is in many senses under siege. As the director of a British Institute for Study of Drug Dependence has noted, "If one looks just at positive policies for the medical treatment of heroin addiction . . . then paradoxically it seems that Britain has on a very much shorter time scale adopted the same medical policies as the U.S. Rather than having anything to teach the U.S., perhaps we should be acknowledging that we have rather more slowly been learning the same lessons" (26, p. 171). The British are now regarded by law enforcement officials in both Canada and the United States as having embarked upon the foolhardy plan of maintaining opiate dependents, only to have later to confess to the folly of their earlier strategies.

Careful analysis of the "British experience" suggests that there is little, if any, evidence of an earlier foolhardiness. The genesis of Britain's "get-tough" approach with opiate dependents can be seen in the Brain II committee's final recommendations in 1965. A collection of leaders from the British medical establishment, the Brain Committee, urged new restrictions on the prescribing of drugs by general practitioners to opiate dependents, and the creation of special treatment units within designated hospitals. The effects of these changes, stimulated by a few over-prescribing doctors, have been far-reaching. In 1984, new opiate dependent patients in Britain are refused injectable heroin and are offered oral methadone and counselling. As one commentator has suggested, there is "evidence that the clinics are moving toward a patient society of two unequal classes: the established injectors, who get their prescriptions regularly, though in reduced dosages, and stay in regular attendance; and the new patients" (26, p. 211). The Chief Inspector of the Drug Branch at Britain's Home Office laments these changes. H. B. Spear notes, "We didn't need clinics. We needed a thousand doctors with one patient each ... In any event, we never asked for clinics. We simply wanted machinery to enable us to deal with the few grossly irresponsible prescribers.... I'd like to see the clinics go back to injectables. It's the street scene that is so much worse now" (26, p. 211).

Professor Arnold Trebach concludes about the changes in the British response to opiate dependence, 1965 to 1982,

> A group of well-intentioned doctors in the clinics, along with their staffs and with the support of the national medical leadership, have applied modern psychiatric principles to many drug abusers. A minority of the addict-patients were helped to develop lives free of drugs, a truly positive outcome. But even larger numbers of addicts, most of whom were dependent primarily on heroin, were repelled by these intellectual principles and soon found themselves purchasing drugs on the black market and intensifying their involvement in criminal subcultures. They went back to being street addicts in the worst sense. But this was not accomplished in the American style, whereby the police invaded the clinics and forced the doctors to stop prescribing drugs for their patients. Rather, it was done in a uniquely English style; the doctors drove the addicts into the arms of the police. (26, p. 219)

It cannot seriously be argued that the lesson of the British experience is that the maintenance of opiate dependents is an inherently flawed experiment. It might be more appropriate to suggest that certain members of the British medical establishment have been taken in by an ideology of coercing abstinence from opiates; clinic doctors have in a very real sense become agents of control, increasingly restricting their distribution of opiates to opiate dependents.

Over the past 25 years there have been many accounts of "the British experience," emanating from both sides of the Atlantic (2, 13, 32). Arnold Trebach's *The Heroin Solution* (26) appears to be both the most comprehensive and most historically current discussion of debates about the evolution of opiate control in the United Kingdom. Sympathetic to the plights of both doctors and addicts, Trebach is able to present a balanced view of the British process.

Opposition to the present structure of opiate control is very much apparent in Britain in 1982. As Professor Trebach notes, "I suspect that the sensible English medical profession will not persist long in its current path. A compromise must evolve soon. Indeed, a countermovement has already started" (26, p. 201). Professor Trebach laments, "In actual clinical situations many doctors are tempted to forcibly "treat" their patients by pushing them off heroin. . . . The result is that the addicts go back to their drugs with a vengeance, usually in greater torment and emotional pain from the frustrating experience of the forced treatment" (26, p. 203).

It is, at the least, clear that there is no consensus of opinion with respect to understanding Britain's response to the phenomenon of opiate dependence. However, British Columbia's Social Credit government emerged with a singular view of the English experience. Vancouver Police Chief Don Winterton, commissioned by the government to report on Britain's response, was unequivocal, if less than convincing, in putting forward his analysis. "There is very little support for heroin maintenance as a method of treatment at this time. The lack of support is based on actual experience," Chief Winterton stated (20). This understanding and the government's ultimate analysis of Britain's response to opiate dependents are, though disappointing, rather unsurprising. A singular view of the British experience could bolster the government's case for Bill 18; presentation of the complexity would only muddy the political waters.

Within the United States, academic literature does not paint a comforting picture of the wisdom of compulsory treatment of opiate dependents. Two major review essays, those of Petersen (18) and Brecher (3) express grave reservations about the social efficacy of such coercion. And Brill and Lieberman's *Authority and Addiction* (4) implies that it is often the absence of coercion that will yield the greatest reward as a response to the phenomenon of opiate dependence. The authors note, "the process of moving an addict from the condition of addiction to that of complete abstinence necessarily . . . requires a tolerance on the part of the rehabilitative agency for repeated relapses to the drugs, whether heroin or other" (4, p. 187). Petersen concludes that American experience with compulsory treatment of the narcotic addict in the community, whether in a parole, probation, or halfway house setting, is less than successful. None of these treatment modalities is dramatically effective in improving the adjustment of addict patients in these settings. Further, it is not established in existing studies that compulsory or authoritarian supervision in the community is more effective than other treatment modes (18).

And yet there are social contexts in which compulsory treatment can be measured as a success, at least in a relative context. McGlothlin suggests a 37 per cent one-year relapse rate among heroin dependents in Singapore, noting, "This is substantially lower than the rate experienced by most heroin treatment programs in the West." The Singapore programme, referred to positively by former B.C. Health Minister Robert McClelland, however, was not without a most significant flaw. McGlothlin (14, 15) has noted the possibility that heroin is simply being displaced by other drugs. It can again be suggested that opiate dependents are turning to other sources of consciousness alteration when faced with a punitive state response to opiate use. From the vantage point of public health, the reality of a displacement effect raises serious concern. It can be argued that alcohol abuse, a common response to the cessation of opiate dependence (24), does not represent a tangible progression (3). Indeed, the social and individual costs of coercing abstinence from opiates must be set fairly in the balance here.

The empirical evidence, blemished though it may be, is not on the side of compulsory treatment. It is not so much that compulsory treatment is by its very nature a contradiction in terms. One can imagine the sense of imposing treatment on those who might have syphilis or the plague; the issue of voluntariness would become irrelevant, subordinated for the greater social good. In the instant case, it is rather the social context into which compulsion is placed that is the basis of our concerns. It does not seem clear that heroin is an inherently contaminating substance; many psychologists appear to have rejected the notion that exposure to heroin redetermines dependence (1); they argue that opiate dependence is a coping mechanism, not triggered by the pharmacology of the given substance. A potent analgesic, heroin can relieve the pain that ordinary waking consciousness presents for some individuals. To the extent that we are honestly concerned with public health, coercion ought to be recognized here as inappropriate; evidence of the benefits of such forms of state intervention has not been forthcoming.

COMPULSORY TREATMENT:
THE QUESTION OF LEGALITY

In the context of Canada's courtrooms, the debate over compulsory treatment has manifested itself as a jurisdictional issue. In *Schneider* v. *The Queen* (22), all three levels of courts, the B.C. Supreme Court, B.C. Court of Appeal, and Supreme Court of Canada, considered the appropriateness of categorizing "narcotics" under the federal criminal law power. Section 91 of the *B.N.A.*

Act was in dispute; the wisdom of defining the legislation as properly provincial was correspondingly at issue.

And yet the reasoning of the judiciary is more complex than this. After hearing ten days of legal argument, Chief Justice McEachern suggested that there were essentially two branches of the case against legitimacy of the legislation in question. McEachern argued first that the effect of the *Hauser* (19) case has been to shift federal jurisdiction over "narcotics" from the criminal law power of s. 91 to the peace, order, and good government clause (22). Accordingly, the Chief Justice continues, "narcotics" must be cast as falling within the exclusive jurisdiction of the federal Parliament; this notion of exclusivity of federal power is arguably central to the subject matter of "narcotics," falling as it does under the general residuary power of the federal government. In this first branch of the case against legitimating the *Heroin Treatment Act*, McEachern sees the court as bound by the decision in *Hauser* to exclude provincial jurisdiction.

Yet there is a second and more fundamental attack on the legislation as colourable. McEachern suggests in his concluding remarks, "I have decided that the Heroin Treatment Act is indeed legislation in relation to Criminal Law. In substance, the Heroin Treatment Act creates a new crime of narcotic dependency which can arise lawfully by repeated use of prescription drugs, or after repeated offences against the Narcotic Control Act. Punishment is provided by way of detention and compulsory treatment" (22). Chief Justice McEachern has essentially concluded that the *Act* is best conceptualized, not as an addendum to the realm of public health, but as an addendum to the realm of criminal punishment.

This was not the view taken by the B.C. Court of Appeal, nor a unanimous Supreme Court of Canada. And yet little effort was taken by either Court to make the case for compulsory detention as a useful form of treatment. While both Justices Dickson and Estey agonize over the legal context of treatment and punishment, they give rather short shrift to the notion that B.C.'s compulsory treatment plan creates a new crime of narcotic dependency. Justice Dickson writes, "It is not an easy matter, I confess, to determine whether the Heroin Treatment Act is a valid provincial health law with what might be regarded as punitive features or whether the pith and substance of the Act is criminal law and therefore invalid. I think on balance however, it was open to the Court of Appeal of British Columbia to conclude, as it did" (22). Justice Estey adds, "Where treatment involves detention, the distinction between treatment and punishment is difficult particularly where in the individual case at some periods in time no other 'treatment' is administered. Punishment and treatment look very much alike in some circumstances. Here the Court of Appeal was satisfied, and I am in respectful agreement, that this is health legislation" (22). Chief Justice Laskin, however, appears to have little doubt about the categorization of the legislation as relating to public health. He simply asserts, "I am in agreement with Dickson, J. that in its thrust as public health legislation in the provinces . . . The Heroin Treatment Act, 1978, is intra vires" (22).

And yet Chief Justice Laskin mis-states the substance of Chief Justice McEachern's two-pronged argument against the validity of the *Act*. Laskin notes of the *Hauser* case, "It appears to be that case, in treating the Narcotic Control Act as an exercise of the federal residuary power to legislate for the peace, order and good government of Canada, that underpinned the reasons of McEachern, invalidating the present provincial Act" (22). While *Hauser* was clearly crucial to a part of Chief Justice McEachern's case against the validity of the *Act*, it was not determinative of the issue. McEachern notes, "it becomes necessary to consider the Plaintiff's second argument that, in any event, the Heroin Treatment Act is in substance legislation in relation to Criminal Law, and could only be enacted by Parliament. On this argument I have decided that the Heroin Treatment Act is indeed legislation in relation to Criminal Law." It appears, then, that McEachern's decision in *Schneider* did not find its sole "underpinning" in *Hauser*, as Chief Justice Laskin would suggest.

It is probably fair to say that the two appeal courts in *Schneider* failed to give a careful delineation of the reasoning that underlies a claim for treatment on the one hand, or punishment on the other. These courts appeared unwilling to look behind the stated intentions of the B.C. government's plan and to examine the reality of compulsory treatment in practice. As the legality of the government's initiative depends upon a constitutional categorization outside the realm of criminal law, the conceptual meaning that one attaches to the *Act* quite literally predetermines legitimacy. Opiate dependents in British Columbia perceived the imposition of the *Act* as a punitive kind of tyranny; they had little difficulty in giving conceptual meaning to the government's initiative (8).

It is perhaps the criminal law power that best forms the focus of any discussion concerning the legality of the *Heroin Treatment Act*. Insofar as the *Act* seeks to punish criminal conduct that has been heretofore unpunished, it does indeed create a new category of criminality with attendant sanctions. There has been, Supreme Court utterances to the contrary, a de facto de-centralization of the criminal law. The jurisdictional debate that closes ranks around the federal residuary power, the criminal law power, and a corresponding catalogue of provincial powers, only serves to mask the more fundamental process of extending definitions of criminality within the provincial realm.

This process of de-centralizing control of "narcotics" seems to be most clearly grasped, at least implicitly, by Chief Justice McEachern. He writes, "In my view, it is impossible to forecast all the various ways in which these two statutes may interact, and it may be that the conflict would not arise in the sense that compliance with one law might involve a breach of the other . . . but it is legislatively unsatisfactory to have both Parliament and one or more of the Legislatures formulating different programmes for the management of the same social problem." McFarlane, J.A. suggests that the *Heroin Treatment Act* in "its pith and substance" is enacted in relation to s. 92(16) of the *B.N.A. Act*, "Generally all Matters of a merely local or private Nature in the Province." While Justice McFarlane would not concede that the *Act* effectively decentralizes the criminal law, he nonetheless allows that certain country-wide social problems may properly have a uniquely provincial response. And yet it might be more appropriate to suggest that upholding the validity of the *Heroin Treatment Act* on the peg of s. 92(16) is merely to reconstitute criminal law's de-centralization by another name.

A recent M.A. thesis at the University of Toronto expresses similar kinds of doubts about the moral logic that underlies the legality of compulsory treatment for opiate dependence. Christopher Millard concluded, after an analysis of the legal issue of jurisdiction, "Treatment per se is obviously a health matter, yet the element of compulsion introduces a level of coercion normally associated with the criminal law or other federal legislation. In view of the problematic nature of coerced treatment from a medical standpoint, and the apparent elusiveness of addiction cures generally, detention for treatment suggests an essentially punitive orientation, with health being merely a secondary aim . . . the criminal law seems to be the most legitimate vehicle for compulsory treatment legislation" (16, p. 63). Millard goes on to argue that the legality of compulsory treatment is very much in question at the present time; the impact of the *Charter of Rights and Freedoms* is unknown. And further, Millard warns, "the Charter might indeed be a powerful challenge to either federal or provincial addiction treatment programmes. . . . The use of imprisonment as a veiled means of detention for treatment has already been rejected by the courts, and any departure from this position would again be subject to constitutional challenge under the Charter" (16, p. 66).

LEGITIMATION AND REPRESSION: THE LURE OF PARADOX

The future of compulsory treatment for opiate dependence is uncertain. While the Supreme Court of Canada has unanimously upheld the legality of British Columbia's initiative, there would appear to be many obstacles in the path of any policy implementation. The threat of a constitutional challenge under the *Charter* would loom as a real possibility; the political opposition to compulsory treatment remains intact. The social efficacy of such a costly programme cannot be demonstrated, and as the recently re-elected Social Credit government works on its promise of budgetary restraint, fiscal generosity is not likely to be forthcoming. In the short term, at least, compulsory treatment is a closed book in British Columbia.

And yet the ideological debate that underlies the issue of compulsory treatment will likely resurface in the future, albeit in somewhat altered form.

It is perhaps not surprising that both proponents and opponents of a state policy of coerced abstinence use similar concepts of legitimation in construction of justifications for the policy choices that they have made. It is said that the intention of British Columbia's compulsory treatment plan was to repress heroin use, in order that individuals would be free from the possibility of such dependence; it is the logic that underlies the industry of "narcotic" control — the selective prohibition of altered states of consciousness. The repression of certain psychoactive substances increases social freedom.

On the other hand, the logic of opponents of compulsory treatment is that such repression cannot be used to further the imperatives of freedom. Freedom from the repression of compulsory treatment in turn signals the possibility of a greater social freedom; there is no reason to believe that drug abuse and drug dependence will flourish in such a context.

And yet the structure of this argument requires further explication. It can be shown that the availability of a given drug does not predetermine individual and collective patterns of use. The availability and the relatively low cost of a plethora of pharmaceuticals have not been sufficient to produce markets that even approach the market of the more costly and more heavily policed marijuana.

It is not the pharmacology of a given substance that determines patterns of drug use and abuse. While the physical consequences of withdrawal from dependence vary with respect to both licit and illicit drugs, the given substance itself is best not understood as the embodiment of the social problem of drug abuse (1). It is not the drug but our relationship with it that is at issue.

The continuing injection of heroin can be understood as a statement of alienation, be it existential or material, from ordinary waking consciousness. In this context, the notion of coercing abstinence appears an ill-considered and repressive policy. To the pain that the opiates often seek to calm is added the pain of imprisonment. We would do well here to remind ourselves of the Le Dain Commission's comments regarding compulsory treatment, comments still appropriate. The Commissioners write,

> The more we attempt to relate compulsory treatment to the criminal law power the more we are obliged to regard it as what many of its critics contend it is—imprisonment under another name. (10, pp. 927–28)

NOTES

1. Personal conversations with prisoners at Mission Penitentiary, Mission, B.C.—with individuals who are both tobacco and opiate dependent—revealed no clear consensus as to the substance that was perceived to be

most productive of dependence. Discussions with individuals outside prison walls have yielded similar findings.
2. B. K. Alexander and P. F. Hadaway (1) have recently described the scholarly literature on opiate addiction as "chaotic and bewildering" and suggest that for "scientific investigation to become productive, the relevant factors eventually must be drawn into an integrative orientation or paradigm rather than tossed into a disorganized heap, from which understanding is expected to arise by some kind of spontaneous combustion. The failure to develop an integrative orientation has left us with a literature that, taken as a whole, seems more an obstacle than an aid to understanding" (1, p. 378).

REFERENCES

1. Alexander, B. K., and Hadaway, P. F. Opiate addiction: The case for an adaptive orientation. *Psychological Bulletin, 92*:367–81 (1982).
2. Bean, P. *The Social Control of Drugs*. Law in Society Series. London: Martin Robertson, 1975.
3. Brecher, E. M., and the Editors of Consumer Reports. *Licit and Illicit Drugs*. Boston: Little, Brown, 1972.
4. Brill, L., and Lieberman, L. *Authority and Addiction*. Boston: Little, Brown, 1969.
5. British Columbia. *Statutes. Heroin Treatment Act*, s.b.c. 1978, c. 24.
6. British Columbia. Ministry of Health. News release, August 3, 1977.
7. British Columbia. Ministry of Health. *A Plan for the Treatment and Rehabilitation of Heroin Users in British Columbia*. April, 1977.
8. Brunke, M. *Some Implications of the Heroin Treatment Act*. Health and Welfare Canada, Non-Medical Use of Drugs Directorate. Ottawa, June, 1978.
9. Bureau of Dangerous Drugs. Health Protection Branch, Department of National Health and Welfare. *Drug Users and Convictions Statistics, 1976–1982*. Ottawa.
10. Canada. Commission of Inquiry into the Non-Medical Use of Drugs. *Final Report*. Ottawa: Information Canada, 1973.
11. Canada. House of Commons. *Debates*. 1961.
12. Green, M. A history of Canadian narcotic control: The formative years. *University of Toronto Faculty of Law Review, 37*:42–79 (1979).
13. Judson, H. *Heroin Addiction in Britain*. New York: Harcourt Brace Jovanovich, 1973.
14. McGlothlin, W. H. Compulsory treatment of opiate addiction in Southeast Asia. Paper presented to a workshop on compulsory treatment of opiate addiction, November 29–30, 1979, Bethesda, Maryland.

15. McGlothlin, W. H., Anglin, M. D., and Wilson, B. D. *An Evaluation of the California Civil Addict Program.* Department of Health, Education and Welfare; Public Health Service; Alcohol, Drug Abuse and Mental Health Administration; NIDA. DHEW pub. no. (ADM) 78–558. Washington, D.C.: U.S. Government Printing Office, 1977.
16. Millard, C. An assessment of the legal implications of compulsory treatment programmes for drug addicts in Canada. Unpublished M.A. thesis, Centre of Criminology, University of Toronto, 1982.
17. Padmore, T. A retrospective on compulsory treatment. *The Journal*: 1980, 16.
18. Petersen, D. M. Some reflections on compulsory treatment of addiction. In: Inciardi, I., and Chambers, C. (eds.). *Drugs and the Criminal Justice System*,143–169. Beverly Hills, Calif.: Sage, 1974.
19. *R. v. Hauser et al.*, [1979] 1 S.C.R. 984, 46 C.C.C. (2d) 481, 98 D.L.R. (3d) 192.
20. Russell, J., and McNicoll, A. Evolution of the British approach to narcotic dependency. Unpublished paper, British Columbia Alcohol and Drug Commission, 1978.
21. Schlaadt, R., and Shannon, P. *Drugs of Choice.* Englewood Cliffs, N.J.: Prentice-Hall, 1982.
22. *Schneider* v. *The Queen* (1980), 49 C.C.C. (2d) 129, 103 D.L.R. (3d) 29 (B.C. S.C.). Reversed [1981] 1 W.W.R. 27, 52 C.C.C. (2d) 321, 111 D.L.R. (3d) 632 (B.C. C.A.). Affirmed [1982] 6 W.W.R. 673, 22 B.C.L.R. 363, 68 C.C.C. (2d) 449 (S.C.C.).
23. *Statutes of Canada.*
    a. *The Opium and Narcotic Drug Act,* S.C. 1908, c. 50.
    b. *The Narcotic Control Act,* S.C. 1961, c. 35.
24. Stevenson, G. H. *Drug Addiction in British Columbia: A Research Survey.* Vancouver, B.C.: University of British Columbia, 1956.
25. *The Globe and Mail.* Editorial. March 23, 1978, 5.
26. Trebach, A. *The Heroin Solution.* New Haven: Yale University Press, 1982.
27. *The Vancouver Province.* August 5, 1977, 1; June 1, 1978, 1.
28. *The Vancouver Sun.* June 3, 1978, 1.
29. *The Victoria Daily Colonist.* July 16, 1980, 1.
30. Webster, C. D. Compulsory treatment of drug addiction: A selective review of the scientific literature. Unpublished manuscript prepared for the Ministry of Justice, Ottawa, 1982.
31. Weil, A. *The Natural Mind.* Boston: Houghton-Mifflin, 1972.
32. Zinberg, N., and Robertson, W. *Drugs and the Public.* New York: Simon and Schuster, 1972.

25

A Justice-based Argument for the Uniform Regulation of Psychoactive Drugs*

CHESTER N. MITCHELL

INTRODUCTION

Over a century ago, Anglo-American laws tolerated prostitution and regulated, for the most part, the nuisance aspects of commercial sex. Then, following various scandals concerning venereal disease, child prostitution, and "white slavery," legislators bowed to pressure exerted by the self-righteous and enacted increasingly Draconian anti-prostitution measures throughout the nineteenth century (108). Often these measures compelled the women involved to submit to medical controls, a strategy still supported by those who would medicalize prostitution (70, 144). A similar wave of intolerance and medical imperialism altered the legal status of drugs and drug users during the same period (29).[1] By 1847, drunkenness had been labelled a "disease of the mind," the American Society for the Promotion of Temperance had been established and the State of New York had for two years banned the public sale of liquor. American lawmakers then moved federally to prohibit non-medical alcohol use, heroin production, and marijuana cultivation (162). By 1921, cigarettes were illegal in 14 states and they remain illegal to those "under age" in 47 states (19, 39, 147). While the prohibition of alcohol and tobacco was largely abandoned through the 1920s, the zealous criminalization of other drug use was continued. This crusade prospered because it served certain purposes, none of which related to justice or public protection. In general disregard for principles of both justice and scientific validity, modern drug control legislation was founded on class prejudice, medical self-interest, cultural chauvinism, racist bigotry, and political scapegoating (15, 27).

This paper is concerned with the regulation of psychoactive or psychotropic drugs. Familiar psychoactives include caffeine, cocaine, alcohol, nicotine, morphine, heroin, mescaline, and diazepam (Valium). Psychoactive substances alter mood by affecting the user's central nervous system, and may act as sleep aids, tranquillizers, or stimulants (61). These drugs are

---

*Reprinted from the *McGill Law Journal 31*, no. 2 (1986): 212–63, with revisions by the author and with revision of the footnote style to be consistent with the format of this book. By permission.

presently segregated into a number of complex, overlapping legal categories. However, according to the scientific evidence detailed below, psychoactives belong to a single, cohesive class and, despite important points of diversity, share the same basic characteristics. That is to say, every psychoactive tends to be habit forming, health impairing, and capable of being used recreationally or medicinally as a symptom reliever (81).

Fairness requires that if all psychoactives are essentially equivalent, they should be assigned to a single regulatory system. There are five possible systems to choose from: criminal law prohibition, medical prescription, rationing, tax-licensing and the free market. In deciding which of these systems would be preferable as a universal plan, I will speculate on which restraints on their own drug use individuals would accept in order to protect themselves from either the drug use of others or the effects of their own drug consumption. Once the drug control question is framed so as to take fairness seriously, reliance on either criminal law or medical controls will be shown to be untenable.

Since selective prohibition and prescription policies now dominate drug regulation, a justice-based reform argument faces two major challenges: the decriminalization of illicit psychoactives and the demedicalization of prescription psychoactives. Legal scholars have focused on the issue of decriminalization, but many decriminalizers only go so far as to advocate the conversion of illicit drugs into quasi-medical substances and the transformation of criminal users into "patients" (see 14, 25, 91, 157). This compromise policy merely shifts drugs and drug users from the control of one inappropriate system to another. It is ill-conceived because drug use is not directly a medical concern. To pretend otherwise is to disguise a legal, ethical, and political problem as a purely technical matter best left to the medical profession (161). This does not imply that technical pharmacological data should be ignored, merely that interpretations of such data should not be accepted on faith alone. For example, it is often assumed uncritically that all new psychoactives should be marked as "medicines" rather than as competitors to alcohol and tobacco (16, 42, 84). It is also assumed that legal classifications reflect major and valid differences between the drugs classified (see 10).

Richard Blum predicts that legal academics in the drug field will assign the fewest drugs to extreme controls and rely least on criminal law sanctions (10). This article bears out Blum's forecast in so far as no drugs are assigned to criminal law or extremist controls. I recommend instead a public law system employing tax disincentives designed to duplicate many of the features of a collective tort action against those responsible for generating drug-related damages. Mild but universal sanctions applied to all drug use will better protect society than extreme penalties applied rarely, haphazardly and unfairly against minority drug use.

THE LEGAL AND SCIENTIFIC CLASSIFICATION OF DRUGS

Divergent Legal Classifications

The industrial nations classify drugs in similar ways, modelled primarily on the American example (82, 87, 175). The central division is between medical and non-medical psychoactives. Non-medical or secular drugs are freely available, like caffeine, or are prohibited to minors and subject to a variety of tax-licensing measures, as is the case with alcohol and tobacco. Use of these three psychoactives constitutes most of the consumption of mood altering substances (164, 173). The less important drugs, in terms of per capita usage, are classified as medicines. The pertinent legislation in Canada is found at the federal level in the *Food and Drugs Act* (159d, and see, generally, 150), the *Narcotic Control Act* (159e), and the *Tobacco Restraint Act* (159f), and at the provincial level, in statutes like Ontario's *Liquor Control Act* (125b).

Medical drugs fall into a confusing array of legal cubbyholes. Some psychoactives are found among the over-the-counter (OTC) preparations and may be purchased without physician approval.[2] Many other psychoactives fall under the general medical heading as available by prescription only.[3] In addition, there exist special status substances. So-called "narcotics," including morphine and cannabis, and "controlled drugs" like methaqualone, may be prescribed but under onerous conditions (120, c. 1041, s. 53). Amphetamine and other "designated drugs" can be prescribed, but only for certain conditions such as narcolepsy. Methadone, the sanctioned heroin substitute, is in a class by itself since its prescription requires approval from the Minister of Health and Welfare (49, G.04.001(4)(a)(i)). "Restricted drugs" such as psilocybin and LSD are available only to persons authorized by regulation (49, J.01.002; 159e, ss. 41, 45; 150). Thalidomide and certain combination products cannot be prescribed under any conditions. Possession and use of medical psychoactives outside approved channels normally carries the risk of minor-to-severe criminal law penalties and, in the case of physicians, the possible loss of their licences to practice (159d, s. 26; 159e, ss. 3–6).

Critics charge that drug classification laws were not well reasoned, well founded, or widely discussed before their enactment (19, 79, 91). The central inconsistency in every legal classification scheme is the cross-category appearance of different members of the same drug group. Sedative-hypnotics like alcohol, diazepam, and the barbiturates occupy three quite distinct legal categories. The same is true for stimulants such as caffeine, theobromine, amphetamine, and cocaine (148). On the proper legal classification of cannabis in particular, the Le Dain Commission reported that

> Cannabis has ... characteristics in common with a wide variety of drugs including alcohol, LSD and mescaline, nitrous oxide, amphetamines, atropine, opiate narcotics, barbiturates and the minor and major tranquilizers. ... [C]annabis has

been shown to have stimulant, sedative, analgesic and psychedelic effects (24, p. 16).

Since cannabis resembles drugs which belong to different legal categories, there is no compelling rational reason to classify it one way or another. Given this open-ended discretion, lawmakers have always been free to classify cannabis as they please.[4]

Pharmaceutical categorizations do not solve the inconsistency in legal classifications. Most pharmaceutical research is commercial, specific, and designed to meet regulatory requirements. Firms test new chemicals in narrow circumstances with a view toward particular uses (75, 89). Specificity of drug action is desired in medical practice and specificity is promoted even when the drug in question has numerous other uses and effects.[5] As a new chemical, THC, the active ingredient in *cannabis sativa*, would probably be tested, approved, and marketed strictly for treatment of glaucoma or as an anti-nausea agent for cancer chemotherapy cases (140). A cannabis based drug, marketed under a brand name such as "Cervil" or "Canab," could be prescribed and ingested with neither physician nor patient suspecting that the medicine was connected with an illicit substance of ill repute (140).

The dozens of apparently precise pharmaceutical categories falsely imply that psychoactives have *only* specific effects and constitute specialized weapons in the arsenal of the well-equipped physician (28). Specificity is of value in medicine and medical classification schemes are too narrow, exclusionary, and misleading for legal purposes. A legal classification scheme requires instead the broadest coverage possible. Laws must take account not only of what a drug now happens to be used for but also of what it could be used for. It would be foolish to approve cannabis for glaucoma treatment or alcohol as a sedative while ignoring the euphoriant and recreational potential of these drugs.

Convergent Scientific Classification

Psychoactive drugs differ, but their differences are less important than their similarities. Unlike politicians, scientists increasingly characterize mood-altering drugs as a single class of substances sharing distinctive similarities regarding mode of action, multi-purpose effects, health impairment, and habit formation. Although no drug's complete and precise mechanisms of action are known (23, 27, 134), it is apparent that psychoactives do not provide nutrients or necessary trace elements, nor do they heal human tissue. Instead, drugs trigger effects by disrupting the organism's biochemistry (58, 134). Through disruption, drugs can temporarily alleviate pain, hunger, or fatigue or overcome boredom, anxiety, or irritability. With varying degrees of success, any psychoactive can serve as symptom reliever, social facilitator, or ceremonial substance. Alcohol is as medical as the prescribed sedatives and these, in turn, can be as intoxicating and recreational as alcohol (36, 61, 78, 82, 97, 164, 179). Broad equivalence is similarly noted among the opiates[6] (78, 139, 142) and the stimulants (26, 139). A significant group of commentators submit that medical psychoactives, illicit drugs, and recreational drugs are comparable and equivalent (64, 92, 106, 139, 162).

All psychoactives appear to be health impairing with damage depending on dosage, duration of use, quality of drug, method of ingestion, condition of user, and type of drug. All psychoactives are potentially dangerous drugs, especially for the most vulnerable users—youngsters, adolescents, and the unborn (134). Unfortunately, assessing the health impact of drug use is impeded by biases which exaggerate illicit drug dangers while downplaying the threat from medical and recreational psychoactives[7] (5, 26, 50, 51, 71, 73, 110, 140, 155). Accurate assessment is also hindered by lack of broad-based, long term comparative studies. Currently recognized "safe" levels of drug intake may well prove to be founded on insensitive or incomplete data.

Finally, every drug capable of triggering pleasant or satisfying effects will be habit forming (78, 134). Actually, any ready source of satisfaction, be it television, gambling, or drugs, can become the focus of psychological dependence or fixation. But in addition, drug use can also lead to physical dependency of various types (44, 67, 168). Addiction is often made the centre point of the drug control debates but habit formation itself is a neutral concept. Drug use is a concern because it is harmful; drug dependency merely compounds that harm. Illicit drugs are no more or less addicting than medical or social drugs (26, 33, 51, 61, 66, 76, 106, 110). Furthermore, the compulsiveness of drug addiction in general has been improperly exaggerated. Even heavy drug users exhibit far more flexibility than proponents of the "disease model" anticipated (7, 44, 61, 81, 106, 141, 145).

DRUG CONTROL AND PRINCIPLES OF JUSTICE

Justification

Justifiable coercive state measures against drug use depend upon two prerequisites: first, that the use of drugs generates real defensive needs and second, that self-help measures and private law remedies provide insufficient self-defence, thus forcing recourse to public law solution (124).

Drug use evidently does create significant defensive needs. In economic terms, drug users impose costs on third parties. Examples of direct drug-related externalities include litter, smoke damage, fires, and a general increase in accidents, errors, and overall social risk (113). The bulk of drug-related costs are borne by users themselves in the form of ill health, incapacity, and shorter life (44). This self-harm element is not a direct component of harm to others. Suicide is not even broadly comparable to murder. Nonetheless, self-harm is rarely pure or isolated. Self-harm does hurt others; the degree and range of harm depend on cost-spreading techniques and social inter-dependence. In a welfare-medicare state, the individual's health is a public issue, as citizens come to realize that their neighbour's drug use, ill health, absenteeism, and lower productivity increase their taxes, costs, and insurance premiums (see 90).

Even if drug-related harms do merit a self-defence response, one must still determine whether public law measures are called for. Informal social restraints are all that primitive societies require in the way of drug controls (105). Similarly, an important anti-smoking mechanism in Western culture is the perception that smoking is no longer intelligent, attractive, or stylish (21). However, while smoking is going out of style, since 1945, alcohol has regained some of its former popularity (103). Informal controls have also failed to cope well with the rapid growth in availability of new and exotic psychoactives. Alcohol's introduction devastated many cultures unprepared for its attractions. Likewise, Western culture was unprepared for the hundreds of new psy-choactive drugs introduced in recent decades. The social practices and atti-tudes limiting use of alcohol, tobacco, coffee, and symptom relievers like opium could not adapt rapidly enough to deal with the new substances (77).

A social control failure does not in itself justify a public law response. An intermediate position based on private law also exists. Drug users commit torts, or civil wrongs, in imposing harm on others. The injured persons could thus initiate private actions against the drug-using defendants. For example, children might sue their drug-using parents for negligence in causing their birth defects. Other drug-related harms might be legally categorized as battery or nuisance.[8]

Tort law, however, is ill-suited in practice to counteract most types of drug-related harm. Most drug-related harm to others is minor, causally un-certain, and spread over a large, indeterminate plaintiff class (52, 138, 170). Transaction costs severely hamper the effective collectivization of small, broad-based interests. Civil procedure is often hostile to collective actions.[9] And even when a class action is launched and a favourable judgment won, a major portion of the award of damages will go toward legal costs (3). The more massive the action, the less the plaintiffs' and attorneys' interests correspond. Collective actions become a hybrid substitute for purely public law (149).

Other problems with a private law response should be noted (130). Prevention of harm is a superior goal to after-injury compensation but tort law is designed to compensate. Civil courts are not inclined or equipped to enforce complicated injunctive remedies. Tort law enforcement necessarily depends on the vagaries of private initiative and is thus unreliable. Even when a single wrong is suffered by an identifiable plaintiff, public ignorance, costs, and attitudes seriously limit recourse to tort law solution (11, 88). Expanding public law has been a justifiable response to tort law's failure to provide adequate deterrence. The incentive that propels tort actions is compensation; deterrence is an optional side-effect. The opposite is true of public law.

Deterrence is the primary goal of criminal law while compensation to the victim is optional.

Since private law fails to deter drug harms adequately, a public law response is justified. However, such a response need not necessarily be modelled on the criminal law.

Proportionality

State coercion is justified solely on the basis of an unmet, bona fide need for collective defense; therefore, the degree of coercion employed must be proportional to the harm defended against (22). Extreme harms, like homicide, call for severe responses whereas minute dangers, like illegal parking, merely justify the mildest legal restraints. The ethical demand for proportional punishment is quite obvious, yet the rule is flaunted by modern drug control legislation.

Three basic methods exist for determining the relative degree of punishment a given wrongdoing deserves. The standard method is to measure the amount of harm caused. Most drug-related harm is minor and comparable to general, chronic nuisances like littering and pollution. Such harms are on a different scale from the severe, acute losses caused by sexual assault, murder, or robbery (117). Drug use does not fit the traditional criminal law model. Drug users do not consume drugs to harm others. The harm to others is usually minor and results indirectly from self-harm. Sedative-hypnotic use, especially alcohol use, increases the probability that the drug user will engage in anti-social acts. We are justified in punishing this wilful creation of risk but this process must be separated from the serious harms that some inebriates commit. Violent crimes are often perpetrated by alcohol-impaired offenders, but the vast majority of alcohol users do not commit violent crimes (6; see also 48). The law should punish only the harm that necessarily flows from acts or attempted acts. What necessarily flows from mass drug use are higher third-party costs, public nuisances, and increased social risk.

When drug consumers under the influence cause serious harm the criminal law should punish that harm alone, not the drug use. Alcohol does not cause murder. Alcohol use, even excessive use, is common. Murder is rare. The criminal law treatment of murder should not be contingent on the presence or absence of drug use. Self-induced drug impairment should rarely serve as even a partial excuse (115). Conversely, drug use should not amplify criminal penalties. By this analysis, statutes that criminalize impaired driving are unethical. An inebriated tavern patron may stagger home in a belligerent mood and kill her spouse but this outcome is such a remote possibility that we do not charge her preventively with being "drunk and dangerous." Yet this is what the law does if the inebriate assumes control of a motor vehicle. Millions of people drive after consuming drugs. The likelihood of any one of those drivers causing serious damage is low although the risk is higher than for non-drugged drivers. All drug-using drivers act in a mildly antisocial manner; some actually drive dangerously and cause severe harm. In many cases where impaired driving charges are laid the driver will in fact have been engaged in dangerous driving but the two offences are different. Dangerous driving is not predictive, nor is it related to the driver's condition. It focuses properly on actual driving behaviour.

Moving to proportionate penalties against drug use will disturb those whose drug use is encouraged or subsidized by the present system. Supporters of criminalization will be displeased as well since their programme is premised on the assumption that use of illicit drugs causes tremendous harm comparable to the consequences of war or plague. Here the test for proportionality is the degree of fear engendered rather than the actual harm caused. Such a test is likely to be unethical since a subjective fear of drugs need not be realistic or fair. Those who fear illicit drug use err in three major respects. First, they attribute severe harm, like murder or robbery, to the drug rather than to the drug-using criminal. Second, they observe the extensive harms caused by criminal prohibitions of drug use and mistakenly blame those harms on the drugs (135). Third, they ignore evidence indicating that illicit drugs are no more harmful than licit or medical psychoactives. The much vilified opiates, for example, are less inherently criminogenic than alcohol (160).

A third method of determining the deserved punishment is the forced-choice analysis (38). Here respondents are directed to choose the lesser of two harms. People would be asked, as an example, whether they would prefer either being offered a chance to buy heroin or being compelled at gunpoint to permit their leg to be crushed. If most people prefer the first choice, we may safely conclude that it should be punished less severely than the second. Contrast this method with the usual survey questionnaire designed to elicit the public's punitive attitudes toward drug use. These surveys normally employ a costless, noncomparative approach by asking, for example: "Do you favour longer prison terms for heroin traffickers?" A "yes" answer to such a question costs the respondent nothing. In contrast, the forced-choice process imposes a type of pricing mechanism. In the example above, a vote for severe penalties against heroin sellers would hypothetically cost a crushed leg. Given such a choice, legislators would immediately retract current laws subjecting heroin traders to life imprisonment.

I suspect that very few people would prefer any physical harm to the opportunity to participate in any of the "victimless crimes." Even lesser harms, like being robbed of ten dollars, would not be chosen, in preference to being offered heroin. That choice is reasonable since in itself selling heroin causes no harm. Consider then the choice between having one's friend, colleague, relative, or neighbour use psychoactive X or being robbed of ten dollars. Most people would likely prefer the first source of harm except where the consumer of the alcohol, antihistamine, or cannabis is their own child. Since in many situations people are indifferent to their neighbour's drug use, I would predict that there are non-criminal harms that would be ranked as more disturbing than drug use. Examples of the nuisances that neighbours inflict on others that might be so ranked include burning garbage outside, keeping barking dogs, leaving grounds unattended, racing motor vehicles, or being rude. The results of a forced-choice analysis should demonstrate that the drug use of others is on a par with nuisances that impose a level of harm far below the threshold needed to justify criminal law penalties.

Fairness

Justified and proportional legal restrictions against drug use must also be fair. Apologists for selective enforcement argue that if we choose to punish A but not B for the same offence, that is not an injustice to A since A deserves punishment independently of what befalls B. K. C. Davis correctly responds that "if equality of treatment is one ingredient of justice, one cannot know whether penalizing A is just without looking at B's case—and C's and D's" (37, p. 170). Therefore, individuals should have constitutional recourse to defend against criminal charges and penalties on grounds of systematic or selective non-enforcement. Similarly, it is unjust to assign alcohol to a given regulatory scheme if nicotine, caffeine, cannabis, and other psychoactives are not also included. This does not imply that every psychoactive would be treated identically any more than every offence in the criminal law system is punished identically. A thorough fairness argument would expand to include non-drug equivalents as well—what Marks calls the "social psychoactives" (106).

Fairness plays a central role in contract theories of justice. Since experience shows that the fairest contracts are those negotiated by equally resourceful parties, it is arguable that the best recipe for deriving fair laws is to put legal contractors into the same position. John Rawls achieves equality theoretically by placing his "original contractors" behind a "veil of ignorance" (131). Legislators devising drug laws from the original position would be apprised of all the historical and scientific information about psychoactive drugs, but they would be ignorant of their own preferences and social position. They would not know, for example, whether they were cocaine importers, tobacco addicts, brewers, college students, marijuana plantation owners, physicians, or law enforcers. Under such constraints, these legislators would not re-invent current drug laws because those laws reflect the unjust exploitation of social power and majoritarian interests.

In the Rawlsian ideal, a legal system should duplicate the results of a voluntary agreement between unbiased and equal contractors. Legal equality and fairness apply to drug users in two respects: equivalent treatment for users of similar substances and equivalence between drug users and persons engaged in equally harmful but non-drug-using behaviours. Systematic equality for drug users means that all psychoactives should be subject to the same uniform control system. Before considering which of the five possible control models is most suitable, this chapter will first examine the justice-based arguments of certain other drug control reformers.

A COMPARATIVE JUSTICE ANALYSIS

Taking Human Rights Semi-seriously

David Richards rests his case for drug law reform on the rights-based approaches of Kant, Rawls, and Gewirth (135). He dismisses the utilitarian framework and criticizes other reformers for relying strictly on a cost-benefit analysis. Richards admits that current drug laws are wasteful and ineffective but he asserts that it is more important to argue that criminalizing drug use violates human rights (136).

Richards rejects prohibition because it fails the test for proportionality. He demonstrates that the reputed criminality of illicit drug users is ridiculously exaggerated, that habituation is miscast as enslavement, and that any degree of illicit use is falsely portrayed as serious abuse. In short, the harm caused by illegal drugs is magnified to match the level of harm that would justify current legal penalties. Law enforcers foster this deception to maintain their self-respect. For Richards, the obvious solution is to lower penalties so that they match the actual harm caused. Richards then dismisses a free market control system because he judges it to be insufficiently restrictive (135).

The problem with Richards' analysis concerns the fairness requirement. Fairness is considered but not in a consistent manner (57, 135). A rationing system for marijuana is rejected on universalist grounds. Richards argues that if rationing would be "inappropriate in the cases of such drugs as alcohol or nicotine, it would seem, *a fortiori*, that it should be rejected in the case of marijuana" (135, p. 681). He labels marijuana rationing "hypocritical" since it ignores the greater harm caused by alcohol and because it does not sufficiently honour personal choice. Richards then tentatively suggests that people "may have a right to take potentially harmful drugs." Yet following this, Richards decides that heroin, mescaline, LSD, and certain other drugs should be available, solely on prescription, from state authorized medical authorities. Prescription is described as a "kind of license" the state gives physicians so that they can exercise "proven medical competence" to minimize drug-related damage (135, pp. 673 ff. and 680).

Richards presents no evidence to prove that either heroin or mescaline is more damaging than alcohol. Nevertheless, he assigns them to a separate control system, a discriminatory policy he condemned when applied to cannabis. Secondly, prescription is ethically equivalent to the compulsory committal Richards earlier rejected as an unwarranted measure (44, 135). A prescription system forces drug users to accept medical supervision. Such coercion is much less onerous than forced confinement in a "detoxication" centre but the ethical difference is merely one of degree. Both surrender individual autonomy to medical authority in a state-run system where physicians serve a police, rather than a medical, role.

Richards understands that psychoactives are used for creative, ceremonial, recreational, and symptomatic relief purposes. This understanding puts into sharper relief his failure to explain why physicians rather than lawyers, bartenders, coaches, teachers, or clerics should have supervisory control over drug use. Richards' claim that physicians exercise proven competence in controlling drug use is unsupported by evidence. On the contrary, the evidence suggests that MDs often prescribe drugs carelessly, even negligently, and that their rehabilitative efforts are consistently marked by failure (77, 104, 112). Many critics identify physicians as part of the drug-abuse problem because of their personal example and their overpromotion of deceptive chemical "solutions" (58, 93, 109).

Richards is also wrong in comparing prescription to a licensing system. Under a licensing scheme, individuals have a right to use drugs, a right subject to certain legal restraints. Under a prescription system, the individual has no right to use the controlled drugs. He may have a right to treatment but this right is limited by the power of medical interests to determine what constitutes "treatment." Almost every drug now classed as illicit or non-medical was once a medical treatment (4, 142). Prescription is much closer to prohibition than licensing.

In *The Heroin Solution*, Arnold Trebach, like Richards, condemns American policy makers because they "criminalized heroin, converted addicts into criminals, and proselytized this repressive policy to the world" (171, p. 289; see also 116). Trebach realizes that people use drugs like heroin for fun and that 90 per cent of heroin users are not "addicts." He also calls for drug control solutions that are "democratic," a term implying a willingness to promote fairness. However, Trebach decriminalizes heroin only to medicalize it. Heroin use is called a disease; he speaks of a global "epidemic" for which there is no "complete cure." Nevertheless, we are urged to "bring addicts into a varied system of medical, caring treatment" (171, p. 289).

Under Trebach's proposal, physicians could prescribe heroin to the "organically ill and the addicted" (171, p. 290). Since he knows most heroin users are not addicts, Trebach must intend to prohibit their access to the drug. They are not sick. Physicians will be free to experiment with every "rational approach" to drug user rehabilitation, including methadone maintenance and Zen Buddhism. In other words, physicians as state agents will be permitted to operate scientifically discredited programmes and to co-opt any religious rituals. Clerics will, of course, not acquire countervailing medical privileges. Trebach's unstated objective is actually the bolstering of a therapeutic state at the expense of a once powerful theocracy. Since heroin is merely a battlefield on which political gains can be amassed, the scientific evidence is immaterial to Trebach (171). Unfortunately, elitist therapeutic controls, like their theocratic predecessors, are potentially much more dangerous than are state criminal controls because they are administered without regard for due process or rule of law.

Utilitarianism and Liberal Pragmatism

John Kaplan, a pioneer cannabis decriminalizer and medicalizer, believes public law restrictions on drug use are justified in terms of both public harm and self-harm (80–83). Justifying state action on the basis of self-harm leads Kaplan into a confrontation with J. S. Mill. Mill's familiar argument is that government is generally not justified in compelling people to act or to forbear from acting merely for their own good or, in other words, that prohibiting the use of alcohol or other drugs is not warranted on self-harm grounds. Mill allowed for two exceptions, however, either of which, Kaplan claims, suffices to defeat a policy of permitting drug use as a matter of right.

Mill's first exception concerned children. He felt that children "must be protected against their own actions." While true, this rule does not justify state action. Mill mistakenly believed that society has "absolute power over [children] during all the early portion of their existence" (111, pp. 15 and 101). But in the main it is parents who control children, not "society." Since real paternalism is far more powerful and important than state controls, the state traditionally has been a minor factor in children's lives (180). Parents hold nearly absolute power over their children's religious, political, ethical, cultural, and dietary frameworks. State prohibitions applying to children alone compete directly with parental control and are usually perceived as violations of parental prerogatives. Mill's rule justifies parental, not state, regulation of children. Parents should limit their child's access to drugs, just as they should prohibit bad posture, poor study habits, rudeness, fighting, and excessive television viewing. The state is not justified in enacting similar prohibitions. Where such attempts are made—for example, Canada and most American states prohibit children's use of tobacco—they are unenforced and irrelevant (113).

According to Mill's second exception, the state should prohibit voluntary slavery because it is "not freedom to be allowed to alienate [one's] freedom" (111, p. 126). Mill's case against absolute freedom of contract in the personal service field, even if accepted, need not be applied because heroin use is not slavery. Kaplan suggests that for "some" heroin users "the metaphor of slavery... is not so farfetched" (83, p. 105). But drug addiction does not seriously restrict choice as evidenced by the millions of alcohol, nicotine, and caffeine addicts who can adequately cope as long as they are permitted to secure a supply legally.

In the end, Kaplan rejects Mill's entire proposition, noting that "no modern state ... has ever followed Mill's principle with respect to all activities" (83,

p. 106). The legislative record of modern states in the drug control field seems to be a shaky basis for an ethical argument. In any event, Mill's rule only applied to self-harming behaviour that did not also harm others. Drug use tends to impose costs on others.

Kaplan then turns to Rawls for support on the self-harm issue. A Rawlsian contractor, Kaplan argues, might consent to laws that made "*reasonable* efforts to prevent his weakness from causing him *great* damage" (83, p. 108 [emphasis added]). This is a valid moral justification for intervention in a case of pure self-harm. The contentious matters are the nature of reasonable limits and the meaning of "great" harm. Kaplan implies that full prohibition could seem reasonable to a risk-averse contractor but that is unlikely in drug regulation since criminal law penalties are usually more detrimental than the self-harm caused by drug use. Some level of legal restraint might be voluntarily accepted but it would not be the criminal law. Kaplan answers critics who charge that present heroin laws grossly exceed traditional levels of paternalism in Western law by identifying an "endless" list of other paternalistic measures from building codes to minimum wage laws (83). Kaplan makes two mistakes here. First, if his other examples are themselves unjust and counterproductive, their alleged consistency with heroin prohibition provides no ethical support (56). Second, Kaplan fails to cite criteria determining the acceptability of paternalism. In many cases high decision-making costs force individuals to transfer some decision-making authority to the government (85). Kaplan avoids such social contract explanations because he wants to equate drug prohibition with consumer protection laws. But the difference in scope and impact of these two types of state intervention is monumental. Heroin prohibition involves criminal penalties and state coercion of the highest order. Pure food laws involve standard setting and minor, non-criminal disincentives usually assessed against businesses.

Kaplan fails to consider seriously the non-prohibitionist tradition in American jurisprudence. The American Constitution does not explicitly guarantee the right to use drugs but the framers probably did not think it necessary to spell out such an obvious personal prerogative. For the same reason, they did not guarantee the right to wear the clothes, eat the food, or sing the songs of one's choice (163). A right to self-medication may be implicitly granted by explicit protections given to the pursuit of happiness (149).[10] It is noteworthy that an Amendment to the Constitution was required to permit the prohibition of alcohol.

Erich Goode adopts the same pragmatic approach as Kaplan but with less recourse to philosophic considerations. Perhaps as a result, Goode's recommendations are more realistic. Goode assumes that "drug use is here to stay, and the only way to eliminate *illegal* drug use is to eliminate the laws outlawing the use of certain drugs" (61, p. 254). For Goode, the central policy issue can be briefly stated: "given a population of heavy drug users ... how can we minimize harm to everyone involved?" (pp. 254–55). He argues that the hysteria over a relatively minor group of heroin users is "misplaced" and that drug laws are prejudiced against young, non-white, working-class, and non-medical users. Goode concludes that "drastic measures" to control drug use are not feasible, and that instead measures to regulate the use and sale of all psychoactives should be considered. Goode does not propose a control programme himself but he is clearly more willing than Kaplan to apply drug controls broadly.

Taking Justice Seriously

Thomas Szasz is perhaps the leading advocate of freeing drug users from both police and medical supervision (163). Szasz realizes that drug use is self-harming, sometimes severely so. Nonetheless, he believes citizens should have the right to ingest any drug just as they have rights to freedom of speech and religious observance. Since this position piggybacks on existing constitutional protections, it implicitly imports legal restraints judged reasonable in other contexts. Self-expression can harm others, hence the state imposes restrictions with respect to libel and slander, sedition, false advertising, copyright infringement, obscenity, hate literature, and so on. Freedom of speech does not excuse a public nuisance created by amplified broadcasts, nor does religious freedom excuse what would otherwise be a serious crime. Neither artistic expression nor divine inspiration excuses murder or assault. Szasz recommends the same legal result for voluntary drug use: a basic right constrained by reasonable laws promoting public defence (163).

This position assumes that protection of autonomy does not depend upon proof of harmlessness. Voting rights and church independence are protected despite the possibility of voters making harmful choices or church members entertaining fantastic delusions. Szasz may agree with Karl Marx that religion is an intoxicating and harmful "opiate of the masses" but Szasz would not on that account prohibit or repress church membership (163).

Since no scientific tests can distinguish licit from illicit drugs, Szasz concludes that the drug question is ethical, not medical. From this perspective the medicalization of drug users raises a parallel between a theocratic and a therapeutic dictatorship. The centuries-long struggle to separate church and state is compared by Szasz to the current legal battles against joint medical-state enterprises such as forced treatment, protected medical monopolies, involuntary committal, and drug prohibition (163). Richards agrees that criminal laws have been abused by "majoritarian legislators" to enforce a specific theocratic ideology, yet he appears to favour the enforcement of a particular medical ideology (135). Szasz does not make that mistake.

Szasz's argument is also more legalistic than Richards' case for human rights because Szasz stresses the need for legal equality. He criticizes drug criminalizers for failing to see that licit drugs as well as "countless other objects in the environment" are as dangerous as the substances we prohibit

(163, p. 267). Criminalizers may respond that, although the existing restrictions are not fair, they at least limit some drug-related harm. But this rationalization does not adequately account for the fact that illicit drugs cause such a small fraction of total drug harm, that any non-biased planner would concentrate on major problems like alcohol and tobacco use. Furthermore, concern for the health of illicit drug users cannot be the real reason for prohibition since these users would be healthier under some less extremist scheme. What then is the purpose of prohibition? Szasz suggests that certain drugs are outlawed as symbols of sin and wickedness. As symbols, these drugs are forced into roles and burdened with fictional characteristics by groups who simultaneously create and purport to solve the "drug problem."

Since Szasz understands that drug use is not significantly more or less dangerous than harmful pastimes we do not prohibit or assign to medical control, he argues that justice precludes dissimilar treatment before the law for drug users (65). Szasz also rejects current control systems since they apply only to certain drugs and are thus unfairly discriminatory (163). Drug laws are unethical, then, because they are not uniform and because they do not deal with equivalent behaviours or wrongdoings consistently. The remaining issue, which is one Szasz does not address, is what level and type of legal restraint on the right to use drugs would be reasonable.

Justice and Regulatory Design

The conclusions drawn from a justice-based analysis depend less on the technique chosen than on the thoroughness, consistency, and empirical accuracy with which that technique is employed. Any of the techniques so far surveyed is capable of producing the same general answers about the design of an optimum drug control system. Consider briefly, in turn, a cost-benefit analysis and a rights-based analysis of drug regulation. According to the cost-benefit technique, regulation aims to achieve the greatest benefits at the lowest costs. Benefits include the amount of harm avoided. This will depend upon the harm caused by the regulated behaviour and the degree to which that behaviour is deterred or positively modified by the regulatory programme. For example, completely deterring behaviour that causes little harm will not achieve significant benefit. Benefits also include compensation paid by wrongdoers to those they injure. Preventing injury is preferable to compensating injury but where injury has occurred, compensation is the best solution. Against such benefits are counterbalanced the costs of regulation. Such costs include enforcement expenses, legal "side-effects," and the impact of regulation on wrongdoers.

Of the five possible regulatory models, both criminal law controls and medical prescription are low benefit–high cost systems. As will be explained below in greater detail, they are low benefit programmes because they fail to deter much drug use. Indeed, both systems may encourage drug use. For example, criminal law prohibitions and attendant media sensationalism serve to advertise the existence and euphoriant properties of illicit drugs. Similarly, medical psychoactives are promoted by their designation as "medicines" and are portrayed as acceptable drug solutions (77). Prohibition and prescription are high cost programmes, first, because they are individualized. That is, they process or treat single individuals one at a time. Moreover, the two systems employ expensive, professional personnel such as lawyers, police, judges, and physicians. The second reason for high costs is that both systems trigger expensive "side-effects." As Kaplan demonstrates, prohibition gives rise to black markets, organized crime, quality control problems, police corruption, and disrespect for the law (27, 33, 34, 83, 129, 181). Prescription control compels physicians to play a police role and thus compromises the ethical and professional duties they owe to their patients.

One of the five regulatory possibilities is a medium benefit–low cost system. This is the free market–private law control programme. It is a medium benefit system because social sanctions (45, 169) and private actions can significantly deter drug-related harms and because damage awards serve to compensate injured parties. It is not a high benefit system because of imperfections in and inherent limits to the available sanctions. The regulatory costs are low because the government's role is small or irrelevant and because social and private law sanctions tend to have minor impact on wrongdoers.

The last two regulatory models considered are rationing and tax-licensing. These tend to be high benefit–low cost programmes for the following reasons. First, both systems offer attractive deterrent potential through either direct limits on drug supplies or price control. Deterrence depends not just on the scale of the penalty or disincentive but on the certainty, frequency, and swiftness of its application. The impact of a mild sanction universally imposed can exceed that of a severe punishment rarely inflicted. Second, tax controls, but not rationing controls, make possible the related payment of compensation to injured persons. With respect to costs, both systems are depersonalized, mass control programmes capable of reducing administrative expenses to pennies per transaction, and of being operated by non-professional personnel. Since neither system imposes major sanctions, affected parties are not unduly burdened, significant black market activity is not sparked and the inducements for police corruption and abuse are limited. A thorough cost-benefit analysis should, therefore, conclude that an optimum drug control scheme will closely resemble the present tax-licensing regulation of alcohol and tobacco. Not surprisingly, these two drugs are not only the major psychoactives consumed, they are the drugs Western culture has had the most time to learn, through trial and error, how to regulate.

Though a rights-based analysis employs different techniques and concepts, similar conclusions about which drug control system is superior can be reached. The concepts that will now be considered may be summarized under the headings of proportionality, equality, and natural rights.

Proportionality in tort law essentially limits a plaintiff's damages to the actual amount of injury suffered. In criminal law, proportionality limits the extent to which the state is justified in imposing penalties; the basic ethical limit established is that punishment should be fitting given the nature of the offence (178; see also 126). Criminal assault and tort battery that involve the merest touching, little apprehension, and minimal harm should be met with a small award of damages and a minor criminal law sentence. Conversely, an assault and battery resulting in severe pain and suffering should be counteracted by a large damage award and a harsh criminal sentence. When the proportionality limit is applied to the minute harm to others caused by an individual act of drug taking, an objective observer must conclude that there is no criminal law penalty small enough to match that level of harm. Likewise, the level of compensation justified will almost always be far below that which a practical tort system can provide (158). Certainly, a court can award damages of 10 dollars or even 10 cents, but very few parties will seek compensation worth far less than the effort expended to gain it.

In most cases, a proportional response to drug use will not include criminal or medical controls because they are "over-repressive." Conversely, proportional responses could include social sanctions, tort damages or injunctions, rationing, taxation, and standards governing time and place for drug use. The scale and nature of such disincentives are in keeping with the scale and nature of drug-related harms.

The second traditional rights-based ethical requirement is equality or fairness—the enjoinder that like cases should be treated alike. As discussed above, the question of whether taking different psychoactive drugs is "like behaviour" may be answered culturally or scientifically. At present, Western culture embodies certain strong biases about drugs so that the subjective-cultural answer is that drug taking in general does not constitute "like behaviour." Scientifically and objectively the opposite conclusion may be reached. Therefore, what is at stake is not the applicability of the equality requirement but rather the equivalence or non-equivalence of psychoactive drug consumption.

If the empirical evidence presented above and the conclusions drawn from it are accepted, then fairness demands that all psychoactives be treated legally as equivalent substances. This does not mean that all drug users would be treated identically; rather they would all be subject to the same general control programme. Equality itself does not determine which control programme should be universally applied. For example, it would be fair as between drug users if the criminal law prohibited all such drug use on pain of death. Similarly, it would be fair if no drugs were prohibited.

Without relying on cost-benefit calculations, the choice of which regulatory programme to universally apply can be arrived at through consensus or public election. It is argued below that if people are forced to make a fair choice and to regulate their own drug use exactly as they regulate the drug use of others, they will reject criminal or medical controls in favour of one of the less intrusive control programmes. Certainly, individuals may employ their own cost-benefit analysis to determine which control system they prefer to inflict on themselves. However, that process of calculation differs substantially from the formalist process adopted by Kaplan whereby the theorist attempts to produce a general cost-benefit conclusion. In the rights-based framework described above, the conclusion depends on individual choice and preference.

The third and final rights-based analysis begins by proclaiming the existence of certain basic, natural, or inalienable rights. For instance, the new *Canadian Charter of Rights and Freedoms* states that everyone has such "fundamental freedoms" as "freedom of conscience and religion" and "freedom of thought, belief, opinion and expression" (159c, Part I).[11] The establishment of such rights is conclusory. No formula is provided by which the selection of certain rights and the exclusion of others can be explained. In this context, a right to use the drugs of one's choice can be promoted in two ways. First, such a right or freedom can simply be proclaimed as part of the basic rights protection package. If such a proclamation is lacking, the second possibility is to argue that a specified right, such as "the right to liberty" guaranteed in section 7 of the *Charter*, extends far enough to cover the disputed action (see 126). Attempts to rule out drug prohibitions in the United States on constitutional grounds have so far failed. The constitutional positions put forward have been logical, attractive, and empirically accurate. They have failed, nonetheless, because of the courts' strong biases in drug matters and because of the courts' reluctance to overrule duly elected legislators (126).

Should either method succeed in establishing a basic right to use the drug of choice, that right will be legally circumscribed in certain ways. The *Charter*, for example, subjects the guaranteed rights "only to such reasonable limits prescribed by law as can be demonstrably justified in a free and democratic society" (159c, Part I, s. 1). In other words, a basic right to use drugs would be subject to legal limits traditionally employed to restrict other basic rights. This would rule out prohibition and prescription since books, churches, and political rallies are not subject to stringent criminal law or medical controls. It would not rule out social sanctions or private law actions since a right to free expression does not excuse libel or other civil obligations. A right to use drugs would also not rule out a tax on drug sales, no-smoking rules for public places, anti-littering ordinances, or even rationing. All of these regulations could be "demonstrably justified" as "reasonable" limits within Western legal traditions.

UNIFORM REGULATION

Criminal Prohibition

In submitting each regulatory scheme to a public-choice test wherein the programme selected must be applied to all psychoactives, it is clear to begin with that uniform prohibition of all drugs is readily ruled out. Other people's drug use imposes minor costs on those injured, so individuals would be unwilling to avoid such costs by subjecting their own drug use to the possibility of criminal penalties. With murder, the calculus is quite different. Individuals willingly bear the small risk of being punished for murder in order to defend themselves against the severe harm of someone murdering them. The Rawlsian contractor's answer to self-harm through drug use would also reject criminal law sanctions because a tobacco habit is less harmful than prison and a criminal record. In practice, the users of tobacco, coffee, alcohol, and diazepam would not criminalize their own behaviour merely to defend themselves against the very minor threat posed by cannabis or cocaine users.

Other obstacles to a universal prohibition are readily noted. Indeed, the costs, disruptions, and social expense of a total drug prohibition are so large that they cannot be seriously contemplated. Since almost everyone would be a drug criminal, there would be a drastic shortage of non-compromised administrators. Furthermore, the millions of people now dependent for their income on the production and sale of drugs would suffer severe financial loss. Alcohol sales alone netted $66.4 billion in the United States in 1984 (132). Since full enforcement would be impossible, universal prohibition would probably extend and amplify the side effects of current prohibitions, namely police corruption, selective enforcement, black markets, organized crime, dubious legal judgments, and international conflict with countries not sharing the same policies (see 82, 133, 137).

Prescription and Medical Supervision

The probable lack of public support for total mandatory prescription is suggested by the fact that only two categories of psychoactives are usually assigned to medical controls. These are new drugs that have no existing body of users to antagonize, and illicit drugs, like heroin, whose users are so heavily punished already that a shift to medical control may represent a relative lessening of restrictions. In contrast, coffee, alcohol, and tobacco users would feel intolerably imposed upon if their drugs were reclassified as "controlled substances." The majority of licit drug users, who are also the majority of voters, would likely reject prescription-only access as too expensive, inconvenient, and demeaning.

Universal prescription is also objectionable because it would provide insufficient social protection against drug harms. The duties, training, and incentives of physicians render them ill-suited to perform the role of social protectors. If physicians were the sole legitimate source not only of Valium but of all alcohol products, they would reap enormous, monopolistic profits from the rapid scripting of alcohol prescriptions and they would buy into distilleries and breweries as they have bought into pharmacies and the pharmaceutical industry (112, 176, 182). Alcohol producers would presumably bribe physicians with gifts, sponsored symposia, free samples, and private "research grants" just as pharmaceutical firms do now. Physicians wanting to act on behalf of social protection would face a major dilemma. If they refused to prescribe alcohol many of their customers would turn to other, "less ethical" physicians. Or, if a group of prescribers organized a joint anti-drug campaign, their customers would frequently turn to adulterated and possibly unsafe black market products. Even physicians convinced of alcohol's overall negative impact could still properly calculate that prescribing alcohol was in the best interests of their client.

As a rule, permissive prescribing would be needed to forestall criminal elements from dominating the trade. This strategy would be forced upon any private group or profession awarded a drug distribution monopoly—either distribute moderately if not generously, or be eclipsed by illicit traders. Within this constraint some incentives variations would occur. The standard, fee-for-service physician would most likely practise assembly-line prescription whereas salaried medics would be more restrictive, either under public plans like the British National Health Service, or private plans like the Kaiser system in California (2, 66).

Physicians as controllers are hindered by their duty to their clients. The role of protector, confidant, and fiduciary usually forces the physician to put individual needs before collective interests. It is redundant and foolish to compromise physicians with police tasks since we can easily empower non-fiduciaries to serve as enforcement agents. As it stands, the law usually gives physicians public police powers without imposing countervailing responsibilities. Physicians are not made liable for the drug-related costs inflicted on other people by their clients. Since physicians do not internalize third-party costs, they are not motivated to curtail drug consumption rates to the extent possible. Physicians could be compelled to bear all the costs of their prescribing choices if the government set annual license-to-prescribe fees at the requisite level. Faced with such fees, physicians would be forced to abandon their drug monopoly because, unlike government, the medical profession lacks the police resources to enforce drug sales at a cost-internalizing price in light of competition from illegal sources. Physicians can therefore only succeed as social protectors if they operate as government agents. Such a partnership is unstable because government can operate effective controls on drug use without any assistance from physicians. Moreover, government is, to some degree, representative of, and responsible to, the public, whereas a private profession is usually elitist and undemocratic.

If universal prescription is unattractive as a social defence measure, might it still be acceptable as a shield against self-harm? Clients seek professional expertise when they lack special knowledge or skills, and where errors would be costly. To reduce risks, clients in many situations delegate authority to physicians (127). However, delegating prescriptive authority is not warranted by this analysis since drug use does not require much technical expertise, because physicians are not the most reliable or cost-effective source of expertise or information about drugs, and because there are important conflicts between the interests of physicians and their patients (76; see also 59, 91, 96).

Physicians systematically fail to act in the best interests of their patients. The literature provides many instances of widespread abusive practices where physicians overpromote drugs, surgeries, and psychotherapies which are unnecessary and counterproductive (1, 30, 63, 69, 104, 172, 182, 183, 186). Practising physicians are not disinterested scientists; they are members of a powerful guild organization (54, 86). Loyalty to the guild and fraternity often supersedes loyalty to patients or to the public. Medical priorities are evidenced in a variety of circumstances: by collusion among physicians not to testify in malpractice suits (41, 101), by the failure of medical associations to remove or restrain unfit members (62, 107), by lobbying efforts against patient protection laws (35, 36, 66, 68), and by chauvinistic aggression against female patients (32, 43, 109).

Physician-client conflicts can be reduced in the drug therapy field if prescribers are in practice made liable for drug-related harm suffered by the drug taker. Physicians are liable in law for drug harms intentionally or negligently inflicted (20), but liability is easily avoided for a number of reasons (158). Drug harms are often subtle, long term and causally uncertain (112). Patients change physicians, take other drugs, and physicians move, retire, or die. In many cases, neither party will link final results with a particular course of drug use. These problems are minimized when the harm is acute or when the prescribed drug is taken for a short, well-defined period. But given the euphoriant potential and popular appeal of psychoactive drugs, such substances attract repeated, chronic, and even lifelong use. This would be true for prescribed alcohol and it has become the case of new sedatives like barbiturates and diazepam. Such developments tend to be ignored or blamed on human perversity since physicians do not intend long-term use to occur (62, 107). Thus new drugs are marketed before the results of chronic consumption are known. If alcohol had been invented in the 1950s instead of diazepam, alcohol would now be prescribed as a safe, effective, non–habit forming sedative or tranquillizer. But as patients began to take alcohol for months and years rather than weeks, its medical gloss would fade and a growing critical literature would warn the public to avoid alcohol just as they are now counselled to avoid the use of benzodiazepines (5, 106).

Since chronic use of psychoactives apparently brings net disvalue to users, physicians would refuse to prescribe except on an emergency basis if they were *de facto* liable for the damage. Emergency-only prescribing would protect people from self-harm. But such extreme medical restraint would fuel a pervasive black market. To curtail the black market, physicians would have to prescribe generously but they could not do that and at the same time accept liability for self-harm to patients. Prescription would then be feasible only on condition that the drug taker assume full responsibility but such a condition would contradict the rationale of compulsory prescription. No private supplier could afford to sell psychoactives to a mass market and be held liable for the resulting damages.

As for technical expertise, much drug use involves social influences, rituals, cultural imperatives, styles, and other matters in which physicians are not expert. Even when technical skill and knowledge are relevant, physicians are questionable sources of expertise. For example, physicians rely heavily on pharmaceutical firms for drug information (66). Both producers and pre-scribers have some interest in looking for benefits and in not looking for long-term consequences. In many reported cases, physicians continue to prescribe a drug despite plain warnings from both producers and government agencies (63, 112). Physicians often resist informing their patients about the drug prescribed; package inserts are not included and contraindications are not mentioned (156). In some countries, physicians protest if pharmacists put the drug's trade name on the container (118, 167). Pharmacists are legally prevented from advising customers directly although they are often more knowledgeable about drugs than are physicians (151). Trade secrets mas-querade as expertise as physicians restrict client access to drug information to amplify client dependency and to elevate their own status and income. According to a number of reports, physicians tend to be poorly trained in pharmacological areas (9, 151). The focus of medical training is crisis intervention—the technical solution of immediate, often life-threatening con-ditions. Non-crisis fields such as nutrition, neurosis, and drug habituation are clearly not marked by medical successes (see 40, 55, 77, 90).

Individuals sometimes require detailed, accurate information about drugs and drug interactions, but that need does not justify a system that also compels them to acquire medical permission to take psychoactive drugs. Nor does it justify a monopoly allowing only physicians, and not nurses, paramedics, pharmacists, or psychologists, to sell such information. It is likely that more informed choices about the use of psychoactive drugs would be made if it were not for forced reliance upon physicians as the sole information source.

Government Rationing

Under rationing controls, drug users would be neither criminalized nor subject to compulsory medical supervision. Individuals would have the right to use drugs in the form and the amounts made available. The only prohibition would be against non-authorized sales.

Rationing by a public body avoids the conflicts inherent in medical controls. Unlike physicians, government exists to promote collective self-defence and is liable for defensive failures. Government health, welfare, and other agencies bear a significant portion of drug-related costs. Government also possesses enforcement resources and the monopoly on police action needed to maintain a restricted supply of drugs.

Rationing would be less intrusive and less expensive than either criminal law or medical controls. Clerks rather than physicians would operate the system and few police resources would be required. Rationing could serve social defence needs by setting ceilings on national drug consumption rates as the Soviet government is presently doing with alcohol. Such ceilings could be restrictive without being prohibitive. For example, a government might decide to cut alcohol consumption by half. Rationing could also prevent self-harm more effectively than would prescription because government has stronger incentives to pursue disease-preventing policies. Reducing overall drug use is the major preventive measure in this field but, in addition, government could selectively ration the more damaging forms of the various drugs. The public could also be provided with comprehensive information about adverse drug effects. Such information could be provided inexpensively through package inserts, warning labels, school instruction, and public service advertising. Drug information is more efficiently conveyed by public agencies and word-of-mouth than by expensive private interviews in a physician's office. Under a rationing scheme, people could still seek professional advice about drugs but they would not be forced to do so.

Rationing systems are not without their faults, as experience with wartime rationing, rent controls, minimum wage laws, and the Soviet "command economy" rationing of many personal goods and services illustrate (60, 98, 165, 166). Rationing coupons are counterfeited. Ceilings are arbitrarily set. The signalling role of market prices is subverted or destroyed. Distribution is often inefficient and competition is reduced. Unproductive disincentives such as waiting in line replace price disincentives. Product quality declines. Bureaucratic systems are vulnerable to political abuse. Multi-tier arrangements evolve, with low rations for the masses and special supplies for foreigners and political elites. Rationing also tends to be cumbersome as it ignores variations in individual preferences.

Despite these drawbacks, Rawlsian contractors would prefer universal drug rationing to either universal prohibition or prescription because rationing would limit externalities and mitigate self-harm more effectively and at a lower cost. An estimation of actual public support should come to the same conclusion. During wartime, voters accept rationing and, as noted above, much of the Soviet economy embodies rationing mechanisms. In addition, many people in the Western world actively call for increased rationing in such areas as rental housing, energy, income, education, and employment opportunities. These demands are understandably met with vigorous opposition and in the case of drugs such opposition would come mainly from users of current recreational drugs since their drugs are the most freely available.

Tax-Licensing Controls

The differences between tax controls and rationing reflect the differences between market allocation and a centrally ordered economy. The rationale for tax controls is to counteract market imperfections, such as pollution and drug-related costs, by forcing prices to account for the full social costs involved. The tax-inflated price signals some degree of official disapproval and manipulates buyers through general economic disincentives. Unlike rationing, tax controls retain the flexibility of market allocations with their allowances for personal preferences. No arbitrary ceilings need to be set. Taxes also raise revenue and thus provide incentives for government to enforce the controls. Like rationing, tax controls would not criminalize or medicalize drug use. Law enforcement resources would focus on the prevention of untaxed sales, not on the harassment of drug users (see 114).

The conceptual objective of tax and licensing controls for distributors, retailers, and on-premise sellers would be to duplicate the results of a class action against drug users. Since government already exists as a collective agency, a public law programme against drug "defendants" is the lowest cost alternative to an actual tort action. Public law controls also avoid certain drawbacks inherent in private law initiatives against chronic, repeated wrong-doing. Courts lack the apparatus to assess and collect small compensatory sums for the duration of the continual tortious acts. Tax controls solve this problem. Taxes are also superior to fines or judgments because these must be extracted directly from the tortfeasor. In contrast, taxes can be collected impersonally at the wholesale or retail level before the tort is committed. Taxes thus pre-emptively limit drug-related harm by reducing drug consumption, whereas fines compensate for or punish harm already caused. On the other hand, the tax is predictive in that it anticipates harm and it is generalizing since it does not distinguish between two persons buying the same amount of drug, although in fact they will impose different costs on third parties. Still, the burden can vary according to the type and amount of drugs used so that in general those generating the highest externalities will pay the most tax. Such approximations and other deviations from the pure individuality of tort law are necessary if liability is to be borne by the millions of drug users.

A regulatory tax based on the tort model must be a fault-based tax. That is, tax level should be proportional to the level of harm caused by the drug use. If alcohol per standard dosage is more harmful than caffeine or cannabis, then the tax on alcohol should be higher. Similarly, tax rates for smokeless tobacco products should be lower than those for cigarettes because of the absence of smoke damage to other persons.

Criminal, medical, and rationing controls attempt to deter drug-related costs but they ignore compensation needs. In contrast, tax controls raise revenue which can be used to finance remedial efforts or to reduce other tax burdens. In either case, an approximation of the plaintiff class would receive some compensatory benefit paid by a general defendant class. Having drug users pay tax compensation directly to government also avoids the legal costs and deadweight losses of a real class action. However, for this system to work, the setting and collecting of tax should probably not be left to revenue departments. The United States Treasury's role in fomenting the present extremist controls is well known (53). Control responsibility should instead be assigned to health, education, or welfare departments.

In addition to tax incentives, a range of injunctive measures is required to regulate non-smoking zones, product quality, returnable bottle systems, advertising standards, warning labels, and so forth. Again, courts are not well suited to administer such long term, continual, and complex regulatory measures.

Tax-licensing controls are also plausible restrictions in terms of self-harm. Price disincentives can be designed to discourage the more damaging modes of drug intake and to encourage less damaging modes. Sniffing, smoking, or injecting drug X is more damaging than eating or drinking the same substance. Tax rates could reflect this difference. Price differentials can similarly dampen demand for the more harmful drugs in a given drug family. Since barbiturates are evidently more damaging than benzodiazepines, they should be more heavily taxed regardless of whether the two drug types are associated with different levels of harm to others. Since tax penalties are quite minor relative to the possibilities for self-harm, drug users are likely to accept such restraints more readily than they would accept the previous models.

Government efforts to limit and prevent self-harm do not mean that government should be liable for self-harm. A major failing of the prescription system is that it holds out the false promise of physician liability. The belief that physicians are liable for self-harm leads patients to assume that physicians would not prescribe any harmful, addicting drug. This presumption would be true if physicians were, in fact as well as in law, responsible for compensating all drug-related damage. But since liability is easily avoided, individuals are inappropriately encouraged to be less defensive, less critical, and less self-reliant than they should be. No such confusion or empty assurances will occur in connection with either tax controls or rationing. People will be forewarned that all psychoactives are harmful and habit forming. They will then bear the cost of that portion of self-harm that is not automatically covered by welfare-medical programmes.

Would Rawlsian contractors accept tax disincentives as a self-protection measure? The answer is not certain. Even with ample warnings about drug effects, some people optimistically assume that they will not become dependent on the drug or that use will not cause them serious damage. If humans naturally discount future risks to some degree then Rawlsian contractors will do likewise. Thus contractors who overestimate their self-control and discount drug risks might be reluctant to bear "needless" tax penalties. However, the contractors would delegate authority to some public body to enforce drug quality and safety standards.

Practical acceptance of tax controls will depend primarily on the trade-off between personal restraint and the avoidance of costs imposed by others. The strongest supporters will be abstainers or light users who suffer more harm from others than they inflict in return. Since these people will pay less in tax than they receive in compensation they will generally welcome tax controls. Opposition will come from those in the higher drug tax brackets who will pay out in compensation more than they receive. Hardest hit will be the heavy, polydrug users, appropriately enough, since they cause the most damage. Current criminalizers will also oppose tax controls because an objective fault-based system necessarily rejects the implicit and subjective indices of fault contained in statutory penalties for drug use offences, which ignore alcohol and nicotine users and punish cannabis and cocaine consumers. (For convenience, reference is made to people as users of a single drug, but most people use a variety of drugs. For example, most serious abusers of any drug are also nicotine addicts (27)).

Free Market Controls

Under this least restrictive alternative, drugs would be dealt with like other commodities. Certain general regulations and laws would therefore apply. New drugs would be tested and quality standards set. False and misleading advertisement would be curtailed (123). Physicians would be liable for harm caused by reasonable reliance on their advice. Producers would be liable for damage resulting from defective products or from failure to warn. The right to use drugs would be subject to the same limitations affecting other rights.

Much of the restrictive potential of free market controls depends upon private law developments and expanding theories of liability (18, 47, 122). Drug use would be inhibited if employees could sue employers for failing to provide a smoke-free environment or if employers could sharply discriminate against drug users in hiring and firing employees. Considerable restraint would also be achieved if drug users such as tobacco smokers were successful in negligence suits against tobacco companies. A finding of negligence could conceivably be based on the manufacturer's failure to warn customers that tobacco was both damaging and addictive. A rash of such actions would force producers to raise prices, thereby deterring some consumption. Drug producers in that tort climate would probably find it less expensive to practise full disclosure. By issuing full and comprehensive warnings they could eventually avoid blame for their customers' self-harm. Drug advertising might be voluntarily eliminated under these conditions. Promotional advertisement would also be abandoned if the courts were to determine that any measure intended to encourage drug use was itself negligent. Under such a doctrine, newspapers, magazines, and other advertising media could be held liable independently.

Since the courts are unlikely to promote revolutionary changes in tort liability for drug-related externalities, a free market system would be less restrictive than either rationing or tax controls. This failure to provide sufficient protection or deterrence could lead Rawlsian contractors to reject free market controls. On the other hand, many business interests would support a free market because of the impetus it would provide to drug sales. Without current excise taxes on alcohol products, alcohol prices would plunge and sales would increase. Alcohol consumption in the United States is below European levels and is, per capita, only about half of what it was in 1850 (103). Potential for major sales increases also exists for tobacco, if not taxed, and for cocaine, cannabis, and opium, if not prohibited. The change would benefit farmers of corn, tobacco, and marijuana, brewers, vintners and distillers, chemical producers, packagers, shippers, and drug retailers. For non-commercial reasons many people would support a free market (or tax controls) because it would eliminate police power over drug use, drug crusades, corruption in the drug control agencies,[12] the scapegoating of drug users by politicians, and much of the life-support system for organized crime. Firmly against free market controls would be the temperance interests, police, organized crime, medical associations, and those agencies burdened by drug-related damages.

CONCLUSION

Assume that the electorate is faced with a binding referendum in which one of the five control systems described above must be selected as the single mode for control of all psychoactive substances. Assume also that the vote would take place after two years of debate, lobbying, and education. With most people's first choice, namely the status quo, eliminated in advance, what would be the result of this hypothetical vote? Universal prohibition and prescription would likely stand as the least preferred alternatives. Among the three plausible contenders, a tax-licensing system would probably be judged the best compromise. Tax controls are familiar from their role in the control of tobacco and alcohol and they are superior to rationing on a number of grounds including greater sensitivity to personal preferences, less need for bureaucratic apparatus, and a capacity to serve a compensatory function. Furthermore, unlike free market controls, tax controls do not leave social protection needs to the uncertain premises and vagaries of private law initiatives.

Whatever the exact outcome of such a public choice operation might be, the salient feature of the exercise is that it would force individuals to include their own drug use and drug abuse in their political calculations.

NOTES

1. The work of Lucy Gaston, Founder of the Anti-Cigarette League, provides a good example of the social climate of that period. See Wallack (174). The propaganda of the period has been successful and durable (95, 185).
2. Since 1976 OTC drugs have been subject to certain general standards set out in the *Food and Drugs Act* (159a and b). Such standards involve conditions of manufacture, labelling, advertising, and sale.
3. Prescription-only psychoactives are listed in Schedule F of the *Food and Drug Regulations* (49). Provincial pharmacy acts may also set out a schedule of prescription drugs, a list that can add to, but not subtract from, the federal list (150).
4. In 13 States marijuana is considered a narcotic but in 37 it is a hallucinogen. In 3 States LSD is also a narcotic. The legal penalties for unauthorized use of these two drug categories vary drastically (see 154).
5. Chlorpromazine, for example, was first hailed as an antihistamine, then subsequently used in the symptomatic treatment of schizophrenia (28).
6. "During the nineteenth century the dominant [opiate] addict type was a middle-aged middle-class or upper-class female and the majority of cases were medical in origin" (33, p. 113).
7. During World War II, tobacco was classified as an "essential crop" in the U.S. and the draft board gave deferments to farmers of tobacco, wheat, and corn (155).
8. Carney (26) suggests that smoking tobacco not only creates a nuisance, it provides an outlet for aggressive acts against other people.
9. Contingency fees are prohibited or severely limited in Canada and England.
10. For an extended analysis of this issue see Oteri (126). The vitality of the constitutional arguments possible in the U.S. contrasts strikingly with the narrow, legalistic and uncritical pre-*Charter* inquiry in Canada. See Laskin (94).
11. *The Canadian Charter of Rights and Freedoms*—Part I of the *Constitution Act, 1982* (159c), being Schedule B of the *Canada Act, 1982* (U.K.), c. 11—is hereinafter referred to as the *Charter*.
12. As one example of bureaucratic corruption in high places, Freemantle (53) claims that Senator Joe McCarthy, an alcohol and morphine addict, was supplied opiates by Harry Anslinger, head of the Narcotics Bureau.

REFERENCES

1. Allentuck, A. *Who Speaks for the Patient?: The Crisis in Canadian Mental Health Care*. Don Mills, Ont.: Burns and MacEachern, 1978.

2. Allsop, J. *Health Policy and the National Health Services*. New York: Longman, 1983.
3. Bailey, G. W. Asbestos: The argument for funds. *The New York Times*. Letters to the Editor, March 7, 1982.
4. Bakalar, J. B., and Grinspoon, L. *Drug Control in a Free Society*. Cambridge: Cambridge University Press, 1981.
5. Bargmann, E., Wolfe, S. M., and Levin, J. *Stopping Valium, Ativan, Centrax, Dalmane, Librium, Paxipan, Restoril, Serax, Tranxene and Yanax*. Washington: Public Citizen, 1982.
6. Bartol, C. *Criminal Behavior—A Psychosocial Approach*. Englewood Cliffs, N.J.: Prentice-Hall, 1980.
7. Bernard, G. An economic analysis of the illicit drug market. *International Journal of the Addictions, 18*:681–700 (1983).
8. Bishop, J., and Yoo, J. H. 'Health scare', excise taxes and advertising ban in the cigarette demand and supply. *Southern Economic Journal, 52*:402–11 (1985).
9. Bloch, H. Toward better systems of drug regulation. In: Landau, R. (ed.). *Regulating New Drugs*. Chicago: University of Chicago Center for Policy Study, 1973.
10. Blum, R. H. Interest groups. In: Blum, R. H., Bovet, D., Moore, J., and Associates (eds.). *Controlling Drugs*. San Francisco: Jossey-Bass, 1974.
11. Blum, W. J., and Kalven, H. Jr. Public law perspectives on a private law problem—auto compensation plans. *University of Chicago Law Review, 31*:641–723 (1964).
12. Blum, R. H., Bovet, D., Moore, J., and Associates (eds.). *Controlling Drugs*. San Francisco: Jossey-Bass, 1974.
13. Bok, S. The ethics of giving placebos. *Scientific American, 231*:17–23 (1974).
14. Bonnie, R. J. Decriminalizing the marijuana user: A drafter's guide. *University of Michigan Law Journal, 11*:3–50 (1977).
15. Bonnie, R. J., and Whitebread, C. H. The forbidden fruit and the tree of knowledge: An inquiry into the legal history of American marijuana prohibition. *Virginia Law Review, 56*:971–1203 (1970).
16. Bovet, D. Medical science and drug classification. In: Blum, R. H., Bovet, D., Moore, J., and Associates (eds.). *Controlling Drugs*. San Francisco: Jossey-Bass, 1974.
17. Boyd, N. The origins of Canadian narcotics legislation: The process of criminalization in historical context. *Dalhousie Law Journal, 8*:102–36 (1984).
18. Brackins, L. W. The liability of physicians, pharmacists, and hospitals for adverse drug reactions. *Defense Law Journal, 34*:273–344 (1985).
19. Brecher, E. M., and the Editors of Consumer Reports. *Licit and Illicit Drugs*. Boston: Little, Brown, 1972.

20. Britain, J. E. Product honesty is the best policy: A comparison of doctors' and manufacturers' duty to disclose drug risks and the importance of consumer expectations in determining product defect. *Northwestern University Law Review*, 79:342–422 (1984).

21. Brody, J. The growing militancy of the nation's nonsmokers. *The New York Times*. January 15, 1984.

22. Brudner, A. Retributivism and the death penalty. *University of Toronto Law Journal*, 30:337–55 (1980).

23. Canada. Commission of Inquiry into the Non-Medical Use of Drugs. *Interim Report*. Ottawa: Queen's Printer, 1970.

24. Canada. Commission of Inquiry into the Non-Medical Use of Drugs. *Cannabis*. Ottawa: Information Canada, 1972.

25. Canada. Commission of Inquiry into the Non-Medical Use of Drugs. *Final Report*. Ottawa: Information Canada, 1973.

26. Carney, R. E. The abuser of tobacco. In: Cull, J. G. and Hardy, R. E. (eds.). *Types of Drug Abusers and Their Abuses*. Springfield, Ill.: Charles C Thomas, 1979.

27. Cashman, S. D. *Prohibition: The Lie of the Land*. New York: Free Press, 1981.

28. Claridge, G. *Drugs and Human Behavior*. New York: Praeger, 1970.

29. Cloyd, J. *Drugs and Information Control*. Westport, Conn.: Greenwood Press, 1982.

30. Cochrane, A. L. *Effectiveness and Efficiency: Random Reflections on Health Services*. London: Nuffield Provincial Hospital, 1972.

31. Consumers Union. *The Medicine Show*. Mount Vernon, N.Y.: Consumers Union of United States, Inc., 1974.

32. Corea, G. *The Hidden Malpractice—How American Medicine Treats Women as Patients and Professionals*. New York: William Morrow, 1977.

33. Courtwright, D. T. *Dark Paradise: Opiate Addiction in America Before 1940*. Cambridge, Mass.: Harvard University Press, 1982.

34. Cox, B., Shirley, J. and Short, M. *The Fall of Scotland Yard*. London: Penguin Books, 1977.

35. Cray, E. *In Failing Health*. Indianapolis, Ind.: Bobbs-Merrill, 1970.

36. Crichton, M. *Five Patients: The Hospital Explained*. New York: Alfred A. Knopf, 1970.

37. Davis, K. C. *Discretionary Justice: A Preliminary Inquiry*. Baton Rouge, La.: Louisiana State University Press, 1969.

38. Davis, M. Setting penalties: What does rape deserve? *Law and Philosophy*, 3:61–110 (1984).

39. Diehl, H. *Tobacco and Youth Health*. New York: McGraw-Hill, 1969.

40. Diehr, P. K., Richardson, W. C., Shortell, S. M., Lo Gerfo, J. P. Increased access to medical care—The impact on health. *Medical Care*, 17:989–99 (1979).

41. Dolan, A. K. Antitrust law and physician dominance of other health practitioners. *Journal of Health Politics, Policy and Law*, 4:675–94 (1980).

42. Dowling, H. F. *Medicine for Man: The Development, Regulation and Use of Prescription Drugs*. New York: Alfred A. Knopf, 1970.

43. Dreifers, C. *Seizing Our Bodies: The Politics of Women's Health*. New York: Vintage Books, 1977.

44. DuPont, R. L. Jr. *Getting Tough on Gateway Drugs: A Guide for the Family*. Washington: American Psychiatric Press, 1985.

45. Ellickson, R. C. The inadequacies of law and economics and other theories of social control. Faculty of Law, University of Toronto, *Law and Economics Workshop Series*. October, 1985.

46. Erickson, P. G. *Cannabis Criminals: The Social Effects of Punishment on Drug Users*. Toronto: ARF Books, 1980.

47. Fern, F. H., and Sichel, W. Evolving two liability theories: Are they taking the pharmaceutical industry into an era of absolute inability? *St. Louis University Law Journal*, 29:763–85 (1985).

48. Fingarette, H., and Hasse, A. *Mental Disabilities and Criminal Responsibility*. Berkeley, Calif.: University of California Press, 1979.

49. *Food and Drug Regulations,* C.R.C. 1978, c. 870.

50. Fort, J. The marijuana user and the abuser of psychedelic-hallucinogens. In: Cull, J. G., and Hardy, R. E. (eds.). *Types of Drug Abusers and Their Abuses*. Springfield, Ill.: Charles C Thomas, 1974.

51. Fredman, S., and Burger, P. E. *Forbidden Cures: How the FDA Suppresses Drugs That Could Save Your Life*. New York: Stein & Sage, 1970.

52. Freedman, W. *Products Liability for Corporate Counsels, Controllers and Product Safety Executives*. New York: Van Nostrand Reinhold, 1984.

53. Freemantle, B. *The Fix: The Inside Story of the World Drug Trade*. London: Michael Joseph, 1985.

54. Freidson, E. *Professional Dominance: The Social Structure of Medical Care*. New York: Atherton Press, 1970.

55. Fried, J. J. *The Vitamin Conspiracy*. New York: Saturday Review Press, 1975.

56. Friedman, M. *Capitalism and Freedom*. Chicago: University of Chicago Press, 1962.

57. Galloway, D. Review of *Sex, Drugs, Death and the Law*, by D. A. J. Richards. *University of Louisville Law Journal*, 34:100 (1984).

58. Garan, D. G. *Against Ourselves: Disorders from Improvements under the Organic Limitedness of Man*. New York: Philosophical Library, 1979.

59. Gellman, R. M. Prescribing privacy: The uncertain role of the physician in the protection of patient privacy. *North Carolina Law Review*, 62:255–94 (1982–83).

60. Goldman, M. I. *Soviet Marketing—Distribution in a Controlling Economy*. New York: Free Press of Glencoe, 1963.

61. Goode, E. *Drugs in American Society*. 2d. ed. New York: Alfred A. Knopf, 1984.

62. Goode, W. J. The protection of the inept. *American Sociological Review*, 32:6–19 (1967).

63. Graedon, J. *The People's Pharmacy*. New York: St. Martin's Press, 1976.

64. Greenberg, S. M. Compounding a felony: Drug abuse and the American legal system. In: Inciardi, J. A., and Chambers, C. D. (eds.). *Drugs and the Criminal Justice System*. Beverly Hills: Sage, 1974.

65. Greenstein, H. M., and DiBianco, P. E. Marijuana laws—a crime against humanity. *Notre Dame Law Review*, 48:314–39 (1972).

66. Grinspoon, L., and Hedblom, P. *The Speed Culture: Amphetamine Use and Abuse in America*. Cambridge, Mass.: Harvard University Press, 1975.

67. Gritz, E. R., and Jarvik, M. E. Psychoactive drugs and social behavior. In: Hammond, K. R., and Joyce, C. R. G. (eds.). *Psychoactive Drugs and Social Judgment: Theory and Research*. New York: Wiley, 1975.

68. Gross, M. L. *The Doctors*. New York: Random House, 1966.

69. Gross, M. L. *The Psychological Society*. New York: Random House, 1978.

70. Hamowy, R. Medicine and the crimination of sin: "Self-abuse" in 19th century America. *Journal of Libertarian Studies*, 1:229–70 (1977).

71. Hartmann, E. *The Sleeping Pill*. New Haven: Yale University Press, 1978.

72. Hellman, A. *Laws Against Marijuana*. Chicago: University of Illinois Press, 1975.

73. Helmer, J. *Drugs and Minority Oppression*. New York: Seabury Press, 1975.

74. Holloban, J., and Lipovenko, D. Many drugs haven't passed modern tests. *The Globe and Mail*. October 18, 1982.

75. Hubbard, W. M. Jr. Preclinical problems of new drug development. In: Landau, R. (ed.). *Regulating New Drugs*. Chicago: University of Chicago Center for Policy Study, 1973.

76. Hughes, R., and Brewin, R. *The Tranquilizing of America*. New York: Harcourt Brace Jovanovich, 1979.

77. Illich, I. *Limits of Medicine*. London: Marion Boyars, 1976.

78. Julien, R. M. *A Primer of Drug Action*. 3d ed. San Francisco: Freeman, 1981.

79. Kalant, H., and Kalant, O. J. *Drugs, Society and Personal Choice*. Toronto: University of Toronto Press, 1971.

80. Kaplan, J. *Marijuana: The New Prohibition*. New York: World, 1970.

81. Kaplan, J. The role of the law in drug control. *Duke Law Journal*:1065–1104 (1971).

82. Kaplan, J. Classification for legal control. In: Blum, R. H., Bovet, D., Moore, J. and Associates (eds.). *Controlling Drugs*. San Francisco: Jossey-Bass, 1974.

83. Kaplan, J. *The Hardest Drug: Heroin and Public Policy*. Chicago: University of Chicago Press, 1983.

84. Kay, D. A. *The International Regulation of Pharmaceutical Drugs*. St. Paul, Minn.: West, 1976.
85. Kelman, S. Regulation and paternalism. *Public Policy*, *129*:219–31 (1981).
86. Kennedy, I. *The Unmasking of Medicine*. London: Allen & Unwin, 1981.
87. King, R. The American system: Legal sanctions to repress drug abuse. In: Inciardi, J. A., and Chambers, C. D. (eds.). *Drugs and the Criminal Justice System*. Beverly Hills: Sage, 1974.
88. Kinsley, M. Fate and lawsuits litigation doesn't work. How about socialism? *The New Republic*. June 14, 1980, 2.
89. Kitch, E. W. The patent system and the new drug application: An evaluation of incentives for private investment in new drug research and marketing. In: Landau, R. (ed.). *Regulating New Drugs*. Chicago: University of Chicago Center for Policy Study, 1973.
90. Knowles, J. H. The responsibility of the individual. In: Knowles, J. H. (ed.). *Doing Better and Feeling Worse: Health in the United States*. New York: Norton, 1977.
91. Koumjian, K. The use of Valium as a form of social control. *Social Science and Medicine*, *15*:245–50 (1981).
92. Kurzman, M. G., and Magell, H. Decriminalizing possession of all controlled substances: An alternative whose time has come. *Contemporary Drug Problems*, *6*:245–59 (1977).
93. Lambert, E. C. *Modern Medical Mistakes*. Bloomington, Ind.: Indiana University Press, 1978.
94. Laskin, J. B. Constitutional authority in relation to drugs and drug use. *Osgoode Hall Law Journal*, *18*:554–83 (1986).
95. Lauderdale, P., and Inverarity, J. Regulation of opiates. *Journal of Drug Issues*, *14*:567–77 (1984).
96. Layne, N. Jr. Restricting access to non-psychoactive medications: Public health necessity or disabling professional prerogative? *Journal of Drug Issues*, *14*:595–610 (1984).
97. Leake, C. D., and Silverman, M. *Alcoholic Beverages in Clinical Medicine*. Chicago: Year Book Medical, 1966.
98. Lerner, A. P. *The Economics of Control*. New York: Macmillan, 1984.
99. Levine, H. R. Unpublished paper, 1971.
100. Levine, H. R. *Legal Dimensions of Drug Abuse in the United States*. Springfield, Ill.: Charles C Thomas, 1974.
101. Lewis, H. R., and Lewis, M. E. *The Medical Offenders*. New York: Simon and Schuster, 1970.
102. Logan, F. *Cannabis—Options for Control*. Sunbury, U.K.: Quartermaine House, 1979.
103. Mäkelä, K., Room, R., Single, E., Sulkunen, P., and Walsh, B. *Alcohol, Society and State*, Vol. 1. Toronto: Addiction Research Foundation, 1981.
104. Malleson, A. *Need Your Doctor Be So Useless?* London: George Allen & Unwin, 1973

105. Maloff, D. Informal social controls and their influence on substance use. *Journal of Drug Issues, 9*:161–65 (1979).

106. Marks, J. *The Benzodiazepines: Use, Overuse, Misuse, Abuse*. Baltimore: University Park Press, 1978.

107. McCleery, R. S., Keelty, L.T., Lam, M., Phillips, R. E., and Quirim, T. M. *One Life—One Physician*. Washington: Public Affairs Press, 1971.

108. McLaren, J. Chasing the social evil: Moral fervour and the evolution of Canada's prostitution laws, 1867–1917. *Canadian Journal of Law and Society, 1*:125–65 (1986).

109. Mendelsohn, R. S. *Male Practice: How Doctors Manipulate Women. Chicago*: Contemporary Books, 1981.

110. Mendelson, W. B. *The Use and Misuse of Sleeping Pills: Clinical Guide*. New York: Plenum, 1986.

111. Mill, J. S. On liberty. In: Wollheim, R. (ed.). *Three Essays*. London: Oxford University Press, 1975.

112. Mintz, M. *The Therapeutic Nightmare*. Boston: Houghton Mifflin, 1965.

113. Mitchell, C. N. A comparative analysis of cannabis regulation. *Queen's Law Journal, 9*:110–42 (1983).

114. Mitchell, C. N. Willingness-to-pay: Taxation and tax evasion. *Memphis State University Law Review, 21*:127–78 (1985).

115. Mitchell, C. N. Culpable mental disorders and criminal liability. *International Journal of Law and Psychiatry, 8*:273–99 (1986).

116. Moore, M. H. Regulating heroin: Kaplan and Trebach on the dilemmas of public policy. *American Bar Foundation Research Journal*:723–31 (1984).

117. Morris, N., and Hawkins, G. *The Honest Politician's Guide to Crime Control*. Chicago: University of Chicago Press, 1969.

118. Muller, M. *The Health of Nations*. London: Faber & Faber, 1982.

119. Murray, J., Williams, T., and Clare, A. Health and social characteristics of long-term psychotropic drug takers. *Social Science and Medicine, 16*:1595–98 (1982).

120. *Narcotic Control Regulations,* C.R.C. 1978, c. 1041.

121. Newman, G. *Just and Painful Punishment*. New York: Macmillan, 1983.

122. Note. The liability of providers of alcohol; Dram Shop Act? *Pepperdine Law Review, 12*:177–213 (1984).

123. Note. Restraints on alcoholic beverage advertising, constitutional analysis. *Notre Dame Law Review, 60*:779–99 (1985).

124. Nozick, R. *Anarchy, State and Utopia*. New York: Basic Books, 1974.

125. Ontario. *Statutes*.
    a. *Health Disciplines Act*, R.S.O. 1980, c. 196.
    b. *Liquor Control Act*, R.S.O. 1980, c. 243.

126. Oteri, J. S., and Silverglate, H. A. The pursuit of pleasure: constitutional dimensions of the marihuana problem. *Suffolk University Law Review, 3*:55–85 (1968).

127. Peltzman, S. The health effects of mandatory prescriptions. Consumer and Corporate Affairs Seminar Series, Carleton University, Ottawa, November 22, 1985.

128. Petursson, H., and Lader, M. H. Benzodiazepine dependence. *British Journal of Addiction*, 76:133–45 (1981).

129. Phinney, R. Scandal on high down under. *The Globe and Mail*. June 15, 1985.

130. Pierce, R. J. Jr. Encouraging safety: The limits of tort law and government regulations. *Vanderbilt Law Review*, 33:1281–1331 (1980).

131. Rawls, J. *A Theory of Justice*. Cambridge, Mass.: Belknap Press, 1971.

132. Reed, J. D. Water, water everywhere. *Time*. May 20, 1985.

133. Regush, N. M. *The Drug Addiction Business*. New York: Dial Press, 1971.

134. Rice, J. *Ups and Downs: Drugging and Doping*. New York: Macmillan, 1972.

135. Richards, D. A. J. Drug use and the rights of the person: A moral argument for decriminalization of certain forms of drug use. *Rutgers Law Review*, 33:607–86 (1981).

136. Richards, D. A. J. *Sex, Drugs, Death and the Law*. Totawa, N.J.: Rowman & Littlefield, 1982.

137. Rock, P. *Drugs and Politics*. New Brunswick, N.J.: Transaction Books, 1977.

138. Rosenberg, D. The causal connection in mass exposure cases: A 'public law' vision of the tort system. *Harvard Law Review*, 97:849–929 (1984).

139. Rosenberg, P. The abusers of stimulants and depressants. In: Cull, J. G., and Hardy, R. E. (eds.). *Types of Drug Abusers and Their Abuses*. Springfield, Ill.: Charles C Thomas, 1974.

140. Rosenblatt, S., and Dodson, R. *Beyond Valium: The Brave New World of Psycho-chemistry*. New York: Putnam, 1981.

141. Rosenthal, M. Partial prohibition of non-medical drug use: A proposal. *Journal of Drug Issues*, 9:437–89 (1979).

142. Rublowsky, J. *The Stoned Age—A History of Drugs in America*. New York: Putnam, 1974.

143. Rudolph, B. Tobacco takes a new road. *Time*. November 18, 1985.

144. Rumack, M. Prostitution: A penal or a medical problem. *Chitty's Law Journal*, 20:49–57 (1972).

145. Russell, M. A. H. Tobacco smoking and nicotine dependence. In: Gibbins, R., Israel, Y., Kalant, H., Popham, R. E., Schmidt, W., and Smart, R. G. (eds.). *Research Advances in Alcohol and Drug Problems*, Vol. 3. New York: Wiley, 1976.

146. Sapolsky, H. M. The political obstacles to the control of cigarette smoking in the United States. *Journal of Health Politics, Policy and Law*, 5:277–90 (1980).

147. Schroeder, R. C. *The Politics of Drugs*. 2d ed. Washington, D.C.: Congressional Quarterly Press, 1980.

148. Schultz, C. B. Statutory classification of cocaine as a narcotic: An illogical anachronism. *American Journal of Law and Medicine, 9*:225–45 (1983).

149. Scott, K. E. Two models of the civil process. *Stanford Law Review, 27*:937–50 (1975).

150. Sellers, E. M., and Sellers, S. Canada. In: Wardell, W. M. (ed.). *Controlling the Use of Therapeutic Drugs: An International Comparison.* Washington: American Enterprise Institute for Public Policy Research, 1978.

151. Silverman, M., and Lee, P. R. *Pills, Profits and Politics.* Berkeley: University of California Press, 1974.

152. Silverman, M., Lee, P. R., and Lydecker, M. *Prescriptions for Death.* Berkeley: University of California Press, 1982.

153. Skolnick, J. Coercion to virtue: The enforcement of morals. *Southern California Law Review, 41*:588–642 (1968).

154. Smart, R. *Forbidden Highs. The Nature, Treatment, and Prevention of Illicit Drug Abuse.* Toronto: Addiction Research Foundation, 1983.

155. Sobel, R. *They Satisfy: The Cigarette in American Life.* Garden City, N.Y.: Anchor Books/Doubleday, 1978.

156. Spake, A. The pushers. In: Dreifers, C. (ed.). *Seizing Our Bodies: The Politics of Women's Health.* New York: Vintage Books, 1977.

157. Stachnik, T. J. The case against criminal penalties for illicit drug use. *American Psychologist, 27*:637–42 (1972).

158. Stapleton, J. Compensating victims of diseases. *Oxford Journal of Legal Studies, 5*:248–68 (1985).

159. *Statutes of Canada.*
    a. *An Act to Amend the Food and Drugs Act,* s.c. 1976–77, c. 28.
    b. *An Act to Amend the Food and Drugs Act,* s.c. 1981, c. 47.
    c. *Constitution Act, 1982* (Part I: *Canadian Charter of Rights and Freedoms*)
    d. *Food and Drugs Act,* r.s.c. 1970, c. F-27.
    e. *Narcotic Control Act,* r.s.c. 1970, c. N-1
    f. *Tobacco Restraint Act,* r.s.c. 1970, c. T-9.

160. Strug, D., Wish, E., Johnson, B., Anderson, K., Miller, T., and Sears, A. The role of alcohol in the crimes of active heroin users. *Crime and Delinquency, 30*:551–67 (1984).

161. Szasz, T. The ethics of addiction. In: Brown, C. C., and Savage, C. (eds.). *The Drug Abuse Controversy.* Baltimore: National Educational Consultants, 1971.

162. Szasz, T. *Ceremonial Chemistry: The Ritual Persecution of Drug Addicts and Pushers.* Garden City, N.Y.: Anchor Press/Doubleday, 1974.

163. Szasz, T. *The Therapeutic State.* Buffalo: Prometheus Books, 1984.

164. Teff, H. *Drugs, Society and the Law.* Westmead, England: Saxon House, 1975.

165. *Time.* Socialism: Trials and Errors. March 13, 1978.

166. *Time.* Definitely not USDA approved. August 23, 1982.

167. Tonkin, M. *South Africa—A Nation of Pill Swallowers.* Johannesburg: Institute for the Study of Man in Africa, 1977.
168. Toronto. *The Globe and Mail.* Smokers in Israel left fuming, July 5, 1985, 6.
169. Toufexis, A. Goodies to the good. *Time.* November 18, 1985.
170. Trauberman, J. Statutory reform of 'toxic torts': Relieving legal, scientific and economic burdens on the chemical victim. *Harvard Environment Law Review,* 7:172–96 (1983).
171. Trebach, A. *The Heroin Solution.* New Haven: Yale University Press, 1982.
172. Tushnet, L. *The Medicine Men.* New York: St. Martin's Press, 1971.
173. Vener, A. M., Krupka, L. R., and Climo, J. J. Drugs (prescription, over-the-counter, social) and the young adult: Use and attitudes. *International Journal of the Addictions, 17:*399–415 (1982).
174. Wallack, L. Mass media and drinking, smoking and drug-taking. *Contemporary Drug Problems, 9:*49–83 (1980).
175. Wardell, W. M. (ed.). *Controlling the Use of Therapeutic Drugs: An International Comparison.* Washington: American Enterprise Institute for Public Policy Research, 1978.
176. Whitaker, R. *Drugs and the Law: The Canadian Scene.* Toronto: Methuen, 1969.
177. Will, G. F. Tobacco vs "Thin Skull Doctrine." Ottawa *Citizen.* February 11, 1985.
178. Williams, G. The aims of the law of tort. *Current Legal Problems,* 4:137–76 (1951).
179. Williams, S. The use of beverage alcohol as medicine, 1790–1860. *Journal of Studies on Alcohol, 41:*543–66 (1980).
180. Wilson, L. C. *Juvenile Court in Canada.* Toronto: Carswell, 1982.
181. Wisotsky, S. Exposing the war on cocaine: The futility and destructiveness of prohibition. *Wisconsin Law Review:*1305–1426 (1983).
182. Wohl, S. M. *The Medical Industrial Complex.* New York: Crown, 1984.
183. Wolcott, D., Fawzy, F., and Coombs, R. Reinforcing networks: The medical, pharmaceutical, mass media and paraphernalia establishments. *Journal of Drug Issues, 14:*223–231 (1984).
184. Young, J. *The Drugtakers.* London: MacGibbon & Kee, 1971.
185. Zentner, J. Heroin: Devil drug or useful medicine? *Journal of Drug Issues, 9:*333–40 (1979).
186. Zilbergeld, B. *The Shrinking of America: Myths of Psychological Change.* Boston: Little, Brown, 1983.

Concluding Remarks:
A Risky Business

Taking drugs is a risky business. Section 1 of this book described how the various illegal substances available on the black market act on the mind and on the body. Drugs are not completely predictable in their psychological or physiological effects. Some of the possible outcomes of drug consumption are very serious indeed, such as dependence or death. Others are epidemiologically more common, but potentially less serious. Some of the hazards can be avoided by choosing less risky drugs or less risky modes of administration, or minimized by adopting moderate patterns of use. Nevertheless, whether a drug is legal or illegal, the first-time user cannot predict what the long-term consequences may be.

All drugs involve risks to health, but the illegal ones also expose the user to the possibility of being searched, arrested, and processed through the criminal justice system. As we saw in Section 5, the immediate consequences of a first conviction for a drug offence may be relatively minor: unpleasant and inconvenient, but not necessarily devastating. Be that as it may, the first offender cannot know what the long-term effects of having a criminal record may be, how many career paths will be blocked or opportunities excluded. Thus, becoming an illicit drug user not only makes one vulnerable to having uninvited guests searching one's living quarters, but can also have serious lifetime consequences.

The illicit drug market is risky big business. On the lower levels, among users, the trade is casual and tends to be integrated into existing friendship networks. As an informal social gesture, bringing a piece of hashish to a dinner party may be no different from presenting a bottle of wine to one's host; by the letter of the law, however, in the former case the guest is liable to life imprisonment. The statistical likelihood of becoming involved in the drug trade increases as illicit drug use becomes more frequent, and heavier users tend to find themselves buying for friends or selling illicit drugs to help pay for personal consumption. Only a small proportion of them will adopt dealing as a primary source of income, but some do, and some of them become more ambitious and take the even higher risks of launching amateur importing endeavours. As we saw in Chapter 20, on the international level the profits of the black market become such that some importing cartels grow to resemble multinational corporations, with profits to match.

Proposing drug policy is a risky business. Illicit drug use is a highly charged and contentious issue. Scientists who study the various aspects of this complex topic soon discover that their conclusions and research reports are received by the various vocal constituencies as proof of political bias. No matter how hard they may try to be neutral and objective, scholars run the risk of being branded as right-wing or left-wing on drug policy, and sometimes by different interest groups as both simultaneously. They must also learn to live with the knowledge that their work may be taken out of context, or used as ammunition in political debates not of their own making. In this, of course, they are not unlike scientists who work in other controversial areas.

Throughout this volume, a common theme has been reiterated: there is widespread agreement that Canada's drug policies should be changed, but little consensus on the nature of the changes needed. It is little wonder, therefore, that there is a paucity of political will for drug law reform. Drug users risk public identification as criminals if they lobby for reform. In the vacuum created by their absence from the public forum, concerned citizens' groups, buttressed by worst-case scenarios and by justifiable fears for the risks young drug users are running, dominate the debate. Not surprisingly, then, politicians prefer not to appear "soft" on drugs and continue to adhere to the status quo.

There are so many unknowns in the drug use field that designing policy becomes a difficult and risky task. Canada's policy of criminal prohibition has been in place for the better part of this century, and has been the dominant model of drug control in the twentieth century. In recent years, some European countries and jurisdictions in the United States have "decriminalized" cannabis possession. These examples afford empirical, cost-benefit analysis of this policy (Chapter 23). Otherwise, innovative policy design must be based on a priori forecasts of the costs and benefits that can be expected if a new policy functions as it should.

What are we going to do about drugs in Canada? The weight of opinion would tend in the direction of doing "something," but it is equivocal with regard to specific policies.

As we have seen in Sections 2 and 3, the original justification for doing something was a moral one. Drug taking was perceived as a vice that could lead to a number of adverse consequences, mostly ones that would undermine the moral fibre of the nation. Today some believe this position is difficult to defend as long as some recreational drugs are legally available, socially sanctioned, and taxed by the government.

The modern justification for doing something is based on concerns for public health and safety. In the minds of some of the contributors to this book, most notably Green and Mitchell (Chapters 12 and 25), this newer orientation does not get us off the horns of the licit-illicit dilemma. If the well-being of Canadians is our concern, we should design our policies to include all drugs that people use recreationally, and, logically, should base our social response on an assessment of the potential for harm of each drug.

Drugs are consumer commodities and thus policies to reduce consumption can be aimed at either the demand, or supply, or both. Demand-reduction policies normally involve manipulation or persuasion of drug users: education, treatment of problem users, or encouraging temperance sentiments. Supply-reduction measures are oriented to the drugs themselves and involve coercion: limiting availability by taxation or regulation, making drugs expensive or hard to obtain, stopping drugs at the border, or seizing those found in the country.

Although criminal prohibition is primarily supply oriented, conventional wisdom assumes that, through deterrence, it also has an effect on demand by threatening users and sellers with sanctions. Research in this area indicates that the effectiveness of deterrence cannot be assumed; it must be examined with respect to individual crimes and, regarding the drug offences, should be evaluated for each drug separately. Most deterrence research which has focused on cannabis (see Chapter 23) has found that perceived risks of being apprehended and punished have negligible demonstrable effect on demand.

In the attempt to assess the supply-side effectiveness of criminal prohibition, the clandestine nature of the drug black market presents many methodological problems. We can measure the quantities of drugs seized by law enforcement agents, but we can only estimate the amount that finds its way to consumers. We can worry about the apparent vicious circle in which drug law enforcement increases the drug trade's profitability and thereby its durability (Chapter 20). That illicit drugs are relatively expensive and not always easy to acquire indicates the degree of success that criminal prohibition has had in limiting availability. Nevertheless, the potential effects of alternative policies on supply can only be a matter for speculation and informed guesswork.

We know from experience with legal drugs that supply-side analysis is of crucial importance. It may be instructive, then, to consider some of the lessons that have been learned about supply and demand reduction from alcohol policy research.

Epidemiological research into alcohol consumption indicates that the availability of this drug is strongly related to the incidence of alcohol-related problems. Indeed, it is reasonable to assume that conditions creating easier access to any drug will increase consumption as well as adverse consequences of use. Easier access includes cost factors such as the amount of time and inconvenience necessary to obtain it, as well as the monetary value of the drug relative to disposable incomes. Hence, alcohol policies imposing taxation, or limitations on numbers of retail outlets, or restrictions on hours of sale, all reduce availability. Thus, criminal prohibition is not the only way to make drugs relatively expensive and difficult to buy.

The availability model is a pure supply-side model, linking substance use problems to per capita consumption of the substance. Because of countervailing attitudes and interests, it serves more as the conscience of alcohol policy than as a practical guide for reform. In practice, policy initiatives are more commonly directed against the consequences of drinking than against consumption itself.

Take, for example, the problem of deaths and injuries on our highways, a significant number of which are alcohol-related. In theory, there are several policy directions that governments could adopt. For example, countries could take measures to cut back automobile production and importation, to tax vehicles out of the market, or to persuade people to give up driving. Instead of such general initiatives, policies tend to be aimed specifically at the dangerous combination of drinking and driving, just as speed limits focus on one particularly risky driving behaviour. As a result, through threat and persuasion, governments have tried to change drivers' attitudes and behaviour in order to reduce impaired driving.

This emphasis on specific substance-related problems rather than on consumption as a whole is reflected in another school of thought in alcohol policy, the "integration" approach. Advocates of this position argue that drinking problems arise because of dysfunctional attitudes and because of ambivalence over societal reactions to adverse consequences of drinking. They propose that alcohol should be demystified and integrated into daily life, in short, that moderate drinking should be encouraged at the expense of excessive drinking.

Needless to say, this integration approach is popular with the alcohol industry, whose members react to restrictive alcohol control policies by claiming that they only reinforce unhealthy attitudes. Scholars who hold that availability is the most important determinant of problems tend to dismiss the integration model as reflecting self-interest rather than good science. They also note instances when new and less risky drinking practices have added to existing problem drinking patterns rather than substituting for them. However, the integration model has never been fully implemented or adequately evaluated. New products have been introduced (such as beverages with lower alcoholic content) and drinking patterns have changed (the increased popularity of drinking wine with meals, for example). Nevertheless, these changes were not accompanied by demand-reduction measures to encourage substitution of the new patterns of use for traditional or higher-risk drinking practices. Thus, the jury is still out on the issue of whether active promotion of moderate drinking accompanied by equally aggressive campaigns against problem patterns of use would reduce the incidence of adverse consequences of drinking.

Just as with alcohol prohibition, the social response to illicit substances has emphasized supply over demand. The experiment of banning alcohol was not followed by a groundswell of temperance sentiment, and the level of demand remained high. This is perhaps not surprising, as to date no society has fully taken up the challenge of a comprehensive demand-reduction program aimed at non-medical drug use, legal or illegal. Arguably, public education about the risks of tobacco smoking has achieved a measure of success, but as long as tobacco advertising continues, the demand-reduction effort cannot be considered comprehensive.

The reasons why there are few new initiatives on the demand side of illicit drug policy making are unclear. Part of the explanation for this oversight may be that demand reduction runs against the tide of our consumer society, where so many resources are devoted to product promotion and the expansion of markets. From this perspective, there is some irony in the observation that marketing firms are hired to design anti-drug media campaigns, with the confidence that they will be just as good at discouraging consumption of unadvertised commodities as they are at encouraging consumption of the products they promote.

Of more importance, perhaps, is the political inertia of the criminal prohibition policy, and the way in which it has imposed its definitions on the universe of discourse about drugs. Although the drug laws are framed in such a way as to suggest that all drugs are not uniformly morally reprehensible, certainly all apprehended drug users are uniformly treated as criminals. Judicial discretion aside, the laws also do not take into account the seriousness of various drug-related activities (sharing a drug vs. selling a drug) or patterns of use (being an infrequent user vs. being an addict). The image communicated by criminal prohibition is that of a monolithic evil that will not be tolerated in any form.

The exploration of successful and sensitive demand-reduction and problem-reduction strategies appears to be the most promising challenge of the future. Initiatives in this area will require clear definition of goals, and some hard questions will have to be answered in their formulation. Is society concerned about drug use per se, or the riskier patterns of use, or the adverse consequences? Does advising moderation in drug use or teaching users how to protect themselves from adverse consequences contradict the message that abstinence would be preferable?

These are questions that lend themselves to rational analysis, but proposals arising from such an endeavour are likely to elicit heated debate. A case in point is the argument against providing birth control advice to sexually active teenagers, on the grounds that it undermines the goal of preserving teenage chastity. In this case, two goals (preventing risky sex and preventing sex) are perceived to be at odds. Cost-benefit analyses of measures to achieve these goals, singly or in combination, accompanied by well-controlled evaluative research, would seem to be a reasonable approach to untangling the apparent contradictions and reducing the emotionalism of the debate.

Our concern in this book has been the illicit drugs, but many of the contributing authors see this problem as one of many, often interlocking, behavioural and social problems. In closing, then, we make one further recommendation. The issue cries out for rational, cost-benefit policy analysis, based on carefully defined goals and amenable to scientific evaluation. However, this endeavour should be grounded in a broad and coherent public health perspective that embraces larger questions about the quality of life of Canadians.

APPENDIX A

Selected Statistics on Convictions for Illicit Drug Use in Canada

Joan A. E. Moreau

Table A.1   Number of Convictions for Selected Drugs in Canada, 1965–1985

Table A.2   Number of Convictions for Selected Drugs by Province, 1980–1985

Table A.3   Conviction Rates for Selected Drugs, Canada and the Provinces, 1975, 1980, and 1985

Table A.4   Sentences Imposed for Simple Possession of Selected Drugs in Canada, 1980 and 1985

Table A.5   Sentences Imposed for Trafficking and Possession for the Purpose of Trafficking of Selected Drugs in Canada, 1980 and 1985

Source: Annual Reports, Bureau of Dangerous Drugs, Health Protection Branch, Health and Welfare Canada, Ottawa.

Table A.1
Number of Convictions for Selected Drugs in Canada, 1965–1985[a]

| Year | Cocaine | Cannabis | Heroin | Hallucinogens[b] | |
				Phencyclidine	FDA, Pt. IV
1965	3	60	266	—	—
1966	1	144	221	—	—
1967	—	586	348	—	—
1968	2	1,429	279	—	—
1969	1	2,964	310	—	—
1970	12	6,270	383	—	1,643
1971	19	9,478	502	—	1,923
1972	44	11,713	923	—	1,709
1973	123	19,929	1,290	19	1,764
1974	237	29,067	798	254	1,986
1975	289	27,367	511	467	1,903
1976	363	39,259	708	484	1,360
1977	420	41,982	636	767	1,069
1978	507	36,079	580	580	1,093
1979	592	36,103	509	448	1,590
1980	850	40,781	309	399	2,402
1981	1,255	43,880	261	498	2,514
1982	1,334	34,886	286	688	1,931
1983	1,592	28,955	295	455	2,171
1984	2,234	26,193	302	347	1,888
1985	2,218	22,510	256	298	1,259

[a] In 1980, the Bureau of Dangerous Drugs started reporting their data in their annual reports over a five-year period, updating the figures for the previous four years. For example, in the 1981 report, the total convictions for cocaine were shown as 1,048; in the latest report (1985) this figure had increased to 1,255. Similarly, each total will be adjusted annually, and therefore caution must be exercised in drawing conclusions about upward or downward trends.

[b] It should be noted that phencyclidine was listed under the *Narcotic Control Act* in 1973. All other hallucinogens are listed under Part IV of the *Food and Drugs Act*, enacted in 1969.

Table A.2
Number of Convictions for Selected Drugs by Province, 1980–1985

					Hallucinogens	
Province	Year	Cocaine	Cannabis	Heroin	Phencyclidine	FDA, Pt. IV
Nfld.	1980	1	965	—	4	30
	1981	1	1,165	—	2	40
	1982	5	690	—	2	25
	1983	3	582	—	1	30
	1984	9	582	—	3	31
	1985	4	507	—	—	25
P.E.I.	1980	—	184	—	2	7
	1981	—	159	—	1	6
	1982	—	91	—	—	5
	1983	1	83	—	1	47
	1984	1	106	—	1	27
	1985	—	73	—	—	3
N.S.	1980	6	1,813	—	2	53
	1981	13	1,762	—	3	67
	1982	11	1,473	1	8	48
	1983	28	1,022	—	1	86
	1984	28	880	—	4	56
	1985	17	605	—	1	45
N.B.	1980	2	919	—	32	34
	1981	5	873	—	14	45
	1982	5	607	—	9	34
	1983	13	523	—	2	38
	1984	19	568	—	12	32
	1985	13	571	1	12	28
Que.	1980	286	4,357	87	234	339
	1981	471	5,564	65	363	411
	1982	556	5,786	59	567	332
	1983	761	5,908	68	390	396
	1984	1,099	4,256	68	287	338
	1985	1,100	3,234	61	255	209
Ont.	1980	242	16,522	34	115	956
	1981	298	17,050	38	106	973
	1982	329	12,830	64	87	682
	1983	367	9,058	60	52	585
	1984	537	8,432	77	32	457
	1985	634	7,433	97	21	336

Table A.2 (continued)
Number of Convictions for Selected Drugs by Province, 1980–1985

| Province | Year | Cocaine | Cannabis | Heroin | Hallucinogens | |
					Phencyclidine	FDA, Pt. IV
Man.	1980	17	1,623	—	1	126
	1981	20	1,951	—	—	140
	1982	17	1,508	—	2	92
	1983	37	1,285	—	—	133
	1984	45	1,243	—	1	117
	1985	29	1,228	1	—	81
Sask.	1980	9	1,912	1	—	96
	1981	23	2,235	1	—	84
	1982	16	1,439	1	—	66
	1983	22	1,384	3	—	117
	1984	19	1,326	—	—	75
	1985	16	1,109	—	—	70
Alta.	1980	102	7,228	32	6	485
	1981	171	7,267	22	7	439
	1982	145	4,867	17	12	330
	1983	153	3,934	11	6	309
	1984	158	3,953	18	4	304
	1985	154	3,802	6	8	207
B.C.	1980	181	5,086	155	3	271
	1981	244	5,620	134	2	294
	1982	248	5,384	144	1	309
	1983	200	4,974	153	2	412
	1984	313	4,624	139	3	436
	1985	238	3,717	90	1	245
Yukon	1980	3	49	—	—	1
	1981	7	76	—	—	5
	1982	2	66	—	—	3
	1983	4	108	—	—	11
	1984	2	113	—	—	10
	1985	6	115	—	—	7
N.W.T.	1980	1	123	—	—	4
	1981	2	158	1	—	10
	1982	—	145	—	—	5
	1983	3	94	—	—	7
	1984	4	110	—	—	5
	1985	7	116	—	—	3

Table A.3
Conviction Rates for Selected Drugs, Canada and the Provinces,
1975, 1980, and 1985[a]

(Rates per 100,000 population aged 16 years and older)

| Province | Year | Cocaine | Cannabis | Heroin | Hallucinogens | |
					Phencyclidine	FDA, Pt. IV
Nfld.	1975	—	114.2	—	3.8	9.8
	1980	0.3	254.2	—	1.1	7.9
	1985	1.0	122.3	—	—	6.0
P.E.I.	1975	1.2	104.5	—	1.2	—
	1980	—	206.7	—	2.2	7.9
	1985	—	77.1	—	—	3.2
N.S.	1975	—	198.4	0.7	6.6	3.8
	1980	1.0	290.1	—	0.3	8.5
	1985	2.5	89.8	—	0.1	6.7
N.B.	1975	0.2	121.4	—	3.9	1.3
	1980	0.4	182.8	—	6.4	6.8
	1985	2.4	105.9	0.2	2.2	5.2
Que.	1975	0.7	60.2	0.9	1.4	15.6
	1980	5.9	89.9	1.8	4.8	7.0
	1985	21.5	63.1	1.2	5.0	4.1
Ont.	1975	1.5	171.7	1.1	5.2	9.9
	1980	3.7	254.5	0.5	1.8	14.7
	1985	9.0	105.5	1.4	0.3	4.8
Man.	1975	3.6	210.2	0.7	1.2	7.6
	1980	2.2	212.6	—	0.1	16.5
	1985	3.6	151.0	0.1	—	10.0
Sask.	1975	0.5	229.9	0.6	0.2	10.1
	1980	1.3	272.8	0.1	—	13.7
	1985	2.1	146.6	—	—	9.3
Alta.	1975	1.2	299.5	5.4	0.9	12.9
	1980	6.5	458.5	2.0	0.4	30.8
	1985	8.8	216.7	0.3	0.5	11.8
B.C.	1975	6.7	309.4	18.2	0.3	15.6
	1980	8.9	249.4	7.6	0.1	13.3
	1985	10.6	165.0	4.0	0.04	10.9
Yukon &	1975	2.6	548.6	—	—	18.4
N.W.T.	1980	9.2	396.3	—	—	11.5
	1985	26.1	462.9	—	—	20.0
Canada	1975	1.8	168.8	3.2	2.9	11.7
	1980	4.7	224.6	1.7	2.2	13.2
	1985	11.4	115.3	1.3	1.5	6.5

[a]Based on population estimates published by Statistics Canada, Ottawa.

Table A.4

Sentences Imposed for Simple Possession of Selected Drugs in Canada, 1980 and 1985

Sentence Imposed	Year	Cannabis		Cocaine		Heroin		Hallucinogens[a]	
		N	%	N	%	N	%	N	%
Fine only	1980	21,973	63.2	313	67.3	34	34.7	863	71.0
	1985	12,541	68.2	924	73.8	30	32.3	532	68.1
Suspended sentence/probation	1980	1,423	4.1	20	4.3	22	22.4	81	6.7
	1985	921	5.0	39	3.1	12	12.9	52	6.7
Absolute/conditional discharge	1980	9,828	28.3	45	9.7	2	2.0	109	9.0
	1985	3,333	18.1	79	6.3	3	3.2	68	8.7
Imprisonment	1980	1,533	4.4	87	18.7	40	40.8	163	13.4
	1985	1,604	8.7	210	16.8	48	51.6	129	16.5
Total sentences[b]	1980	34,757	100.0	465	100.0	98	100.0	1,216	100.0
	1985	18,399	100.0	1,252	100.0	93	100.0	781	100.0

[a] Hallucinogens do not include phencyclidine, as sentencing information is not available for this drug. The figures shown here represent convictions for the *Food and Drugs Act*, Part IV, only.
[b] Excludes those sentences classified as "Other" by the Bureau of Dangerous Drugs. Also, note that the figures in the percentage columns may not total 100.0, due to rounding.

Table A.5

Sentences Imposed for Trafficking and Possession for the Purpose of Trafficking of Selected Drugs in Canada, 1980 and 1985

Sentence Imposed	Year	Cannabis		Cocaine		Heroin		Hallucinogens[a]	
		N	%	N	%	N	%	N	%
Non-imprisonment	1980	1,708	32.1	65	17.5	34	16.8	310	26.4
	1985	1,307	34.2	242	25.6	16	10.5	137	29.0
Imprisonment									
<1 year	1980	3,173	59.6	120	32.3	36	17.8	695	59.1
	1985	2,189	57.3	404	42.7	36	23.7	265	56.0
1 year – < 2 years	1980	372	7.0	88	23.7	49	24.3	141	12.0
	1985	284	7.4	199	21.0	38	25.0	59	12.5
2 years and over	1980	72	1.4	98	26.4	83	41.1	30	2.6
	1985	38	1.0	101	10.7	62	40.8	12	2.5
Total sentences[b]	1980	5,325	100.0	371	100.0	202	100.0	1,176	100.0
	1985	3,818	100.0	946	100.0	152	100.0	473	100.0

[a] Hallucinogens do not include phencyclidine, as sentencing information is not available for this drug. The figures shown here represent convictions for the *Food and Drugs Act*, Part IV, only.
[b] Excludes those sentences classified as "Other" by the Bureau of Dangerous Drugs. Also, note that the figures in the percentage columns may not total 100.0, due to rounding.

BIOGRAPHICAL NOTES

Bruce Alexander (Ph.D.) is a Professor of Psychology at Simon Fraser University. He received his doctorate in comparative psychology from the University of Wisconsin in 1966. After a few years of research in primate behaviour, he became interested in drug issues and, since 1970, has undertaken research in rat psychopharmacology, family therapy with addicts, and drug use among university students. He is currently working on a book relating psychological theory to Canadian drug policy.

Judith Blackwell (Ph.D.) began her research into the non-medical use of drugs as a member of the research staff of the Le Dain Commission. Since then, she has been a Policy Advisor for Health and Welfare Canada and from 1980 to 1987 was a Research Scientist at the Addiction Research Foundation of Ontario. Her doctoral research at the London School of Economics focused on the ways in which heroin users minimize the risks of adverse consequences of use, including addiction. Her research interests include epidemiology, the sociology of deviant behaviour, the meaning and nature of dependence, and the analysis of drug policy in Canada, the United Kingdom, and the United States. In 1987, she became a member of the Department of Sociology at Brock University, St. Catharines, Ontario.

Neil Boyd (LL.M.) is an Associate Professor and Associate Director of the School of Criminology at Simon Fraser University; he is currently Director of the Criminology Research Centre. Professor Boyd has written extensively on the subjects of drug control policy and substance criminalization. He is part-author and editor of the text *The Social Dimensions of Law* (Prentice-Hall, 1986), and is currently writing a book on murder.

Michael Bozarth (Ph.D.) is currently an Associate Professor in the Department of Psychology, State University of New York at Buffalo. He is affiliated with the Center for Studies in Behavioral Neurobiology and the Department of Psychology at Concordia University. His research interests involve the study of brain reward systems with a specific focus on how addictive drugs interact with these systems.

Robert Coambs (Ph.D.) holds a doctorate in psychology from the University of Toronto. He is currently a Scientist with the smoking research program at the Addiction Research Foundation of Ontario. His research has been concerned with personality theories of addiction and the reinforcing properties of opiates. His current research focuses on the assessment of cognitive effects of nicotine, diazepam and alcohol, and the influence these effects have on sustaining substance abuse.

Patricia Erickson (Ph.D.) is Head of Drug Policy Research within the Prevention Studies Department of the Addiction Research Foundation, and she lectures in the undergraduate program in criminology at the University of Toronto. She was a researcher with the Centre of Criminology before joining the ARF in 1973. She is the author of *Cannabis Criminals: The Social Effects of Punishment on Drug Users* (ARF Books, 1980) and one of the authors of *The Steel Drug: Cocaine in Perspective* (Lexington Books, 1987). Her other publications and interests are in the areas of the police role, comparative juvenile justice systems, and deterrence. She received her doctorate in social administration from the University of Glasgow, Scotland.

Kevin O'Brien Fehr (Ph.D.), Science Educator at the Addiction Research Foundation of Ontario's School for Addiction Studies, has a background in behavioural pharmacology. For several years, she worked as a Scientist in the Documentation Section of the Foundation, specializing in the toxicology of illicit drugs. She lectures across Canada on non-medical drug use, to both general and professional audiences.

P. James Giffen (M.A.) is Professor Emeritus of Sociology at the University of Toronto and author of sundry writings on official rates of deviance, alcohol, lesser drugs, and the sociology of law.

Melvyn Green (LL.B.) has been a barrister with the Toronto firm of Ruby and Edwardh since 1981. His practice is almost exclusively devoted to criminal litigation, a substantial portion of which involves drug cases. He is an Associate Editor of the *Canadian Rights Reporter*, and a frequent lecturer at the Addiction Research Foundation of Ontario's School for Addiction Studies. Mr. Green has taught sociology at Carleton University, has served as Research Associate for the Le Dain Commission, has consulted on drug policy and legislative reform for Health and Welfare Canada, and has worked on a number of drug research projects in the United States and England. Mr. Green has written extensively on non-medical drug use and, in particular, on the history of Canadian drug control efforts.

Patricia Hadaway (Ph.D.) holds a doctorate in psychology from Simon Fraser University, and is currently working at Malaspina College in Nanaimo, British Columbia. Her research interests include factors leading to addiction (including smoking behaviour). She is also interested in the civil rights of smokers and other drug users.

John Hagan (Ph.D.) is Professor of Sociology and Law at the University of Toronto. He is currently studying the imposition of sanctions on securities violators and the entry and advancement of women and men in the legal profession. He is an Associate Editor of the *American Sociological Review*, an International Consulting Editor for the *American Journal of Sociology*, and serves on the editorial boards of several other American and Canadian journals. His recent books include *Modern Criminology* (McGraw-Hill, 1985) and *The Disreputable Pleasures* (McGraw-Hill Ryerson, 1984).

Riley Hinson (Ph.D.) is currently Associate Professor of Psychology at the University of Western Ontario in London, Ontario. He has published several articles in the areas of behavioural pharmacology and learning. Since 1984, he has been President of the Section on Psychopharmacology of the Canadian Psychological Association.

Marvin Krank (Ph.D.) is an Assistant Professor of Psychology at Mount Allison University in Sackville, New Brunswick. He is currently researching the effects of drug conditioning on drug-taking behaviour.

Sylvia Lambert (B.A.) is a graduate in sociology from the University of Toronto. As a Senior Research Assistant with the Addiction Research Foundation, she has co-authored several articles on the chronic drunkenness offender and drinking among homosexuals. She has also edited the papers from various symposia held at the ARF into book form.

Christopher Millard (LL.M.) is a graduate of the University of Sheffield, and the Centre of Criminology and the Faculty of Law, University of Toronto. In 1985 he published *Legal Protection of Computer Programs and Data* (Carswell). He is a researcher with the firm Clifford-Turner in London, England, and lectures internationally on topics related to the protection of software and data.

Chester Mitchell (LL.M.) is presently an Associate Professor of Law at Carleton University, Ottawa. His major research interests include drug regulation, the professions, criminal law, taxation, and the economic analysis of law. He is the author of numerous scholarly articles on these topics.

Joan Moreau has been with the Addiction Research Foundation of Ontario for 25 years. In her capacity as a Senior Research Assistant, she has supplied much of the data base used in alcohol policy research. She has done many in-house statistical reports and, until 1976, was responsible for the "Statistical

Supplement" of the Foundation's *Annual Report*. She is presently working in the Drug Policy Research Program; her current interest is the legal aspects of illicit drug use, and she is creating a sound data base for research in this area.

Glenn Murray (M.A.) completed his M.A. in criminology at the University of Toronto in 1979. From 1979 to 1986, he worked at the Addiction Research Foundation of Ontario, where his most recent position was Research Associate in Drug Policy Research. He is currently a Ph.D. candidate in sociology at York University, where he is completing course work in the sociology of law and preparing a thesis on the social history of patent medicine legislation. He has published several articles in law, criminology, and drug journals, and he is one of the authors of *The Steel Drug: Cocaine in Perspective* (Lexington Books, 1987). His other interests include methodological and theoretical issues in deterrence research and the application of social control theory to drug use.

Irving Rootman (Ph.D.) is Chief of Health Promotion Studies in the Health Promotion Directorate of Health and Welfare Canada. He was formerly Chief of Epidemiological and Social Research for the Non-Medical Use of Drugs Directorate of Health and Welfare Canada. He has been a technical advisor, consultant, and staff member for the World Health Organization and is currently a member of the WHO Expert Panel on Drug and Alcohol-Related Problems. He is also currently the Chairman of the Professional Advisory Board of the Addiction Research Foundation. He has numerous publications in the substance abuse field and in health promotion.

Shepard Siegel (Ph.D.) is currently Professor of Psychology at McMaster University in Hamilton, Ontario. He has published extensively in the areas of learning and psychopharmacology, and is on the editorial boards of several journals. In 1985, he was the recipient of the Canadian Psychological Association's Distinguished Psychopharmacologist Award.

Eric Single (Ph.D.) is a Senior Scientist with the Addiction Research Foundation of Ontario and a Professor of Preventive Medicine and Biostatistics at the University of Toronto. He holds a doctorate in sociology from Columbia University, and he has published extensively in the areas of alcohol and illicit drug policy issues. Professor Single was involved in a number of World Health Organization projects concerning alcohol issues, and he was a principal investigator in the WHO "International Study of Alcohol Control Experiences." He is currently engaged in tavern studies, and he has been working with the Liquor Licence Board of Ontario on a review of the provincial liquor regulations.

Reginald Smart (Ph.D.) holds a doctorate in psychology from the University of Toronto and is currently Director of the Prevention Studies Department at the Addiction Research Foundation of Ontario. He has a long-standing interest in the international aspects of drug abuse and has often been a consultant for the World Health Organization. He is the author of *Forbidden Highs: The Nature, Treatment, and Prevention of Illicit Drug Abuse* (Addiction Research Foundation, 1983) and other books on alcohol and drugs.

Robert Solomon (LL.M.) is currently a Professor in the Faculty of Law at the University of Western Ontario in London, Ontario. He has been involved in research on drug law and policy for over 15 years. He has published widely on various aspects of the illicit international heroin trade, the Canadian drug trade, and the development of Canadian drug and alcohol laws. He has served as a consultant to Health and Welfare Canada, the Law Reform Commission of Canada, the Attorney General's Department of British Columbia, and the Addiction Research Foundation of Ontario. In recent years, he has focused on various aspects of alcohol law and regulation.

Kenneth Stoddart (Ph.D.) is a member of the Department of Anthropology and Sociology at the University of British Columbia. His interests include ethnomethodology, ethnographic field methods, urban ethnography, and contemporary lifestyles. During the early 1970s, Dr. Stoddart did observational research for the Commission of Inquiry into the Non-Medical Use of Drugs.

Christopher Webster (Ph.D.) is Head of the Department of Psychology and Research Scientist at the Clarke Institute of Psychiatry in Toronto, and Professor of Psychiatry, Psychology, and Criminology at the University of Toronto. Following several years as Research Scientist at the Addiction Research Foundation, he spent nearly a decade as Research Scientist at the Metropolitan Toronto Forensic Service (METFORS), Clarke Institute of Psychiatry. In 1982 he published, with R. J. Menzies and M. A. Jackson, *Clinical Assessment Before Trial* (Butterworths), and has written various monographs and many articles within the domain of forensic psychiatry and psychology.

Roy Wise (Ph.D.) is Professor of Psychology and Director of the Center for Studies in Behavioral Neurobiology at Concordia University. His research deals with the rewarding effects of drugs and brain stimulation, and he has recently served as a member of the Board of Scientific Councilors for the Addiction Research Center of the National Institute on Drug Abuse (U.S.A.).

INDEX

Abstinence, 136, 144, 145, 146, 171, 200,
    395, 396, 398, 399, 400, 404, 448
  syndrome, 24, 231
Accidents, driving, 201
Acetaminophen, 35, 201
Acquired immune deficiency syndrome
    (AIDS), 210
Addicts, 95, 98, 99, 100, 101, 103, 106,
    108, 110, 111, 141, 145, 146, 147,
    159, 163, 171, 181, 222, 235, 259,
    263, 302, 309, 325, 331, 351, 358,
    359, 371, 393, 394, 398, 399, 415,
    417, 418, 434, 448. *See also*
    Addiction
  convicted, 105
  criminal, 135–36, 160, 161, 234, 236,
    349, 352, 363
  heroin, 57, 107, 142, 148, 178, 307,
    396
  hidden, 143
  marijuana, 96
  morphine, 233
  narcotic, 64, 105, 167, 182, 352
  nicotine, 432
  opiate, 57, 63, 64, 144, 307, 339, 354
  population, 89, 232
  registered, 102, 104
Addiction, 63, 67, 95, 98, 100, 103, 104,
    105, 111, 132, 134–35, 137, 140,
    143, 144–47, 149, 158, 162, 302,
    305, 307, 312, 349, 351, 363, 396,
    399, 411, 418. *See also* Addicts
  alcohol, 63
  cures, 403
  heroin, 51, 63, 102, 107, 306, 397
  iatrogenic, 141
  opiate, 51, 54, 63, 64, 66, 139, 141,
    142, 144, 145, 147, 148, 150, 405
  re-addiction, 147
Addiction Research Foundation (Ont.),
    105, 215, 219, 223, 225, 352, 353

Administration, of drug, 26, 43, 45, 47,
    48, 49, 57, 58, 59, 146, 149
  chronic, 21, 32
  intravenous, 36, 38, 194
  long-term, 31
  modes of, 1, 2, 3, 198, 202, 205, 233,
    444
  oral, 15, 40
  routes of, 15, 41
  self-administration, 51, 52, 53, 54, 141,
    143, 145, 148, 353
  subcutaneous, 16
Adulteration Act, 118
Advertising, 73, 74, 76, 429, 433, 447
Afghanistan, 331
Agents, drug, 48
  anti-anxiety, 29, 30–31
  hypnotic, 31, 32
Agents, of the state, 417
Alberta, 239, 261
Alcohol, 1, 9, 14, 17, 18, 19, 20, 21, 23,
    24, 28, 29, 31, 32, 41, 67, 70, 71, 74,
    76, 78, 88, 91, 106, 117, 131, 132,
    133, 134, 144, 148, 159, 160, 162,
    168, 171, 182, 183, 186, 197, 198,
    199, 205, 215, 226, 230, 231, 241,
    279, 337, 343, 352, 356, 392, 396,
    397, 400, 407, 408, 409, 410, 411,
    412, 413, 414, 415, 417, 419, 422,
    425, 426, 427, 430, 433, 447. *See
    also* Alcoholism
Alcohol and Drug Commission of British
    Columbia, 221, 394
Alcoholics Anonymous, 165
Alcoholism, 18, 24, 164, 168, 171, 217,
    231
Alex G. Brown Memorial Clinic, 104, 352
Allergies, 32
American Bureau of Narcotics, 104, 106
American Medical Association, 80
Amphetamines, 21, 30, 38–40, 41, 118,

124, 145, 147, 148, 198, 214, 234, 237, 338, 348, 355, 362, 409
Analgesics, 28, 66, 232, 392, 400
  non-opioid, 35
  opioid, 28, 33–37, 48
Anesthetics, 9, 15, 17, 22, 29, 40, 46, 66
Anorexia, 36, 45
Anoxia, 41
Anslinger, H. J., 104, 105, 110, 111, 181, 349, 434
Antibiotics, 15
Antihistamines, 22, 32, 33, 35, 36, 414, 434
Anti-Saloon League, 182
Anxiety, 23, 24, 25, 29, 30, 31, 33, 38, 41, 47, 48, 298, 375, 410
Arousal, 6, 9
Arrest, 95, 96, 99, 102, 106, 117, 118, 119, 132, 136, 160, 163, 214, 245, 246, 256, 259, 260, 264–71, 275, 278, 279, 280, 291–98, 316, 350, 372, 373, 375, 376, 378, 380, 382, 385
  patterns, 291
ASA, 15, 35
Atropine, 409
Attitudes, 2, 49, 181, 190, 222, 275, 342, 343, 356, 374, 375, 381, 385, 412, 414, 446, 447
Australia, 328
Autonomic nervous system, 6, 7, 22, 35, 38
Availability, 48, 49, 71, 161, 193, 205, 238, 329, 330, 339, 393, 404, 412, 446, 447

Bad trips, 46, 48
Baking soda, 40
Barbiturates, 19, 20, 24, 31, 32, 106, 118, 124, 189, 343, 355, 396, 409, 427, 430
Behaviour, 6, 21, 22, 148, 149, 162, 164, 177, 178, 179, 181, 183, 196, 197, 213, 217, 218, 219, 222, 232, 255, 270, 294, 317, 323, 346, 352, 373, 383, 395, 419, 421, 425
  aggressive, 159
  antisocial, 160, 161, 165, 176
  bizarre, 39, 41, 47
  compulsive, 27
  coping, 66
  criminal, 165, 170
  deviant, 252, 257
  disinhibited, 9

drinking, 134
driving, 414, 447
  drug-induced, 201
  drug-related, 132, 137
  drug-seeking, 25–26, 143
  drug-using, 137, 184, 186, 193
  "like," 423
  non-drug-using, 415
  violent, 23, 41, 47
Benzedrine, 38
Benzodiazepines, 9, 21, 30, 31, 32, 427, 430
Bill 18 (B.C.), 393–96, 399
Bill S-19 (Ont.), 308, 342, 356, 357, 370
Blood alcohol level, 18
Blood pressure, 6, 7, 8, 37, 38, 47
B.N.A. Act, 400, 403
Bolivia, 332
Brain, 9, 14, 15, 16, 17, 19, 20, 21, 22, 24, 26, 29, 34, 36, 40, 42, 358
  atrophy of, 23
  damage, 44
  function, 6, 7, 8, 23
Britain, 73, 104, 106, 110, 141, 162, 182, 230, 231, 235, 241, 283, 351, 397, 398, 399, 434
British Columbia, 89–91, 93, 94, 96, 97, 103, 105, 107, 109, 166, 167, 215, 220, 222, 231, 232, 233, 235, 236, 238, 239, 240, 261, 271, 281, 309, 352, 392, 393, 394, 396, 397, 402, 403
  Supreme Court, 304, 395, 400
British Columbia Medical Association, 102
"British experience," with opiate dependence, 398–99
Bromides, 32
Bronchitis, 23, 44
Bureau of Dangerous Drugs, 160, 235, 238, 244, 306, 362, 393
  Drug Users Index, 221
Burlingame Treaty, 109
Burma, 331

Cacti, 237
Caffeine, 28, 37, 38, 39, 205, 407, 409, 412, 415, 425, 430
Calgary Drug Information Crisis Centre, 220–21
Canada, 30, 33, 35, 36, 38, 42, 67, 70, 71, 72, 73, 74, 76, 77–82, 88, 89, 90, 91, 94, 95, 96, 100, 101, 102, 103, 106, 107, 109, 117, 122, 139, 163,

181, 182, 186, 188, 197, 211, 213, 215, 216, 218, 219, 220, 222, 223, 224, 225, 231, 232, 233, 234, 235, 238, 240, 241, 242, 259, 260, 261, 265, 283, 295, 301, 302, 308, 310, 311, 314, 320, 324, 328, 331, 333–34, 336, 343, 354, 359, 361, 363, 370, 371, 372, 373, 374, 376, 380, 385, 392, 398, 409, 418, 434, 445

Canada Evidence Act, 377
Canadian Addiction Foundation, 357
Canadian Association of Chiefs of Police, 309
Canadian Bar Association, 312, 357, 370
Canadian Bill of Rights, 279, 354, 380
Canadian Charter of Rights and Freedoms (Charter), 117, 259, 260, 264, 270, 271, 275, 278, 279, 280, 281, 284, 325, 345, 346, 347, 354, 370, 380, 381, 403, 424, 434
Canadian Medical Association (CMA), 105, 163, 164, 312, 370
Canadian Pharmaceutical Association (C.Ph.A.), 81, 84, 92
Canadian Public Health Association, 225
Cancer, 2, 410. *See also* Carcinogenesis
lung, 25, 201, 211
Cannabidiol (CBD), 42
Cannabinol (CBN), 42
Cannabis, 2, 17, 19, 20, 21, 23, 24, 28, 42–45, 69, 70, 96, 99, 100, 107, 108, 110, 118, 119, 120, 121–22, 125, 126, 133–34, 181, 186, 187, 189, 192, 198, 209, 222, 230, 235, 236, 237, 239, 240, 241, 260, 261, 264, 291, 292, 295, 296, 298, 302, 304, 305, 306, 307–309, 316, 317, 324, 327, 329, 330, 331, 332, 333, 337, 339, 342, 343, 344, 345, 355, 356, 357, 358, 359, 360, 370, 371, 372, 373, 374, 378, 381, 382, 383, 384, 385, 396, 404, 407, 409, 410, 414, 415, 416, 418, 430, 433, 434, 445, 446
Carcinogenesis, 22, 23. *See also* Cancer
Cardiovascular disease, 23. *See also* Heart
Central nervous system (CNS), 1, 3, 6, 8, 20, 28–36, 37–42, 48, 194, 407
Characteristics, 193, 217, 218, 220, 221, 223, 261, 297, 318
behavioural, 25
offender, 314, 315–16

Charter. See *Canadian Charter of Rights and Freedoms*
Children, 76, 418
China, 73, 101, 109, 110, 331
"China White," 333
Chinese Exclusion Act, 109
Chinese Immigration Act, 1885, 90, 97
Chinese Regulation Act, 90
Chloral hydrate, 32
Chlordiazepoxide, 30
Chlorpromazine, 434
Cigarettes. *See* Tobacco
Cirrhosis, 23
Civil liberties, 100, 108, 264, 278, 294, 346, 350, 354, 363, 378–81
Clinics, 95, 164, 351, 352, 353, 356, 398
maintenance, 104
narcotics, 102, 103, 104
Clonidine, 144
CNS. *See* Central nervous system
Cocaine, 3, 7, 8, 15, 16, 21, 22, 30, 37, 40–42, 48, 51, 53, 54, 70, 74, 75, 76, 77, 83, 84, 92, 93, 94, 118, 119, 147, 148, 181, 182, 186, 214, 230, 233, 235, 238, 240, 241, 260, 261, 302, 304, 305, 307, 327, 329, 330, 331, 332, 334, 339, 343, 345, 348, 356, 407, 409, 433
free base, 40
free-basing, 55, 145
hydrochloride, 40, 52
street, 40
Code. See *Criminal Code*
Codeine, 9, 10, 34, 35, 119, 238
Coffee. *See* Caffeine
Cognition, 48
Colombia, 329, 332
Commission of Inquiry into the Non-Medical Use of Drugs. *See* Le Dain Commission
Commitment, compulsory. *See* Treatment: compulsory commitment for
Concentration, 6, 23, 46, 48
Conditioning, 57, 145, 146
Consumption, 2, 21, 123, 135, 136, 159, 172, 189, 211, 214, 215, 241, 261, 383, 386, 408, 423, 426, 427, 430, 432, 444, 445, 447, 448
alcohol, 18, 88, 134, 171, 198, 217, 429, 433, 446
cannabis, 384
morphine, 4, 67, 143, 147, 234
opiate, 64, 66, 143, 233
oral, 64

Control(s), 76, 119, 120, 190, 194, 267, 268, 277, 298, 311, 314, 331, 338, 339, 349, 359, 379, 381, 385, 392, 393, 399, 404, 425, 428, 429
 of addicts, 353
 crime, 295
 drug, 72, 163, 187, 189, 197, 198, 199, 200, 205, 325, 343, 354, 408, 411–24, 445
 free market, 432–33
 international, 94–95, 328–30, 362
 loss of, 172
 price, 422
 psychomotor, 6, 9
 quality, 189, 422
 social, 182, 196, 201, 237, 301, 309, 324, 360
 strategies, 203
 systems, 202, 348, 353, 360, 361, 416, 421, 424, 433
 tax-licensing, 430–32
Convention on Psychotropic Substances, 187
Convictions, 94, 98, 99, 100, 101, 105, 106, 119, 121, 192, 214, 233, 234, 260, 270, 271, 276, 281, 303, 311, 314, 345, 353, 372, 373, 375, 377, 378, 385, 394, 444
 cannabis, 107, 235, 239, 240, 293, 308, 317, 370, 371, 374
 cocaine, 240, 307
 heroin, 238, 261, 393
 LSD, 307
 possession, 120, 306, 308, 363
 summary, 107, 120, 124, 125, 265, 279, 344, 351, 355, 376
Convulsions, 53
Cortical function, 47
Council on Drug Abuse, 357
Counterculture, 107
"Crack," 40, 241
"Crash," 41
Cravings, 42, 63, 66, 67, 133, 141, 145, 146, 148, 161, 172
Crime, 96, 104, 106, 117, 118, 122, 132, 135, 136, 160, 162–64, 166, 169, 170, 175, 176, 177, 180, 181, 183, 184, 198, 201, 202, 209, 212, 214, 231, 259, 265, 295, 303, 328, 329, 339, 351, 356, 372, 374, 378, 401, 413, 420, 446. *See also* Offences
 organized, 101, 102, 121, 422, 425, 533
 rates, 252

 victimless, 292
Criminal(s), 88, 94, 95, 100, 104, 106, 119, 135, 159, 163, 172, 176, 263, 270, 298, 339, 352, 354, 360, 393, 417, 445, 448. *See also* Offenders
 cannabis, 262, 291–298, 314–320
 history, 317
 intent, 351
 justice system, 160, 161, 169, 245, 259, 260, 304, 348, 361, 371, 373, 374, 380, 383, 384, 393, 444
 label, 307, 310
 record, 308, 310, 316, 317, 319, 320, 346, 356, 357, 372, 373, 375, 376–78, 382, 383, 385, 425, 444
Criminal Code, 117, 118, 119, 122, 125, 259, 261, 264, 265, 267, 268, 271–74, 276, 277, 279, 324, 347, 356, 377, 382
Criminalization, 261, 301, 302, 307, 310, 311, 314, 316–18, 320, 356, 375–76, 382, 385, 386, 407, 414
Criminal Law Amendment Act, 122, 308, 346
Criminal Law Reform Bill, 346
Criminal Records Act, 377, 378, 382
Cuba, 330
Curran, R., 103, 111, 353
Customs Act, 283
Customs agents, 332

Dealers, 3, 107, 136, 137, 261, 276, 292, 296, 328
Death, 22, 31, 32, 33, 36, 41, 51, 54, 57, 58, 60, 193, 194, 209, 210, 214, 336, 371, 385, 423, 444, 447
Death sentence. *See* Penalties: death
Decriminalization, 309, 344, 345, 357, 358, 359, 374, 382, 408
Delirium tremens (DTS), 32
Delta-9-tetrahydrocannabinol. *See* THC
Delusions, 46, 47
Demerol, 35
Dependence, 5, 22, 27, 42, 49, 58, 132, 134, 135, 137, 158, 162–63, 165, 167, 168, 169, 172, 193, 202, 231, 276, 307, 355, 397, 404, 405, 444
 alcohol, 159, 160, 161, 164, 166, 170, 171, 241, 242, 396
 heroin, 40, 160, 165, 166, 168, 236
 liability, 25, 32, 33, 34, 38, 201
 physical, 31, 36, 40, 45, 46, 47, 65, 144, 147, 394–95, 411

psychological, 31, 194, 411
  opiate, 36, 88, 159, 161, 307, 325, 359, 393–400, 402, 403
  opioid, 36
Deportation, 99, 100, 110
Depression, 25, 29, 33, 38, 146, 183. *See also* Mood
  CNS, 42
  of medullary function, 54
  respiratory, 22, 31, 32, 35, 41, 44, 47, 57
DES, 176
DET, 348
Deterrence, 345, 360, 372, 412, 413, 422, 433, 446
Detoxification, 144, 146
  centres, 160, 165, 417
Deviance, 134, 137, 175–83, 184, 361
Dextroamphetamine, 38
Dextrose, 58, 59, 60
Diacetylmorphine. *See* Heroin
"Dial-a-writ." *See* Telewarrants
Diarrhea, 37, 141
Diazepam, 9, 30, 41, 407, 409, 425, 426, 427
Diethylpropion, 39
Dilaudid, 35
Dimethyltryptamine. *See* DMT
Diphenhydramine, 32
Disease, 36, 39, 45, 142, 158, 210, 230, 241, 417. *See also* Infections
  cardiovascular, 23, 209
  mental, 96, 168
  model, 142, 161–64, 165, 168
  venereal, 407
Division of Narcotic Control, 97, 98, 100, 163, 349, 353, 363
DMT (dimethyltryptamine), 124, 237, 302, 348
Dope fiends, 166, 170, 233, 354
Dose, 1, 2, 4, 8, 9, 12, 14, 15, 22, 23, 36, 37, 39, 40, 43, 49, 52, 60, 64, 76, 82, 140, 143, 144, 163, 353
  higher, 13, 20, 24, 31, 32, 33, 35, 38, 41, 46, 47, 48, 57, 58, 59, 141, 237, 238
  lower, 10, 31, 34, 41, 44, 46, 47, 48, 59
  maintenance, 95, 99, 102, 106, 352
  therapeutic, 30, 31, 141
"Double doctoring," 118, 122–23, 124, 345, 346
Drinking, 132, 134, 159, 160, 161, 162,

164, 168, 170, 171, 231, 407, 446, 447. *See also* Intoxication
Drugs, 1, 24, 44, 54, 58, 78, 95, 120, 121, 123, 127, 162, 186, 210, 230, 238, 263, 270, 291, 312, 331, 352, 359, 399, 413, 429. *See also* specific drugs; Effects; Narcotics; Use; Users
  absorption, 14–17
  addictive, 80
  agonist, 10, 36
  antagonist, 10–12
  bureaucracies, 88, 97–100, 108, 111
  classification, 409–11
  controlled, 124, 125, 213, 338, 339, 344, 346, 347, 348, 355, 362, 409, 417
  crusade, 96
  dangerous, 82, 330, 347, 348, 411
  depressant, 6, 28, 32, 41, 48, 124
  designated, 362, 409
  "designer," 205, 241, 333
  experience, 2
  experts, 89
  "gateway," 133–34
  illicit, 3, 29, 70, 119, 135, 136, 158, 159, 160, 171, 214, 215, 216, 217, 219, 220, 221, 222, 224, 226, 234, 235, 236, 241, 242, 260, 261, 274, 275, 277, 292, 297, 303, 304, 305, 306, 307–9, 311, 324, 326, 329, 333, 334, 343, 379, 392, 396, 404, 408, 414, 416, 420, 422, 425, 444, 446, 448
  licit, 28, 48, 71, 99, 117, 136, 215, 220, 242, 325, 336, 343, 392, 404, 407, 420, 446
  medical, 409
  over-the-counter (OTC), 434
  prescription, 28, 123, 401, 434
  psychoactive, 1, 3, 5, 6–12, 17, 21, 25, 26, 28, 46, 49, 325, 327, 407, 408, 409, 410, 411, 412, 414, 415, 416, 417, 420, 422, 423, 425, 427, 428, 431, 434
psychotropic, 342, 407
reaction, 1, 2
receptors, 10
recreational, 233, 411, 430, 445
restricted, 124–25, 302, 338, 339, 342, 344, 346, 347, 348, 355, 362, 409
scares, 349, 350, 351, 355, 361–2
scene, 216, 218, 234, 348
scheduled, 94, 99

searches, 274–78
sedative, 7
squads, 281, 283, 298, 299
subculture, 223, 232, 307
stimulant, 51
synthetic, 14
therapeutic, 16, 347
volatile, 15, 17
Drunkenness. See Drinking
Durkheim, 73
"Dust." See PCP
Dysphoria, 38

Education, 135, 165, 166, 193, 338, 386,
    429, 433, 446, 447
  drug, 102, 187, 192
  medical, 236
  programs, 358
Effects, 36, 40, 43, 45, 57, 96, 97, 182,
    192, 193, 271, 278, 279, 310, 316,
    336, 349, 350, 356, 360, 371, 382,
    392, 397, 411, 446
  adverse, 22, 23, 25, 26, 231, 329, 376,
    429
  analgesic, 63, 410
  aversive, 26
  behavioural, 22, 23, 46, 53
  deterrent, 99, 374
  drug, 2, 3, 4, 5, 6, 7, 9–17, 19, 20, 41,
    49, 58, 89, 132, 149, 151, 161, 198,
    385, 431
  lethal, 59
  mood-modifying, 1
  non-medical, 83
  pharmacological, 26, 42, 48, 76, 186,
    196, 198, 199
  physiological, 22, 23, 35, 38, 41, 44,
    46, 47, 91, 93, 107, 108, 196, 444
  psychological, 23, 42, 64, 107, 196,
    358, 359, 444
  psychotomimetic, 23
  of punishment, 291
  rewarding, 52
  sedative, 32, 33, 35, 410
  therapeutic, 1
  toxic, 13, 21–24, 39, 48, 54
Endocrine system, 22, 37
Endorphins, 10, 26, 34, 148
Enforcement, 94, 98, 108, 248, 249–52,
    259, 260, 261, 269–70, 271, 276,
    277, 278, 279, 281, 283, 303, 310,
    330, 343, 348, 360, 415, 421, 425,
    429
  hegemony, 349, 351–55

law, 49, 89, 95, 100–101, 102–103,
    104, 163, 164, 165, 171, 187, 192,
    199, 214, 215, 238, 291, 294, 295,
    297, 298, 326, 327, 328, 329, 331,
    332, 333, 337, 338, 370, 380, 381,
    398, 412, 426, 430, 446
  narcotics, 245, 252, 253–56, 263
  network, 349, 350, 353
  powers, 69, 119, 264, 372, 374,
    378–81, 383
  problems, 100, 350
England. See Britain
Entrapment, 298
Environment, 58, 59, 60, 63, 64, 65, 97,
    143, 145, 147, 170, 210, 257, 385,
    420
Ephedrine, 38, 39
Epilepsy, 22, 31
Erythroxylum coca, 40. See also Cocaine
Ethchlorvynol, 32
Ether, 40
Eucaine, 94, 348
Euthanasia, 3
Excise Act, 283

FDA. See Food and Drugs Act
"Federal Crowns," 353
Federal-Provincial Task Force on Heroin
    Epidemiology, 215
Federal-Provincial Working Group on
    Drug Monitoring, 216, 225
Fenfluramine, 39
Fentanyl, 333
Flashbacks, 44, 46
Flurazepam, 30
Food and Drugs Act (FDA), 69, 70, 117,
    118, 123–25, 175, 197, 240, 261,
    264, 265, 271, 272, 273, 274, 276,
    277, 278, 283, 302, 307, 311, 337,
    338, 342, 344, 345, 346, 347, 355,
    356, 357, 409, 434
France, 101

Gastritis, 23
Glaucoma, 410
Glue sniffing, 15
Glutethimide, 32
Great Britain. See Britain

Hague Opium Convention, 94–95
Hallucinations, 24, 39, 41, 44, 46, 47, 48
Hallucinogens, 23, 24, 28, 32, 33, 42–48,
    236, 237, 240, 261, 333, 338, 356,
    434

Hangover, 25, 30
Harrison Act, 95, 182
Hashish, 43, 189, 209, 214, 237, 238, 298, 331, 444
"Hash" oil, 43, 189, 298
Headache, 31, 38, 41
Health, 51, 53, 80, 81, 105, 108, 193, 194, 201, 202, 225, 230, 314, 323, 355, 357, 358, 359, 372, 374, 403, 410, 411, 412, 421
care services, 83
mental, 167, 192
problems, 29, 176, 304
public, 49, 57, 70, 88, 232, 396, 400, 401, 445, 448
Health Promotion Directorate, 215, 216, 370
Heart, 6, 17, 22, 23, 36
Hepatitis, 201
Heroin, 3, 7, 12, 15, 16, 21, 22, 34, 35, 36, 41, 51, 53, 57, 58, 59, 60, 63, 64, 66, 69, 82, 83, 89, 92, 95, 101, 111, 119, 121, 133, 134, 135, 136, 139, 141, 142, 159, 163, 164, 166, 187, 189, 198, 202, 215, 222, 232, 233, 234, 235, 236, 238, 241, 260, 261, 270, 281, 282, 302, 305, 306, 307, 329, 331, 333, 355, 379, 382, 393, 394, 397, 398, 400, 404, 407, 414, 416, 417, 425
hydrochloride, 52
maintenance, 309, 339, 399
trade, 106–108
Heroin Treatment Act, 394, 395, 401, 402, 403
"High," 28, 35, 36, 43, 312
Highway Traffic Act, 276
Hippies, 237
Homicide, 26, 160, 413
Hormones, 15
"Horse tranquillizer." *See* PCP
Hydrocodone, 34, 35
Hydromorphone, 34, 35
Hypertension, 22, 47
Hyperthermia, 41, 47, 48
Hypnotics, 30, 31–33
Hypotension, 44
Hypoxia, 57

Identification of Criminals Act, 271
Illness. *See* Disease
Immigration, 376
Asian, 182
Chinese, 89–91, 97, 99, 109, 110

Japanese, 91
Immune system, 22, 45, 210, 358
Incest, 160
Infections, 36, 39. *See also* Disease
systemic, 26
viral, 23
Inhalants, 9, 33
Inhalation, 15, 16
Injection, 58, 59, 60, 64, 146
intramuscular, 16
intravenous (IV), 4, 16, 36, 55, 202
self-injection, 142, 143
subcutaneous, 16
Inositol, 40
Insomnia, 24, 30, 31, 32, 45
Insulin, 15, 148
Interpretation Act, 117, 264, 272, 274
Intoxication, 9, 20, 30, 31, 32, 33, 46, 160, 161. *See also* Drinking
amphetamine, 38
syndrome, 44
Iran, 331

"Jogger's high," 26
"Joint," 19, 43, 119, 120, 121, 125, 293, 296, 299, 309, 373, 382
Junkie, 63, 64, 65, 135, 136, 141, 144, 150, 159, 160, 166

Kidneys, 17, 18
"Killer weed," 21
King, Mackenzie, 91, 92, 93, 96, 97, 108, 109, 110, 181

Laos, 331
Laurier, Sir Wilfrid, 76
Law, 48, 49, 72, 73, 75, 77, 80, 82, 83, 90, 92, 93, 96, 105, 125, 126, 128, 167, 177, 186, 187, 195, 196, 199, 211, 232, 233, 245, 246, 260, 261, 264, 270, 275, 277, 278, 292, 294, 297, 299, 301, 305, 312, 318, 320, 325, 336, 337, 339, 342, 352, 353, 355, 356, 357, 358, 359, 361, 362, 370, 371–72, 374, 375, 379, 380, 381, 384, 385, 394, 395, 407, 410, 411, 414, 418, 426, 427, 431, 432, 444, 448. *See also* Enforcement: law
cannabis, 107, 262, 373
common, 265, 267, 268, 271, 272, 273, 274, 276, 279, 282, 283, 303
criminal, 68, 69, 71, 88, 89, 97, 98, 99, 100, 101, 108, 181, 193, 197, 203, 204, 206, 267, 268, 306, 307, 311,

314, 324, 338, 343, 347, 349, 360, 400, 401, 402, 403, 404, 408, 409, 413, 415, 419, 420, 423, 424, 429
drug, 69, 70, 89, 91, 94, 97, 100, 102, 104, 108, 110, 127, 163, 181, 203, 213, 230, 259, 263, 274, 291, 309, 310, 343, 345, 348, 349, 354, 372, 378, 383, 407, 413, 415, 416, 420, 421
fair, 415
immigration, 100
mental health, 168, 169
narcotics, 97, 181, 182, 254, 255, 298, 349, 350
reform, 70, 323, 324, 345, 360, 416, 445
respect for, 316, 317
sociology of, 345
temperance, 182, 183
tort, 280, 412, 423, 430
U.S., 276
Law Reform Commission of Canada, 281, 283, 346, 360
Learning, 6, 9, 21, 23, 52, 58
Lebanon, 331
Le Dain Commission, 70, 71, 107, 108, 187, 192, 197, 200, 203, 218, 219, 237, 238, 262, 291, 301, 307, 308, 309, 324, 325, 336–43, 345, 346, 347, 356, 359, 362, 370, 404, 409
Legislation. See Law
Libido, 36, 38
Librium, 30. See chlordiazepoxide
Liquor Control Act (Ont.), 409
Liver, 17, 18, 20, 22, 34
LSD. (lysergic acid diethylamide), 10, 45–46, 47, 48, 70, 107, 118, 124, 134, 234, 235, 236, 237, 240, 302, 307, 311, 333, 336, 337, 348, 355, 409, 416, 434
Lungs, 6, 7, 14, 17, 36, 41, 43, 44, 45, 358
Lysergic acid diethylamide. See LSD

Mafia, 101, 106, 111, 330
"Mainlining," 16
Malnutrition, 39, 201
Mannitol, 46
Marijuana. See Cannabis
Matsqui, 105, 111, 166, 170, 352
McCarthy, Senator Joe, 434
MDA (methylenedioxyamphetamine), 48, 124, 237, 240, 302

MDMA (methylenedioxymethamphetamine), 48
Medication. See Medicine
Medicine, 5, 39, 42, 95, 118, 123, 141, 210, 230, 231, 234, 354, 408, 409, 410, 422
companies, 88
dose, 14
in hospital, 66
industry, 109, 230
legislation, 75
non-medical use of, 92
patent, 70, 72, 73–82, 93, 230, 233
profession of, 78, 83
quack, 76
self-medication, 83, 100, 143, 230, 231, 232, 233, 327
Melanby effect, 20
Memory, 6, 9, 23, 39, 44, 47, 48, 194
short-term, 31, 43
Men, drug use by, 239, 240
Meperidine, 33, 35
Mescaline, 237, 311, 407, 409, 416
Metabolic disease concept, 142
Metabolism, 147
Methadone, 17, 34, 35, 36, 144, 214, 223, 395, 398, 409
maintenance, 105, 106, 148, 165, 170, 171, 339, 353, 359, 361, 417
Methamphetamine, 38, 40, 70, 214, 333, 337, 348
Methaqualone, 32, 333, 409
Methylenedioxyamphetamine. See MDA
Methylenedioxymethamphetamine. See MDMA
Methylphenidate, 38–39
Methylphenylisonipecotonitrile, 362
Methyprylon, 32
Mexico, 329
Mice, 1
Midwives, Irish, 2
Model, 165, 422
availability, 446
control, 190, 416
criminal law, 413
disease, 142, 158, 161–62, 163, 167, 170, 171, 411
drug control, 188
integration, 447
justice, 360
medical, 168, 169
moral failure, 158, 159–61, 164, 168, 170

opportunities-incentive, 360
prohibition, 138, 188, 189, 190
rehabilitation, 360
sin, 158, 166, 167, 171
tort, 430
vice, 190
Monkeys, 63, 67
Monoacetylmorphine, 35. *See also*
  Heroin
Mood, 2, 6, 10, 20, 21, 25, 30, 39, 42, 47,
  407, 409. *See also* Depression
  changes, 34
  depression, 23, 24, 40
  elevation, 37
  enhancement, 31, 33, 35, 36, 38, 41
  swings, 31, 32
Morbidity, 205, 210, 230
Morphine, 4, 9, 10, 21, 34, 35, 36, 58,
  64, 65, 66, 67, 70, 74, 82, 83, 89, 92,
  94, 95, 141, 143, 146, 147, 232,
  233, 234, 348, 407, 409
Mortality, 54, 57, 58, 59, 205, 209, 210,
  230
  rate, 51, 53, 54
Motivation
  acquired, 148
  for drug use, 2
Mouth, 48, 281
Mulock, Sir William, 78
Murphy, Mrs. Emily (Judge), 96, 104,
  105, 139, 358, 371, 372
Muscles, 6, 7
Mushrooms, 47, 237, 240

Naloxone, 10, 12, 21, 36, 144
Naltrexone, 36
Narcolepsy, 38, 362, 409
Narcotic Addiction Foundation (B.C.),
  103, 106, 352, 353
Narcotic Control Act (NCA), 69, 70, 72,
  105–106, 107, 117, 118–23, 125,
  126, 163, 167, 175, 186, 197, 206,
  238, 240, 261, 263, 264, 265, 271,
  272, 273, 274, 276, 277, 278, 283,
  298, 302, 305, 307, 311, 337, 338,
  339, 343, 345, 346, 347, 348, 352,
  354, 355, 371, 373, 378, 392, 400,
  402, 409
Narcotic Control Regulations, 122, 163,
  353
Narcotic Division. *See* Division of Narcotic Control
Narcotics, 63, 64, 65, 100, 105, 106, 118,
  119, 120, 122, 181, 245, 252, 302,
  303, 304, 339, 345, 349, 350, 354,
  356, 371, 378, 394, 395, 400, 401,
  402, 409, 434
National Organization for the Reform of
  Marijuana Laws, 363
Nausea, 25, 26, 35, 36, 37, 41, 46, 47
  anti-nausea agent, 110
NCA. See *Narcotic Control Act*
Netherlands Narcotics Working Party,
  187, 193, 194, 196, 201
Neurons, 3, 6, 7, 8, 9, 12, 17, 20, 24
Neurotransmitters, 8, 12
Nicaragua, 332
Nicotine. *See* Tobacco: nicotine
Nitroglycerine, 16
Nitrous oxide, 409
Non-Medical Use of Drugs Directorate,
  215
North America, 43, 64, 106, 163, 181,
  210, 235, 237, 327, 329, 332
Northwest Territories, 239, 261
Nostrums, 74, 75, 80, 81, 83, 230
Novahistex DH, 35
Nova Scotia, 230
Nytol, 32

Oakala, 352
Obesity, 38, 362
Offences, 69, 70, 92, 94, 99, 100, 103,
  119, 127, 159, 181, 192, 197, 213,
  221, 238, 245, 246, 249, 254, 256,
  262, 263, 264, 267, 268, 269, 270,
  272, 275, 281, 284, 293, 304, 305,
  307, 308, 309, 310, 314, 317, 324,
  338, 343, 346, 348, 350, 354, 357,
  362, 363, 386, 414, 415, 423, 432,
  444. *See also* Crime
  cannabis possession, 371–81, 382–84
  drinking and driving, 375
  dual procedure, 117, 124, 125, 126
  first, 118, 120, 123, 342, 363, 373
  indictable, 117, 118, 121, 122, 265,
    266, 271, 273, 276, 279, 345, 347
  sex, 360
  summary conviction, 117, 118, 122,
    266, 279, 303, 351, 356
  trafficking, 105, 261, 352, 355, 382,
    383
Offenders, 93, 121, 259, 268, 272, 296,
  308, 316–18, 346, 353, 372, 374,
  382, 413, 444. *See also* Criminals
  cannabis, 107, 119, 260, 261, 264, 291,
  292, 314, 318, 319, 356, 373, 375,
  376, 377, 378, 380

Chinese, 99, 101
chronic drunkenness, 160
drug, 94, 97, 105, 125, 126, 265, 275, 276, 306, 310
heroin, 119, 373
Ontario, 75, 76, 77, 94, 95, 105, 216, 219, 223, 261, 276, 318, 319, 352
Court of Appeal, 269, 303, 304, 305, 306, 307
Ontario Medical Council, 78
Operation Intercept, 329
Opiates, 57, 58, 59, 63, 64, 66, 67, 88, 92, 95, 108, 119, 139, 140, 141, 142, 143, 144, 145, 146, 147, 148, 160, 186, 202, 214, 230, 232, 233, 238, 263, 327, 328, 331, 339, 343, 359, 392, 396, 398, 399, 400, 404, 411, 414. *See also* Heroin; Opium
dependence. *See* Dependence: opiate
maintenance, 104, 163, 394
Opioids, 9, 20, 23, 24, 26, 33–37
Opium, 34, 70, 72, 74, 75, 76, 77, 78, 82, 83, 88, 91, 95, 100, 101, 110, 118, 119, 121–22, 141, 181, 182, 230, 233, 234, 270, 323, 329, 348, 361, 394, 433. *See also* Opiates
dens, 231, 232, 331
manufacturers, 92
merchants, 90
poppy, 34, 327, 332, 345, 392
Opium Act, 82, 83, 92, 93, 96
Opium and Drug Act, 93–94, 348
Opium and Narcotic Drug Act, 95, 98
Opium and Narcotic Drug Branch, 349. *See also* Division of Narcotic Control
Ottawa, 83, 233, 271, 376
Ouimet Committee, 203, 206
Overdose, 12, 16, 49, 57, 58, 60, 132
barbiturate, 32
benzodiazepine, 31
opioid, 36
risk of, 16
Oxycodone, 34, 35

Pain, 6, 10, 16, 24, 28, 33, 34, 35, 47, 143, 163, 164, 371, 392, 400, 404, 410, 423
Pakistan, 331
Panic, 38, 44, 362
Papaver somniferum. See Opium: poppy
Paraldehyde, 32
Paranoia, 41, 44, 46, 47

Paraphernalia, drug, 25, 254, 275
Parkinsonism. *See* Parkinson's disease
Parkinson's disease, 38, 362
Patients, 30, 34, 66, 132, 140, 142, 143, 161, 165, 166, 169, 172, 233, 309, 352, 353, 399, 400, 408, 410, 422, 427, 428, 431
cancer, 141
dependent, 163, 164, 398
methadone, 144, 214. *See also* Methadone
psychiatric, 3, 24
PCP (phencyclidine), 21, 46–47, 69, 118, 119, 186, 206, 237, 240, 261, 348
Peace officer, 378. *See also* Police
Penalties, 69, 70, 82, 95, 102, 103, 104, 105, 110, 117, 119, 120, 122, 123, 124, 125, 127, 179, 186, 187, 192, 301–303, 304, 308, 311, 339, 342, 343, 344, 345, 346, 347, 350, 352, 355, 356, 357, 358, 362, 363, 373, 374, 382, 408, 409, 413, 414, 415, 416, 419, 422, 423, 425, 431, 432, 434. *See also* Convictions
death, 302, 392
Penicillin G procaine, 51
Pentazocine, 21, 32, 36
Pentobarbital sodium, 51
Perception, 6, 23, 42, 74, 194, 216, 245, 301
self-perception, 317
Percocet, 35
Percodan, 35
Personality, 2, 47
Pharmaceutical Association. *See* Canadian Pharmaceutical Association
Pharmacists, 70, 75, 76, 77, 78, 79, 80, 81, 83, 161, 221, 230, 347, 428
Pharmacology, 1, 2, 5, 49, 132, 133, 137, 160, 400, 404. *See also* Psychopharmacology
Pharmacy Act, 76
Phencyclidine. *See* PCP
Phenobarbitol, 31, 32
Phenylpropanolamine. *See* PPA
Physicians, 70, 74, 75, 76, 77, 78, 83, 92, 94, 95, 102, 103, 141, 162, 163, 230, 233, 347, 353, 362, 363, 409, 410, 415, 416, 417, 422, 425, 426, 427, 428, 429, 431, 432
Pipe, 40, 43, 120
Placebo, 2, 58, 148, 350
Poisons, 42, 214

Police, 69, 88, 89, 102, 103, 104, 106, 107, 120, 121, 189, 212, 214, 218, 221, 223, 244, 245, 246, 248, 249, 250, 251, 259, 279, 281, 283, 292, 293, 294, 299, 307, 308, 314, 316, 317, 318, 319, 320, 326, 328, 330, 333, 343, 349, 350, 351, 352, 353, 355, 357, 360, 371, 375, 376, 379, 380, 385, 394, 398, 417, 422, 429
American, 96
behaviour, 295–98
corruption, 425
discretion, 125, 373
initiative, 348
municipal, 93, 94, 100
powers, 99, 108, 117, 118, 119, 168, 260, 263, 264–71, 271–78, 280, 291, 295, 373, 426, 433. *See also* Search and seizure
provincial, 94
records, 377
-work, 252–56
Policy, 69, 131, 137, 163, 164, 166, 167, 170, 186, 187, 188, 192, 197, 198, 200, 205, 249, 257, 279, 282, 295, 299, 301, 302, 306, 308, 309, 311, 314, 325, 329, 342, 343, 351, 359, 370, 371, 380, 383, 384, 386, 397, 404, 408, 416, 419, 425, 429, 446, 447
analysis, 71, 327, 448
drug, 2, 70, 97, 100, 101, 108, 163, 190, 193, 195, 196, 199, 202, 204, 206, 260, 264, 323, 324, 326, 336, 337, 355, 444, 445, 448
foreign, 330, 331, 332
international, 328–30
narcotics, 97, 108, 183
prohibitionist, 385
proposals, 71
Poppy, opium. *See* Opium: poppy
Potency, of drug, 12, 14
PPA (phenylpropanolamine), 38, 39
Prescription, 122, 125, 141, 163, 176, 233, 238, 398, 408, 409, 416, 417, 421, 422, 424, 425–28, 429, 431, 433
scams, 355
Prescription shopping. *See* "Double doctoring"
Prices, 95, 233, 238, 314, 328, 329, 330, 426, 429, 430, 431, 432
street, 106
Prince Edward Island, 219, 358
Prison, 97, 104, 120

Prohibitions, 63, 71, 88, 181, 182, 183, 186, 202, 281, 298, 304, 314, 324, 342, 370, 372, 373, 374, 384, 386, 404, 416, 417, 418, 419, 420, 421, 424, 428, 429, 433
alcohol, 101, 407, 447
cigarette, 109
criminal, 93–100, 192, 320, 375, 408, 414, 422, 425, 445, 446, 448
opium, 91–93
Proprietary or Patent Medicine Act, 72, 82, 92
Prosecution, 98, 106, 107, 117, 163, 167, 276, 312
Prosecutors, 278, 279, 306, 349, 350, 353, 360, 380
federal, 98, 125, 302, 303, 308, 373, 376
special, 98
Prostitutes, 95, 161, 232, 296
Prostitution, 104, 135, 136, 407
Proteins, 10, 16, 17
Propylhexedrine, 39
"Pseudohallucinations," 47
Psilocybin, 47–48, 124, 237, 240, 302, 409
Psychoactives. *See* Drugs: psychoactive
Psychopharmacology, 1, 2, 3, 27
Psychosis, 23, 31
acute, 38, 44, 201
chronic, 24, 44
paranoid, 25, 39
toxic, 41, 46, 47
Pulmonary edema, 57

Quacks, 80
medicines, 76
Quarantine, argument, 168, 169
Quebec, 94, 95, 260, 261
Quinine, 57, 65

Raid, police, 292, 380
Hull, 282, 379
Landmark Hotel, 275, 282, 378
Ranta committee, 351
Rape, 160, 263
Rationing, drug, 416, 422, 423, 424, 428–30, 431, 433
Rats, 1, 3, 4, 51, 52, 58, 59, 60, 63, 64, 65, 66, 67, 143, 146, 147, 247
RCMP (Royal Canadian Mounted Police), 97, 98, 99, 100, 106, 163, 234, 265, 271, 276, 277, 283, 299, 309, 310,

328, 331, 337, 346, 349, 362, 376
  drug squad, 102, 263, 265
Regulations, 69, 73, 77, 105, 408, 409,
  419, 421, 422, 425–33, 445. *See also*
  Narcotic Control Regulations
Respiration. *See* Lungs
Reverse onus, 347, 350, 354
Richards, Keith, 260, 306, 307
Risk, 26, 49, 70, 95, 106, 111, 133, 134,
  137, 161, 171, 186, 187, 190, 192,
  193, 194, 195, 196, 198, 199, 200,
  201, 202, 203, 204, 205, 206, 211,
  239, 241, 264, 268, 312, 324, 330,
  333, 357, 374, 409, 411, 413, 425,
  427, 432, 445, 446, 447
  accident, 23
  addiction, 100
  dependence, 30
  health, 372, 383, 385, 386, 444
  infection, 16
  overdose, 16
  populations at, 2
Royal Canadian Mounted Police. *See*
  RCMP
Royal Commission of Inquiry into the
  Non-Medical Use of Drugs. *See*
  Le Dain Commission
Royal Commission on Chinese and
  Japanese Immigration, 91
Royal Commission on Chinese
  Immigration, 90, 232
Royal Commission to Investigate Alleged
  Chinese Frauds and Opium
  Smoking on the Pacific Coast, 93
"Rush," 16, 35, 38, 64

Sale, of drugs, 384, 392, 420, 424, 425,
  426, 428, 430, 433, 434
  legalized, 339
Schedule, drug, 94, 99, 100, 118, 124,
  125, 348, 373
Schizophrenia, 39, 44, 46, 434
"Script doctors," 96
Search and seizure, 94, 96, 99, 117, 213,
  259, 264, 271–74, 275, 278, 281,
  284, 295, 346, 378. *See also* Police:
  powers
Secobarbital, 31, 32
Sedatives, 8, 29, 47, 144, 410, 427
  sedative-hypnotics, 24, 30, 31, 32, 409
Seizures, 22, 24, 25, 30, 31, 32, 33, 41,
  47, 48
  clonicotonic, 53
Senate, 77, 78, 79, 82, 92, 342

Special Committee on the Traffic in
  Narcotic Drugs in Canada, 103–105,
  106, 110, 163, 351, 352
Serum testosterone, 45
Set, 1, 210
  factors, 1, 2
Setting, 1, 2, 146, 210, 292, 294, 338,
  397, 399, 400
  variables, 4
Shafer Commission, 187, 192, 196, 202,
  203
Shanghai Opium Commission, 93, 94,
  110
Sharman, Col. C. H. L., 349, 350, 362
"Shrooms," 47
Sickness model, 161–64, 165, 168
Sin model, 159, 162–64
Single Convention on Narcotic Drugs,
  385
Sinsemilla, 43
Skid row, 160, 170
"Skin popping," 16
Sleeping pills, 28, 29, 30
Smokers. *See also* Smoking
  cannabis, 2, 43, 44–45, 133, 363
  Chinese, of opium, 88, 92, 96, 99, 349
  cocaine, 40
  opium, 88, 92, 96, 99, 231, 232, 349
  tobacco, 2, 45, 88, 211, 432
Smoking, 16, 40, 43, 232, 411, 412, 431,
  447. *See also* Smokers
  cannabis, 2, 15, 44, 119, 120, 209, 309
  damage, 430
  opium, 72, 89, 90, 91, 92, 93, 94, 109,
  233, 392
  tobacco, 2, 15
Smuggling, 93, 100, 106, 328, 330, 333
"Snorting," 40
Snuff, 16
Social gospel movement, 77
Soldiers, 66, 141, 142, 146
  addicts, 64
Solvents, 15, 17, 64, 336, 343
Sominex, 32
South America, 40, 332
Speech, 6, 47
"Speed," 198, 337
  freaks, 237, 241
"Speedball," 41
Spinal cord, 6
"Spliffs," 43
Spree, cocaine, 41
Stimulants, 24, 28, 48, 51, 124, 343, 407,
  409, 410

CNS, 37–42
"look-alike," 38
STP, 237, 348
Stress, 146
Stroke, 22, 39
Studies
  "double-blind," 2
  key informant, 216–17, 224
  observational, 217–18, 224
  special, 222–24
Sugar, 121
Supreme Court of Canada, 259, 260,
    273, 278, 279, 280, 281, 283, 284,
    311, 325, 347, 350, 381, 400, 401,
    402, 403
Surveys, 237, 240
  household, 225, 239
  population, 218–20, 222
  student, 225, 239
Sympathetic nervous system, 41
Synesthesia, 46, 47
Systems, 431
  British, 351, 359, 361
  control, 416, 421, 424, 433
  recording and reporting, 220–22

Talwin, 36
Tar, 2, 22
Taverns, 275, 293, 378, 379, 413
Tax, 81, 90, 91, 411, 422, 424, 430, 431,
    433
  disincentives, 408
Tea, 73
Telewarrants, 273–74, 346–47
Temperance movement, 162, 183, 231,
    433, 446, 447
Temperature, 6
Thailand, 331
Thalidomide, 176, 302, 355, 409
THC, 17, 19, 42, 43, 44, 46, 410. *See also*
  Cannabis
Theft, 104, 213
Theobromine, 409
Therapy, 165, 166
  drug, 30, 36, 163, 359, 427
Thiopental, 31
Thought, abstract, 6, 9, 23, 44
Tobacco, 23, 28, 43, 69, 71, 88, 92, 145,
    147, 148, 171, 186, 197, 199, 200,
    215, 216, 337, 343, 392, 396, 404,
    408, 412, 422, 425, 430, 433, 434, 447
  industry, 93
  nicotine, 2, 8, 16, 22, 25, 37, 205, 407,
    415, 416, 432

smoke, 2, 15, 22
Tobacco Restraint Act, 409
"Tokes," 43
Tolerance, to drugs, 4, 20–21, 23, 26,
    31, 33, 36, 39, 41, 44, 46, 47, 52, 57,
    59, 65
  cross-tolerance, 21
  morphine, 58
Toxicity, 13, 21, 26, 31, 38, 41, 49
  acute, 22–23
  chronic, 23–24, 44
  cocaine, 51
  heroin, 51
Traffic, drug. *See* Trafficking
Traffickers, 97, 100, 102, 103, 104, 237,
    253, 260, 293, 311, 328, 332, 333,
    349, 353, 379, 414. *See also*
    Trafficking
Trafficking, 93, 101, 105, 108, 111, 118,
    120–21, 122, 124, 125, 192, 254,
    261, 270, 276, 302, 303, 304, 305,
    309, 326, 327, 329, 330, 331, 339,
    343, 344, 347, 348, 350, 351, 352,
    354, 355, 356, 362, 363, 373, 384,
    386. *See also* Traffickers
Tranquillizers, 30, 66, 396, 407, 409, 427
Treatment, 3, 26, 27, 30, 32, 33, 36, 42,
    44, 49, 73–74, 83, 89, 100, 101–106,
    107, 135, 141, 142, 144, 145, 147,
    148, 164, 165, 170, 171, 172, 182,
    189, 193, 214, 215, 221, 223, 238,
    240, 298, 306, 307, 316, 317, 338,
    339, 343, 353, 363, 398, 415, 420,
    421, 446
  compulsory, 168, 169, 325, 393, 394,
    395, 396–403
  compulsory commitment for, 167–69,
    352, 359, 395
  custodial, 97, 104, 105
  of epilepsy, 31
  medical, 160, 162, 397, 417
  programmes, 95, 111, 132, 166, 351,
    360, 361, 362, 393, 400, 403
Tremor, 31, 32, 35, 36, 41
Triazolam, 30
Tripelennamine, 21, 32, 36
"Ts and blues," 21, 32, 36
"Ts and Rs," 21
Trudeau, Pierre Elliott, 299, 309
Turkey, 328

United Kingdom. *See* Britain
United States, 3, 36, 48, 67, 69, 76, 89,
    90, 95, 101, 103, 107, 108, 109, 111,

133, 141, 142, 146, 162, 182, 183, 189, 230, 232, 233, 236, 276, 295, 327, 328, 329, 330, 332, 354, 359, 362, 363, 380, 398, 399, 424, 425, 431, 433, 445

Urine, 43, 363

Use, drug, 23, 25, 26, 43, 96, 124, 131, 135, 136, 137–38, 144, 158, 165, 175, 177, 179, 183, 184, 186, 189, 190, 196, 197, 201, 203, 213, 215, 218, 221, 224, 225, 230, 231, 232, 241, 259, 277, 294, 302, 305, 306, 307, 347, 355, 382, 386, 400, 408, 411, 412, 414, 415, 416, 419, 423, 425, 427, 428, 429, 430, 432. *See also* Drugs; Users

  addictive, 139, 142
  alcohol, 160, 168, 170, 176, 178, 216, 217, 413, 418
  amphetamine, 39, 176, 237
  barbiturate, 176, 343
  cannabis, 187, 209, 210, 219, 220, 222, 223, 234, 236, 237, 239, 263, 291, 295, 301, 308, 309, 310, 311, 317, 318, 324, 357, 358, 370, 372, 374, 383, 384, 385
  cocaine, 51, 54, 187, 220, 233, 240, 361
  compulsive, 25, 31
  heroin, 65, 107, 108, 145, 166, 168, 171, 236, 239, 244, 245, 247, 252, 257, 363, 392, 394, 404, 418
  long-term, 20
  medical, 38, 234, 343, 347
  morphine, 361
  multiple, 192, 242
  narcotics, 181, 182, 256. *See also* Narcotics
  non-medical, 5, 28, 31, 35, 46, 48, 70, 71, 72, 88, 89, 90, 95, 100, 118, 171, 193, 194, 199, 200, 202, 240, 323, 336, 337, 338, 342, 343, 407, 447
  opium, 92, 93
  patent medicine, 82, 83
  patterns of, 132, 133, 172, 195, 198, 205, 214, 220, 223, 242, 261, 264, 374, 404, 444, 447, 448
  regular, 33
  tobacco, 418
  youthful, 350, 351, 354, 361

Users, drug, 1, 5, 6, 9, 21, 22, 23, 24, 26, 27, 47, 48, 49, 54, 69, 70, 88, 96, 108, 133, 136, 137, 143, 161, 167,

170, 171, 172, 210, 213, 214, 215, 220, 234, 241, 259, 260, 262, 263, 294, 310, 323, 324, 342, 343, 349, 350, 354, 359, 361, 380, 404, 413, 415, 416, 421, 423, 428, 430, 431, 433, 444, 446, 448. *See also* specific drugs; Drugs; Use

  addicted, 239
  amphetamine, 30, 238
  cannabis, 2, 17, 19, 29, 43, 44, 107, 131, 132, 134, 178, 179, 182, 198, 235, 239, 291, 292, 297, 308, 314, 315, 372, 384, 425
  characteristics, 2, 219, 221
  cocaine, 15, 30, 40, 41, 132, 134, 135, 238, 240, 425
  compulsive, 25, 45
  criminal, 233, 408
  daily, 32, 45
  dealer, 3
  dependent, 135, 238
  experienced, 15, 44, 57
  heavy, 219, 411, 419
  heroin, 4, 15, 107, 131, 132, 134, 135, 141, 142, 168, 189, 212, 223, 235, 236, 238, 244, 245, 246, 247, 248, 249, 256, 257, 270, 281, 306, 329, 393, 394, 395, 417, 418, 420
  LSD, 131, 355
  methadone. *See* Methadone
  methamphetamine, 39, 41
  naive, 34, 43, 44
  narcotics, 238, 351
  non-dependent, 135
  non-medical, 28, 31, 35, 36, 38, 39, 338, 420
  opiate, 232, 235, 392
  opioid, 36
  opium, 93
  quack medicine, 76
  street, 16, 30, 33, 35
  young, 29, 237, 295, 356, 445

Valium. *See* Diazepam
Vancouver Community Chest, 102, 103
Vancouver Medical Association, 76
Vertigo, 41
Veterans. *See* Soldiers
Vices, 71, 88, 135, 162, 190, 232, 233, 445
Viet Nam, 64, 66, 101, 141, 142, 146
Violations. *See* Offences
Violence, 23, 26, 41, 47, 194, 202, 296, 297, 298, 304, 358, 371, 384

Vision, blurred, 47
Vitamins, 5
Vomiting. *See* Nausea

Warrant, 264, 265–66, 267, 280, 284,
   292, 293
  search, 99, 272–73, 276, 277, 281, 282,
    346, 350, 379
  telephonic, 273–74, 346–47
"Weed oil," 120
who. *See* World Health Organization
Withdrawal, 39, 65, 160, 182, 194, 346,
   404
  alcohol, 30
  amphetamine, 41

  reactions, 24, 36
  symptoms, 25, 47, 143, 144–47, 172
  syndromes, 31, 32, 45
Women, 1, 45, 150, 239, 247, 281
  pregnant, 2
Women's Christian Temperance Union,
  182
World Health Organization (who), 221,
  225, 348, 362
Writs of assistance, 99, 110, 259, 273–74,
  277, 278, 283, 284, 346, 350, 370,
  379

Young Offenders Act, 271
Yukon, 239, 261